Caribbean–South American plate interact

edited by

Hans G. Avé Lallemant
Department of Earth Science
Rice University
Houston, Texas 77251-1892
USA

Virginia B. Sisson
American Museum of
Natural History
New York, New York 10024-5192
USA

THE
GEOLOGICAL
SOCIETY
OF AMERICA

Special Paper 394

3300 Penrose Place, P.O. Box 9140 ▪ Boulder, Colorado 80301-9140 USA

2005

Published by The Geological Society of America, Inc.
3300 Penrose Place, P.O. Box 9140, Boulder, Colorado 80301-9140, USA

www.geosociety.org

Printed in U.S.A.

GSA Books Science Editor: Abhijit Basu

Library of Congress Cataloging-in-Publication Data

Caribbean–South American plate interactions, Venezuela / edited by Hans G. Avé Lallemant, and Virginia B. Sisson
   p. cm. -- (Special paper ; 394)
  Includes bibliographical references and index.
  ISBN 0-8137-2394-9 (pbk.)
   1. Geology, Structural--Caribbean Area. 2. 1. Geology, Structural--Venezuela. 3. Plate tectonics--Caribbean Area. 4. Plate tectonics--Venezuela. 5. Orogenic belts--Caribbean Area. I. Avé Lallemant, Hans G. II Sisson, Virginia Baker. III Special papers (Geological Society of America) ; 394.

Qe631.A1C37 2005
551'09729—dc22   2005049456

Cover: Looking to the east from the village of Rincón del Pirata (~5 km east of Puerto Cabello). The rocks on the background (Cordillera de la Costa belt) are moderately to steeply northward-dipping layers of mostly graphite- and mica-schists containing lenses of eclogite that often have a rind of blueschist (see Chapters 6 and 7). Coral reefs in the foreground are dead; they may have been uplifted during a major earthquake that hit the area in 1812 (see Chapter 3). **Back cover:** Microphotographs of a trondhjemite mylonite sample from the Cordillera de la Costa belt; west coast of the Ensenada de Patanemo (~10 km east of Puerto Cabello). Both images were taken with crossed nichols; additionally, a 1-λ-quartz plate was inserted for the bottom photo. Quartz grains in two conjugate shear zones are strongly deformed by crystal-plastic mechanisms; the quartz {0001} crystallographic planes are rotated into parallelism with the two shear zone boundaries. Extension axis is parallel to the acute bisector of the shear zones and parallel to regional sub-horizontal, ENE-trending extension axis.

10 9 8 7 6 5 4 3 2 1

Contents

Part III: (Par)autochthonous Belts

Geological Society of America
Special Paper 394
2005

Prologue

Hans G. Avé Lallemant*
Virginia B. Sisson*
Department of Earth Science, MS-126, Rice University, Houston, Texas 77251-1892, USA

INTRODUCTION

This volume presents the results of about 20 years of field-work in northern Venezuela by students and faculty at Rice University and collaborators from several other universities. A geographic map of northern onshore and offshore Venezuela covering most of the areas discussed in this volume is shown in Figure 1. A simplified tectonic map of north-central Venezuela is shown in Figure 2. The locations of the study areas are shown on Figure 3.

The research presented in this book was guided to a large extent by Geological Society of America Memoirs 98 (Hess, 1966), 130 (Donnelly, 1971), 132 (Shagam et al., 1972), and 162 (Bonini et al., 1984). A very useful source of information was the Decade of North American Geology, volume H, pro-duced by the Geological Society of America (Dengo and Case, 1990). Another useful source was the Geological Map of the Caribbean produced by the Institut Français du Pétrole (1990). Unpublished geological maps made by geologists of Creole (Exxon), and unpublished studies by Venezuelan oil companies and universities were also important in planning. Since the publication of the 1984 GSA Memoir (Bonini et al.), major progress has been made as a lot of new data has been collected constraining the nature and the history of the Caribbean plate and the continental margin of northern Venezuela. Important sources of information dealing with the geology of Venezuela are in González de Juana et al. (1980) and the "Código Geológico de Venezuela" (Petróleo de Venezuela, S.A., 2004).

The first comprehensive plate tectonic model for the origin and development of the Caribbean–South American plate

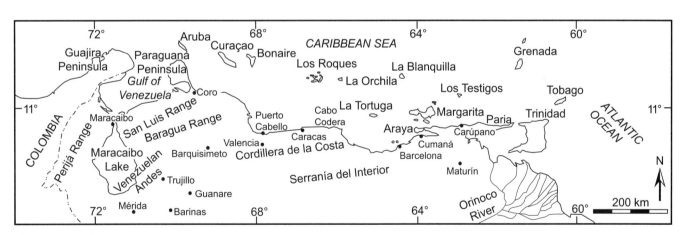

Figure 1. Map of northern Venezuela.

*E-mails: ave@rice.edu; j_sisson@netzero.com

Avé Lallemant, H.G., and Sisson, V.B., 2005, Prologue, *in* Avé Lallemant, H.G., and Sisson, V.B., eds., Caribbean–South American plate interactions, Venezuela: Geological Society of America Special Paper 394, p. 1–5, doi: 10.1130/2005.2394(00). For permission to copy, contact editing@geosociety.org. ©2005 Geological Society of America.

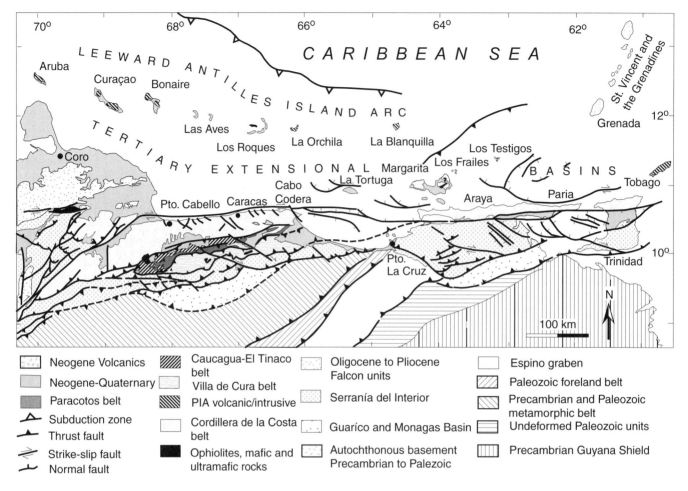

Figure 2. Simplified tectonic map of north-central Venezuela.

boundary was published by Pindell et al. in 1988. Since then, many refinements were made by Pindell and his co-workers (see Chapter 1, this volume).

TECTONICS

Neotectonics

The boundaries of the Caribbean plate are reasonably well established by seismicity along its western, northern, and eastern margins (e.g., U.S. Geological Survey [USGS] and MIDAS, 1998). The southern boundary is not well defined because it is a wide (locally 500 km) zone of distributed shear, and the displacement rates are small. The recent displacements and displacement rates along the Caribbean–South American plate boundary zones are consequently not very well known. Relative to South America, the Caribbean plate moves eastward at a rate of 21 mm/yr; it moves southward at ~10 mm/yr in the western Caribbean, and in the east, near Trinidad, the two plates diverge slightly (Pérez et al., 2001; Weber et al., 2001). A major complication is the northward tectonic extrusion of the Maracaibo block (e.g., Burke, 1988).

Paleotectonics

Extrapolation of neotectonic displacement rates to the past is difficult. However, Pindell et al. (1988) were able to make reasonable tectonic maps based on seafloor magnetic anomalies. Most plate kinematic models of the Caribbean region converged and are quite similar to the one by Pindell et al. (this volume). From the late Triassic to the Late Cretaceous, North and South America diverged in a NW-SE direction, creating between them the Proto-Caribbean lithosphere. The Farallon plate was subducted northeastward underneath the Americas and the Proto-Caribbean. At ca. 120 Ma, the polarity of subduction changed along the Central American portion of the volcanic arc, possibly because subduction ceased due to collision of a buoyant crustal block. The Farallon plate and the northeast-facing Antilles volcanic arc moved northeastward, injecting itself between the Americas and consuming the Proto-Caribbean lithosphere. At ca. 110 Ma, the Panama–Costa Rica arc formed far to the west, isolating a piece of the Farallon plate to form the (neo-) Caribbean plate. In mid-Eocene time, the Antilles arc collided with the Bahama Banks and the Caribbean plate started

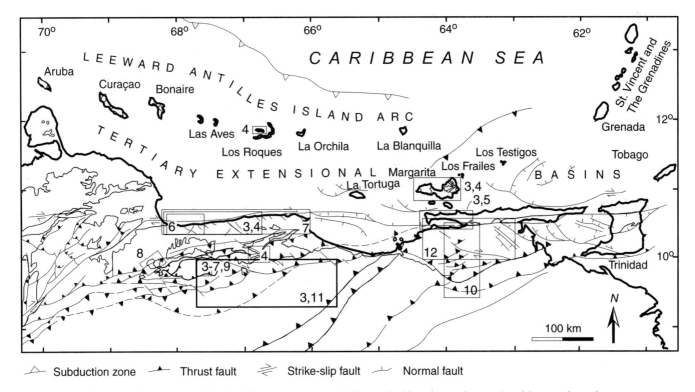

⊿— Subduction zone   ⊾— Thrust fault   ⇌ Strike-slip fault   ⊥— Normal fault

Figure 3. Location map of study areas. Numbered boxes represent each chapter in this volume; chapters 1 and 2 cover the entire map.

moving to the ESE, colliding very obliquely and diachronously with the South American plate.

Whereas Pindell's models suggest that the Caribbean plate was formed far to the west of today's position, alternative models have been proposed in which the plate formed where it resides today (e.g., Meschede, 1998). The arguments pro and con are presented by Pindell et al. (1988; this volume)

REGIONAL GEOLOGY

The Caribbean–South American plate boundary zone between 63°W and 69°W is a very wide zone of distributed shear. It can be subdivided from north to south into the following EW-trending belts (Fig. 2): South Caribbean deformed belt, Leeward Antilles volcanic island arc, a belt of Tertiary extensional basins, and the Caribbean Mountain system. An overview of the geology is given by Ostos et al. (this volume, Chapter 2).

South Caribbean Deformed Belt

This belt is a reasonably well defined belt north of the Leeward Antilles. Seismic reflection data indicate that it consists of thick Cretaceous to Tertiary sedimentary rocks that are being subducted toward the south (e.g., Case et al., 1990).

Leeward Volcanic Island Arc

The Leeward Antilles volcanic island arc crops out from the Los Monjes Archipelago (~100 km due west of Aruba) in the west to the Los Testigos Archipelago in the east. The archipelagos consist of plutonic, volcanic, and volcaniclastic rocks mostly of volcanic island arc composition (e.g., Beets et al., 1984). K-Ar dating of rocks from the Leeward Antilles suggests that magmatism was shut off earlier in the west (ca. 90 Ma) than in the east (ca. 40 Ma) (Santamaría and Schubert, 1974). On the basis of geochemical data, it has been suggested recently that some of the islands are underlain by oceanic plateau basalts without or with minor volcanic island arc material (e.g., White et al., 1999), whereas the island of Bonaire is built up completely of island arc rocks (Thompson et al., 2004).

Belt of Tertiary Basins

Between the Antilles and the mainland of Venezuela, deep sedimentary basins occur. They formed during the Tertiary and are related to plate-boundary parallel extension (e.g., Ysaccis, 1997). This extension may be related to displacement partitioning: in an arcuate volcanic island arc, the arc-parallel component of convergence increases with the increase of obliquity (the angle between convergence and the normal to the arc), causing extension (Avé Lallemant and Guth, 1990). Alternatively, arc-parallel extension is caused by displacements along en echelon strike-slip faults (e.g., Mann and Gordon, 1996). These models are not mutually exclusive.

Caribbean Mountain System

Superficially, the Caribbean Mountain system resembles a classical fold and thrust belt with a nonmetamorphic foreland fold and thrust belt in the south and an igneous, metamorphic hinterland in the north. However, the foreland belt formed in the Tertiary, whereas the age of metamorphism is generally Mesozoic, and igneous rocks are Cretaceous to lower Paleozoic in age (Sisson et al., this volume, Chapter 3). The tectonic settings of igneous rocks in this belt are discussed by Ostos and Sisson (this volume, Chapter 4).

The Caribbean Mountain system (Fig. 2) is subdivided from north to south into the Cordillera de la Costa belt, Caucagua–El Tinaco belt, Loma de Hierro–Paracotos belt, Villa de Cura belt, and the Serranía del Interior foreland fold and thrust belt (Bellizzia and Dengo, 1990).

Cordillera de la Costa Belt

The Cordillera de la Costa belt is exposed from Puerto Cabello in the west to Cabo Codera in the east. The belt can be correlated with rock associations on Margarita Island and the Araya and Paria Peninsulas (e.g., Bellizzia and Dengo, 1990). It is a subduction mélange (Avé Lallemant and Sisson, 1993) consisting of knockers of eclogite, blueschist, marble, quartzite, granite, and granitic gneiss in a matrix of mica schist, graphite schist, and serpentinite. The eclogite formed at great depth (~75 km) in mid-Cretaceous time (e.g., Stöckhert et al., 1995), but retrograded following a high-pressure–low-temperature (HP-LT) path typical of collisional terranes (Sisson et al., 1997). Fluid inclusions in several generations of quartz veins elucidate the exhumation history of these rocks (Sisson et al., this volume, Chapter 5). Geochemical compositions of the eclogites and their country rocks indicate the importance of fluids both in prograde and retrograde situations (Sorensen et al., this volume, Chapter 6).

Deformation structures in the high *P-T* belt that formed during retrograde greenschist and epidote-amphibolite metamorphism indicate NS shortening and EW dextral simple shear, and EW (Avé Lallemant, 1997) plate boundary parallel extension may have been an important mechanism of exhumation (Avé Lallemant and Sisson, this volume, Chapter 7).

Caucagua–El Tinaco Belt

The Caucagua–El Tinaco belt consists of gneisses, amphibolites, peridotites, and younger upper Paleozoic to Cretaceous volcanic and sedimentary rocks. K-Ar and Rb-Sr ages of the basement rocks range from 945 to 112 Ma. A new amphibole $^{40}Ar/^{39}Ar$ determination of the Tinaquillo complex yielded an age of 146 Ma (Sisson et al., this volume, Chapter 3). The Tinaquillo

peridotites are mylonites that may have formed during Jurassic rifting (Ostos et al., this volume, Chapter 8).

Paracotos Belt

The Paracotos belt consists of coarse- to fine-grained clastic rocks and limestone of possibly Late Cretaceous age. At the contact with the Caucagua–El Tinaco, slices of serpentinite and disrupted ophiolite occur (Loma de Hierro peridotite). Serpentinites occur at the contact with the Villa de Cura belt as well.

Villa de Cura Belt

The protolith of the Villa de Cura belt is a sequence of volcanic arc basalts and volcaniclastic rocks (Unger et al., this volume, Chapter 9). It was metamorphosed at blueschist facies conditions in mid-Cretaceous time (e.g., Smith et al., 1999). The belt is not a mélange, but consists of four coherent imbricate slices each recrystallized at slightly different conditions (e.g., Smith et al., 1999). Together, these four assemblages display a prograde metamorphic history with only little retrograde overprint, typical of Franciscan-type blueschist terranes.

Serranía del Interior

The Serranía del Interior fold and thrust belt consists of Upper Cretaceous to upper Tertiary autochthonous to parautochthonous clastic rocks. As with the Leeward Antilles, it is believed that the Serranía fold and thrust belt is older in the west (Eocene) and younger in eastern Venezuela (Miocene). It may not be realistic to construct balanced cross sections through the belt because very little is known about the geometries and rock types at greater depth. Even so, Hung (this volume, Chapter 10) made six hypothetical reconstructed NS cross sections based on several assumptions. He shows that NS shortenings can be as low as 15 km and as large as 115 km.

Apatite fission-track ages in north-central Venezuela are generally Oligocene to Miocene in age, indicating a deformation event related to the passage of the Antilles volcanic arc. In north-central as well as in eastern Venezuela, there are two populations of apatite fission-track ages: one Eocene and the other Miocene (Pérez de Armas, this volume, Chapter 11; Locke, this volume, Chapter 12). The younger dates are probably related to the oblique collision of the arc; the older dates suggest that N-S contraction occurred long before the Antilles reached the area.

ACKNOWLEDGMENTS

The single most important advisor in this project was Albert (Bert) W. Bally; he was always ready to help, and he reviewed both the Prologue and the Epilogue. Discussions with Bert as well as with Peter Vail and André Droxler were enlightening. Jon Blickwede was particularly helpful in matters of logistics. We owe gratitude to the Universidad Central de Venezuela (Caracas) and Litos, CA (Caracas), who helped us solve logistical problems.

Most projects described in this volume were funded by National Science Foundation grants EAR-8517383, EAR-9019243, EAR-

9304377, and EAR-9706521, and the American Chemical Society Petroleum Research Fund grant 27788-AC2, and by oil companies (Amono, Apex, Conoco, Exxon, Mobil, and Pérez-Companc).

We are indebted to the following persons for their careful and thoughtful reviews of the papers submitted for publication in this volume: Bert Bally, Mike Carr, Mark Cloos, Carlos Dengo, Bob Erlich, John Garver, Dick George, Emery Goodman, Keith James, Kenneth Johnson, James Joyce, Gerard Klaver, Will Lamb, Paul Layer, John Lewis, Ed Lidiak, Jim Mattinson, Ian Norton, Bill Leeman, Paul O'Sullivan, Terry Pavlis, Mary Roden-Tice, Dietrich Roeder, Art Snoke, Basil Tikoff, John Weber, and Aaron Yoshinobu.

REFERENCES CITED

Avé Lallemant, H.G., and Guth, L.R., 1990, Role of extensional tectonics in exhumation of eclogites and blueschists in an oblique subduction setting: Northwestern Venezuela: Geology, v. 18, p. 950–953, doi: 10.1130/0091-7613(1990)018<0950:ROETIE>2.3.CO;2.

Avé Lallemant, H.G., 1997, Transpression, displacement partitioning, and exhumation in the eastern Caribbean–South American plate boundary zone: Tectonics, v. 16, p. 272–289, doi: 10.1029/96TC03725.

Avé Lallemant, H.G., and Sisson, V.B., 1993, Caribbean–South American plate interactions: Constraints from the Cordillera de la Costa Belt, Venezuela, *in* Pindell, J.L., and Perkins, B.F., eds., Mesozoic and early Cenozoic development of the Gulf of Mexico and Caribbean region: Proceedings, Gulf Coast Section, SEPM Foundation 13th Annual Research Conference: Austin, Texas, Society for Sedimentary Geology (SEPM) Foundation, Earth Enterprises, p. 211–219.

Beets, D.J., Maresch, W.V., Klaver, G.T., Mottana, A., Bocchio, R., Beunk, F.F., and Monen, H.P., 1984, Magmatic rock series and high pressure metamorphism as constraints on the tectonic history of the southern Caribbean, *in* Bonini, W.E., Hargraves, R.B., and Shagam, R., eds., The Caribbean–South American plate boundary and regional tectonics: Geological Society of America Memoir 162, p. 95–130.

Bellizzia, A., and Dengo, G., 1990, The Caribbean Mountain system, northern South America; A summary, *in* Dengo, G., and Case, J.E., eds., The Caribbean region: Boulder, Colorado, Geological Society of America, The Geology of North America, v. H, p. 167–175.

Bonini, W.E., and Hargraves, R.B., and Shagam, R., editors, 1984, The Caribbean–South American plate boundary and regional tectonics: Geological Society of America Memoir 162, 421 p.

Burke, K., 1988, Tectonic evolution of the Caribbean: Annual Reviews of Earth and Planetary Sciences, v. 16, p. 201–230, doi: 10.1146/annurev.ea.16.050188.001221.

Case, J.E., MacDonald, W.D., and Fox, P.J., 1990, Caribbean crustal provinces; Seismic and gravity evidence, *in* Dengo, G., and Case, J.E., eds., The Caribbean Region: Boulder, Colorado, Geological Society of America, The Geology of North America, v. H, p. 15–36.

Dengo, G., and Case, J.E., editors, 1990, The Caribbean region: Boulder, Colorado, Geological Society of America, The Geology of North America, v. H, 528 p.

Donnelly, T.W., editor, 1971, Caribbean geophysical, tectonic, and petrologic studies: Geological Society of America Memoir 130, 224 p.

González de Juana, C., Iturralde de Arozena, J.M., and Picard, X., 1980, Geología de Venezuela y de sus cuencas petrolíferas: Caracas, Foninves, v. 1, 407 p.

Hess, H.H., editor, 1966, Caribbean Geological Investigations: Geological Society of America Memoir 98, 310 p.

Institut Français du Pétrole, 1990, Geological map of the Caribbean: Paris, Edition Technip, scale 1:2,500,000.

Mann, P., and Gordon, M.B., 1996, Tectonic uplift and exhumation of blueschist belts along transpressional strike-slip fault zones, *in* Bebout, G.E., Scholl, D.W., Kirby, S.H., and Platt, J.P., eds., Subduction, top to bottom: American Geophysical Union Geophysical Monograph 96, p. 143–154.

Meschede, M., 1998, The impossible Galapagos connection: geometric constraints for a near-American origin of the Caribbean plate: Geologische Rundschau, v. 87, p. 200–205, doi: 10.1007/s005310050202.

Petróleo de Venezuela, Sociedad Anónima (PDVSA), 2004, Código Geológico de Venezuela: http://www.pdv.com/lexico/ (Accessed April 2004).

Pérez, O.J., Bilham, R., Bendick, R., Velandia, J.R., Hernandez, N., Moncayo, C., Hoyer, M., and Kozuch, M., 2001, Velocity field across the southern Caribbean plate boundary and estimates of Caribbean–South American plate motion using GPS geodesy 1994–2000: Geophysical Research Letters, v. 28, no. 15, p. 2987–2990, doi: 10.1029/2001GL013183.

Pindell, J.L., Cande, S.C., Pitman, W.C., III, Rowley, D.B., Dewey, J.F., Labrecque, J., and Haxby, W., 1988, A plate-kinematic framework for models of Caribbean evolution: Tectonophysics, v. 155, p. 121–138, doi: 10.1016/0040-1951(88)90262-4.

Santamaría, F., and Schubert, C., 1974, Geochemistry and geochronology of the southern Caribbean–northern Venezuela plate boundary: Geological Society of America Bulletin, v. 85, p. 1085–1098, doi: 10.1130/0016-7606(1974)85<1085:GAGOTS>2.0.CO;2.

Shagam, R., Hargraves, R.B., Morgan, W.J., Van Houten, F.B., Burk, C.A., Holland, H.D., and Hollister, L.C., editors, 1972, Studies in earth and space sciences: A memoir in honor of Harry Hammond Hess: Geological Society of America Memoir 132, 683 p.

Sisson, V.B., Ertan, I.E., and Avé Lallemant, H.G., 1997, High pressure (~2000 MPa) kyanite- and glaucophane-bearing pelitic schist and eclogite from Cordillera de la Costa belt, Venezuela: Journal of Petrology, v. 38, p. 65–83, doi: 10.1093/petrology/38.1.65.

Smith, C.A., Sisson, V.B., Avé Lallemant, H.G., and Copeland, P., 1999, Two contrasting pressure-temperature-time paths in the Villa de Cura blueschist belt, Venezuela: Possible evidence for late Cretaceous initiation of subduction in the Caribbean: Geological Society of America Bulletin, v. 111, no. 6, p. 831–848, doi: 10.1130/0016-7606(1999)111<0831:TCPTTP>2.3.CO;2.

Stöckhert, B., Maresch, W.V., Brix, M., Kaiser, C., Toetz, A., Kluge, R., and Kruckhaus-Lueder, G., 1995, Crustal history of Margarita Island (Venezuela) in detail: Constraints on the Caribbean plate-tectonic scenario: Geology, v. 23, no. 9, p. 787–790, doi: 10.1130/0091-7613(1995)023<0787:CHOMIV>2.3.CO;2.

Thompson, P.M.E., Kempton, P.D., White, R.V., Saunders, A.D., Kerr, A.C., Tarney, J., and Pringle, M.S., 2004, Elemental, Hf-Nd isotopic and geochronological constraints on an island arc sequence associated with the Cretaceous Caribbean plateau, Bonaire, Dutch Antilles: Lithos, v. 74, p. 91–116, doi: 10.1016/j.lithos.2004.01.004.

U.S. Geological Survey (USGS) National Earthquake Information Center and Middle America Seismograph (MIDAS) Consortium, 1998, Caribbean Seismicity 1900–1994: USGS Open-File Report 98-223, map scale 1:6,500,000.

Weber, J.C., Dixon, T.H., DeMets, C., Ambeh, P., Jansma, P., Mattioli, G., Saleh, J., Sella, G., Biham, R., and Pérez, O., 2001, GPS estimate of relative motion between the Caribbean and South American plates, and geologic implications for Trinidad and Venezuela: Geology, v. 29, no. 1, p. 75–78, doi: 10.1130/0091-7613(2001)029<0075:GEORMB>2.0.CO;2.

White, R.V., Tarney, J., Kerr, A.C., Saunders, A.D., Kempton, P.D., Pringle, M.S., and Klaver, G.T., 1999, Modification of an oceanic plateau, Aruba, Dutch Caribbean: Implications for the generation of continental crust: Lithos, v. 46, no. 1, p. 43–68, doi: 10.1016/S0024-4937(98)00061-9.

Ysaccis, R., 1997, Tertiary evolution of the northeastern Venezuela offshore [Ph.D. Dissertation]: Houston, Texas, Rice University, 285 p.

MANUSCRIPT ACCEPTED BY THE SOCIETY 5 APRIL 2005

Geological Society of America
Special Paper 394
2005

Plate-kinematics and crustal dynamics of circum-Caribbean arc-continent interactions: Tectonic controls on basin development in Proto-Caribbean margins

James Pindell*
Lorcan Kennan
Tectonic Analysis, Ltd., Chestnut House, Burton Park, Duncton, West Sussex GU28 0LH, UK
Walter V. Maresch
Institut für Geologie, Mineralogie und Geophysik, Ruhr-Universität Bochum, D-44780 Bochum, Germany
Klaus-Peter Stanek
Institut für Geologie, TU Bergakademie Freiberg, Bernhard-von-Cotta-Strasse 2, D-09596 Freiberg, Germany
Grenville Draper
Department of Earth Sciences, Florida International University, Miami, Florida 33199, USA
Roger Higgs
Geoclastica Ltd., 16 Norham End, Norham Road, Oxford OX2 6SG, UK

ABSTRACT

The American margins of the Caribbean comprise basins and accreted terranes recording a polyphase tectonic history. Plate kinematic models and reconstructions back to the Jurassic show that Mesozoic separation of the Americas produced passive margins that were overridden diachronously from west to east by allochthonous Caribbean plate–related arc and oceanic complexes. *P-T-t* and structural data, sedimentary provenance, and basin-subsidence studies constrain this history. Caribbean lithosphere is Pacific-derived and was engulfed between the Americas during their westward drift as the Atlantic Ocean opened. This began ca. 120 Ma with development of a west-dipping Benioff zone between Central America and the northern Andes, now marked by the Guatemalan and Cuban sutures in North America and by the northern Colombian and Venezuelan "sutures" of South America, persisting today as the Lesser Antilles subduction zone. Most Caribbean high-pressure metamorphic complexes originated at this subduction zone, which probably formed by arc-polarity reversal at an earlier west-facing Inter-American Arc and was probably caused by westward acceleration of the Americas. The mainly 90 Ma Caribbean basalts were extruded onto preexisting Caribbean crust ~30 m.y. later and are not causally linked to the reversal. The Great Caribbean Arc originated at this trench and evolved up to the present, acquiring the shape of the preexisting Proto-Caribbean Seaway. The uplift and cooling history of arc and forearc terranes, and history of basin opening and subsidence, can be tied to stages of Caribbean plate motion in a coherent, internally consistent regional model that provides the basis for further studies.

Keywords: Caribbean, plate tectonics, Pacific origin, paleogeographic evolution, arc-continent interaction, arc-polarity reversal, backarc spreading, Proto-Caribbean, Cuba, Venezuela, Trinidad, Mexico, Guatemala.

*Also at Department of Earth Science, MS-126, Rice University, Houston, Texas 77005, USA; e-mail: jim@tectonicanalysis.com

Pindell, J., Kennan, L., Maresch, W.V., Stanek, K.-P., Draper, G., and Higgs, R., 2005, Plate-kinematics and crustal dynamics of circum-Caribbean arc-continent interactions: Tectonic controls on basin development in Proto-Caribbean margins, *in* Avé Lallemant, H.G., and Sisson, V.B., eds., Caribbean–South American plate interactions, Venezuela: Geological Society of America Special Paper 394, p. 7–52, doi: 10.1130/2005.2394(01). For permission to copy, contact editing@geosociety.org. ©2005 Geological Society of America.

INTRODUCTION

Basin and structural development at the Caribbean plate's boundaries with North and South America were strongly controlled by regional plate motions associated with the breakup of Pangea, opening of the Proto-Caribbean arm of the Atlantic Ocean, and the progressive engulfment of a swath of Pacific oceanic crust (now part of Caribbean plate) between the Americas as they drifted west from Africa. Thus, a passive margin phase of stratigraphic development preceded arc-continent interactions and syntectonic basin development along the Caribbean-American margins (Fig. 1).

As the American plates began their separation in the Triassic to Neocomian, passive margins formed along northern South America and southern North America, and an east-dipping subduction zone defined the western limits of continental crust along the Cordilleran margin, producing a continuous continental arc crossing from North to South America. However, as continental separation increased during the Neocomian, this trench became lengthened across the widening inter-American gap, giving rise to the hypothetical concept of an "Inter-American Arc" connect-

ing the Andes and Mexico. This arc would have been situated, at first, above the east-dipping subduction zone, allowing Pacific crust to subduct beneath North and South America and the Proto-Caribbean, but in order for Pacific crust to eventually enter the widening gap between the Americas, subduction polarity must have reversed, becoming west-dipping.

We develop and review arguments that this subduction polarity reversal occurred during the Aptian and that subsequent plate motions allowed Pacific-derived crust to enter the Proto-Caribbean Seaway between the Americas. Thus, the hypothetical Inter-American Arc should form the roots of arc complexes that defined the leading edge of the Pacific-derived crust. Burke (1988) termed this arc the Great Caribbean Arc.

As circum-Caribbean plate kinematics have become better constrained (contrast Ladd [1976] and Pindell et al. [1988]), the Pacific origin of the Caribbean plate has become more firmly established (Burke et al., 1978, 1984; Pindell and Dewey, 1982; Burke, 1988; Pindell, 1990). Increasing confidence in a Pacific origin for the Caribbean plate, to the west of the Intra-American Arc, has led to many of the allochthonous complexes of southern

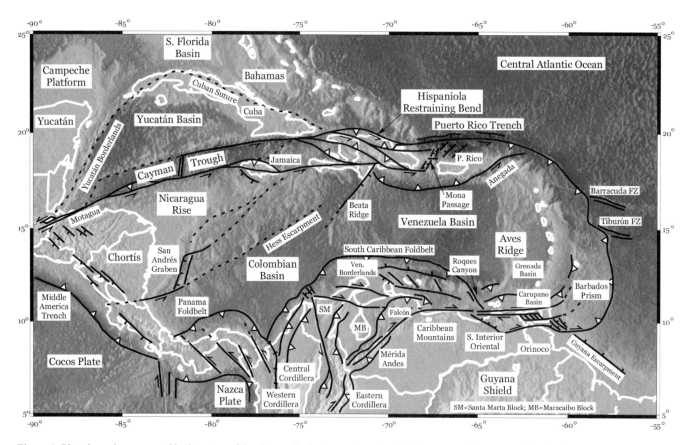

Figure 1. Plate-boundary map and bathymetry of the circum-Caribbean region, showing key tectonic features and geological provinces discussed in the text. Leading and trailing boundaries of the Caribbean plate are subduction zones associated with active volcanic arcs (Lesser Antilles and Panama–Costa Rica arcs, respectively). The southern plate boundary with Colombia, Venezuela, and Trinidad is wide, diffuse, and complex; strain is partitioned between thrust faulting and strike-slip faulting associated with development of pull-apart basins. Similarly, prior to the Eocene collision of Cuba with the Bahamas Bank, the northern plate boundary was also wide and complexly partitioned. Post-collision, the plate boundary was reorganized, with motion now concentrated on the relatively simple Cayman Trough in the west, whereas complexly partitioned thrust and strike-slip faulting continues in the Puerto Rico segment.

North America and northern South America, including much of the western flank of the northern Andes, being tied through lithology, chronology, and/or geochemistry to the Caribbean plate, to its arcs, and to its subduction-accretion complex (Donnelly et al., 1990; Snoke, 1991; Reynaud et al., 1999; Snoke et al., 2001). However, identifying a terrane as "Caribbean-related" is only the first step to understanding how that terrane fits into the long-lived Caribbean–South American interaction, and significant effort is required to reconstruct the various complexes into a coherent and detailed understanding of this progressive "Caribbean Orogeny."

This paper examines the history of tectonic interactions of the Great Caribbean Arc and the Caribbean plate with the North and South American continental margins. We employ and integrate plate kinematics, pressure-temperature-time (*P-T-t*) data of metamorphic complexes in arc-related terranes, other geochronological data, periodicity of arc magmatism, seismic tomography, basin and arc stratigraphy, and regional structure, set within the above general evolutionary scheme.

Several of the allochthonous complexes on both of the American margins possess high pressure–low temperature (HP-LT) and other metamorphic rocks whose *P-T-t* paths can help to define the history of subduction and subsequent tectonic events leading to their obduction onto the American margins. Integration of this information with structural and stratigraphic data that show a fairly consistent west-to-east younging of terrane emplacement and basin subsidence along both northern and southern margins of the Caribbean allows us to constrain the origin of various Caribbean terranes and the timing and processes of continent-ocean interactions.

Here, we briefly review the history of progressive obduction of allochthonous metamorphic complexes recorded along the southern North American passive margin (Fig. 2). Before we can address such interaction, the Chortís Block (continental crust beneath southern Guatemala, Honduras, Nicaragua, El Salvador, and western parts of Nicaragua Rise) of today's Caribbean plate must be restored to the southwest margin of Mexico for mid-Cretaceous and older times (prior to its incorporation into the Caribbean plate; Figs. 3 and 4; Pindell and Dewey, 1982; Johnson, 1990; Schaaf et al., 1995) to avoid overlap with the known Jurassic position of the South American plate. Once this is done, a northeastward younging of deformation, which we interpret as a result of Caribbean arc–continent interactions, can be documented starting in Chortís (mid-Albian; Horne et al., 1974), progressing to southern Yucatán (Senonian; Rosenfeld, 1993) and along the Belize margin (Rosencrantz, 1990). Finally, emplacement of the arc in the Bahamas (early to middle Eocene; Pszczółkowski, 1999) was made possible by the opening of the Paleogene Yucatán Basin, allowing the leading edge of the Caribbean plate to advance to the northeast while most of the Caribbean plate moved in a more easterly direction with respect to North America. The origin of some of the allochthonous complexes along this margin remains problematic and is discussed below.

The broad, diffuse Caribbean–South American plate-boundary zone (Fig. 1) is also strongly controlled by regional tectonics.

In the west, continental crust of the northern Andean terranes is escaping the east-west convergence in Colombia and is extruding northward across Caribbean lithosphere at the north-vergent South Caribbean Deformed Belt (Dewey and Pindell, 1985; van der Hilst and Mann, 1994). Basement-involved deformation has occurred since at least 25 Ma, penetrating several hundred km into the South American continent, allowing South America to acquire an arcuate, hanging-wall geometry necessary for long-term subduction of the southern part of the Caribbean plate (Pindell et al., 1998). In the eastern portion of the plate-boundary zone, primary structures more closely reflect Caribbean–South America relative motion (east-west shear) because the two plates have no large, independent Andean terranes between them.

Despite these complexities, this late Cenozoic tectonic setting for the South American margin tells only a part of the full history of Caribbean–South American interaction. Earlier development involves the emplacement of a fairly continuous belt of oceanic-related and arc-related rocks along northern South America (Fig. 2). It was thought previously that the collision of an arc directly with the northern South American margin had driven Cretaceous metamorphism of these arc complexes more or less in situ (e.g., Maresch, 1974; Beets et al., 1984). However, analysis of sedimentary provenance (e.g., van Houten, 1976) and subsidence history in northern South American sedimentary basins (Dewey and Pindell, 1986; Pindell et al., 1991) strongly supports the idea of a Pacific or Inter-American Arc origin for the allochthons. They occur in structural and basinal settings that record a protracted, west-to-east diachronous (Late Cretaceous along the Andes, Paleogene in northern Colombia–western Venezuela, and Neogene in Eastern Venezuela–Trinidad) history of arc-continent collision and obduction of allochthonous materials onto the South American margin, consistent with the Pacific-origin model (Pindell and Barrett, 1990; Pindell and Erikson, 1994; Pindell and Tabbutt, 1995).

It is generally considered that the South American margin onto which the Caribbean allochthons were obducted was an Atlantic-type passive margin (Speed, 1985; Pindell et al., 1988) that faced the Mesozoic Proto-Caribbean Seaway (Figs. 3 and 4; Pindell, 1985b). However, this generality now needs partial revision, owing to the fact that 60–200 km of north-south shortening has occurred across the Proto-Caribbean Seaway since the Paleocene (Pindell et al., 1988; Müller et al., 1999), starting well before the arrival of the Caribbean plate from the west. We follow Pindell et al. (1991, 1998), Higgs and Pindell (2001), and Pindell and Kennan (2001a, 2001b) and consider that this shortening was taken up by southward-dipping subduction of Proto-Caribbean crust beneath northern South America (see position of this Cenozoic trench on Figs. 5D–G), although subduction has not progressed enough to generate arc magmatism. Hence, at least the Venezuela portion of the South American margin was not passive at the actual time of emplacement of the Caribbean allochthons.

As developed in this paper, the refined tectonic, metamorphic, and geochronologic constraints on Caribbean evolution allow us to better define the controls on basin development along the American (Proto-Caribbean) margins and to separate the geo-

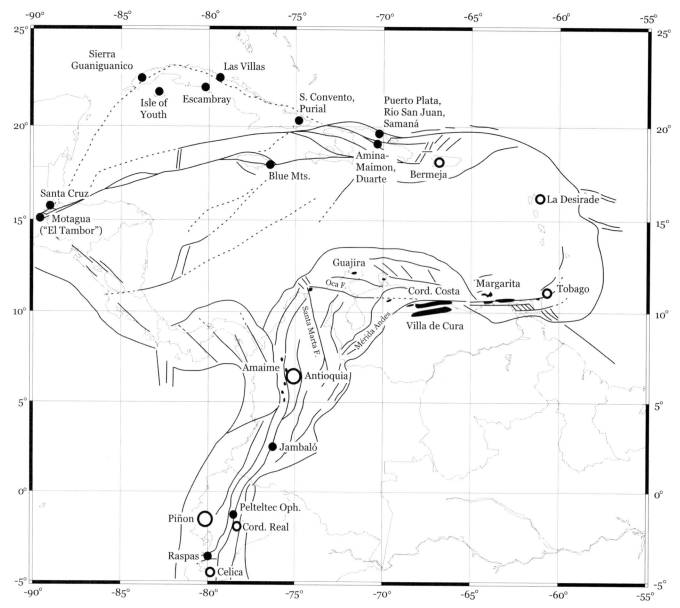

Figure 2. Map of circum-Caribbean region and northern Andes of Peru, Ecuador, and Colombia, showing the locations of high-pressure–low-temperature rocks (filled circles) and other key localities discussed in this paper (unfilled circles). Rocks as far south as −5° are included because the trailing edge of the Caribbean plate was initiated at approximately this latitude prior to northeastward migration during the Late Cretaceous and Cenozoic. F—fault.

logical developments that result from interaction with the Caribbean plate from those that pre-date any Caribbean influence. This paper will provide the framework for more detailed work and for other types of studies.

PROTO-CARIBBEAN RIFTED MARGINS AND CARIBBEAN EVOLUTION

The breakup of western Pangea involved Middle Jurassic to Late Jurassic rifting and seafloor spreading in the Gulf of Mexico, the Proto-Caribbean, and the Colombian Marginal seaways

(Figs. 3 and 4). Although spreading in the Gulf of Mexico stopped in the earliest Cretaceous, it continued in the Proto-Caribbean and Colombian Marginal seaways into the Late Cretaceous producing, by that time, a wide oceanic gap between North and South America into which the Caribbean plate was progressively inserted from the Pacific realm. Figures 3 and 4 show modeled positions of the rifts and transfer zones of the various ocean-continent boundaries. The northern Venezuela-Trinidad margin rifted from eastern Yucatán, and the northwestern Colombia margin rifted from southern Mexico–eastern Chortís. The southern Colombia-Peru margin formed the eastern flank of an Early Cretaceous backarc basin

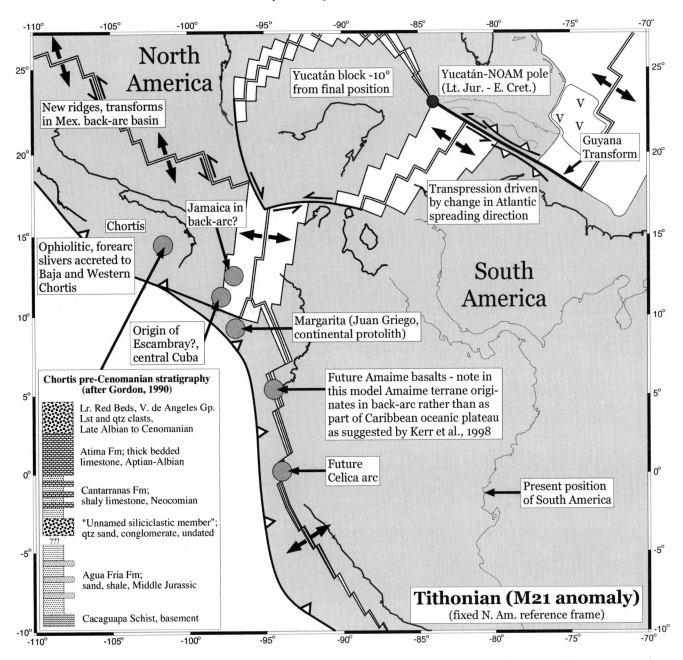

Figure 3. Paleotectonic reconstruction of the Americas at anomaly M-21 (ca. 150 Ma), drawn in a fixed North America reference frame; rotation parameters for the Americas after Pindell et al. (1988), Gulf of Mexico and Caribbean paleogeography modeled according to Pindell and Kennan (2001b), and Pacific plate boundaries schematic but in keeping with the motions of Engebretson et al. (1985). Separation of the Americas was not yet sufficient for Yucatán to have rotated into its final position (it was still constrained by Colombia). Zone of sinistral transform motion where Yucatán and northwest Venezuela interact connects the Proto-Caribbean and Colombian Marginal seaways to east and west. Reconstructed relative positions and contexts of some key localities are shown. Lr.—lower; Lst—limestone; qtz—quartz; V.—Valle.

between the South American autochthon and the continental roots of an arc system that later evolved into part of the Great Caribbean Arc. Incorporated into Figures 3 and 4 is a palinspastic restoration for the northern Andes that retracts Cenozoic transcurrent offsets of 150 km (dextral), 110 km (sinistral), and 120 km (dextral) on

the Mérida, Santa Marta, and Oca fault zones, respectively, which collectively requires 180 km of associated orthogonal shortening across the northern part of the Eastern Cordillera of Colombia (Pindell et al., 1998, 2000). To the east, ~80 km of dextral transpressive shear has been removed from the parautochthonous Serranía del

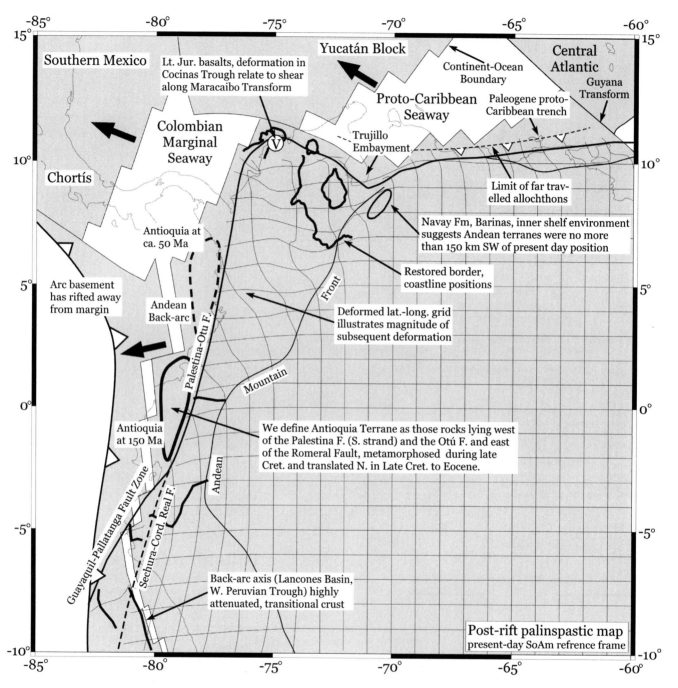

Figure 4. Palinspastic reconstruction of northern South America at 150 Ma (note fixed South America reference frame); rotations as in Figure 3. A deformed latitude-longitude grid (areas of known parautochthonous and autochthonous Jurassic-Cretaceous rocks only) shows the effects of undoing subsequent contraction and strike-slip deformation and provides a more reliable framework for modeling geological evolution. For example, the Guajira Peninsula of northern Colombia probably lay as much as 500 km west-southwest of its present position. The grid ends at the eastern limit of highly allochthonous terranes bounded by the Guayaquil-Pallatanga-Palestina-Otú faults. The Antioquia terrane is shown to the west of the Palestina-Otú fault, and some 500 km south of its present position, in order to lie adjacent to middle Cretaceous synorogenic deposits known in Ecuador but not at its present position in Colombia. To the west of Antioquia are shown the proposed Andean backarc and the arc, rifted entirely from the continental margin. The arc shape shown is drawn to connect with the trench along western North America. F—fault.

Interior–Trinidad foldbelt (Erikson and Pindell, 1998; Pindell and Kennan, 2001a). Along the Andes, for reasons discussed later, it is likely that the "Antioquia terrane" of the northwestern central Cordillera of Colombia has migrated northward an uncertain distance along the Palestina-Otú fault zone. This terrane was overridden by ophiolites and metamorphosed in the Late Cretaceous, but rocks immediately east of the Palestina-Otú fault were not (McCourt et al., 1984), and terrane allochthoneity is potentially large (several hundred km).

Inherent to Figures 3 and 4, and to any model outlining the breakup of Pangea, is the need for a west-facing arc system defining the western margins of the American plates in order to explain the well-known Triassic-Jurassic magmatic belt from at least California to Peru (Jaillard et al., 1990; Jones et al., 1995; Romeuf et al., 1997; Noble et al., 1997). In the Jurassic (Fig. 3), this west-facing arc system must also have spanned the widening gap between Chortís and the Andes, but relative motion along the trench must have become highly oblique by the Early Cretaceous, and arc-parallel transcurrent motions and internal extension were probably severe. It is not clear if a northeast-dipping Benioff zone was maintained, and eventually this portion of the Cordilleran arc system must have reversed its polarity to east-facing (west-dipping subduction) in order for the Pacific crust of today's Caribbean plate to become inserted between the Americas (Fig. 5). Estimates for the time of the reversal range from Aptian (e.g., this paper; Mattson, 1979; Pindell and Dewey, 1982; Snoke, 1991; Draper et al., 1996; Snoke and Noble, 2001), to Campanian (e.g., Burke, 1988; Kerr et al., 1998).

Our "Pacific-origin" model for Caribbean evolution is outlined in Figure 5 and honors the seven plate-kinematic, magmatic, stratigraphic, and paleobiogeographic arguments for the Pacific origin outlined by Pindell (1990). However, "intra-American" models for the origin of the Caribbean crust (i.e., derived from Proto-Caribbean lithosphere that formed between the Americas) persist (Meschede and Frisch, 1998; Kerr et al., 1999; James, 2002). Here, we further affirm the Pacific origin of the Caribbean plate by noting that intra-American origin models predict the following contradictions of Caribbean geology:

1. Inception of arc magmatism in the Greater Antilles Arc would be younger in intra-American origin models than that in the Costa Rica–Panama Arc, whereas the opposite is true (Maurrasse, 1990; Donnelly et al., 1990; Lebrón and Perfit, 1993; Calvo and Bolz, 1994; Stöckhert et al., 1995; Draper et al., 1996; Hauff et al., 2000; Stanek et al., 2000; Maresch et al., 2000).

2. Passive margin conditions in Colombia, western Venezuela, and Yucatán would have ceased by the Albian had the Caribbean arcs formed between the Americas, whereas they persisted well into the Late Cretaceous (Pindell and Erikson, 1994; Villamil and Pindell, 1998; Villamil, 1999; Erlich et al., 2000).

3. The Proto-Caribbean Seaway was not as large as the area of the Caribbean plate until Campanian (Pindell et al., 1988; Müller et al., 1999), but recent seismic data (e.g., Driscoll and Diebold, 1999) argue against seafloor spreading in the Caribbean plate as young as Campanian, which is required in intra-Ameri-

can origin models to explain the size of the Caribbean plate. Rather, the data indicate that ocean-plateau basalts were erupted upon a preexisting ocean floor at ca. 90 Ma, with no detectable plate growth thereafter.

4. If we consider the enormous area of Caribbean lithosphere that has been subducted beneath Colombia and western Venezuela as indicated by seismic tomography (van der Hilst and Mann, 1994), then the Proto-Caribbean was *never* wide enough to have housed the entire Caribbean plate, which must therefore have been situated west of Guajira (Fig. 2) until after Maastrichtian time.

Figure 5 portrays the arc-polarity reversal at the Inter-American Arc as Aptian. In the following section, we review existing Caribbean *P-T-t* data that are critical among our reasons for interpreting the Aptian as the time of initial southwest-dipping subduction in the Great Caribbean Arc, and, hence, of the arc-polarity reversal as well.

P-T-t DATA FROM CIRCUM-CARIBBEAN METAMORPHIC TERRANES

Metamorphic petrology and geochronology of Early to Late Cretaceous rocks of the circum-Caribbean region (Table 1 and references therein) point to an Aptian onset of southwestward dipping subduction beneath the Great Caribbean Arc, and hence to early Aptian subduction-polarity reversal. For several reasons, caution must be exercised when interpreting the data of Table 1. Geochronological systems such as Rb-Sr and K-Ar yield cooling ages only and require careful analysis. Incomplete resetting during multiple metamorphic events may lead to meaningless results. During HP-LT metamorphism, some minerals may incorporate excess argon, leading to higher apparent ages.

Blueschist and other HP-LT assemblages ranging in age from ca. 125 Ma to ca. 70 Ma are found in Guatemala, Cuba, Dominican Republic, Jamaica, northern Venezuela and Colombia, but not in Puerto Rico (the Bermeja complex is greenschist-amphibolite facies meta-ophiolite). Protoliths include fragments

---

Figure 5 (*following pages*). (A–H) Model for the evolution of the Caribbean region from 120 Ma to 19 Ma, drawn in North American reference frame and simplified from similar maps in Pindell and Kennan (2001b). The model is geometrically viable and satisfies primary geological constraints. In particular, the spreading between North and South America, and the need to keep the Andean margin compressive since 100–120 Ma while the northern Caribbean interacts with southern Mexico, Yucatán, and the Bahamas, places strong constraints on the position, rate of migration and rate of rotation of the Caribbean plate. NOAM—North America; SOAM—South America; CAR—Caribbean plate; FAR—Farallon plate; KUL—Kula plate; NAm—North American plate; SAm—South American plate; HS—hotspot; RRF—ridge-ridge-fault; V—volcanic; Oc—oceanic; CAY—Cayman; CC—Central Cordillera; DR—Dominican Republic; EC—Eastern Cordillera; ESC—Escambray; HA—Haiti; HUAL—Huallaga Basin; MAR—Margarita; MOC—Mocoa; MS—Muertos Shelf; NC—Northern Cordillera; OCA—Oca Fault; PI—Isle of Pines or Isle of Youth; PR—Puerto Rico; SANT—Santiago Basin; SWH—Southwest Haiti; SMB—Santa Marta–Bucaramanga fault; TOB—Tobago; VIR—Virgin Islands.

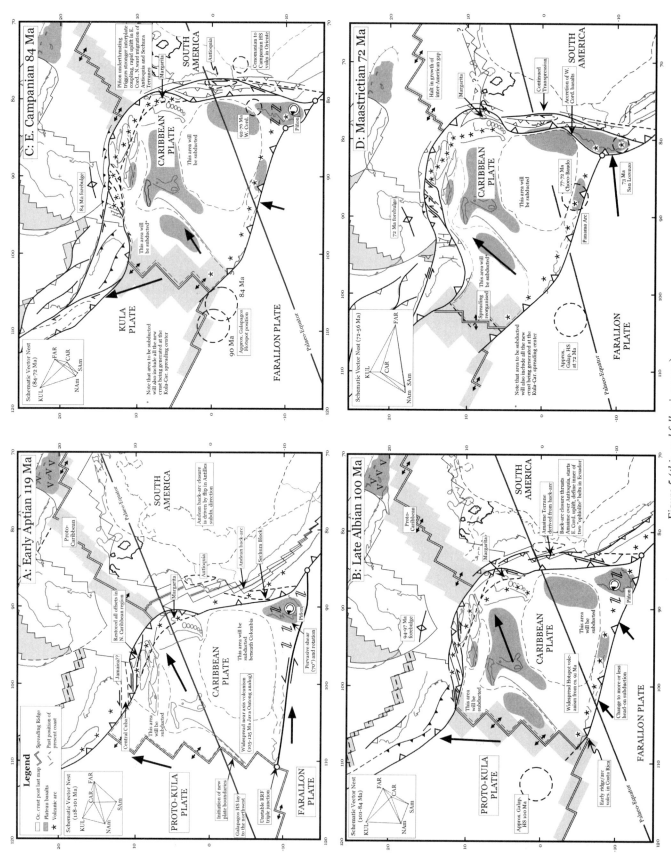

Figure 5 (*this and following page*).

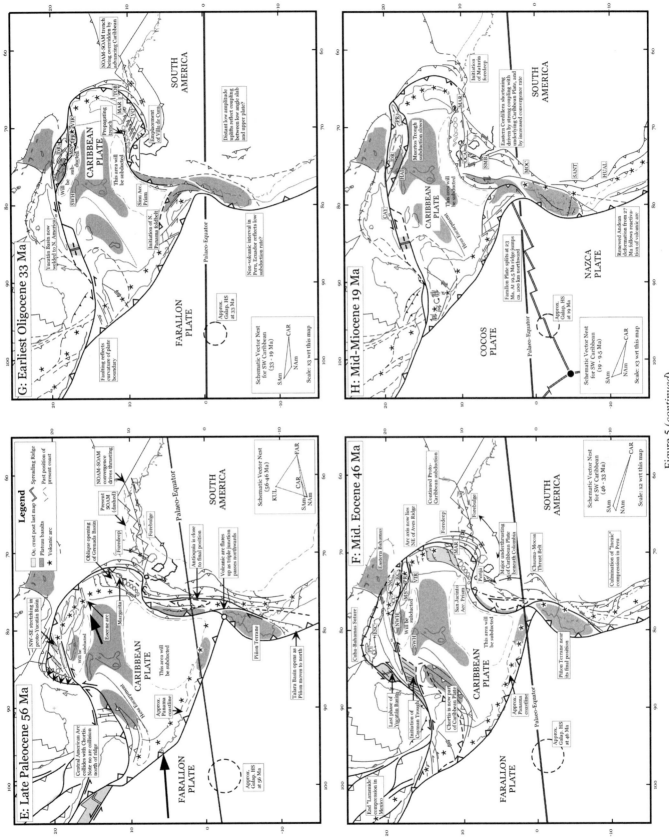

Figure 5 (*continued*).

TABLE 1. TIMING OF METAMORPHISM, IGNEOUS ACTIVITY, AND COOLING IN SUBDUCTION COMPLEXES AROUND THE CARIBBEAN

Complex	Location	Lithology	Protolith	Dating	Interpretation	References
Northern margin						
Motagua Fault Zone	Guatemala	HP blueschists, eclogites and jadeiites as inclusions in fault bounded serpentinites; eclogites more common on south side of MFZ	Probably Proto-Caribbean oceanic crust formed at spreading center between southern Mexico and Colombia	116–125 Ma Ar-Ar Phen (south side Motagua); 65–77 Ma Ar-Ar Phen (south side Motagua); 78–63.7 Ma Ar-Ar; 58.5 ± 3.7 Ma K-Ar	The oldest ages may come from preexisting HP-LT rocks from the Pacific-facing trench south of Chortis. However, revised ages for Cretaceous stages indicate an Aptian age for metamorphism, matching both geochronologic and stratigraphic data elsewhere in the Caribbean (Fig. 6), suggesting these too formed during arc-polarity reversal to the southwest of their present location. Ca. 65 Ma ages are interpreted as time of collision between leading edge of Caribbean Arc and southern margin of Yucatán, unroofing HP-LT rocks that formed as Proto-Caribbean oceanic crust subducted beneath the Great Caribbean Arc. Older rocks now lie on the south side of the MFZ associated with slivers of Chortis basement, but regional reconstructions suggest this juxtaposition is probably as young as Oligocene-Miocene, related to eastward motion of Chortis relative to Yucatán during opening of the Cayman Trough farther east.	Bertrand et al., 1978; Harlow, 1994; Harlow et al., 2002; McBirney et al., 1967; Sisson et al., 2003; Sutter, 1979; Gradstein et al., 2004
Blue Mountains	Jamaica	Greenschists, blueschists, amphibolites, serpentinites	MORB, probably of Proto-Caribbean origin	48.8 ± 1.3 K-Ar Bt; 52.9 ± 1.4 Ma K-Ar Bt; 76.5 ± 2.1 Ma K-Ar Hbl; all ages reset	Metamorphic rocks underlie Campanian-Maastrichtian arc rocks, cherts. Not clear if relationship is structural or stratigraphic. Overlain unconformably by Eocene strata (post-date latest cooling ages?). If unconformable, then metamorphism and uplift may relate to subduction-polarity reversal event.	Draper et al., 1976; Draper, 1979, 1986; Lewis et al., 1973
Cangre Belt	Western Cuba	Blueschist-facies metabasite lenses in metacarbonate and quartz-mica schist	Jurassic (to Lower Cretaceous) passive margin sediments	119 ± 10 K-Ar WM	Blueschist-facies metamorphic belt overthrust north onto weakly metamorphosed Sierra Guaniguanico (allochthonous Late Jurassic passive margin strata) prior to Eocene.	Somin and Millán, 1972, 1981; Millán, 1988
Escambray	Central Cuba	Eclogite, blueschist and marble lenses in carbonate-mica and quartz-mica schists; ferruginous metaquartzites	Jurassic to Lower Cretaceous carbonate and clastic sediments and volcanics deposited on southwest margin off the Bahamas platform	160–140 Ma U-Pb Zr; 106–102 Ma U-Pb Zr; 71 ± 1 Ma U-Pb Ti; 65–70 Ma Ar-Ar, Rb-Sr WM; 58–66 Ma FT Zr; 40–60 Ma FT Ap	Protolith includes Late Jurassic to Early Cretaceous marbles and quartzites derived from southeast margin of Chortis Block. Zircons in some eclogite lenses yield Proterozoic upper intercept age, Late Jurassic lower intercept: metamorphism in a pre-Caribbean Late Jurassic subduction environment? Otherwise HP-LT (up to 630 °C, 25 kbar) metamorphism in west-dipping trench at 118–102 Ma followed by uplift. Juxtaposed with Mabujina arc tholeiites before 80–90 Ma intrusion by non-metamorphic igneous rocks. Continued cooling to <350 °C by ca. 65 Ma. Exhumation may have been driven by tangential extension associated with opening of Yucatán basin. Unconformably overlain by middle Eocene chalks. Barrovian metamorphism on Isle of Youth is older than 72 Ma.	Somin and Millán, 1981; Renne et al., 1989; Somin et al., 1992; Stanek, 2000; Grafe et al., 2001; Maresch et al., 2003
Mabujina	Central Cuba	Amphibolite-facies metavolcanics, gneisses, metasediments	PIA of the Greater Antillean Arc	>110 Ma Pb-Pb Zr; 87–80 Ma cross-cutting granitic intrusives; 74–72 Ma Rb-Sr, Ar-Ar Bt, WM	Somin and Millán, 1981; Bibikova et al. 1988; Stanek, 2000; Grafe et al., 2001

TABLE 1. TIMING OF METAMORPHISM, IGNEOUS ACTIVITY, AND COOLING IN SUBDUCTION COMPLEXES AROUND THE CARIBBEAN (continued)

Complex	Location	Lithology	Protolith	Dating	Interpretation	References
Northern Serpentinitic Mélange	Central Cuba	Eclogite slivers in serpentinitic mélange	Probably Proto-Caribbean oceanic crust	115–103 Ma Ar-Ar WM, amphibole; 118 Ma Rb-Sr isochron		García-Casco et al., 2002
Isle of Youth	Offshore southwest Cuba	Marble, carbonate-mica, and quartz-mica schists	Jurassic (to Lower Cretaceous) passive margin sediments	72–68 Ma Ar-Ar Bt, WM; 68–60 Ma cross-cutting subvolcanic dikes		Millán 1975; Somin and Millán 1977; García-Casco et al., 2001
Purial	Eastern Cuba	HP-LT metabasite and gneiss	Protolith unknown	105–103 U-Pb Zr; 82 Ma K-Ar isochron	Basement of the Oriente nappe stack	Hatten et al., 1989; Somin et al., 1992
Puerto Plata, Río San Juan, Samaná	Northern Dominican Republic	Garnet-bearing blueschists and eclogite, metagranitoids, serpentinite mélange	MORB, probably of Proto-Caribbean origin	ca. 100 Ma Ar-Ar on glaucophane (?); 120 ± 100, 125 ± 50, and 250 ± 100 Ma, all K-Ar on glaucophane; 78 ± 30 Ma Sm-Nd eclogite, 90 ± 10 Ma Rb-Sr eclogite, 98 ± 3 Lu-Hf eclogite, 70 Ma and 85 Ma Rb-Sr isochrons on metagranites; 85 ± 2 Ma Ar-Ar hornblende; 62 ± 2 Ma Ar-Ar phengite; 37–39 Ma K-Ar phengite; 25–50 Ar-Ar phengite	98 Ma Lu-Hf age pinpoints time of eclogite formation thought to be associated with post-flip westward subduction. Suggests polarity reversal is older than 100 Ma. Large spread in ages and peak metamorphic P-T conditions points to complex arrays of P-T-t paths in subduction zone. Mid-crustal levels generally reached by Eocene.	Joyce and Aronson, 1989; Draper and Nagle, 1991; Krebs et al., 1999, 2003; Perfit and McCulloch, 1982; Gonçalves et al., 2000; Catlos and Sorensen, 2003
Duarte	Central Dominican Republic	Metagabbros, metabasalts, cherts	Mixed ages, Oceanic Plateau Basalt affinities	86.1 ± 1.3 Ma Ar-Ar, 86.7 ± 1.6 Ma Ar-Ar, both on plateau basalts (Caribbean origin?); 123–148 Ma K-Ar on associated metatonalites and gabbros	Duarte complex is highly heterogenous. Oldest components may be Jurassic oceanic plateau with cherts (possible correlation to early Caribbean Piñon of Ecuador) or fragments of early Cretaceous forearc (basement to Amina-Maimón arc). Older ages may be misleading due to later structural juxtaposition, excess Ar, etc.	Lapierre et al., 1999; Draper and Lewis, 1989, 1991
Amina-Maimón Los Ranchos	Central Dominican Republic	Greenschist metavolcanic mylonite, metavolcanics, volcaniclastics	Neocomian Primitive Island Arc	Metamorphism and penetrative deformation must predate 110 Ma	Early Cretaceous arc is metamorphosed (>10 km depth), uplifted, and eroded prior to ca. 110 Ma Hatillo Limestone. In turn overlain by Tireo calc-alkaline arc is 93–89 Ma ± younger dacites.	Draper et al., 1996
La Desirade	Northern Lesser Antilles	Pillow basalts, cherts, plagiogranite, basic dykes	147–140 Ma U-Pb Zr; end-Jurassic (faunal age)		Associated with Pacific affinity cherts. Probably formed at a Pacific spreading center and represents basement of Caribbean plate.	Mattinson et al., 1980; Montgomery et al., 1994

TABLE 1. TIMING OF METAMORPHISM, IGNEOUS ACTIVITY, AND COOLING IN SUBDUCTION COMPLEXES AROUND THE CARIBBEAN (continued)

Complex	Location	Lithology	Protolith	Dating	Interpretation	References
Southern margin						
North Coast schist	Tobago	Greenschist metavolcanic rocks, volcaniclastic rocks	Pyroclastic, epiclastic fringe to (Primitive?) Island Arc	120 Ma or older Ar-Ar from PIA; 105–103 Ma Ar-Ar from TVG and TPS; 113–102 Ma K-Ar from TVG, TPS	Aptian and older PIA rocks are metamorphosed prior to late Aptian–Albian plutonism and volcanism, also of "primitive island arc" character.	Snoke et al., 2001; Snoke et al., 1990; Speed and Smith-Horowitz, 1998
La Rinconada	Margarita, Venezuela	Metabasalts, metagabbros and ultrabasics; trondhjemites	MORB, probably of Proto-Caribbean origin	116–109 Ma U-Pb Zr concordant	Continental fragment juxtaposed after 109 Ma with MORB formed in backarc or Colombian marginal seaway in a subduction zone. No similar aged MORB known from Caribbean Plate. Peak metamorphic conditions of up to 650 °C/20 kbar reached before 86 Ma when El Salado granite was intruded, still at ~25 km depth. We infer HP-LT metamorphism in west-dipping subduction zone immediately after subduction polarity reversal, followed by exhumation continuing into Oligocene.	Stöckhert et al., 1995; Maresch et al., 2000
Juan Griego	Margarita, Venezuela	Quartz-feldspar gneiss and garnet-mica schists, granitoid intrusives, marbles	Continental sedimentary and/ or igneous rocks	315 Ma U-Pb Zr upper intercept augen gneiss; 86 Ma U-Pb Zr and 90–80 Ma Ar-Ar WM on unmetamorphosed El Salado Pluton; 66 Ma Ar-Ar amph in dyke; 55–50 Ma K-Ar WM in recrystallized schist; 53–36 Ma Zr FT; 23 ± 2 Ma apatite FT		Stöckhert et al., 1995; Maresch et al., 2000
Villa de Cura	Venezuela	Metavolcanics, metavolcaniclastics; four metamorphic zones, from north to south: (1) pumpellyite-actinolite, (2) glaucophane-lawsonite, (3) glaucophane-epidote, and (4) barroisite	Volcanic island arc and associated clastic fringe	79.8 ± 0.4 Ma Ar-Ar WM for the three N zones; 96.8–96.3 Ma Ar-Ar barrositic amphibole; 91.1–89.5 Ma Ar-Ar WM for barroisite zone; 101–77 Ma K-Ar amph; 87–82 Ma K-Ar WM; 107–98 Ma K-Ar Hbl from ultrabasic intrusive complex (excess Ar?); 43.4–41.9 Ma Zr FT on Tinaco diorite 10 km to N; 6.1 Ma Ap FT on Tinaco diorite 30 km to W	HP-LT metamorphism of a >100 Ma protolith in forearc to west-dipping subduction zone. Adjacent bodies of rock reached peak metamorphism between 96 Ma and 78 Ma. The significance of 107–98 ages from associated non-metamorphic ultrabasic intrusives remains unclear. Ongoing cooling and unroofing prior to emplacement during Oligocene-Miocene. We consider it unlikely that a subduction polarity reversal could have occurred in the interval 96–78 Ma, ruling out trench "choking" by Caribbean Igneous Plateau at ca. 90 Ma as proposed by others.	Smith et al., 1999; Hebeda et al., 1984; Skerlec and Hargraves, 1980; Kohn et al., 1984

Continued

TABLE 1. TIMING OF METAMORPHISM, IGNEOUS ACTIVITY, AND COOLING IN SUBDUCTION COMPLEXES AROUND THE CARIBBEAN (continued)

Complex	Location	Lithology	Protolith	Dating	Interpretation	References
Cordillera de la Costa	Venezuela	Serpentinites, leucotonalitic gneisses, amphibolites, actinolite-garnet-mica-chlorite schists, blueschists ("oceanic assemblage"); graphite-garnet-mica schists, marbles, quartzites, quartz-feldspar gneisses ("continental assemblage"); metagranites and augengneisses	Very heterogeneous. "Oceanic assemblage" comprises dismembered meta-ophiolite, juxtaposed with "continental assemblage" of probable passive margin origin; deformed and metamorphosed intrusive rocks; some gneisses may be basement to passive margin strata	494 ± 52, 467 ± 52 Ma U-Pb on "basement gneisses"; 753, 735, 155, 32 Ma K-Ar on amphibolites; 77–76 Ma K-Ar from metadiorites, possibly originally cross-cutting intrusives?; AFT and ZFT data show protracted cooling history into the late Cenozoic	Blueschist metamorphism probably occurred at west-dipping subduction zone, as also inferred for Margarita and Villa de Cura HP-LT rocks. Relationships of HP-LT rocks to greenschist-grade "passive margin" protoliths are not clear, nor is the original depositional location of these "passive margin" rocks: are they para-autochthonous parts of the central Venezuelan margin or do they derive from farther west?	Morgan, 1967, 1970; Avé Lallemant and Sisson, 1993; Sisson et al., 1997
Northwest Guajira	Northern Colombia	Garnet-bearing eclogite, greenschists, amphibolite, serpentinite mélange		48 ± 4 Ma K-Ar ?whole rock? on diorite stock that post-dates metamorphism, emplacement; unroofing recorded by eclogite clasts in ?Oligocene conglomerate	Metamorphism and initial unroofing during middle or late Cretaceous (unconformably overlain by Maastrichtian strata offshore) emplacement of leading edge of Caribbean in latest Cretaceous, prior to Eocene emplacement or unroofing of non-metamorphic stock.	Green et al., 1968
Western South America						
Antioquia	Central Colombia	HT-LP (Abukuma) pre–220 Ma	Paleozoic clastic sediments	Locations for data not known; 120–108 Ma K-Ar; 75–57 Ma K-Ar	Early cluster may relate to proposed backarc closure. Late cluster may relate to exhumation driven by Caribbean underthrusting. Overlain by early Albian (ca. 110–100 Ma) sediments prior to overthrusting by Amaime Terrane.	McCourt et al., 1984; Bourgois et al., 1987
Amaime	Central Colombia	Basalts, pillow lavas, ?komatiites?		163 ± 10–131 ± 9 Ma ?K-Ar WR?; 126 ± 12 Ma K-Ar Hbl (all above from Cauca Ophiolite); intruded by 113–99 Ma Buga Batholith (?post-metamorphic?)	Pre-Albian age and intrusion by arc (?) Buga Batholith suggest formation within narrow Andean backarc during Early Cretaceous. Nappes emplaced east onto the Central Cordillera after 110–100 Ma.	McCourt et al., 1984; Restrepo and Toussaint 1974; Restrepo and Toussaint, 1976
Jambaló	Central Colombia	HP-LT metamorphics	Not known	125 ± 15 Ma K-Ar WR; 104 ± 14 Ma K-Ar WR	Possibly protolith or metamorphic-uplift ages. Here we interpret driving mechanism for metamorphism to be eastward overthrusting of arc over backarc basin. Associated with eastward thrusting of Amaime (backarc basalts).	Orrego et al., 1980; Feininger, 1982; De Souza et al., 1984

Continued

TABLE 1. TIMING OF METAMORPHISM, IGNEOUS ACTIVITY, AND COOLING IN SUBDUCTION COMPLEXES AROUND THE CARIBBEAN (continued)

Complex	Location	Lithology	Protolith	Dating	Interpretation	References
Raspas	SW Ecuador	Garnet-kyanite–bearing schists, omphacite-garnet eclogites, sheared serpentinites	N-MORB, E-MORB, quartzose and shaley clastic sediments of continental origin	221–228 Ma, method not known; continental protolith age; 132 ± 5 Ma K-Ar phengite; 80–70 Ma reset ages from adjacent non–HP-LT metamorphics	Highly sheared. Generally south-dipping structures may reflect Late Cretaceous accretion of Piñon Terrane. Context of ?Barremian-Aptian blueschist uncertain—does it indicate polarity reversal and terrane accretion earlier in south than north?	Malfrère et al., 1999; Arculus et al., 1999; Aspden et al., 1995; Feininger and Silberman, 1982
Other relevant data						
Cordillera Real	Ecuador	Granitoids, metavolcanics, and clastic metasediments	Backarc and arc granites and transitional crust	144 Ma U-Pb Zr is youngest intrusive age; 125–145 Ma K-Ar ages may be partial reset; 60–100 Ma K-Ar ages are widespread	We suggest that ca. 145 Ma marks time of final opening of backarc, rifting the arc away from the margin. From 100 Ma, backarc was closed, associated with dextral transpressive deformation, accretion of Piñon Terrane (overlain by late Cretaceous quartzose sediments), and large magnitude clockwise rotation.	Litherland et al., 1994 Noble et al., 1997
Celica-Ayabaca	Ecuador, Peru	Andesite		113 Ma K-Ar ?WR? on cross-cutting pluton	Aptian or older andesitic Celica volcanics with continental signature are intruded by Late Aptian plutons. Overlain unconformably by Albian-Cenomanian volcaniclastics. No clearly Albian or younger arc (e.g., lavas, pyroclastics). Ayabaca volcanics of N. Peru are similar. Not dated but note no significant volcanic influence in Albian and younger sediments in nearby West Peru Trough.	Kennerley, 1980; Berrones et al., 1993; Jaillard et al., 1996
Casma	Peru	Greenschist	Andesites, volcaniclastics	102 Ma K-Ar on granitoids	Greenschist metamorphism of Aptian?-Albian volcaniclastics predates late Albian, 102 Ma, plutonism.	Cobbing et al., 1981

Note: HP-LT—high-pressure–low temperature; MORB—mid-oceanic-ridge basalt; E-MORB—enriched MORB; N-MORB—normal MORB; amph—amphibole; Ap—apatite; Bt—biotite; Hbl—hornblende; Lu-Hf—letetium-hafnium; Phen—phengite; Ti—titanite; WM—white mica; WR—whole rock; Zr—zircon; AFT—apatite fission-track age; FT—fission track; MFZ—Motagua Fault Zone; PIA—Primitive Island Arc; TPS—Tobago Plutonic Suite; TVG—Tobago Volcanic Group; ZFT—zircon fission-track age.

of Paleozoic continental crust (Margarita) and continent-derived sedimentary rocks that formed the basement or forearc of the Inter-American Arc (which formed as the Americas separated in the Late Jurassic and Early Cretaceous), as well as volcanic ocean floor and arc rocks.

In Guatemala, HP-LT rocks are found on north and south sides of the Motagua Fault Zone (Harlow et al., 2003), associated with the dismembered ophiolite, serpentinite bodies mapped the "El Tambor Group." Recent mapping shows that jadeitites and albitites are common in both north and south, but that eclogite and blueschist are much more common in the southern exposures. Ar-Ar ages on phengites are consistently 116–125 Ma in the south and, north of the Motagua Fault, are consistently 65–77 Ma (Sisson et al., 2003). In both cases, these ages are interpreted to be at or near peak-metamorphism and, together with the lithological contrast, suggest that two discrete belts of HP-LT rocks formed during two discrete events and may have been separated by up to several hundred kilometers prior to Cenozoic sinistral motion on the Motagua Fault. In both belts, the nature of the protolith is unclear (possibly volcanic rocks of primitive arc or oceanic origin). The original position of the southern belt with respect to the Great Caribbean Arc at the time of subduction polarity reversal is also unclear, such that this older belt may have formed very early in the polarity reversal event on the north flank of the arc or may contain rocks metamorphosed at the older west-facing trench prior to the reversal event. In neither belt is there any age data indicating a significant event occurring at ca. 90 Ma.

In Cuba, Late Jurassic equilibration of the U-Pb isotopic system is found in the zircons of some rare eclogites (Grafe et al., 2001), but the nature (i.e., magmatic, metamorphic, etc.) of the thermal event is at present enigmatic. We interpret this older material to have been incorporated into the Inter-American Arc (Fig. 3) as it swept past the southern end of the Chortís block (where Jurassic igneous rocks in a clastic and carbonate sedimentary sequence similar to the Cuban protoliths are present; Gordon, 1990). Primitive island-arc (PIA) volcanic protoliths are found in Cuba (Los Pasos Formation; Stanek et al., 2000) and Tobago (North Coast Schist; Snoke et al., 2001) with minimum ages of 110 Ma, and some older metatonalites and metagabbros are known. Pacific-derived Jurassic mid-oceanic-ridge basalt (MORB) crust and associated chert is present in La Desirade. MORBs (La Rinconada unit) erupted at 116–109 Ma are found in Margarita (Stöckhert et al., 1995), which is consistent with an origin at the spreading center in the Colombian Marginal Seaway, to the east of the Intra-American oceanic island arc (Fig. 5).

In central Colombia and Ecuador, blueschists are also found as highly sheared fault-bounded slivers along the Romeral-Peltetec Suture and in the El Oro Belt of southern Ecuador. K-Ar ages from Raspas (southern Ecuador) and Jambaló (southern Colombia) range from 125 to 132 Ma (Aspden and McCourt, 1986; Aspden et al., 1992, 1995). Both the field relationships and the ages are less easy to interpret than those in Cuba and Margarita, and it is not clear if the HP-LT rocks here directly relate to the polarity-reversal event. In the El Oro Belt of southernmost

Ecuador, the Raspas blueschists are found north of both an Early Cretaceous arc and associated continental fragments and, if we account for at least 60°–90° of clockwise rotation (Mourier et al., 1988a), appear to lie on the west side (Pacific-facing) of the Early Cretaceous arc. Farther north, in central Ecuador, fragments of continental to transitional crust found to the west of the Peltetec ophiolite suture are inferred to be the trace of the "Andean backarc" or southern part of the "Colombian Marginal Seaway" (Fig. 4). However, the Jambaló blueschists are found farther north in Colombia and have no associated continental or arc fragments to the west or farther north along the trace of the Romeral Fault. Thus, although the blueschists might have originated during oblique closure of the Andean backarc basin, with the ages indicating onset of polarity reversal prior to the Aptian, it is also possible that the blueschists could have formed on the southwest side of the older, pre-reversal Inter-American Arc. If they did form on the southwest side of that arc, they must have been sheared into place during the intense southwest-northeast dextral slip that occurred in northern South America during the Cretaceous at the southeastern margin of the Caribbean plate.

Throughout the circum-Caribbean region, HP-LT metamorphism could have occurred at either the east-dipping subduction zone (prior to polarity reversal) or the west-dipping subduction zone (after polarity reversal), and we would expect significant unroofing to occur during the arc-polarity reversal event itself, because of the probability of transient doubly-vergent underthrusting beneath the arc. We conclude for the following reasons that the reversal occurred at, or at most a few million years before, 115–120 Ma:

1. With the possible exception of the rare Late Jurassic zircon ages from Cuba noted above (probably protolith ages) and a few slightly older K-Ar or Ar-Ar ages found in Andean terranes and in Guatemala, no HP-LT metamorphic rocks with ages older than ca. 120 Ma are known in the circum-Caribbean.

2. Potentially rapid burial and unroofing events are recorded in Cuba, Hispaniola, and Puerto Rico, where greenschist-grade metamorphic rocks were exhumed and then unconformably overlain by Albian limestones, and in Tobago, where the greenschist-grade North Coast Schist was intruded by the unmetamorphosed Tobago Volcanic Suite at ca. 105 Ma (Snoke et al., 2001). Part of the Villa de Cura Complex in Venezuela may also have been buried and exhumed at this time as metamorphic components of the Villa de Cura were intruded by unmetamorphosed 108–98 Ma ultrabasic rocks (Hebeda et al., 1984; Smith et al., 1999).

3. In *P-T-t* loops of HP-LT metamorphic rocks around the Caribbean, the 90–20 Ma interval is generally characterized by exhumation processes and not interrupted by burial or prograde metamorphic events, consistent with polarity reversal occurring before that time. Nowhere is peak HP-LT metamorphism recorded at ca. 85 Ma, as would be expected if subduction of the buoyant ca. 90 Ma Caribbean Large Igneous Province was the cause of polarity reversal, as argued by Burke (1988) and Kerr et al. (1998).

Numerous processes may lead to exhumation of HP rocks in the Great Arc, including arc-parallel stretching (mainly Late Cretaceous), obduction of forearc materials onto rifted continental margins (Late Cretaceous–Paleogene), low-angle detachment at intra-arc basins (Maastrichtian–Paleocene at Yucatán Basin), extensional detachment during creation of intra-arc pull-apart basins (early to middle Eocene at Grenada Basin), and possibly vertical extrusion along high-angle transpressive faults (Late Cretaceous in Andes terranes). All of these possibilities are discussed below.

APTIAN SUBDUCTION POLARITY REVERSAL: INTER-AMERICAN ARC BECOMES THE GREAT CARIBBEAN ARC

Constraints on Timing

Seven independent lines of evidence point to the Aptian as the time of the subduction polarity reversal that transformed the Inter-American Arc (southwest-facing) into the Great Caribbean Arc (northeast-facing). At no other time in the histories of the various parts of the Caribbean arc system was there such a profound change in depositional, magmatic, structural, and geochemical conditions (Fig. 6). Furthermore, the changes that occurred were very similar in many of the older arc fragments. This suggests that the various arc fragments once lay much closer together than they do today, an argument that itself points to the Early Cretaceous, when the gap between the Americas was still relatively small.

Onset of HP-LT Metamorphism

As shown in Table 1, circum-Caribbean HP metamorphic rocks indicate peak metamorphism dating back to the Aptian (119–112 Ma). The older age from the Escambray complex, Cuba (Table 1), appears to be exotic to the Inter-American Arc and Neocomian ages from the Motagua Fault Zone, and the northern Andes

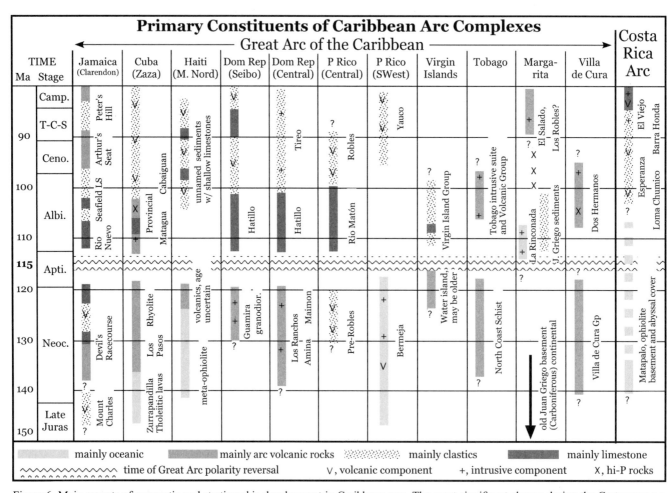

Figure 6. Main aspects of magmatic and stratigraphic development in Caribbean arcs. The most significant change during the Cretaceous occurred at ca. 120–115 Ma. Note lack of significant changes at 80–90 Ma, a time proposed for polarity reversal by other authors. Prior to the Aptian subduction polarity reversal and associated hiatus, nearly all Caribbean terranes show evidence of primitive island-arc magmatism, but it is not clear if these formed at a west-facing Inter-American Arc (requiring polarity reversal), or if they were dragged across the inter-American gap by transform motion. The complete lack of continental influence in the pre-Aptian stratigraphies of the arc pieces argues for an intra-oceanic arc (formed in the Inter-American gap), rather than an arc that was sheared away from Chortís. Camp.—Campanian; T-C-S—Turonian-Coniacian-Santonian; Ceno.—Cenomanian; Albi.—Albian; Apti.—Aptian; Neoc.—Neocomian; Juras—Jurassic; M. Nord—middle and north.

may be from HP-LT rocks that predate the polarity reversal and were emplaced along strike-slip faults at the flanks of the Caribbean plate. We interpret the Aptian onset of HP metamorphism in Cuba and Margarita as dating the inception of the southwest-dipping Benioff zone. Most of the Aptian and younger HP ages are from rocks on the northeast side of the Great Caribbean Arc; therefore, if the polarity reversal occurred any later than Aptian, it would have been necessary for HP rocks on the southwestern flank of the arc to pass beneath the higher temperature arc axis to be exhumed on the northeastern flank of the arc, which we think highly unlikely.

Hiatus in Volcano-Sedimentary History

In areas of the Great Caribbean Arc where pre-Albian arc rocks are present, a strong Aptian hiatus separates the older, usually metamorphosed rocks from little- or non-metamorphosed Albian and younger rocks (Fig. 6). Possible causes for this hiatus are (1) strong uplift in the wedge of arc material above the opposing Benioff zones during the transient arc polarity reversal, (2) tectonic unroofing due to arc-parallel extension (Draper, 2001), and (3) erosion at localized transpressional(?) uplifts along the Inter-American Arc prior to polarity reversal (or a combination of both).

Development of a Limestone Platform upon Parts of the Aptian Hiatus

In Cuba, Hispaniola, and Puerto Rico, the units beneath the Aptian hiatus are commonly metamorphosed to or near to greenschist grade and unconformably overlain by the unmetamorphosed Albian, shallow water, fossil-bearing Provincial, Hatillo, and Río Matón limestones, respectively. In Tobago, the greenschist-grade North Coast Schist (of PIA geochemical character; Jackson et al., 1988) is also deeply eroded and overlain by extrusive volcanics and intruded by plutons, both of the less-metamorphosed Tobago Volcanic Group, dated paleontologically and isotopically as middle Albian (Snoke et al., 2001; Snoke and Noble, 2001).

Shift in the Positions of Magmatic Axes

In at least the Hispaniolan and possibly the Cuban portions of the Great Caribbean Arc, the magmatic axis appears to have shifted southwest from the pre-Aptian to the Albian. In Hispaniola, we consider the Los Ranchos and Maimón Formations as pre-reversal arc and the Tireo Formation, which lies some 20–60 km southwest of Los Ranchos Formation (Bowin, 1966; Lewis and Draper, 1990), as post-reversal arc. In central Cuba (which we suggest represents only the forearc of the Great Arc; Paleocene opening of the Yucatán [intra-arc] Basin separated the Cuban forearc from the bulk of the Great Arc's magmatic axis beneath Cayman Ridge), the occurrence of the Los Pasos Formation (primitive, pre-reversal arc lavas) some 10–30 km northeast of the Cabaiguan Formation (evolved, post-reversal arc lavas) (Stanek, 2000) might suggest a southwesterly shift in the magmatic axis as well. The shift may also have occurred at the Aves Ridge portion of the arc, such that pre-reversal arc lithologies such as the La Desirade Complex (Mattinson et al., 1980) and the North Coast Schist of Tobago

have occupied a forearc position since the reversal. The shift in the magmatic axis may also explain why HP-LT metamorphic rocks from the pre-reversal subduction zone have not clearly been recognized. The post-reversal arc may have buried and/or destroyed them.

Change in Arc Magmatic Chemistry

Magma chemistry is dramatically different above and below the Aptian discontinuity in some parts of the arc. Donnelly et al. (1990) and Lebrón and Perfit (1993) pointed out that in the Greater Antilles, pre-Albian arc magmas are generally PIA tholeiites, whereas Albian and younger magmas are mainly calc-alkaline (CA). The change from PIA to enriched CA magmas may pertain to differing sedimentary and/or crustal materials entering the Benioff zone before and after the reversal (Lebrón and Perfit, 1993; Pindell, 1993).

Emplacement of Nappes in Hispaniola

Draper et al. (1996) showed that the mylonitization and inverted metamorphism in the Maimón Schist and the development of penetrative fabrics in the Neocomian Los Ranchos Formation of central Hispaniola record a significant orogenic event, probably the northward thrusting of peridotites over these two units. Because the two units are overlain by the undeformed lower middle Albian Hatillo Limestone, the deformation must have occurred during the Aptian to early Albian. Draper et al. (1996) concluded that the timing of deformation coincides with the timing of the change in arc magmatism from PIA to CA, and that the orogenic event was related to arc-polarity reversal.

Geometric Simplicity

At 120 Ma (start of Aptian), the Inter-American Arc was very short and likely quite straight, bridging the juvenile gap between Mexico and Ecuador. By 80 Ma (Campanian), the arc would have been nearly 2000 km long and likely quite arcuate or cusped. We consider that reversal would have been far more complex, longer-lived, and comprised several significant sub-events once a long and arcuate arc geometry had been established. In the Campanian, it is difficult to pick out *any* regional arc event (Fig. 6), let alone one as complex as might be expected were the arc 2000 km long.

Cause of the Arc-Polarity Reversal

Much of the crust of the Caribbean plate is ~20 km thick (Case et al., 1990), and widespread basaltic extrusions (Caribbean basaltic plateau marked by seismic reflector B″) are believed to be at least partially responsible for the abnormal thickness. Burke et al. (1978) considered that this abnormal thickness would cause excessive buoyancy relative to "normal" oceanic crust. They, as well as Livaccari et al. (1981), Burke (1988), Kerr et al. (1998), and White et al. (1999) invoked choking of the west-facing (inter-American) trench by the arrival of this abnormally thick Caribbean crust as the cause for (Santonian–Campanian) polarity reversal. However, if the Caribbean plateau is 90 Ma, then it could not have driven our Aptian polarity reversal. But we are so confident in the Aptian age for polarity reversal (or onset of west-dipping subduction) that we doubt the plateau-trench choking hypothesis altogether. Large regions of Caribbean lithosphere *have* been subducted, such as the 900 km long Benioff zone imaged by seismic tomography beneath the Maracaibo region (van der Hilst and Mann, 1994), the "pre-subduction" area of which is shown on Figure 5.

Choking by very young (and therefore buoyant) crust at the Cordilleran trench is another possibility. However, seafloor spreading must also have been ongoing in the Proto-Caribbean Seaway at the time of the reversal, such that the age of crust on the east side of the arc may have been, if anything, younger than that entering the trench on the west. Another feasible hypothesis is that an east-facing intra-oceanic arc from farther out in the Pacific arrived at the west-facing Inter-American Arc and that the ensuing arc-arc collision was "won" by the east-facing arc, but so far parts of only a single pre-Albian magmatic axis have been recognized. Still another possibility is that east-dipping subduction drastically accelerated in the Aptian, but subduction *rate* is not often considered to be a strong control on tectonic style in the overriding plate (Jarrard, 1986).

Pindell (1993) noted the above timing discrepancy and recognized that Aptian arc polarity reversal was analogous to, and coeval with, the onset of compressive arc behavior (sensu Dewey, 1980, where trenchward advance of the overriding plate exceeds trench rollback, thereby increasing plate coupling and triggering backarc thrusting). Such compressive arc style is seen in Mexico (Sedlock et al., 1993), the Sevier fold-and-thrust belt of the western United States, and the West Peruvian Trough along the Andes (closure of backarc; Jaillard, 1994). This suggested a hemispheric-scale driving mechanism that spanned two continents on different plates and led to the proposal that the Aptian initiation of opening of the Equatorial Atlantic (Pindell, 1985b) and an Aptian doubling of spreading rate in the Central Atlantic (Klitgord and Schouten, 1986) caused the onset of compressive arc conditions. Such a profound change in the style of Cordilleran arcs over such large areas of two continents suggests to us that arrival of an oceanic plateau, or even a collection of plateaus, was not the driver of the Inter-American Arc polarity reversal. We favor the Aptian acceleration of Atlantic spreading as the dominant cause of the hemispheric scale onset of arc compression and reversal of the Inter-American Arc, which, upon reversal of its polarity, became the Great Caribbean Arc.

Our model, then, requires that the Caribbean Plateau basalts erupted onto a swath of Pacific-derived crust that was progressively engulfed by the American continents. In addition, Calvo and Bolz (1994) cite evidence for the Albian (ca. 100 Ma) onset of arc magmatism (calc-alkaline volcaniclastic turbidites) in Costa Rica. If this is true, then the Caribbean plate was already defined by plate boundaries in the Albian, at least three of which were subduction zones dipping Caribbean-ward at the time of the plateau basalt extrusion (Fig. 5). At the time of plateau basalt eruption, these subduction zones were relatively young, and subducted slabs did not penetrate deep enough to restrict plumes ris-

ing from the deep mantle. Kerr et al. (1998) propose that a subsidiary pulse of Caribbean basalt extrusion occurred at 72–78 Ma, which postdates the arc's collision with both the Yucatán and Colombian margins and thus must be well after reversal. Thus, we do not see any serious restraint on whether the main 90 Ma basalt pulse occurred before or after the reversal and, in our view, the extrusion of the Caribbean basalts is not an argument for or against the timing of the reversal. Central and southern Texas and the Oriente Basin of Ecuador also experienced basaltic magmatism between 90 and 100 Ma (Byerly, 1991; Barragán and Baby, 1999) that clearly had nothing to do with the Caribbean plate.

Paleogeographic Depiction of the Subduction-Polarity Reversal

The early breakup of western Pangea entailed the northwestward departure of North America from Africa–South America, but much of Mexico lagged behind North America by sinistral transform motion on one or more intra-continental transform faults such as the Texas Lineament and Trans-Mexican Volcanic Belt Lineament (Pindell and Dewey, 1982; Anderson and Schmidt, 1983). By the Late Jurassic, seafloor spreading in the Proto-Caribbean and Colombian Marginal Seaway was probably linked to the Pacific trench by a major transform fault passing along the south side of Chortís, because the stratigraphic sequences of Chortís and southern Mexico are very similar for the Early Cretaceous. Thus, one can infer that the original (Jurassic) east-dipping Cordilleran arc should have persisted for some time as the gap between the Americas grew, and hence there is a reason for the former existence of an east-dipping Benioff zone that initially spanned the widening gap between Chortís and the Andes (Fig. 3). Within the span of the Late Jurassic to Neocomian, however, motion at this Benioff zone may have become so oblique that an overlying magmatic arc was not developed. Relative plate motion at this boundary certainly had a strong sinistral component (Engebretson et al., 1985; Avé Lallemant and Oldow, 1988). Boreal Jurassic radiolarian cherts have been found in several Antillean islands (Montgomery et al., 1994), suggesting, in our view, southward terrane migration along the Mexico-Chortís margin prior to the subduction polarity reversal. Pre-Albian PIA rocks form "basement" throughout the Caribbean islands, but whether these rocks were extruded at an Inter-American Arc south of Mexico-Chortís formed above the east-dipping subduction zone, or were stripped from an intra-oceanic arc that lay outboard of the backarc basins of southern Mexico-Chortís and were carried southward along a mainly transform margin, is not clear. The primitive nature of the Antillean basement rocks suggests an intra-oceanic origin, which is more compatible with extrusion at an Inter-American Arc than with strike-slip removal from the Chortís continental block.

Thus, in the Early Cretaceous, there was either an elongating, highly sinistral, southwest-facing primitive arc system (Fig. 7A) or a sinistral shear system of unknown complexity with little or no Benioff zone (Fig. 7C) across the widening inter-American gap. This plate boundary would become the site of southwest-dipping

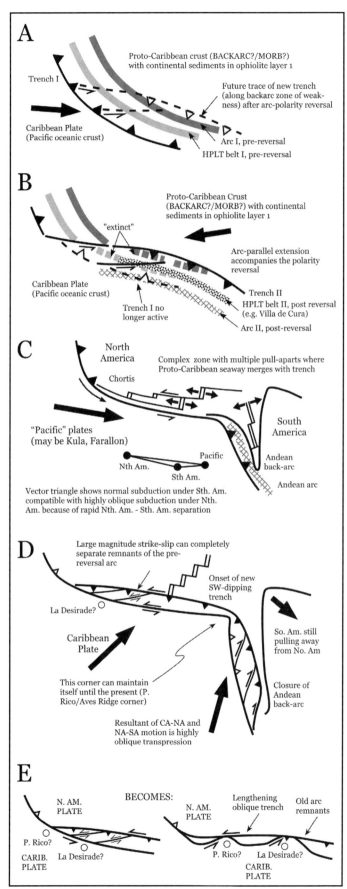

subduction by the Aptian (Figs. 7B, 7D, and 8). If the circum-Caribbean pre-Albian primitive arc materials were carried into the Inter-American gap from outboard of Chortís by sinistral transcurrent motions along a complex shear system, then a northeastward-dipping subduction zone is not necessarily required, and hence the Aptian "event" earmarked in Figure 6 may have comprised the onset of southwest-dipping subduction at a preexisting transform zone rather than a true arc-polarity reversal (Fig. 7D). However, the general lack of quartz, continental sediments, or isotopic indicators of continental influence in the pre-Aptian primitive Caribbean arcs (e.g., Frost and Snoke, 1989; Donnelly et al., 1990) suggests that the Inter-American Arc was intra-oceanic.

Figures 7A and 7B schematically show the effects of polarity reversal at a sinistrally oblique trench for typical slab dips of 30° to 45°. In such a transpressive geometric model for reversal, axis-parallel extension along the arc should be an important process. The features of Figure 7B are generally recognized in the geology of the Caribbean arcs; namely, (1) the "new" arc axis can form southwest or west of the "old" arc (e.g., Cuba, Hispaniola); (2) the old arc, and even parts of the Pacific-derived Caribbean plate, can thus end up within the forearc of the new arc (e.g., the Los Pasos Formation relative to the Cabaiguan Formation in Cuba; the Los Ranchos and Maimón Formations relative to the Tireo Formation in Hispaniola; La Desirade and North Coast Schist terranes relative to Aves Ridge in the eastern Caribbean;

Figure 7. Models for the subduction-polarity reversal at the Inter-American Arc (North American end shown here; a mirror image could apply in the south). In (A) and (B), a southwest-facing primitive arc is replaced by a northeast-facing arc, with consequent reversal of the positions of high-pressure–low temperature (HP-LT) and high-temperature–low pressure (HT-LP) metamorphic zones. Note that we also show east-west–trending "cross-arc transform faults," which link the new Antilles trench to the continued east-dipping subduction zone in Mexico-Chortís and farther north. The degree of development of a preexisting arc is highly dependent on the direction and obliquity of "Pacific" relative plate motion. We show an extremely oblique case in (C) with little or no preexisting arc because the margin was strongly sinistral, with only a small component of subduction beneath the Proto-Caribbean, and also show how seafloor spreading in the Proto-Caribbean may merge with the Mexican trench, across one or more significant transforms south of Chortís. Parts of the new subduction zone may have nucleated along ridge segments and transforms of the Proto-Caribbean spreading ridge immediately adjacent to the original arc; thus, post-reversal forearc rocks (e.g., boninites of pre-Albian age and mid-oceanic-ridge basalt [MORB]-like basalt blocks in the northern Cuban ophiolite mélange noted by Kerr et al., 1999) may have a geochemistry consistent with a "backarc" origin or with melting due to spreading center subduction following polarity reversal. (D) shows a regional scale snapshot after subduction polarity reversal. Note that the transforms that link the two trenches must lengthen dramatically as Caribbean–American relative motion continues. One important consequence is that arc-parallel extension can be so severe that remnants of the pre-reversal arc can be strung out to the point where Pacific-origin crust of the Caribbean plate can be carried into the forearc position of the new arc as the Caribbean walls of the cross-arc faults become part of the hanging wall above the new trench (E). This may explain the apparent anomaly of Pacific-derived cherts (Montgomery et al., 1994) being present in the Antilles forearc in Hispaniola, Puerto Rico, and La Desirade. CA-NA—Caribbean–North America; NA-SA—North America–South America.

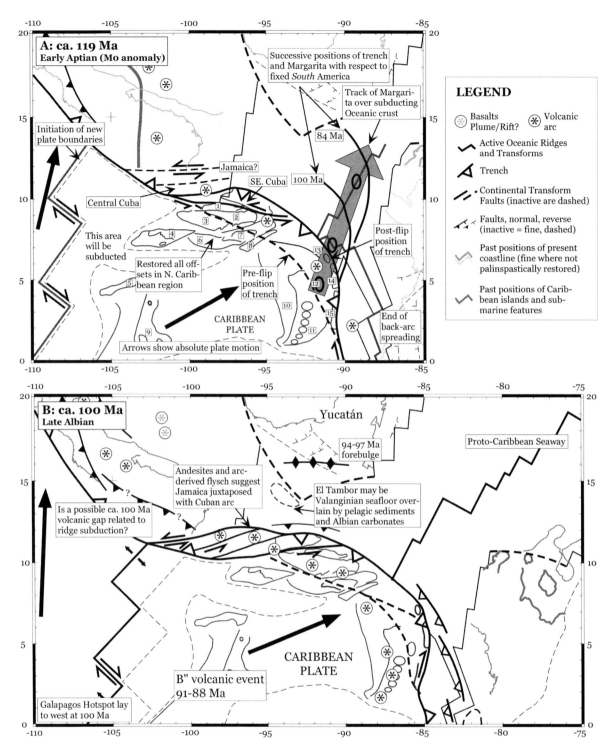

Figure 8. Detailed depiction of paleogeography of the subduction-polarity reversal, modified after Pindell and Kennan (2001b). (A) Inferred position of the Inter-American Arc immediately after the reversal. Note that the inter-American gap is quite narrow and we must restore large magnitudes of strike-slip in the northern Caribbean and arc-parallel rather than arc-normal extension in the Grenada Basin to allow the Caribbean plate to fit through. Key terranes are identified. We have also shown the modeled track of Margarita relative to South America and successive positions of the trench at 100 Ma and 84 Ma. The track passes close to spreading ridges active at 110 Ma, allowing the accretion of 110 Ma basalts prior to high-pressure–low-temperature metamorphism. (B) Modeled position of the Caribbean plate at 100 Ma. In the northern Caribbean, the Cuban terranes are lengthening east-west above the new southwest-dipping subduction zone. In the south, the modeled track of Margarita is consistent with slightly transpressive dextral motion relative to South America, allowing it to pass north of Guajira at 72 Ma. In the northwest, we suggest that the Caribbean plate was bounded by a ridge system, which may explain the "Icelandic" character of soon-to-be-erupted plateau basalts. This is also consistent with the lack of arc activity in Chortís and the lack of younger arc accretion in southern Mexico. Index to numbered localities: 1—Northern Cordillera, Dominican Republic; 2—eastern Cordillera; 3—central Cordillera; 4—central Haiti; 5—southern Haiti; 6—Muertos forearc; 7—Puerto Rico; 8—Virgin Islands; 9—Beata Ridge; 10—Aves Ridge; 11—Leeward Antilles; 12—Margarita (Juan Griego protolith); 13—Tobago; 14—Paria-Araya Peninsula; 15—Villa de Cura. M0—M0 oceanic magnetic anomaly.

Villa de Cura complex relative to Leeward Antilles Arc in the southern Caribbean; and (3) the transfer faults crossing from trench to trench may be the origin of faults of that orientation in Cuba (e.g., La Trocha Fault), and dextral ductile shear strains mapped in Margarita may also pertain to such faulting (but of opposite sense, being located at the southeast end of the arc).

Once southwestward-dipping subduction had been initiated, Figure 8 shows how the American plates began to engulf the Caribbean lithosphere, the main points of which are (1) seafloor spreading continued in the Proto-Caribbean because the American plates continued to separate until ca. 85–90 Ma, after which the Proto-Caribbean ridge was effectively dead; (2) the Great Caribbean Arc must have lengthened to match this progressive separation, presumably by arc-parallel extension and by en echelon strike-slip faulting; (3) Albian and younger calc-alkaline magmatism continually intruded the arc as extension continued such that the arc began to acquire local paleogeographies that are recognizable today shortly after 100 Ma; (4) the western end of the Great Caribbean Arc began to override and subduct elements of the North American margin immediately after polarity reversal; (5) the eastern end of the arc began to override and subduct elements of the South American margin, including the Andean backarc basin, immediately after polarity reversal; (6) the arc went on to collide obliquely with the margins of the American continents in the Late Cretaceous. Only the central portion of the Great Arc (i.e., the Greater Antilles and the Aves Ridge–Leeward Antilles and their forearcs) would eventually fit through the gap between Yucatán and Guajira Peninsula.

NORTH AMERICA–GREAT CARIBBEAN ARC INTERACTIONS

Sinistral Oblique Collision between the Great Arc and Central America–Yucatán

At the North American end of the Great Arc, polarity reversal involved large-scale sinistral displacements along en echelon transfer faults that connected the Mexican trench to the Greater Antilles (Great Arc) trench. These faults lengthened the arc and allowed the Caribbean plate to enter the Proto-Caribbean realm (Figs. 7 and 8) and are probable precursors to the La Trocha, Pinar, Cauto, and other such faults crossing Cuba that were reactivated in the Maastrichtian to Eocene (Stanek et al., 2000). The faults also allowed fragments of the pre-reversal Inter-American Arc to become entirely separated (Fig. 7E), such that Caribbean plate rocks (parts of Puerto Rico and La Desiràde) or fragments of the pre-reversal forearc, including HP-LT rocks, could be pulled into the forearc of the younger west-dipping subduction zone.

The early history of the Jamaican portion of the Great Arc is murky at best. Today, Jamaica forms the eastern tip of Nicaragua Rise, but appears to be intra-oceanic; thus, a continent-oceanic arc boundary between Jamaica and Chortís likely occurs somewhere along Nicaragua Rise. From the inferred paleogeographies of Fig-

ures 5, 7, and 8, we deduce that Jamaica originated (Lower Devil's Racecourse Formation) southeast of Chortís and northwest of the Central Cuban terranes (but was still part of the Inter-American Arc), such that the sinistral transpressive shear noted above (Fig. 7) carried central Cuba east of Jamaica and carried Jamaica east of southern Chortís. Unfortunately, we do not know well enough when peak HP metamorphism was reached in the Blue Mountains of Jamaica, and thus it is difficult to define which subduction polarity produced the HP metamorphism. Draper (1986) suggested a single north-dipping Benioff Zone for Jamaica with the Blue Mountains HP rocks lying south of the arc axis, such that Upper Cretaceous arc magmatic intrusions in or near the Blue Mountains pertain to a steepening of that Benioff Zone. This might be feasible if the Blue Mountain HP metamorphism is Aptian or older, but if future geochronological work indicates a late Aptian or younger age for these rocks, as we expect will be the case, then the Blue Mountains HP suite probably originated from southwest-dipping subduction like those in Cuba, and was subsequently uplifted by faulting in the forearc. Transtensional collapse of the central Cuban terrane off of Jamaica during arc-parallel extension may be a possible cause of uplift. The Blue Mountains HP rocks might then have been intruded by magmas derived from rejuvenated *north-dipping* subduction of *Caribbean* crust beneath Chortís-Nicaragua Rise (Fig. 5D and 5E), *after* the Great Arc's Maastrichtian collision with Yucatán (see below). Part of the basis for this latter interpretation is that Jamaica remained volcanically active into the Eocene, long after collision with Yucatán (Pindell and Barrett, 1990).

The original context of the pre-Aptian HP-LT rocks south of the Motagua Fault is even less clear. If polarity reversal in this area is slightly older than in Cuba, then it is possible that they comprise part of the forearc of Jamaica and were emplaced ahead of Jamaica onto the Yucatán margin during the Late Cretaceous. In this case, they must have lain north of the Motagua Fault until Neogene time. Alternatively, if the Motagua HP-LT rocks were part of the Pacific-facing forearc prior to polarity reversal, axis-parallel extension within the Great Arc (Fig. 7E), separating Jamaica from southeastern Chortís, would allow them to lie west of Jamaica at time of collision with Yucatán, and be carried east by up to 500 km to their present position by Cenozoic sinistral motion on one of the strands of the Motagua Fault Zone.

Partial subduction of the attenuated southern margin of the continental Chortís Block (where Jurassic continental quartz-bearing strata are known; see lithologic column, Fig. 3), initiated by transpressive thrusting during and after polarity reversal, is an appealing origin for the quartzofeldspathic protoliths of the Escambray metamorphic complex of Cuba, as well as some of the HP blocks in the serpentinite mélanges of Las Villas. Las Villas mélanges also yield rare Grenville ages in their protolith (Somin and Millán, 1981; Renne et al., 1989; Grafe et al., 2001), again consistent with Chortís as an origin (e.g., Honduras; Manton, 1996). Four distinct nappes in the Escambray complex show northward ductile shearing, which may pertain to this early south-dipping subduction (Stanek, 2000). We suggest that thinned parts of the rifted margin of the Chortís Block, or quartzose sediments derived therefrom, were included in the downgoing Proto-Caribbean slab. HP-LT conditions were reached at Escambray and Las Villas Complex by 106 Ma (middle Albian).

The eastern Chortís margin may also have been the origin of the Isle of Youth (Isle of Pines) metamorphic complex, given that Somin and Millán (1981) have identified similarities between the protoliths of Escambray and Isle of Youth. The Barrovian metamorphism in the Isle of Youth indicates a quite different crustal setting to the higher-pressure metamorphic rocks of Escambray, possibly within a nappe pile at the western end of the arc. Other possibilities include an origin as a fragment of Chortís basement (if the metamorphism is old) or its passive margin cover (intercalated volcanics could be of proto-Caribbean origin or from the pre-reversal Inter-American Arc) or the passive margin cover of southernmost Yucatán. It could have been metamorphosed prior to polarity reversal, or within the root of the post-reversal Antilles arc during the middle Cretaceous, or during latest Cretaceous (in the case of a Yucatán origin). Distinguishing between these requires more accurate dating of protolith age and of peak metamorphism than is currently available; $^{40}Ar/^{39}Ar$ cooling ages (Garcia-Casco et al., 2001) simply constrain peak metamorphism to early Maastrichtian or older.

The central Cuban rocks were progressively uplifted through middle and Late Cretaceous. Given the oblique subduction history for this interval in Figures 5 and 8, this was likely due to arc-parallel stretching. At the same time, several km of post-reversal arc lavas had accumulated in southern central Cuba, which we interpret as pertaining to southward subduction of Proto-Caribbean crust. The primary plutonic-magmatic axis of the Cuban portion of the Great Arc was probably situated farther south in what is now the Cayman Ridge (the intra-arc Yucatán Basin had not yet opened; see below and also Pindell and Barrett, 1990), as suggested by the Cayman Ridge's far thicker crustal root (Case et al., 1990) relative to that of the Cuban "arc" rocks, beneath which lie the overthrust Bahamas carbonates. Thus, the "Central Cuban arc terrane," north of the Yucatán and Caúto basins and east of Pinar Fault (defining the boundary with Western Cuba), likely comprises mainly forearc elements of the Great Arc, where a number of "arc" intrusions and volcanic flows do occur, but where accreted sedimentary terranes, ophiolites, and HP and other metamorphic terranes are the rule. This interpretation is consistent with structural interpretations that the Cuban arc-related rocks comprise only relatively thin, obducted nappes above the underthrusted Bahamian carbonate section (Hempton and Barros, 1993; Draper and Barros, 1994).

Between 90 and 80 Ma, less-metamorphosed granitic pegmatites cut the contact between the Escambray HP rocks and the amphibolite grade base of the arc basement (Mabujina unit), indicating that significant uplift of the composite Escambray-Mabujina units had occurred by that time (Stanek et al., 2000; Grafe et al., 2001). The Campanian migration of the Great Arc toward the southern fringe of the Yucatán passive margin should have caused further shallowing of the subduction angle and a progressive southward shift of the magmatic axis. We suggest that this is why volcanism ceased in the central Cuban terrane by the Maastrichtian; if

our reconstruction is correct, arc magmatism should have continued in the Yucatán Basin, a Maastrichtian–early Eocene intra-arc basin, and/or Cayman Ridge, as it did in the Oriente Province of Cuba where no significant intra-arc basin was present.

By the Campanian, north-vergent collision was imminent between the Great Arc and the southern Yucatán margin as marked by the drowning of the Cobán carbonate-evaporite platform beneath upward-deepening Campur Formation carbonates and the onset of Sépur clastic (including ophiolitic debris) flysch deposition (Rosenfeld, 1993). By the Maastrichtian, El Tambór and Santa Cruz ophiolites overthrust the Sépur foredeep basin, but it is not clear if these ophiolites represent the Great Arc's forearc basement or obducted Proto-Caribbean material; Giunta et al. (2002) suggest that both MORB and arc basalts are present. The Cuban part of the Great Arc was likely situated just east of Jamaica and avoided direct collision with the southern Yucatán margin such that it, but not Jamaica, continued to migrate toward the Bahamas thereafter. Thus, the Guatemalan ophiolites likely represent the Jamaican part of the Great Arc's forearc; new biostratigraphic assessments in Jamaica suggest that a primary orogenic pulse occurred in Jamaica during the Maastrichtian (Mitchell, 2003), matching the time of forearc emplacement onto northern Guatemala.

By 70 Ma (late Maastrichtian), the part of the Great Caribbean Arc that did not get blocked by southern Yucatán was passing through the narrowest point between the Americas, the gap between Yucatán and Guajira. Beyond this bottleneck, toward the northeast, the Proto-Caribbean margins became farther apart. However, a clear record of uninterrupted diachronous arc-continent collision exists along all Proto-Caribbean margins (Pindell and Barrett, 1990), and therefore, the arc must have undergone arc-parallel lengthening during further migration in order to accommodate the widening shape of the Proto-Caribbean. Arc-parallel extension was achieved at both ends of the Great Arc by opening of two intra-arc basins, the Yucatán and Grenada Basins, driven, we suggest, by trench rollback forces. Intra-arc rifting separated mainly forearc elements (Cuba in the northwest, and the composite Villa de Cura–Tobago terrane in the southeast) from the main Late Cretaceous magmatic axes. These forearc elements went on to collide with the American margins, which is why the American margins are today the sites of HP-LT and other Caribbean metamorphic complexes.

Evolution of the Yucatán Basin and Collision of the Cuban Forearc with Yucatán-Bahamas

Figure 9D shows the present structure of the Yucatán Basin and Cuba. Three distinct sets of faults dominate the region. Set 1 (Figs. 9A, 9B) comprises northeast- to east-northeast–striking extensional basement faults across much of the Yucatán Basin and Cayman Rise, which we believe record the north-northwest–south-southeast extension direction associated with generation of oceanic crust in Yucatán Basin. Set 2 (Fig. 9C) comprises high-angle block faults within arc-related crust along the Cayman Ridge that are probably younger than set 1 faults

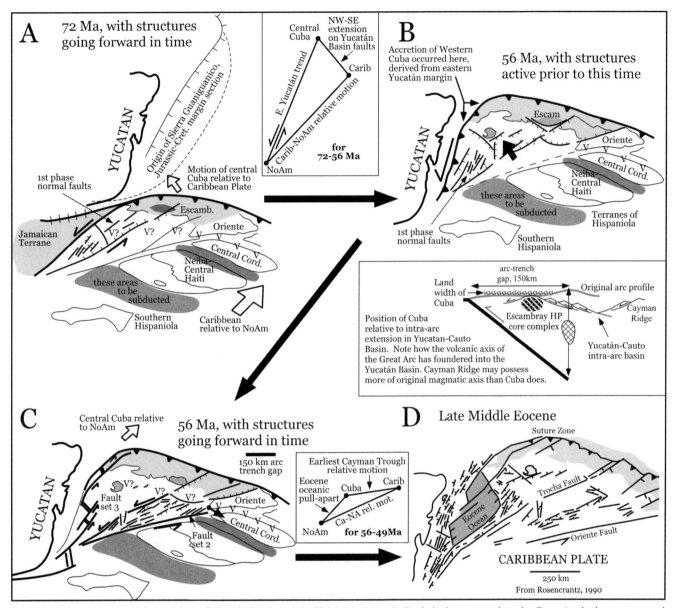

Figure 9. Three-stage model for opening of Yucatán Basin. (A) At 72 Ma, the Yucatán Basin had not opened, as the Great Arc had not yet passed through the Yucatán-Guajira bottleneck. (B) From 72 to 56 Ma, rollback of Proto-Caribbean oceanic crust (Fig. 10) sucked the northwest forearc flank of the Great Arc (i.e., Cuban portion) northwest with respect to the Caribbean plate, resulting in set 1 normal faults and oblique collision with Yucatán. (C) At ca. 56 Ma, tearing of the overthrust Proto-Caribbean slab along Yucatán (Fig. 10) caused the rollback direction to change from northwest to northeast, toward the Bahamas (slab was not yet torn there). We suggest the set 3 pull-apart formed above this tear, consistent with northeast-directed final suturing of Cuba with the Bahamas. (D) Late Eocene to present structure at the same scale as models A, B, and C. This model requires onset of Cayman Trough faulting by ca. 56 Ma; Rosencrantz et al. (1988) interpreted marine magnetic anomalies back to 50 Ma, and the 200-km-wide stretched, non-oceanic ends of the Trough suggest that motion began somewhat earlier. Ca-NA—Caribbean–North America; HP—high pressure; NoAm—North America; V—volcanism.

and that probably pertain to initial sinistral motion along the Cayman Trough transform. Set 3 (Fig. 9C), following Rosencrantz's (1990) interpretation, comprises faults defining a discrete north-northeast–striking pull-apart basin in the western Yucatán Basin. Northeast to east-northeast–striking faults crossing onshore Cuba (e.g., La Trocha, Cauto faults) correlate with, and probably belong to, fault set 1. These faults are mainly

extensional, step down to the east in the onshore, and moved during the Maastrichtian to Eocene, judging from fault growth in flanking sediments (Iturralde-Vinent, 2000, personal commun.). Although untested by drilling as yet, the faults of the first set in the basin are probably of the same age. Rosencrantz (1990) cogently argues that set 3 (pull-apart basin) faults are early to middle Eocene and younger than the creation of the bulk of the Yucatán Basin. Set

3 faults transformed plate motion along the Pinar Fault into the Eocene Cuban thrust belt.

Given the general northeast migration of the Caribbean plate relative to North America during the early Paleogene, the north-northwest–south-southeast opening direction of the Yucatán Basin suggested by set 1 faults may initially seem anomalous but is actually required in the three-plate system: North America–Cuban forearc–Caribbean plate/Cayman Ridge (Fig. 9, vector triangle for 72–56 Ma, which defines motions for the 72–56 Ma interval). Note that the North America–Caribbean relative motion direction was more easterly than the trend of the eastern Yucatán Proto-Caribbean margin. Maastrichtian–Paleocene extension at set 1 faults and associated generation of quasi-oceanic crust in the

Yucatán Basin allowed the Cuban forearc to migrate transpressively north-northeast along the Yucatán margin (Fig. 9B), while the rest of the Caribbean plate moved in a more eastward direction. We suggest that at least some set 1 faults were southeast-dipping low-angle detachments, such that the Cayman Ridge (arc) collapsed off the Escambray and Isle of Youth footwalls during the early opening of Yucatán Basin. Following Draper (2001), we suggest, therefore, that Escambray and Isle of Youth are extensional metamorphic core complexes as is suggested by their flat-lying and domal foliation patterns. The extension was driven by rollback of the Middle Jurassic Proto-Caribbean crust ahead of Cuba (Fig. 10), and we suggest that the 68 Ma $^{40}Ar/^{39}Ar$ age on Isle of Youth metamorphic rocks (Garcia-Casco et al., 2001) and

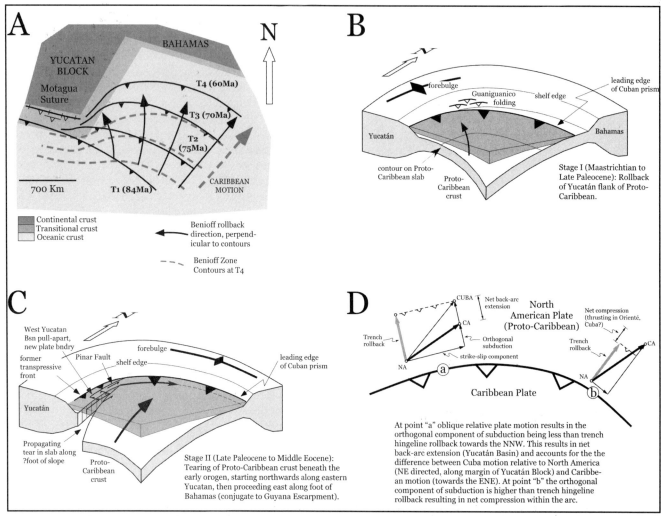

Figure 10. Block diagram of Proto-Caribbean rollback geometry beneath advancing Cuban terranes. (A) Schematic structure contours dashed on subducting slab; rollback vectors relative to Yucatán (arrows) and successive trench positions. Times T1–T4 are dated as ca. 84 Ma, 75 Ma, 70 Ma, and 60 Ma. (B) From 72 to 56 Ma, rollback toward Yucatán drove oblique thrusting in the Sierra Guaniguanico to the northwest of the opening Yucatán Basin. (C) Starting at ca. 56 Ma, rollback and extension orientations changed to southwest-northeast. We suggest this required tearing of the Proto-Caribbean slab southeast of Yucatán and was accompanied by a new oceanic pull-apart opening in the Yucatán Basin. Slab tearing led to rebound as the footwall unloaded, starting initially in Yucatán and migrating northeast and then east around the Cuban Orogen by the Eocene. (D) Vectors nets show that at very oblique margins (point a) rollback of the subducting plate can exceed the orthogonal component of subduction, resulting in extension within the forearc, in contrast to less oblique margins (point b) where the rollback of the subducting plate is unlikely to exceed the orthogonal component of subduction, resulting in continued compression within the forearc. CA—Caribbean; NA—North America.

the 60–70 Ma zircon fission track ages from Escambray (Stanek et al., 2000) date this tectonic unroofing.

By 56 Ma, set 3 faults (pull-apart) began to form in the western Yucatán Basin, following oblique collision between the Cuban forearc and the Yucatán margin. This oblique collision had imbricated the eastern Yucatán passive margin strata into the Sierra Guaniguanico fold-thrust belt (Pindell, 1985b; Hutson et al., 1998; Pszczólkowski, 1999). The set 3 pull-apart basin appears to have formed coevally (early to middle Eocene) with initial transform motion on the Oriente Fault of Cayman Trough (Fig. 8C; Rosencrantz et al., 1988), signaling a change in the regional kinematics. Thereafter, a new three-plate system, North America–Cuba/Yucatán Basin/Cayman Ridge–Caribbean plate, took over, the relative motions of which are shown in the lower vector triangle of Figure 9. The set 3 pull-apart (comprising Pinar Fault) allowed Cuba–Yucatán Basin to migrate toward eventual collision with the Bahamas, while the early Cayman Trough transform system became the site of Yucatán Basin–Caribbean relative plate motion. It is important to note that prior to final collision of Cuba with the Bahamas, the early Cayman Trough itself must have been moving north toward North America, following the Yucatán Basin plate. This also implies a component of north-directed compression in northern Central America and explains the more complex, disorganized structure of the easternmost and westernmost Cayman Trough. Following suturing of Cuba with the Bahamas, the Cayman Trough represents the relative motion between the Caribbean plate and North America.

Note that this two-stage model (Fig. 9) does *not* invoke synchronous backarc spreading (set 1 faults of Yucatán Basin) and arc-continent collision (Cuba–Bahamas). In this model, the composite Cuban forearc–Yucatán Basin terrane (second stage of Fig. 9) can move as an independent platelet between the Caribbean and North American plates, and the Cuba–Bahamas collision could ultimately have been driven by Caribbean–North America relative motion in the absence of a passive backarc spreading center. Thus, total contraction in the collision may have exceeded that which would be expected if Proto-Caribbean rollback were the only driving mechanism.

Seismic tomography data (van der Hilst, 1990) clearly image the Proto-Caribbean slab subducted beneath the Antilles and also clearly show that, to the east of the Dominican Republic, this slab has torn away from the North American plate and is sinking into the deep mantle. We expect that the overthrust Proto-Caribbean slab started to drop off into the mantle upon or shortly following collision of the Great Arc with the North American plate. In such a diachronous collision from southern Yucatán to the Bahamas, slab drop off must also have occurred diachronously, by progressive tearing: Maastrichtian at the Motagua Suture Zone, Paleocene along eastern Yucatán, and Eocene at the Bahamas. Thus, the cause for central Cuba's kinematic change from north-northwest to northeast at 56 Ma, relative to North America, was probably the cessation of the rollback driving mechanism upon

Paleocene oblique collision along eastern Yucatán, because the subducting slab started to tear in that area.

We suggest that the set 3 pull-apart basin ("Eocene Ocean" in Fig. 9D) formed directly above the propagating Paleocene-Eocene tear between Yucatán (i.e., North America) and the Proto-Caribbean, such that further rollback would have been restricted to the eastern side of the tear and in a north-northeast direction. Thus, the Cuban forearc terrane would have been pulled, after 56 Ma, toward the Bahamas rather than toward Yucatán. Our two-stage model is supported by structural field studies (Gordon et al., 1997) that indicate northwest shortening and maximum stress during the Paleocene and north-south maximum stress due to sinistral transpression between the Pinar Fault and the offshore thrust belt during early to early middle Eocene.

As the tear in the slab propagated northward, we predict that isostatic rebound would occur in the North American margin to form a deep post-orogenic unconformity whose onset should young to the north. Such an unconformity does exist (e.g., middle Eocene hiatus in Cuba of Pszczólkowski, 1999), but it is difficult to demonstrate the northward-younging in Yucatán of its *onset*, because the erosional surface can remain subaerial for significant amounts of time thereafter. Rapid Paleocene–lower Eocene carbonate accumulation rates in the Bahamas ahead of the Cuban thrustbelt (Paulus, 1972) attest to Proto-Caribbean slab-pull and arrival of the Cuban terranes during that time, followed by a strong middle Eocene unconformity. Uplift surely occurred during imbrication of the Cuban nappes as they overrode the Bahamas margin, but the unconformity most certainly was severely enhanced by isostatic rebound due to slab drop off at the end of the orogeny. The fact that arc magmatism continued in the Oriente area of Cuba until ca. 45 Ma demonstrates that the tear had not propagated that far east until after that time.

Figure 10 explores how trench rollback initially drove northwestward extension (set 1 faults and seafloor spreading) in the Yucatán Basin. As the Great Arc encountered southern Yucatán, structural contours on the descending Proto-Caribbean slab would necessarily become warped as shown in Figure 10A (note contours for T4). As the obliquity of subduction direction at the trench increased, rollback velocity would begin to dominate the orthogonal rate at which Proto-Caribbean crust actually entered the trench (Fig. 10D). This would impart an extensional stress on the arc in a direction perpendicular to the Proto-Caribbean structural contours and parallel to the rollback direction (northnorthwest). Thus, the leading edge of the arc was pulled toward eastern Yucatán while the rest of the Caribbean plate migrated to the north-northeast. Structural style at the plate *interface* along the eastern Yucatán Block was sinistrally transpressive. As the Cuban forearc terrane encountered the eastern Yucatán margin, the Yucatán margin strata were imbricated and accreted into the growing Cuban thrustbelt (Sierra Guaniguanico of western Cuba); structural imbrication and metamorphism there are both Paleocene (Gordon et al., 1997).

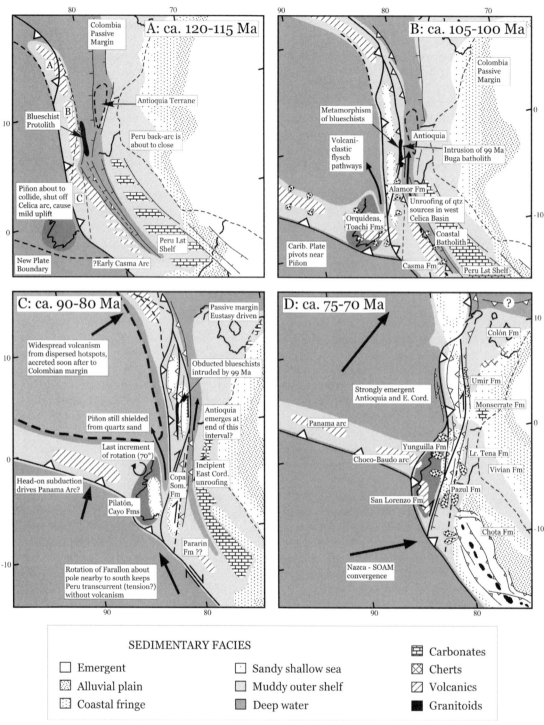

Figure 11. Snapshots of northern Central Andes development from 120 to 70 Ma, as discussed in the text. Positions of the trailing edge of the Caribbean plate off northern Peru are constrained by position of its leading edge off Yucatán, by equatorial paleomagnetic data from allochthonous Ecuadorian terranes, and by absence of arc volcanism farther north in the Ecuadorian and Colombian autochthon. Note the north-northeast–directed diachronous transpression of the former Andean backarc and northward migration of the Panama triple junction. Enhanced rate of uplift and erosion in the Andes from 84 Ma is driven by increased subduction of Caribbean crust beneath the Andes, related to the end of oceanic spreading between the Americas. Locations on (A): A—Margarita and Tobago portion of the pre-Aptian arc; B—arc fragments accreted to western Colombia; C—Amotape, Tahuín, and Chaucha terranes of northern Peru and southern Ecuador.

SOUTH AMERICA–GREAT CARIBBEAN ARC INTERACTIONS

Setting of Northern South America Prior to Caribbean Interaction: The "Andean Backarc Basin"

As with the northwest end of the Great Arc, the southeast end was also the site of HP-LT metamorphism dating back to at least the Aptian (Table 1). Such metamorphic rocks occur in Margarita, the Villa de Cura complex, and the Cordillera de la Costa of Venezuela, all of which lie on the eastern flank of the Great Arc of the Caribbean as reconstructed here. HP-LT rocks also occur along the Romeral–Peltetec Suture of Colombia and, although less easily interpreted, also probably formed along the eastern flank of the Great Arc. Again, unless we invoke keel-hauling to bring such old HP rocks under the arc from the western to eastern flank of the arc, the polarity reversal must be Aptian or older.

Figures 5 and 11 show the general south-to-north diachronous closure of the Andean backarc basin and arc-continent collision between the offshore arc (Great Arc) and the South American autochthon. One of the most important features to note in these maps is that, prior to the middle and Late Cretaceous, almost the entire Ecuadorian and Colombian margin is thought to have been essentially a passive margin, facing either the "Colombian Marginal Seaway" or the "Andean Backarc Basin." Both of these features were largely destroyed during proposed interaction with the Caribbean plate, and thus the key features that indicate their existence and nature warrant brief review:

- We define the Colombian Marginal Seaway as lying outboard of the Colombian passive margin. The arc to the west was intra-oceanic, founded on pre-reversal PIA rocks. The floor of the basin comprised entirely oceanic crust of Proto-Caribbean origin.
- We define the "Andean Backarc Basin" as that part of the Peruvian to southern Colombian margins separated from the passive margin by a narrower basin and with an arc founded on continental or transitional crust lying out to the west. The floor of the basin comprised highly stretched continental crust (central Peru) to transitional and possibly oceanic crust in northernmost Peru and Ecuador.
- There is strong paleogeographic evidence for the Colombian passive margin. Facies mapping in Colombia (Tectonic Analysis, 1998; Villamil, 1999) shows no sign of an active margin setting in the central Cordillera and areas to the east prior to the Late Cretaceous. There are no unambiguous remnants of a continental volcanic arc after the Late Jurassic, little or no volcanic material derived from an arc is found in the Magdalena Basin or areas to the east, and there is no indication prior to the Late Cretaceous of any west-derived sediment of arc or continent derivation.
- Plate reconstructions show that, prior to the Late Jurassic, Colombia (north of ~4°) was the conjugate margin to Chortís, and that the tail of Chortís (including our proposed protolith for central Cuba) extended at least this far south. Thus,

the South American portion of the early "Intra-American Arc," above an east-dipping subduction zone and founded on stretched continental crust, must lie south of the latitude of Bogotá (see also maps in Jaillard et al., 1990).

- The lack of pre-Late Cretaceous active margin indicators in Colombia north of Bogotá and in Venezuela, and the fact that the Great Arc of the Caribbean forms the leading edge of the Caribbean plate, thus suggest that in South America the "Intra-American Arc," which rifted away from the passive margin, was the template for the Great Arc.
- In the Ecuadorian Cordillera Real, as in Colombia, the latest intrusive ages are Late Jurassic (Litherland et al., 1994, Noble et al., 1997) and only prior to Early to Middle Jurassic can volcanism with both extensional and subduction affinities be found in the Subandes and inner foreland basin (Romeuf et al., 1997).
- Volcanic components of the Cordillera show a geochemistry indicative of progressively more transitional crust to the west, and still farther west remnants of ophiolite (probable Early Cretaceous age) are found at ~2°S with no intervening Early Cretaceous arc. Thus, we suggest these are the remnants of "oceanic crust" formed in a backarc basin and that any arc of Early Cretaceous age lay farther to the west.
- To the west of these ophiolites, the "Chaucha Terrane" ("B" on Fig. 11A) comprises poorly exposed granite and metamorphic Paleozoic rocks with a Mesozoic clastic fringe on its eastern side ("Guamote Terrane" of Litherland et al., 1994). Farther west, middle Cretaceous and younger arc rocks are separated from this terrane by a second ophiolite suture. We propose that these continental fragments are the dismembered basement to the arc on the west side of the backarc basin. To the south, the Celica Volcanics in the Lancones Basin (e.g., Jaillard et al., 1999) are mainly andesites with a geochemical signature indicating underlying continental basement ("C" on Fig. 11A). These rocks are nearly in situ. Although separated from "stable" South America by significant north-south shear zones, paleomagnetic and other data (Mourier et al., 1988a, 1998b) indicate that they are not displaced significantly north of their latitude of origin.
- A pre-Albian "mafic arch" beneath the Coastal Batholith of western Peru is apparent from gravity data (Wilson, 1985). It lies immediately west of the "West Peruvian Trough" passive margin basin (Cobbing et al., 1981) and probably represents the highly stretched, but not truly oceanic, axis of the backarc basin. Farther south, rift basins with continental and basaltic fill, but no indication of oceanic crust, can be traced as far as northernmost Argentina, 500 km east of the arc (Salfity and Marquillas, 1994).
- The basement rocks of Margarita ("A" on Fig. 11A), where high-pressure rocks have both continental crust of Carboniferous age and oceanic crust of Albian age, are the final pieces required to reconstruct the Inter-American Arc. During the Late Jurassic, as South and North America separated,

they must have lain south of the southern end of Chortís and the future Cuban terranes. They must have been north of the future Chaucha Terrane of Ecuador and thus are shown on our maps within the Inter-American Arc to the west of southern Colombia. This fragment of continental crust lay sufficiently far north along the Inter-American Arc that it was able to pass by the Guajira peninsula during subsequent motion (Fig. 8). The backarc basin and Colombian marginal seaway to the northeast are interpreted to be the original site of the oceanic protoliths, which were structurally juxtaposed with the continental crust before 90 Ma.

Following opening of the backarc basin, compression, with strong uplift and cooling of metamorphic terranes, dominated northern South America from the Aptian on, identical in age to the arc-polarity reversal farther north. Thus, we believe that these two events are genetically linked and that backarc basin closure, and accretion of fragments of arc terranes along Ecuador and western Colombia throughout the Late Cretaceous, was driven by relative motions of the Caribbean and South American plates. Because separation of South America from North America continued into at least the Campanian, relative motion was much more north-south oriented than in the northern Caribbean (see vector nests within Figs. 5A and 5B), consistent with the dextral transpressive tectonic style indicated by field studies (e.g., Litherland et al., 1994). During the Cenozoic, the arc continued to migrate along northern South America, all the way to Trinidad. In the sections below, we will trace this prolonged arc-continent interaction, looking first at the arc itself, and then examining the Andes of Ecuador–Colombia, and the Venezuela-Trinidad portions of northern South America, thus documenting the tectonic controls on basin development in northern South America.

The Caribbean Plate and the Eastern End of the Great Arc

Margarita, Tobago (Tobago terrane), and the Villa de Cura complex of Venezuela comprise forearc elements of the Great Arc whose metamorphism indicates burial to varying depths. In Margarita, two very different protoliths have reached HP conditions (Stöckhert et al., 1995; Maresch et al., 2000). The Juan Griego unit protolith had two components, Carboniferous gneisses and Aptian-Albian (*Heterohelix*-bearing) sedimentary rocks. Carboniferous gneisses are characteristic of the central Cordillera of Colombia and Ecuador, some of which must have been rifted from the South American autochthon in the Late Jurassic as the Andean backarc basin formed (magmatism ceased in Colombia's central Cordillera remnant arc by 140 Ma; Irving, 1975). Backarc extension and spreading was presumably driven by subduction rollback of Pacific lithosphere; the basin persisted as marine during the Neocomian to at least the Albian. In contrast, the La Rinconada unit protolith was an oceanic MORB crystallized between 109 and 116 Ma (Stöckhert et al., 1995; Maresch et al., 2000). Thus, we suggest that both the Juan Griego unit and La Rinconada unit protoliths derive from the Andean backarc basin (Figs. 5, 8, and 11); if the protoliths came from different parts of that basin, then they

were juxtaposed by faulting as they were taken down together to depths as great as 50 km. By 90 Ma, they had already begun to cool (Stöckhert et al., 1995; Maresch et al., 2000).

A broadly similar initial metamorphic history may apply to both the Villa de Cura complex and parts of the Cordillera de la Costa (Smith et al., 1999; Sisson et al., this volume, Chapter 3; Sorenson et al., this volume; Unger et al., this volume), but we will focus on the Margarita and other data to interpret some of the younger stages of Caribbean–South American interaction on the Caribbean side. By 86 Ma, as the arc converged obliquely with western Ecuador and Colombia, Margarita's HP suite had been elevated to ~25 km depth, as indicated by cross-cutting arc magmas (Stöckhert et al., 1995; Maresch et al., 2000). As with Cuba, arc-parallel extension is a viable mechanism for uplift, given the strong obliquity of subduction; alternatively, attempted subduction of a progressively thickening continental margin may have been the cause. Possible explanations for the intrusion of arc magmas into HP rocks at this depth include: (1) forearc magmatism, (2) widening of the forearc by addition of migrating terranes from further north along the plate edge, and (3) steepening of the subduction angle for a variety of possible reasons. Ductile dextral shear fabrics and a greenschist overprint were then imparted on both the HP suites and the 86 Ma arc magmatic rocks, indicating that Margarita was situated within the Late Cretaceous dextral transpressive plate boundary zone between the Caribbean and South American plates. Additional uplift of the HP rocks occurred during this shearing, possibly as vertically extruded wedges under transpression, and by 66 Ma as the Great Arc passed through the Yucatán-Guajira bottleneck, the Margarita Complex had been elevated to a depth of ~15 km.

Aruba presents a case that may also occur in other Leeward Antilles islands. The Aruba Batholith (83 Ma) intrudes the Aruba Lava Formation that has been interpreted as ca. 90 Ma Caribbean Plateau basalts (White et al., 1999), leading them to propose 85–88 Ma as the time of the arc polarity reversal. In that model, the Aruba Lava Formation (Caribbean Plateau basalts) choked an east-dipping subduction zone such that, after reversal, the basalts were situated above the new west-dipping Benioff zone, which produced new arc magmas (Aruba Batholith). If the Aruba Lava Formation does, in fact, represent the Caribbean basalt plateau, an alternative model consistent with Aptian polarity reversal and the paleogeography shown in Figure 8 would be that Aruba was situated within the Caribbean interior plateau province at 90 Ma, beyond the "reach" of the post-Aptian west-dipping Benioff zone, but strike-slip removal and incorporation of Caribbean hanging-wall elements into the Western Cordillera of Colombia during dextral oblique collision of the arc with northwest South America caused Aruba to move into the arc axis above the slab by 83 Ma. However, there is a prominent interval up to 100 m thick in the Aruba Lava Formation characterized by coarse conglomerates, paleosols, and accretionary lapilli tuffs clearly indicating subaerial conditions (Beets et al., 1984; A. Snoke, 2003, personal commun.). Thus, the Aruba Lava Formation may have an arc origin as opposed to being part of the Caribbean Plateau basalt province.

After passing through the Yucatán-Guajira bottleneck, in the Paleocene, the Great Arc must have undergone a significant arc-parallel lengthening in order to maintain oblique collision along both the northwestern and the southern Proto-Caribbean margins. Opening of the Yucatán Basin was examined above as one example of this process (Fig. 9), and opening of the Grenada intra-arc basin may be another. Pindell and Barrett (1990) reviewed structural, magnetic, magmatic, and kinematic arguments for a north-south growing dextral pull-apart model for Grenada Basin. Bird et al. (1993, 1999) claimed that magnetics do not support this model, and argued instead for arc-normal expansion of the basin. However, we caution against over-interpreting low-reliability low-latitude magnetic anomalies and note that east-west opening cannot account for early to middle Eocene emplacement of nappes onto the western Venezuelan margin (see section on Venezuela, below). It is possible, however, that the basin opened in two stages, the first one dominated by north-south dextral shear, thereby creating the very sharp western wall of the basin (former strike-slip fault) and explaining the kinematic requirement for forearc obduction in Maracaibo, followed by a period of more southeastward-directed opening and mafic intrusion in the basin itself.

The important point here is that rock units in Margarita cooled very rapidly between 50 and 55 Ma (early Eocene). In the north-south opening model for Grenada Basin, which pulls the Leeward Antilles arc fragments out of the position now occupied by the basin (Pindell and Barrett, 1990), Margarita lies very near the southern rifted margin of the basin (Fig. 5). Thus, Margarita likely formed the footwall to an asymmetric detachment at the site of Grenada Basin. If so, the cooling ages of 50–55 Ma in Margarita may record the time of opening of Grenada Basin. This period matches the time of peak foredeep subsidence in northeastern Maracaibo Basin as allochthonous Caribbean nappes were emplaced southeastward in the Falcón region (Bockmeulen et al., 1983). Therefore, as with central Cuba, rollback of Proto-Caribbean lithosphere toward the continental margin appears to have caused intra-arc extension in the Great Arc, thereby creating Grenada Basin. Margarita was analogous to the south flank of central Cuba during this Paleogene phase of arc lengthening; it was part of the Great Arc's forearc, which was sucked by trench rollback from under the flank of the Great Arc and toward the Proto-Caribbean passive margin with which it eventually collided. Once the Margarita basement units had been tectonically unroofed in the middle Eocene, subsequent dextral-oblique Caribbean–South American collision caused further progressive uplift and cooling of most allochthonous southern Caribbean rocks.

Late Cretaceous and Paleogene of Peru, Ecuador, and Colombia

The lack of younger faulting or volcanism strongly suggests that the Caribbean plate had reached its present size or larger by ca. 90 Ma (Driscoll and Diebold, 1999). Its northern edge was situated south of the Yucatán Block prior to the Campanian (and would collide with southern Mexico during the Maastrichtian), and thus the southern, trailing, edge of the Caribbean plate must have been situated in the vicinity of northern Peru at this time (Figs. 5, 11). As the Caribbean plate then migrated north, the southern edge of the plate also migrated northward along western South America, reaching its present position at 4°N (southern tip of Panama-Baúdo arc) by the Eocene. Following the Early Cretaceous passive margin stage, deformation in the northern Central Andes was therefore first driven by Caribbean interactions and only later, after the Panama Arc had migrated north of any given point, by interaction with the Farallon and Nazca plates. North of 4°N, Andean deformation is still controlled by Caribbean interactions.

There is clear evidence for significant tectonic changes that are probably directly related to the Aptian polarity inversion event in the Great Arc. At ca. 120–115 Ma (Fig. 11A), volcanism ceased in the Celica Arc of northernmost Peru and southern Ecuador. Subduction of the newly isolated Caribbean plate beneath the active arc along the backarc basin farther north also ceased, and subduction of "Pacific" (Phoenix, Proto-Farallon) plates began beneath the new Panama–Costa Rica arc (initiated in the Albian; Calvo and Bolz, 1994). In Ecuador, the extinct arc (Jaillard et al., 1996), associated plutons (115 Ma; Kennerley, 1980), forearc, and underlying continental basement (Amotape-Tahuín; Aspden et al., 1995) were uplifted and eroded prior to deposition of southwest-derived volcaniclastic flysch (Alamór Formation; Jaillard et al., 1996). At this time, the oceanic plateau basement of the Piñon Terrane (123 Ma; Reynaud et al., 1999) of western Ecuador lay close to the paleoequator (Roperch et al., 1987), consistent with a position at the trailing edge of the Caribbean plate. The presence of large mafic clasts in basal Talara Basin sediments in Peru (Pecora et al., 1999) indicates that until the Paleocene, the Piñon Terrane still lay 300–500 km south of its present position. The newly formed Panama–Costa Rica Trench at the trailing edge of the Caribbean plate now accommodated most of the eastward convergence of the "Pacific" oceanic plates. Caribbean–South American relative motion was near north-northeast–directed dextral transpression. To the south of the Panama triple junction, volcanism and associated plutonism continued in Peru (Casma Group; Cobbing et al., 1981) during the Albian.

The Caribbean–South America plate boundary remained transpressional, causing closure of the Andean backarc basin and metamorphism of blueschists, which are found today along the Romeral-Peltetec Suture—the west flank of the Colombian central Cordillera and Ecuadorian Cordillera Real (Aspden and McCourt, 1986). Basalts were thrust eastward out of the backarc axis and over Albian limestones on the Antioquia Block, burying the western flank of the Colombian central Cordillera to at least 10–15 km depth, sufficient to drive greenschist-type metamorphism and to reset K-Ar ages. In this model, we propose that the Antioquia Block lay at least 300–400 km south of its present position at 120–100 Ma, close to present day Ecuador, because nowhere in northern or central Colombia have mid-Cretaceous synorogenic deposits or metamorphism been identified. Northward motion of the Antioquia Block (along the Palestina-Otú fault system) to its present position in the central Cordillera can be constrained to the time between backarc basin closure (110–120 Ma) and the late Eocene deposition of the Chorro Group in the Middle Magdalena Basin (overlap assemblage).

Dextral transpression continued during the Albian-Cenomanian (Fig. 11B and 11C), but as separation between the Americas slowed by 84 Ma, relative motion of the Caribbean with respect to South America became more east-west. Initially, this resulted in a higher component of contraction across the closed former backarc basin, and may be the cause of the consistent 85–65 Ma peak in K-Ar cooling ages in the Cordillera Real of Ecuador (Litherland et al., 1994) and the central Cordillera of Colombia (McCourt et al., 1984). From the Maastrichtian on, the east-west component of Caribbean-Colombia convergence was taken up by the establishment of east-dipping subduction of the Caribbean beneath Colombia (Fig. 11D). Seismic tomography data (van der Hilst and Mann, 1994) clearly show an enormous area of the Caribbean plate, which was subsequently subducted eastward beneath Colombia. This reorganization of subduction initiated the accretion of young Caribbean oceanic plateau basalts to the Colombian western Cordillera.

In contrast, in northernmost Colombia, the original Caribbean–over–South America vergence was maintained and the Ruma metamorphic belt was emplaced by the Paleocene onto the northwest Guajira margin, driving latest Maastrichtian–Paleocene foredeep subsidence in the Cesar Basin (Molina Formation). An important river flowed north through this basin, providing immature clastic sediments to the trench ahead of the Caribbean plate. These clastic sediments were then accreted into the Caribbean accretionary prism and later emplaced onto the Falcón portion of the Venezuelan margin (Matatére Formation).

Other aspects of the regional geology also strongly support the picture of south to north diachronous transpression indicated in Figure 11. Inception of the Andean foredeep (indicated by passage of a "peripheral bulge unconformity" and markedly increased rates of subsidence) youngs from south to north. The West Peruvian Trough may have been incorporated into the foredeep as early as the Cenomanian in Peru (Jaillard, 1993, 1994), the Putumayo-Llanos Basin during the Turonian–Santonian, and the César Basin (northernmost Colombia) during the Maastrichtian (Tectonic Analysis, 1998, unpublished report). As the west-east component of relative plate motion increased, underthrusting of the Colombian margin by the Caribbean plate caused Maastrichtian emergence of the northward-migrating Antioquia Terrane, from which west-derived clastic sediments were shed into the Middle Magdalena Valley for the first time (Cimmarona-Umir Formations; Villamil, 1999). Whereas the early Andean foreland was terrestrial to the south of Vaupes Arch by the Maastrichtian (Lower Tena Formation in Ecuador; Chota Formation in Peru; Mourier et al., 1988c), it was still open marine in the north (Colón Formation; Villamil, 1999).

Interaction of the trailing edge of the Caribbean plate (Panama Arc) with South America was also clearly diachronous, leaving an unmistakable imprint on the forearc basins and the Andean arc system. The San Lorenzo intra-oceanic volcanic arc was accreted to the western Piñon Terrane during the latest Cretaceous and/or early Paleocene, and the Piñon Terrane was then accreted to northernmost Peru and southern Ecuador. The Macuchi Arc was accreted to central Ecuador and southern Colombia during the Eocene. Uplift of the extinct Early Cretaceous Celica Arc and forearc basement blocks led to forearc limestones giving way to volcaniclastic sediments in the Celica-Lancones area (Copa Sombrero Formation; Jaillard et al., 1999). Maastrichtian continent-derived siliciclastic turbidites overlap the accreted terranes of the western Cordillera (Yunguilla Formation; Henderson, 1979; Jaillard et al., 1999; Reynaud et al., 1999; Kerr et al., 2002), while red beds derived from the Cordillera Real were deposited over marine carbonate and shale sequences in the foreland (Jaillard, 1997). Farther west, the Piñon terrane was the site of mostly pelagic sedimentation, with minor local volcaniclastic components, during the Late Cretaceous (Calentura, Cayo, Pilatón Formations; Reynaud et al., 1999) and had not yet been accreted. All of these accreted terranes lie west of the Pallatanga Fault, site of still active dextral faulting (5–7 mm/yr; Trenkamp et al., 2002) and were probably accreted at least 200 km south of their present site, in the area of present-day northern Peru.

Once the Panama triple junction passed to the north, subduction of the Nazca plate beneath South America (which occurred at roughly 5 times the rate of Caribbean subduction) resulted in the reestablishment of andesitic arc volcanism by earliest Eocene in southern Ecuador and middle to late Eocene in southern Colombia. Unmetamorphosed stitching plutons of Eocene age clearly indicate that accretion of basalts and deep-sea sediments had ceased in the Western Cordillera (Kerr et al., 1997). Subsequent northward migration of the Piñon Terrane was driven by oblique subduction of the Nazca plate beneath Ecuador, and its onset is probably indicated by initiation of rapid subsidence in the Talara Basin (northern Peru) during the Eocene. The tail of the terrane is marked by progressively younger onset of subsidence northward into the Progreso and Guayaquil basins of Ecuador (Jaillard et al., 1996).

Paleogene Underthrusting of Caribbean Crust beneath Colombia and the Development of "Negative Flexure" Basins

Progressive early Andean uplift continued into the Paleogene, producing a regional unconformity that affected the central Cordillera, the Lower, Middle, and Upper Magdalena basins, the Putumayo Basin, and parts of the Llanos Basin. The style of uplift can be inferred from the erosional unconformity in the Magdalena Valley; Cretaceous strata beneath the unconformity generally form a deeply eroded, east-dipping homocline (eroded section of ~5 km in the west, diminishing eastward; Pindell et al., 1998). The broad homocline suggests a flexural origin rather than a typical thrust-belt behind a foreland basin. We propose that this unconformity was produced by the obduction and telescoping of the Colombian crust westward onto the Caribbean plate (Figs. 12 and 13). In order for this to be the case, westward drift of Colombia would need to exceed the rollback velocity of the Caribbean Benioff zone. To the east of the area of unconformity, a broad sag-like basin is recorded by up to 300 m of Paleocene and early Eocene deposits (Fig. 13).

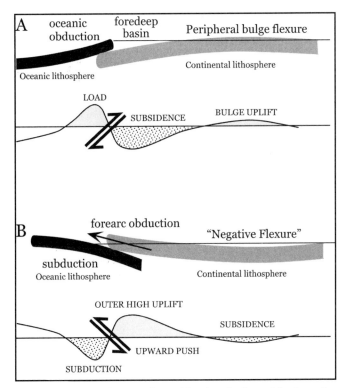

Figure 12. Contrasts between flexural foredeep basins and the "negative flexure" model proposed for the Paleogene development of Colombia. (A) Flexural foredeep basins reflect subsidence adjacent to a load (e.g., a foreland fold-thrust belt) placed on an elastic lithospheric plate. (B) In contrast, "negative flexure" basins can form as a result of the onset of obduction of continental crust onto oceanic crust to form a new subduction zone (i.e., in cases where the overriding plate moves toward the trench faster than the subducting plate rolls back). In such cases, outer highs are flexurally uplifted by the subducting oceanic slab while the interior will sag. Because this is an elastic flexural process, the wavelength of the sag basin will be comparable to the width of flexural forebulges, typically 200–300 km. Where subduction is sufficiently fast, arc development will eventually overprint the records of these early synsubduction basins. However, the early Paleogene sections in Colombia and eastern Venezuela–Trinidad appear to be two cases where subduction was sufficiently slow that the record of the "negative flexure" can be seen.

We coin the term "negative flexure basin" to describe this depocenter, and suggest that such basins may be a standard feature of the onset of subduction beneath formerly passive continental margins, whereby the outer edge of the margin is uplifted anywhere up to 10 km due to underthrusting of the oceanic slab.

The early Paleogene strata in the Colombian negative flexural basin predate significant thrusting, orogen growth, and arc volcanism within the Andes, most of which are of Oligocene and younger age, the palinspastic effects of which have been removed in Figure 13. The Paleogene stratigraphy of this area overlies a post-foredeep unconformity (top of the Maastrichtian foreland) and comprises basal fluvial sandstones (lower Socha, Barco, lower Regadera Formations) overlain by lacustrine shales (upper Socha, upper Regadera Formations). Marine incursion into this basin ("Lake Socha") was intermittent, over a sill at the

rising forebulge in the Caribbean region (produced by southeast-directed overthrusting by leading Caribbean nappes). Ongoing uplift and erosion of the central Cordillera eventually resulted in filling of this basin by the early Eocene and deposition of the regressive lower Mirador sandstones.

The negative flexure basin was short-lived. It appears that rollback of Caribbean lithosphere allowed a relaxation of the earlier uplift, as Colombia's advance over the Caribbean plate slowed from ~20 mm/yr to 10 mm/yr in the late middle and late Eocene (Pindell et al., 1998). This led to subsidence of the Colombian hanging wall and unflexing of the South American lithosphere, renewed sedimentation at the previously erosive margins of the negative flexure basin (Chorro Group onlaps westward onto central Cordillera), and rebound of the core of the negative flexure, producing an erosional unconformity at the top of the negative flexure fill (a second, higher, "Eocene unconformity") and the retreat of sedimentation northward toward modern Lake Maracaibo.

Continued thrusting of Colombia over the downgoing Caribbean plate cooled the base of the Colombian lithosphere over the following 10 m.y., driving further regional subsidence and renewed deposition, namely the upper Mirador and equivalent transgressive sandstones, and the eventual re-establishment of widespread lacustrine and intermittently marine conditions in a younger basin ("Lake Concentración"; Pindell et al., 1998). The rate and magnitude of this younger pre-Andean subsidence, as indicated by stratal thicknesses, are consistent with known rates of conductive cooling (Tectonic Analysis, 1998, unpublished report).

Paleogene Underthrusting of Proto-Caribbean Crust beneath Eastern Venezuela and Trinidad

Concurrently, to the east in the Paleocene to Eocene, several tens of km of plate convergence occurred between the Americas across the Proto-Caribbean that must have been taken up at structures between the Bahamas and northern South America. Caribbean seismic tomography (van der Hilst, 1990) and regional stratigraphy suggested to Pindell et al. (1991, 1998) and Pindell and Kennan (2001a, 2001b) that this convergence accumulated as the eastern Venezuela–Trinidadian continental crust overthrust the Proto-Caribbean oceanic lithosphere and caused considerable uplift and erosion (Figs. 14 and 15). Recent and ongoing field studies by the authors are confirming and expanding upon long-lived concepts (Guppy, 1911; Hedberg, 1937; Higgs, 2000) of a Paleogene northern outer high along eastern Venezuela and Trinidad (the "North Trinidad Basement High" of Pindell and Kennan, 2002) that provided erosional detritus toward the south. In the northernmost Serranía del Interior, erosion of probable Paleocene age cut down locally to the Barremian level of the Barranquín Formation (Vierbuchen, 1984), and in the subsurface of the Caroni Basin and northern flank of the Central Range of Trinidad, erosion of probable Eocene-Oligocene age cut variably to Eocene, Paleocene, and mid-Cretaceous levels. A second negative flexural trough formed south of this outer high, but unlike the Paleogene trough

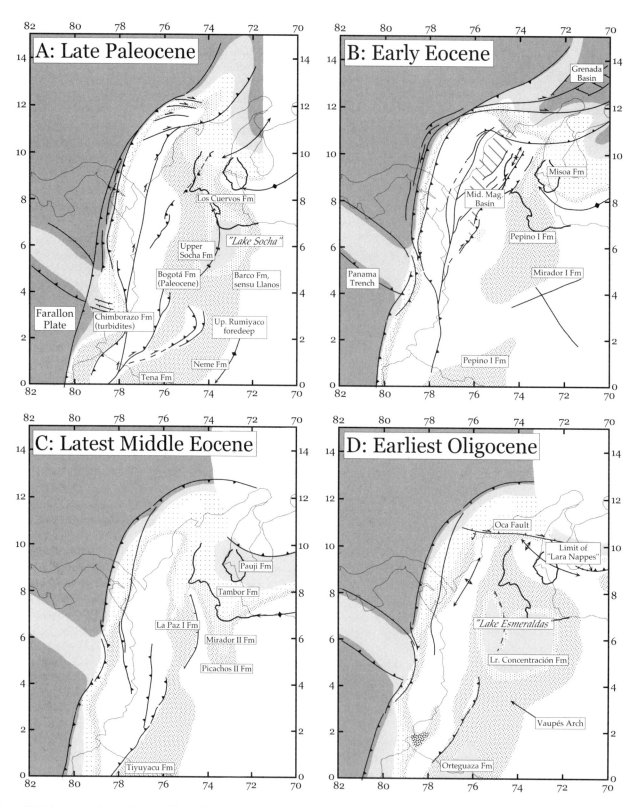

Figure 13. Paleogeographic evolution of Colombian "negative flexure" basins, derived partly from Pindell et al. (1998). (A) Maastrichtian-Paleocene underthrusting resulted in uplift of the central Cordillera, eastward tilting, and erosion, which is recorded in the Middle Magdalena Basin and development of a negative flexure basin in the eastern Cordillera and Llanos region farther east, without associated large-magnitude overthrusting. (B) Ongoing uplift and erosion of the central Cordillera eventually resulted in regressive sandstones filling this basin by the early Eocene. (C) Slowing subduction and sinking of the Caribbean plate resulted in "unflexing" of the basin, reducing accommodation space and resulting in a subtle overlying unconformity. (D) Continued subsidence of the Caribbean slab, and cooling of the base of the South American lithosphere, resulted in long-wavelength thermal subsidence and development of a wide lacustrine basin in the absence of associated thrusting. Facies patterns as in Figure 11.

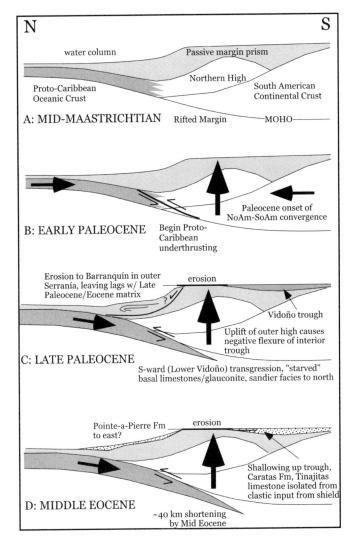

Figure 14. Hypothetical cross sections of the onset of subduction beneath northern South America. As in Colombia, onset of subduction led to the uplift of an outer high, which was a possible source area for sediments deposited in the "negative flexure" basin to the south.

of Colombia, this trough continued as a marine depocenter that remained connected to the ocean in its eastern and probably its western end. The northern flank of this trough in Paleocene–early Oligocene time received north-derived "orogenic" fan-delta slope sediments including sandy mudstones and turbidites (Vidoño [northern facies], Chaudière [northern facies], Pointe-a-Pierre, and San Fernando [northern facies] Formations), whereas the southern flank was starved of clastics: the Paleocene of Venezuela is characterized by authigenic glauconitic greensands and carbonates (southern Vidoño, possibly Soldado), and the Paleocene-Eocene of Trinidad lacks sand altogether (Lizard Springs and Navet Formations). In Venezuela, the Caratas Formation sands filled much of the trough in the Eocene, due to its proximity to the Shield. In the Oligocene, this basin configuration was changed by drowning of the northern outer high due to the arrival by then of the Caribbean

prism's foredeep basin, as the Caribbean plate came ever closer to eastern Venezuela and Trinidad (Fig. 15).

A large volume of mid-Cretaceous hydrocarbon source rocks was probably eroded from the northern outer high. This pre-Caribbean uplift and unroofing of Cretaceous section may explain why fission track studies of northerly Barranquín Formation strata (Locke and Garver, this volume) show depositional rather than Neogene, synorogenic ages (lack of sufficient burial due to prior erosion). Because the total amount of Proto-Caribbean subduction at this margin is very small, ~70 km in eastern Venezuela–Trinidad and ~150 km in western Venezuela (Pindell et al., 1998), a subduction-related magmatic arc has not formed along the margin. Therefore, the record of this marine negative flexural basin has been preserved.

Cenozoic Dextral-Oblique Caribbean–South America Collision in Venezuela and Trinidad

Although the northern Andean terranes of northwest South America are currently being extruded northward (relative to the Guyana Shield) onto the Caribbean plate at the South Caribbean foldbelt (Fig. 1; Mann and Burke, 1984; van der Hilst and Mann, 1994), this plate boundary geometry has developed only since middle Oligocene time (Dewey and Pindell, 1985; Pindell et al., 1998). Prior to the Oligocene, from Santa Marta Massif eastward, initial Caribbean–South America interaction was southward vergent, such that oceanic material was emplaced by dextral transpression onto the former South American margin (Fig. 2). This emplacement of allochthonous material is well recorded by the eastwardly-younging Caribbean foredeep basin (Pindell, 1985a; Dewey and Pindell, 1986; Pindell et al., 1988), which started in the Paleocene at César Basin, Colombia, and continued until the middle Miocene in eastern Venezuela–Trinidad. The onset of Andean extrusion onto the Caribbean plate coincides with a westward acceleration of South America across the mantle (Pindell et al., 1998), and we believe that coupling between the North Andean and Caribbean lithospheres and collision of buoyant parts of the Panama Arc with western Colombia have combined to cause strong, roughly east-west contraction in the eastern Cordillera of Colombia at roughly the same azimuth as Caribbean–South American relative motion. This "Andean" development has involved a foldbelt polarity reversal, probably eastward-younging from offshore western Colombia, which accommodated continued convergence, after arc collision, between the Caribbean and South America (Fig. 5). The Oligocene-Recent extrusion of the northern Andes has taken advantage of the free-face provided by these early north-vergent structures. Foredeep sections have formed in the basinal areas adjacent to the zone of strong Andean strain, which are critical to hydrocarbon maturation history in these basins.

Thus, dextral oblique collision between the Caribbean and South American crusts, with local complexities, characterizes the Paleocene to middle Miocene of the southern Caribbean margin (Pindell et al., 1988; Audemard and Serrano, 2001). After the Great Caribbean Arc rounded the Guajira corner, eastward-

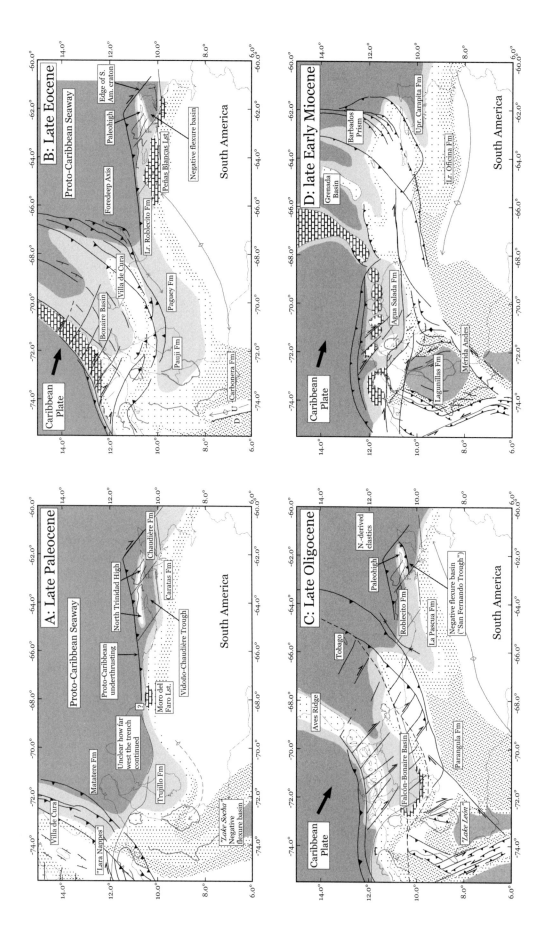

Figure 15. Caribbean–Venezuela/Trinidad arc–continent interactions, simplified from Pindell et al. (1998). (A) By late Paleocene, the leading edge of the Caribbean plate was driving foredeep subsidence in the Maracaibo area. In the east, a negative-flexure basin (coined here the "Vidoño–Chaudière Trough") was the consequence of onset of subduction of Proto-Caribbean lithosphere beneath northern South America. (B) By late Eocene, foredeep subsidence had spread to central Venezuela. Migration of the associated flexural forebulge into eastern Venezuela provided a source for sediments deposited in the negative flexure trough. (C) By late Oligocene, the Caribbean foldbelt reached central Venezuela and the foredeep had encroached upon eastern Venezuela. Basement-involved faulting may have accentuated uplift of the North Trinidad Basement High, such that coarse clastics were deposited southward into what we term here the "San Fernando Trough." Note the restored coastline of Northern Range of Trinidad, showing the extent of subsequent transpressive deformations. (D) By late early Miocene, the Proto-Caribbean subduction zone and associated outer high were inactive and incorporated into the Caribbean foredeep. Facies patterns as in Figure 11.

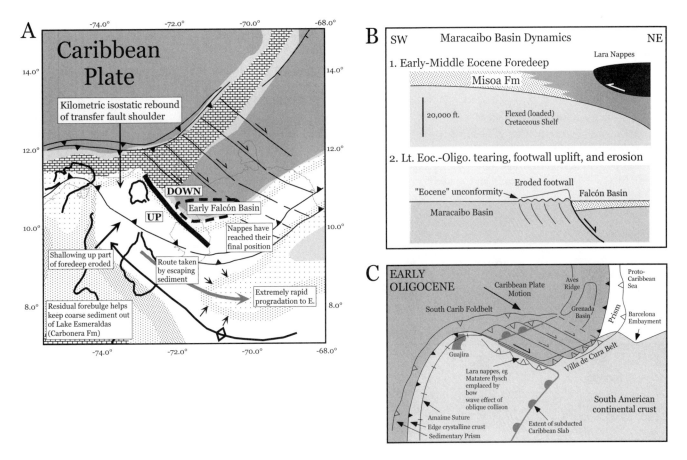

Figure 16. (A) Middle Oligocene reconstruction of the Maracaibo-Falcón area. Southeast-directed thrusting stalled over the thicker continental crust of the Maracaibo Basin but continued over the transitional to oceanic crust northeast of the Mesozoic Maracaibo Transform (see Figs. 4 and 5). (B) Tearing of the downgoing plate led to flexural rebound in the northeast Maracaibo Basin and onset of subsidence in the Falcón Basin. (C) Overview of the complex, lengthening transfer zone that developed between areas of subducting Caribbean plate (northern Colombia) and overriding Caribbean plate (central Venezuela). Facies patterns as in Figure 11.

younging foredeep development from the Maracaibo to Maturín basins, as well as eastward-younging cooling ages of obducted and metamorphosed parautochthonous rocks involved in the collision (Foland et al., 1992), attest to continuous, west-to-east collision along the plate interface. Rounding of Guajira Peninsula and initial collision in western Venezuela was assisted by arc-parallel lengthening as the Grenada Basin opened (Figs. 5 and 15). The north-south opening model of Grenada Basin suggests that the Leeward Antilles Arc originated east of, and is equivalent to, the southern half of Aves Ridge (Pindell and Barrett, 1990). In all our paleogeographic-kinematic modeling, there is insufficient space to bring the Great Arc through the Yucatán-Guajira bottleneck if the Leeward Antilles islands originated along strike of, rather than in front of, the southern Aves Ridge.

It is not clear how far west the Paleogene Proto-Caribbean Trench of eastern Venezuela had developed as Caribbean–South America collision ensued (Fig. 15). It is possible that north-south contraction between the Americas at the longitude of western Venezuela was achieved by downwarping of Proto-Caribbean

crust beneath the Caribbean Arc, such that there was no kinematic need for a trench in the west (Pindell et al., 1998). In the east, however, this mechanism is not viable in the Paleogene, because the Caribbean plate was too far west, and seismic tomography and Paleogene stratigraphy support the existence of a Proto-Caribbean Trench there. Thus, for at least the eastern portion of this margin, the Caribbean plate has obliquely overthrust the preexisting trace of the Proto-Caribbean Trench. To the east of Trinidad, toward the North America–South America pole of rotation for this boundary, contraction has been so small, and the mid-Atlantic Ridge was so near, that the eastward continuation of the Proto-Caribbean Trench for much of Cenozoic time has not been identified clearly (Pindell and Kennan, 2001a, 2001b).

Within the Caribbean oblique collisional history, a secondary development occurred in the northern Maracaibo–Falcón region, where the Trujillo Embayment existed in the original passive margin (Fig. 4). As the Lara Nappes were emplaced toward the southeast across this embayment in the Eocene-Oligocene, the emplacement direction was parallel to the western side of the embayment (Fig. 16).

Thus, the thrust belt north of the Maracaibo Basin is a transpressional lateral ramp rather than a south-directed thrust front, but a significant load was still imparted on northern Maracaibo Basin. However, shortening progressed so far to the southeast toward central Venezuela that the autochthonous South American lithosphere was forced to tear, northeastern side down, to accommodate the continued shortening. The effect of this was that the western side of the tear rebounded isostatically, leading to several km of late Eocene–early Oligocene uplift and erosion in northern Maracaibo Basin. This event most certainly arrested hydrocarbon maturation that had been in progress in northern Maracaibo Basin due to early and middle Eocene foredeep deposition. In addition, tearing of the autochthon probably facilitated the Oligocene emplacement of basalts in the Falcón Basin section (Muessig, 1978).

Another secondary development was the late middle Miocene change in Caribbean–South American relative motion direction (Pindell, 1994; Pindell et al., 1998). Prior to 12 Ma, Caribbean–South America motion was directed east-southeast, whereas relative motion since 12 Ma has been directed slightly north of east;

GPS studies confirm this for the present day (Weber et al., 2001). Figure 17 shows three "snapshots" of this late Cenozoic evolution in the eastern Venezuela–Trinidad area, showing: (1) end of oblique collision, (2) onset of transcurrent plate boundary development, and (3) post–4 Ma dextral transpression across the region.

In the Miocene, until ca. 12 Ma, dextral oblique thrusting in the Serranía del Interior of Venezuela and the Nariva Fold Belt of Trinidad was accompanied by foredeep loading in Maturín and Southern basins. However, after the 12 Ma relative motion change, late Miocene sediments in the Maturín and Southern basins step northward and bury deeper thrust structures with little or no evidence for further thrusting in the subsurface thrust wedge. Between 12 and 4 Ma, east-west motion between the Caribbean and South American plates appears to have become strongly partitioned along the Cariaco–El Pilar fault zones, stepping southward across the late Miocene to Recent Gulf of Paria pull-apart basin, along which there is evidence for subtle collapse of the middle Miocene allochthons back to the north. Farther east, along the Central Range and south to the Point Radix–Darien

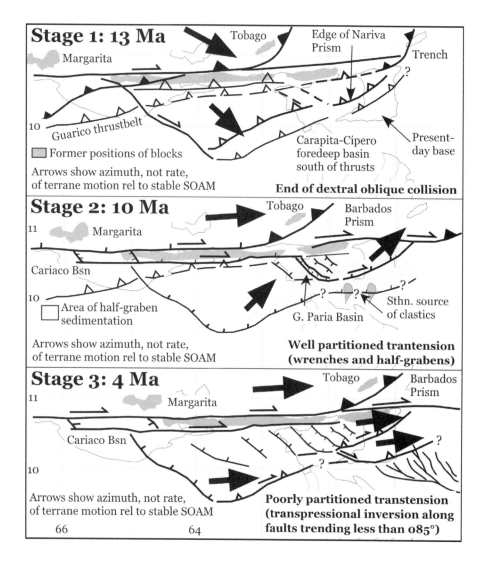

Figure 17. Proposed map view evolution of eastern Venezuela and Trinidad since 12 Ma, modified after Pindell and Kennan (2001a). Stage 1 shows the end of oblique collision of the Caribbean plate. During Stage 2, transtensional movements between the Caribbean and South American (SOAM on figure) plates were well partitioned into strike-slip at the Coche–North Coast Fault and Gulf of Paria pull-apart basin and northward listric extension along the half-graben faults in the Maturín and the South Trinidad basins. Finally, in Stage 3, the Caribbean and South American plates become more strongly coupled, possibly because the deep root of the Antilles arc could not override the North Trinidad High of South American lithosphere. As a result, both contractional and strike-slip faulting, with associated pull-apart formation, spread southeast from their late Miocene location.

Ridge Fault Zone, displacement was transpressional because reactivated middle Miocene thrust structures were oriented slightly counterclockwise of late Miocene relative plate motion.

A third secondary development is seen at ca. 4 Ma, documented by the onset of shortening in the Southern Basin of Trinidad, enhanced transpressional uplift in the Central Range, onset of significant subsidence in the Columbus Channel and eastern offshore areas (drowning of late Miocene deltas by Pliocene shelf sediments), enhanced rates of pull-apart formation in the Gulf of Paria and of transpression in the eastern offshore, and initiation of extensional collapse (Wood, 2000) of the foredeep basin fill toward the Atlantic south of the Darien Ridge (Pindell and Kennan, 2001a). The strong partitioning of strain appears to have broken down, and little or no significant strike-slip on the North Coast Fault Zone can be recognized since 4 Ma (Tectonic Analysis, 2002, unpublished seismic interpretation). The Caribbean plate appears to have become more strongly coupled with deeper basement of South America, possibly because the deep root of the Antilles volcanic arc (Margarita Ridge) began to encounter the northern limit of the North Trinidad Basement High (Pindell and Kennan, 2002).

SUMMARY DEPICTION OF TECTONIC STYLES OF SELECT ARC-CONTINENT INTERACTIONS

Figure 18A–N shows a series of schematic maps and cross sections summarizing proposed and possible mechanisms for arc-continent interaction between elements of the Caribbean plate and the Americas and outlining the context of key HP-LT occurrences.

At ca. 120 Ma, west-dipping subduction of Proto-Caribbean oceanic crust was initiated by subduction polarity reversal beneath the Great Arc. We envision that the new Great Arc trench was connected to the ongoing, east-dipping western Chortís trench by an ever-lengthening transfer zone of arc-parallel stretching and through-going, propeller-shaped, sinistral shear zones (Fig. 18A). The cross section (Fig. 18B) shows the sutured subduction or strike-slip zone between Pacific-derived (Caribbean plate) crust and the former Inter-American Arc, the through-going sinistral shear zones, and newly-initiated oblique subduction of thinned Chortís passive margin beneath the Great Arc. The protolith for the Escambray Massif, Cuba, was probably Jurassic quartzose sandstone and carbonate from part of the Chortís passive margin. Protoliths of other Caribbean HP complexes include (1) Proto-Caribbean oceanic crust (e.g., Río San Juan Complex, Dominican Republic); (2) fragments of the former northeastern fringe of the Inter-American Arc that entered the trench immediately upon reversal, or sometime later by subduction erosion of the Great Arc hanging wall (e.g., Villa de Cura Complex); and (3) continental blocks of the Inter-American Arc that may have been rifted from the Americas during Neocomian intra-arc spreading (e.g., Juan Griego Unit, Margarita). Although Sisson et al. (2003) suggested that the southern Motagua HP-LT rocks, which formed from oceanic crust and give Ar-Ar ages of 116–125 Ma, may pertain to an early collision between Chortís and Mexico, two other possible origins worth noting are

(1) Proto-Caribbean or Inter-American Arc crust that was subducted at 120 Ma, like other Caribbean HP complexes (although this does not explain apparent ages at the old end of Sisson et al.'s [2003] age range); and (2) Pacific crust (like that at Baja California; Baldwin and Harrison, 1989) subducted at the west-facing trench near the southern end of Chortís shortly prior to subduction polarity reversal (ca. 130 Ma), such that initial exhumation (toward the end of the 116–125 Ma interval) may directly relate to arc-parallel stretching within the lengthening sinistral transfer zone between the Chortís and Great Arc trenches during the subduction polarity reversal. Such an origin may best explain the possible Jurassic HP components in Cuba's Escambray complex (Maresch et al., 2003), as well as possible 118 Ma components in the Northern Serpentinite Mélange (García-Casco et al., 2002).

In the Late Cretaceous, the Great Arc migrated northeast over Proto-Caribbean oceanic crust toward sinistral-oblique collision with Yucatán at ca. 70 Ma (Fig. 18C). The south Motagua HP-LT rocks may have formed the hanging wall of the trench at this time in the two possible origins for them suggested above, but not if they were formed by Chortís-Mexico collision. The ophiolites and mélanges later emplaced onto the Yucatán margin are interpreted to form part of the accretionary wedge above subducting Cretaceous Proto-Caribbean oceanic crust (Fig. 18D). Proto-Caribbean oceanic crust also likely formed the protolith for the younger, northern Motagua HP-LT rocks, and may only have been subducted shortly before Maastrichtian collision. This Late Cretaceous collision event exhumed HP-LT rocks and thrust less-metamorphosed ophiolites and ophiolite mélange (Santa Cruz, Cuchumantanes) onto the Yucatán margin, driving subsidence of the Maastrichtian Sepúr foredeep (Fig. 18E). Highly oblique collision between the Great Arc and Yucatán may have allowed slivers of older HP-LT rocks to be left behind north of a "Proto-Motagua Fault" and south of the younger HP-LT belt, while most were carried farther east (i.e., Jamaican and Cuban HP rocks). Alternatively, the southern Motagua HP-LT rocks may have been emplaced after passage of the Great Arc to the east, with the southern Yucatán margin forming the northwestern side of the sinistral shear zones that link the Chortís and Caribbean trenches. Relative motions between the Great Arc, the easternmost end of Chortís, and southern Yucatán during the Late Cretaceous are likely to have been complex. Our maps suggest that sinistral transtension is likely, and may play a role exhuming the younger HP-LT rocks in Yucatán. Finally, during the middle to late Cenozoic (Fig. 18F), strike-slip on the Motagua Fault, linked to opening of the Cayman Trough, juxtaposed the Chortís Block and southern Yucatán, and the older and younger HP-LT suites reached their current relative positions. We consider that south-directed thrusting in this highly transpressive zone may have placed the older, more southerly HP-LT suite onto the Chortís Block, because we are confident that prior to this time Chortís lay well west of the Great Arc–Yucatán suture zone (Pindell and Dewey, 1982), and we are not convinced that a former oceanic basin ever existed between Chortís and southwest Mexico that may have produced these rocks. The trace of the neotectonic Motagua Fault appears

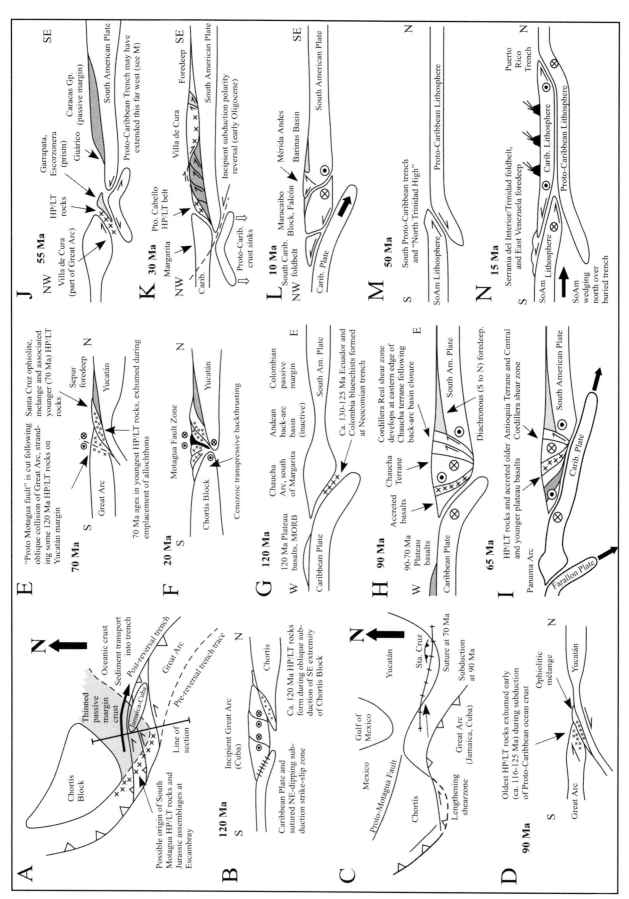

Figure 18. Schematic maps and cross sections, not necessarily to scale, illustrating the proposed and possible mechanisms of formation and emplacement of allochthons and associated high-pressure–low-temperature (HP-LT) rocks on the margins of North and South America. MORB—mid-oceanic-ridge basalt; SoAm—South America.

to follow the boundary between older (ca. 120 Ma) and younger (70 Ma) HP-LT belts, suggesting that prior to the ?Miocene (age of emplacement onto Chortís?), the older HP-LT suite lay some distance west of its present position.

A similar scenario, with dextral strike-slip along the southeast flanks of the Caribbean plate linking southwest-dipping subduction beneath the Great Arc with ongoing northeast-dipping subduction beneath the Central Andes, appears to best explain the age and location of HP-LT rocks and associated structures in Ecuador and Colombia. A schematic cross section of the northern Andes at ca. 120 Ma (Fig. 18G), located south of the paleoposition of Margarita at approximately the latitude of present-day Ecuador, shows key Andean elements at the time of subduction polarity reversal farther north. The Chaucha Terrane (rifted blocks of Carboniferous to Jurassic continental crust) is interpreted as the basement of an arc formed due to subduction of "Pacific" oceanic crust beneath South America prior to 120 Ma, and there is no evidence of arc activity from 120 to 60 Ma north of Peru. The blueschists in Ecuador and Colombia are older than those in Cuba and Margarita and lie west or northwest of the Chaucha (pre-reversal) arc and forearc fragments, suggesting that they formed in the "Pacific" subduction zone prior to subduction polarity reversal. Continued opening of the Proto-Caribbean Seaway after the subduction polarity reversal resulted in highly oblique dextral relative motion between the Caribbean and South America, in contrast to the head-on subduction beneath the Great Arc farther north. The oblique closure of the Andean backarc basin formed the Cordillera Real of Ecuador and the Central Cordillera of Colombia, and inactive fragments of the former Inter-American Arc were stranded in Ecuador (Chaucha Terrane, Fig. 18H). Some slivers of the passive margin were transported several hundred km north of their original position in Ecuador (e.g., Antioquia Terrane of central Cordillera, Colombia). As in the north, this zone of transpressive shear deformation must have lengthened northward with time, and interaction between the leading edge of the Caribbean must have youngened from south to north. Several lines of evidence support this conclusion. Exhumation of parts of the shear zone in central Ecuador is pre-Campanian (cooling ages, first appearance of "orogenic" clastic sediments), but the first west-derived, "orogenic" sediments are of Maastrichtian age in the Middle Magdalena valley. Also, unconformities and sequence boundaries related to northward migration of the Caribbean foredeep are Coniacian-Santonian age in southern Colombia, but are of late Maastrichtian age in northernmost Colombia.

A ca. 70–65 Ma section through Colombia (Fig. 18I), slightly north of that shown in Figure 18H, shows no fragments of the former arc. Instead, blueschists, serpentinites, and fragments of ca. 120 Ma plateau basalts, derived from the Caribbean plate, are juxtaposed directly against the central Cordillera–Antioquia Terrane along the line of the present-day Romeral Fault. Remnants of the arc may be present in the subsurface of the Lower Magdalena Basin, and arc or forearc remnants outcrop on the Guajira Peninsula and farther east. Campanian termination of Proto-Caribbean seafloor spreading (Pindell et al., 1988) caused Caribbean–South America relative motion to change from northeast to east, trigger-

ing, in the west, renewed low-angle, non-volcanic, subduction of Caribbean crust beneath South America. This led to the accretion of Caribbean Plateau Basalts in the Western Cordillera and development of an accretionary prism of offscraped Caribbean plate strata (San Jacinto Belt). The Panama Arc, which marks the trailing edge of the Caribbean plate, still lay to the southwest at this time, but began to underthrust the Colombian margin during the Paleogene, driving eastward thrusting in and east of the Central Cordillera at the latitude of the Upper Magdalena Valley (Chusma belt), and leading to the establishment of a volcanic arc in southern Colombia that was produced by subduction of Farallon crust south of the Panama Arc–Andean Trench triple junction.

By Paleogene time, the leading edge of the Caribbean plate had rounded the Guajira Peninsula of Colombia. The dextral-oblique opening of the Grenada backarc basin (Pindell and Barrett, 1990) allowed the Caribbean arc and forearc to be thrust southeastward onto the western Venezuelan margin. Figure 18J shows northern Venezuela during the early Eocene, shortly before obduction of the Villa de Cura allochthon. The Eocene Garrapata (and possibly the Los Cajones Member of Guárico and the Escorzonera Formations) allochthonous rocks (prism) have an arc-orogenic character and are interpreted to have formed ahead of the Caribbean arc and forearc. The bulk of the quartz-turbiditic Guárico Formation is shown in a slope and rise position north of older passive margin section, and the Caracas Group is shown as pre-Cretaceous passive margin section overlying extended Paleozoic continental crust. As noted earlier, it is not clear if the Proto-Caribbean Trench along northern South America, well-developed to the east (see below), had propagated this far west. If it had, then the Caribbean prism must have overridden the trace of the Proto-Caribbean trench, as opposed to a simple passive margin, before emplacement onto the Venezuelan margin, and the hanging wall of the Proto-Caribbean trench may have contributed to the Garrapata and other orogenic facies. During the late Eocene and through Oligocene time, the Villa de Cura allochthon (partly HP-LT metamorphosed arc and MORB rocks) was emplaced over the Caracas Group, which was strongly deformed, forming a duplex beneath a major Caribbean sole thrust marked by HP-LT rocks (Fig. 18K). The primitive (PIA) character of parts of the Villa de Cura Group suggests to us a partly pre-polarity reversal (i.e., older than 120 Ma) age for protoliths, in keeping with the ages of other PIA rocks in the Great Arc. The northern portion of this sole thrust could be interpreted to coincide with the coastal Puerto Cabello HP-LT rocks. The Garrapata-Escorzonera-?Cajones prism, the Guárico Formation, and the Upper Cretaceous cover of the passive margin (Querecual and Mucaria Formations) were detached from the underlying, mostly older Caracas Group and thrust ahead of the Villa de Cura allochthon, driving subsidence in the La Pascua–Roblecito foredeep. Although Smith et al. (1999) proposed a western Colombian derivation of Paleozoic continental components in the Puerto Cabello zone, another alternative origin to consider is the basement beneath the Caracas Group. Because the Caracas Group was itself detached from its basement, the Caribbean sole thrust may have been able to incorporate Paleozoic basement material, perhaps leading to a complex mix of lithologies and protoliths seen in the Puerto Cabello complex (Avé Lallemant and Sisson, 1993). Caribbean plate oceanic and arc rocks of Margarita and the Leeward Antilles lay to the north of the Puerto Cabello area.

Toward the end of or after emplacement of the Caribbean allochthons in northern Colombia and western Venezuela, the accreted arc material and elements of South American basement began to be backthrusted onto the Caribbean plate (Fig. 18K and 18L; note section L is drawn somewhat west of K to include Maracaibo Basin). Northward thrusting is limited in central Venezuela, north of the Morón Fault, but was strongly enhanced in the Maracaibo area by northward tectonic escape of the triangular Maracaibo Block between the Santa-Marta-Bucaramanga and Boconó faults.

Figure 18M summarizes eastern Venezuela–Trinidad during the Paleogene, where a Proto-Caribbean Trench developed prior to the arrival of the Caribbean plate from the west to accommodate north-south convergence between North and South America, producing an outer high in the Paleogene. Subduction was minor (<150 km) and slow and did not produce a volcanic arc on northern South America. During the Miocene to Recent (Fig. 18N), the Caribbean plate migrated into the line of section from the west, burying the northern edge of South American continental basement and driving southeast-directed thrusting in Venezuela (Serranía del Interior Oriental) and Trinidad (Naparima belt). Continued convergence between North and South America has enhanced the apparent "wedging" of South America between the Caribbean and Proto-Caribbean plates. Volcanism on the Caribbean plate has been confined to those areas where a significant asthenospheric wedge existed above the subducting Proto-Caribbean plate, and thus, volcanism has probably been shut off diachronously from west to east during the oblique Caribbean–South America collision.

CONCLUSIONS

The American continental margins of the Caribbean region formed during Jurassic continental breakup of Pangea and originally faced the Proto-Caribbean Seaway in which seafloor spreading resulted from separation of North and South America. These margins were later overridden diachronously by allochthonous arc and oceanic complexes that were part of the Caribbean plate or its accretionary complex. The stratigraphic and structural development of the American margins was strongly controlled by tectonic events prior to and including these arc-continent interactions.

Caribbean lithosphere originated in the Pacific and was progressively engulfed between the Americas after Aptian time by the inception of a west-dipping Benioff zone in the widening gap between the Chortís Block and the northern Andes. This trench is now marked by the Motagua (Guatemalan) and Cuban sutures of southern North America, and by the Ruma (Guajira) and Villa de Cura (Venezuela) nappes of northern South America, and persists today as the Lesser Antilles subduction zone. Most Caribbean HP metamorphic complexes originated at this east-facing Aptian and

younger subduction zone. Arc-polarity reversal at an earlier (Neocomian) west-facing Inter-American Arc is implied, but the site of this "arc" may have been dominated by sinistral transform motions between two oceanic plates rather than by significant amounts of east-dipping subduction. Geochronologic data and metamorphic relations of the HP complexes, as well as the arc magmatic and structural histories of today's pieces of the Great Arc, all support a roughly 120 Ma age for this polarity reversal event, with uplift and exhumation well under way prior to 90 Ma. Several HP complexes along the Ecuadorian and southern Colombian Andes, and two Caribbean HP complexes (south Motagua, Guatemala, and parts of Escambray, Cuba) possess components that pre-date the Aptian; this suggests that they originated along the west-facing Inter-American Arc (like those in Baja California; Baldwin and Harrison, 1989) prior to polarity-reversal, but were then intimately involved with the arc-polarity reversal and part of the subsequent migration of the Great Arc. Processes that we can tie to progressive exhumation of HP rocks in the Great Caribbean Arc include arc-parallel stretching, obduction of forearc materials onto continental rifted margins (e.g., north Motagua), and low-angle detachment at intra-arc basins (Yucatán and Grenada Basins, final cooling at Escambray and Margarita). Counterflow within the subduction complex is also possible. A number of Caribbean HP complexes were considerably uplifted by 90 Ma, and we consider that arc-parallel stretching (Avé Lallemant and Guth, 1990) by various processes at the highly oblique northwestern and southeastern portions of the Great Arc subduction zone (as opposed to the more head-on, northeastern part of the Great Arc) was a major factor in the progressive uplift histories.

Given the clear Aptian age (ca. 120 Ma) for the onset of polarity reversal, which was achieved by the Albian, the 90 Ma Caribbean Basalt Plateau could not have played a role in triggering the polarity reversal. Rather, the Caribbean basalts were extruded onto preexisting Caribbean crust after polarity reversal and during engulfment by the Americas. Polarity reversal was probably triggered, instead, by the westward acceleration of the Americas, thereby causing strong compression at the entire Cordilleran arc system. Oceanic plateau basalts were able to erupt onto the Caribbean Basin because that lithosphere remained almost fixed relative to a deep mantle reference frame, and the bounding subduction zones were young and did not root deeply enough into the mantle by 90 Ma to block the paths of plumes to the surface.

Evidence increasingly suggests that amagmatic, Paleogene subduction of Proto-Caribbean lithosphere occurred beneath eastern Venezuela and Trinidad, ahead of the migrating Caribbean plate, which accommodated the well-documented Cenozoic convergence between North and South America. Subduction of Caribbean crust beneath western Colombia also began in Maastrichtian time. In both settings, strong uplift occurred in the hanging walls close to the trench as subduction began, while shallow subaqueous troughs formed landward of these highs in the apparent absence of bounding thrusts. We propose a new class of basin to describe this condition, the "negative flexure basin," produced as a consequence of flexure during the onset of subduction at a preexisting passive margin. The early Paleogene sections of Colombia and eastern Venezuela–Trinidad provide epicontinental and pericontinental examples, respectively.

Finally, stratigraphic and structural style was altered dramatically in eastern Venezuela and Trinidad at ca. 12 Ma, when Caribbean–South America relative motion changed from east-southeast–directed to east-directed. Since 4 Ma, increased coupling between the Lesser Antilles Arc and deep South American basement has resulted in less partitioning of interplate shear and the *onset* of transpressive shortening in southern Trinidad, coeval with pull-apart basin formation in the Gulf of Paria, where little recent thrusting is recorded.

ACKNOWLEDGMENTS

This paper has grown out of years of "sessions" among the authors at many international meetings, field trips, workshops, and informal get-togethers. There are many others to thank for critical input into this synthesis: Sam Algar, Claudia Arango, Felipe Audemard, Hans Avé Lallemant, Bert Bally, Steve Barrett, Tony Barros, the late Alirio Bellizzia, Dale Bird, Terry Blair, Kevin Burke, Barry Carr-Brown, Antonio García-Casco, Julio Cristancho, John Dewey, Juan di Croce, Steve Donovan, Dave Engebretson, Johan Erikson, Bob Erlich, John Frampton, Francia Galea, Richard P. George Jr., Giuseppe Giunta, Friedemann Grafe, Mark Hempton, Manuel Iturralde-Vinent, Trevor Jackson, Keith James, Chris Johnson, Jim Joyce, Andrew Kerr, Tony King, Hans Krause, Martin Krebbs, Dave Larue, John Lewis, Jairo Lugo, Oliver Macsotay, Paul Mann, Florentin Maurrasse, Javier Meneses-Rocha, Martin Meschede, Ernesto Miranda, Simon Mitchell, Homer Montgomery, Krishna Persad, Nelly Pimentel, Tony Ramlackhansingh, Ted Robinson, Eric Rosencrantz, Josh Rosenfeld, Jinny Sisson, Art Snoke, Mercedes Socas, the late Bob (R.C.) Speed, Pat Thompson, Rob van der Hilst, Tomas Villamil, John Weber, and Roz White are only some of them. We are also grateful to the various sponsors of many work programs by Tectonic Analysis Inc. and Ltd. over the years, as well as Petróleos de Venezuela (PDVSA), Petrotrin, Ecopetrol, Pemex, and the Ministries of Trinidad and Tobago and Venezuela; they have made this type of synthesis work possible. Finally, we would like to thank Art Snoke and an anonymous reviewer for their penetrative comments, helpful criticisms, and suggestions.

REFERENCES CITED

Anderson, T.H., and Schmidt, V.A., 1983, The evolution of Middle America and the Gulf of Mexico–Caribbean Sea region during Mesozoic time: Geological Society of America Bulletin, v. 94, p. 941–966, doi: 10.1130/0016-7606(1983)94<941:TEOMAA>2.0.CO;2.

Arculus, R.J., Lapierre, H., and Jaillard, E., 1999, Geochemical window into subduction and accretion processes: Raspas metamorphic complex, Ecuador: Geology, v. 27, p. 547–550, doi: 10.1130/0091-7613(1999)027<0547:GWISAA>2.3.CO;2.

Aspden, J.A., and McCourt, W.J., 1986, Mesozoic oceanic terrane in the central Andes of Colombia: Geology, v. 14, p. 415–418, doi: 10.1130/0091-7613(1986)14<415:MOTITC>2.0.CO;2.

Aspden, J.A., Harrison, S.M., and Rundle, C.C., 1992, New geochronological control for the tectono-magmatic evolution of metamorphic basement, Cordillera Real and the El Oro Province, Ecuador: Journal of South American Earth Sciences, v. 6, p. 77–96, doi: 10.1016/0895-9811(92)90019-U.

Aspden, J.A., Bonilla, W., and Duque, P., 1995, The El Oro Complex, Ecuador: Geology and economic mineral deposits: British Geological Survey, Overseas Geology and Mineral Resources v. 67, 63 p.

Audemard, F.E., and Serrano, I.C., 2001, Future petroliferous provinces of Venezuela, in Downey, M.W., Threet, J.C., and Morgan, W.A., eds., Petroleum provinces of the twenty-first century: American Association of Petroleum Geologists Memoir 74, p. 353–373.

Avé Lallemant, H.G., and Oldow, J.S., 1988, Early Mesozoic southward migration of Cordilleran transpressional terranes: Tectonics, v. 7, p. 1057–1088.

Avé Lallemant, H.G., and Guth, L.R., 1990, Role of extensional tectonics in exhumation of blueschists in an oblique subduction setting, Northeastern Venezuela: Geology, v. 18, p. 950–953, doi: 10.1130/0091-7613(1990)018<0950:ROETIE>2.3.CO;2.

Avé Lallemant, H.G., and Sisson, V.B., 1993, Caribbean–South America plate interactions: Constraints from the Cordillera de la Costa belt, Venezuela, in Pindell, J.L., and Perkins, B.F, eds., Mesozoic and early Cenozoic development of the Gulf of Mexico and Caribbean region—A context for hydrocarbon exploration, Proceedings, Gulf Coast Section, SEPM Foundation 13th Annual Research Conference: Houston, Texas, Society for Sedimentary Geology (SEPM) Foundation, p. 211–219.

Baldwin, S.L., and Harrison, T.M., 1989, Geochronology of blueschists from west-central Baja California and the timing of uplift of subduction complexes: Journal of Geology, v. 97, p. 149–163.

Barragán, R., and Baby, P., 1999, A Cretaceous hotspot in the Ecuadorian Oriente Basin, Geochemical, Geochronological and Tectonic Indicator, in Proceedings, Fourth International Symposium on Andean Geodynamics, Göttingen, Germany, October 1999: Paris, France, Institut de recherché pour le développement (IRD), p. 283–286.

Beets, D., Maresch, W., Klaver, G., Mottana, A., Bocchio, R., Beunk, F., and Monen, H., 1984, Magmatic rock series and high-pressure metamorphic as constraints on the tectonic history of the southern Caribbean, in Bonini, W., Hargraves, R., and Shagam R., eds., The Caribbean–South American plate boundary and regional tectonics: Geological Society of America Memoir 162, p. 95–130.

Berrones, G., Jaillard, E., Ordoñez, M., Bengtson, P., Benitez, S., Jimenez, N., and Zambrano, I., 1993, Stratigraphy of the "Celica-Lancones Basin" (southwestern Ecuador-northwestern Peru), Tectonic implications, in Proceedings, Second International Symposium on Andean Geodynamics, Oxford, September 1993: Paris, France, Institut Français de recherché scientifique pour le développement en cooperation (ORSTOM), p. 283–286.

Bertrand, J., Delaloye, D., Fontignie, D., and Vuagnat, M., 1978, Ages K-Ar sur diverses ophiolites et roches associates de la Cordillere centrale du Guatemala (K-Ar ages of diverse ophiolites and rocks associated with the central Cordillera of Guatemala): Bulletin Suisse de Mineralogie et Petrographie, v. 58, p. 405–412.

Bibikova, E., Somin, M.L., Gracheva, T.V., Makarov, V.A., Millán, G., and Chukoliukov, Y.A., 1988, First results of the U-Pb dating of metamorphic rocks from the arc of the Greater Antilles: Ages of the Mabujina Complex of Cuba: Dokladi Akademii Nauk, v. 301, p. 924–928.

Bird, D.E., Hall, S.A., Casey, J.F., and Millegan, P.S., 1993, Interpretation of magnetic anomalies over the Grenada Basin: Tectonics, v. 12, p. 1267–1279.

Bird, D.E., Hall, S.A., Casey, J.F., and Millegan, P.S., 1999, Tectonic evolution of the Grenada Basin, in Mann, P., ed., Caribbean basins: Amsterdam, Elsevier, Sedimentary Basins of the World, v. 4, p. 389–416.

Bockmeulen, H., Barker, C., and Dickey, P.A., 1983, Geology and geochemistry of crude oils, Bolivar coastal fields, Venezuela: AAPG Bulletin, v. 67, no. 2, p. 242–270.

Bourgois, J., Toussaint, J.F., Gonzalez, H., Azema, J., Calle, B., Desmet, A., Murcia, L.A., Acevedo, A.P., Parra, E., and Tournon, J., 1987, Geological history of the Cretaceous ophiolitic complexes of northwestern South America (Colombian Andes): Tectonophysics, v. 143, p. 307–327, doi: 10.1016/0040-1951(87)90215-0.

Bowin, C.O., 1966, Geology of the central Dominican-Republic (A case history of part of an island arc), in Hess, H.H., ed., Caribbean geological investigations: Geological Society of American Memoir 98, p. 11–84.

Burke, K., 1988, Tectonic evolution of the Caribbean: Annual Review of Earth and Planetary Sciences, v. 16, p. 201–230, doi: 10.1146/annurev.ea.16.050188.001221.

Burke, K., Fox, P.J., and Şengör, A.M.C., 1978, Buoyant ocean floor and the evolution of the Caribbean: Journal of Geophysical Research B, v. 83, p. 3949–3954

Burke, K., Cooper, C., Dewey, J.F., Mann, P., and Pindell, J.L., 1984, Caribbean tectonics and relative plate motions, in Bonini, W.E., and Hargraves, R.B., and Shagam, R., eds., The Caribbean–South America plate boundary and regional tectonics: Geological Society of America Memoir 162, p. 31–64.

Byerly, G.R., 1991, Igneous activity, in Salvador, A., ed., The Gulf of Mexico basin: Boulder, Colorado, Geological Society of America, Geology of North America, v. J, p. 91–108.

Calvo, C., and Bolz, A., 1994, Der älteste kalkalkaline Inselbogen-Vulkanismus in Costa Rica; Marine Pyroklastika der Formation Loma Chumico (Alb bis Campan) [The oldest calcalkaline island arc volcanism in Costa Rica; Marine tephra deposits from the Loma Chumico Formation (Albian to Campanian)]: Profil, v. 7, p. 235–264.

Case, J.E., MacDonald, W.D., and Fox, P.J., 1990, Caribbean crustal provinces: Seismic and gravity evidence, in Dengo, G., and Case, J.E., eds., The Caribbean region: Boulder, Colorado, Geological Society of America, Geology of North America, v. H, p. 15–36.

Catlos, E.J., and Sorensen, S.S., 2003, Phengite-based chronology of K- and Ba-rich fluid flow in two paleosubduction zones: Science, v. 299, p. 92–95.

Cobbing, E.J., Pitcher, W.S., Wilson, J., Baldock, J., Taylor, W., McCourt, W., and Snelling, N.J., 1981, The geology of the Western Cordillera of northern Peru: London, Overseas Memoir of the Institute of Geological Sciences, v. 5, 143 p.

de Souza, H.A.F., Espinosa, A., and Delaloye, M., 1984, K-Ar ages of basic rocks in the Patia valley, southwest Colombia: Tectonophysics, v. 107, p. 135–145, doi: 10.1016/0040-1951(84)90031-3.

Dewey, J.F., 1980, Episodicity, sequence, and style at convergent plate boundaries, in Strangway, D.W., ed., The continental crust and its mineral deposits: Geological Association of Canada Special Paper 20, p. 553–573.

Dewey, J.F., and Pindell, J.L., 1985, Neogene block tectonics of eastern Turkey and northern South America: Continental applications of the finite difference method: Tectonics, v. 4, p. 71–83.

Dewey, J.F., and Pindell, J.L., 1986, Neogene block tectonics of eastern Turkey and northern South America: Continental applications of the finite difference method: Reply: Tectonics, v. 5, p. 703–705.

Donnelly, T.W., Beets, D., Carr, M.J., Jackson, T., Klaver, G., Lewis, J., Maury, R., Schellekens, H., Smith, A.L., Wadge, G., and Westercamp, D., 1990, History and tectonic setting of Caribbean magmatism, in Dengo, G., and Case, J.E., eds., The Caribbean region: Boulder, Colorado, Geological Society of America, Geology of North America, v. H, p. 339–374.

Draper, G., 1979, Tectonics of the regionally metamorphosed rocks of eastern Jamaica, [Ph.D. thesis]: Kingston, Jamaica, University of the West Indies, 277 p.

Draper, G., 1986, Blueschists and associated rocks in eastern Jamaica and their significance for Cretaceous plate-margin development in the northern Caribbean: Geological Society of America Bulletin, v. 97, p. 48–60, doi: 10.1130/0016-7606(1986)97<48:BAARIE>2.0.CO;2.

Draper, G., 2001, The southern metamorphic terranes of Cuba as metamorphic core complexes exhumed by low angle extensional faulting: Abstracts and Programs of the 4° Congreso Cubano de Geología y Minería, La Habana, Cuba, March 19–23, 2001 (CD-ROM Folder Geol~1, file 004~1.HTM).

Draper, G., and Barros, J.A., 1994, Cuba, in Donovan S.K. and Jackson, T.A., eds., Caribbean geology: An introduction: Kingston, Jamaica, University of the West Indies Publishers Association/University of the West Indies Press, p. 65–86.

Draper, G., and Lewis, J.F., 1989, Petrology and structural development of the Duarte complex, Central Dominican Republic: A preliminary account and some tectonic implications, in Transactions, 10th Caribbean Geological Conference: Cartagena, Colombia, August 1983, p. 103–112.

Draper, G., and Lewis, J.F., 1991, Metamorphic belts in Central Hispaniola, in Mann, P., Draper, G., and Lewis, J., eds., Geologic and tectonic development of the North America–Caribbean plate boundary in Hispaniola: Geological Society of America Special Paper 262, p. 9–45.

Draper, G., and Nagle, F., 1991, Geology, structure, and tectonic development of the Rio San Juan complex, northern Dominican-Republic, in Mann, P., Draper, G., and Lewis, J., eds., geologic and tectonic development of the North America–Caribbean plate boundary in Hispaniola: Geological Society of America Special Paper 262, p. 77–91.

Draper, G., Harding, R.R., Horsfield, W.T., Kemp, A.W., and Tresham, A.E., 1976, Low grade metamorphic belt in Jamaica and its tectonic implica-

tions: Geological Society of America Bulletin, v. 87, p. 1283–1290, doi: 10.1130/0016-7606(1976)87<1283:LMBIJA>2.0.CO;2.

Draper, G., Gutierrez, G., and Lewis, J.F., 1996, Thrust emplacement of the Hispaniola peridotite belt: Orogenic expression of the mid-Cretaceous Caribbean arc polarity reversal?: Geology, v. 24, p. 1143–1146, doi: 10.1130/0091-7613(1996)024<1143:TEOTHP>2.3.CO;2.

Driscoll, N.W., and Diebold, J.B., 1999, Tectonic and stratigraphic development of the eastern Caribbean: New Constraints from multichannel seismic data, in Mann, P., ed., Caribbean Basins: Amsterdam, Elsevier, Sedimentary Basins of the World, v. 4, p. 591–626.

Engebretson, D.C., Gordon, R.G., and Cox, A., 1985, Relative motions between oceanic and continental plates in the Pacific basin: Geological Society of America Special Paper 206, 59 p.

Erikson, J.P., and Pindell, J.L., 1998, Cretaceous through Eocene sedimentation and paleogeography of a passive margin in northeastern Venezuela, in Pindell, J.L., and Drake, C., eds., Paleogeographic evolution and non-glacial eustasy, North America: Society for Sedimentary Geology (SEPM) Special Publication 58, p. 217–259.

Erlich, R.N., Macsotay, O., Nederbragt, A.J., and Lorente, M.A., 2000, Birth and death of the Late Cretaceous "La Luna Sea," and origin of the Tres Esquinas phosphorites: Journal of South American Earth Sciences, v. 13, p. 21–45, doi: 10.1016/S0895-9811(00)00016-X.

Feininger, T., 1982, Glaucophane schist in the Andes at Jambaló: Canadian Mineralogist, v. 20, p. 41–47.

Feininger, T., and Silberman, M.L., 1982, K-Ar geochronology of basement rocks on the northern flanks of the Huancabamba deflection, Ecuador: U.S. Geological Survey Open-File Report 82-206, 21 p.

Foland, K.A., Speed, R., and Weber, J., 1992, Geochronologic studies of the hinterland of the Caribbean mountains orogen of Venezuela and Trinidad: Geological Society of America Abstracts with Programs, v. 24, no. 7, p. 149.

Frost, C.D., and Snoke, A.W., 1989, Tobago, West Indies, a fragment of a Mesozoic oceanic island arc: Petrochemical evidence: Journal of the Geological Society, v. 146, p. 953–964.

García-Casco, A., Torres-Roldán, R.L., Millán, G., Monié, P., and Haissen, F., 2001, High-grade metamorphism and hydrous melting of metapelites in the Pinos terrane (W Cuba): Evidence for crustal thickening and extension in the northern Caribbean collisional belt: Journal of Metamorphic Geology, v. 19, p. 697–715.

García-Casco, A., Torres-Roldan, R.L., Millán, G., Monié, P., and Schneider, J., 2002, Oscillatory zoning in eclogitic garnet and amphibole, Northern Serpentinite Mélange, Cuba: A record of tectonic instability during subduction?: Journal of Metamorphic Geology, v. 20, p. 581–598, doi: 10.1046/j.1525-1314.2002.00390.x.

Giunta, G., Beccaluva, L., Coltori, M., Cutrupia, D., Mota, B., Padoa, E., and Siena, F., Dengo, C., Harlow, G.E., and Rosenfeld, J., 2002, The Motagua suture zone in Guatemala: IGCP 433 Workshop and second Italian–Latin American Geological Meeting guidebook, Edizioni ETS, Pisa, Gennaio, 41 p.

Gonçalves, P., Guillot, S., Lardeaux, J.-M., Nicolleta, C., and Mercier de Lepinay, B., 2000, Thrusting and sinistral wrenching in a pre-Eocene HP-LT Caribbean accretionary wedge (Samaná Peninsula, Dominican Republic): Geodinamica Acta, v. 13, p. 119–132., doi: 10.1016/S0985-3111(00)00116-9

Gordon, M.B., 1990, The Chortís Block is a continental, pre-Mesozoic terrane, in Larue, D.K., and Draper, G., eds., Transactions of the 12th Caribbean geological conference: Transactions of the Caribbean Geological Conference [Memorias, Conferencia Geológica del Caribe], p. 505–512.

Gordon, M.B., Mann, P., Caceres, D., and Flores, R., 1997, Cenozoic tectonic history of the North America–Caribbean plate boundary zone in western Cuba: Journal of Geophysical Research B, v. 102, p. 10,055–10,082, doi: 10.1029/96JB03177

Gradstein, F.M., Ogg, J.G., and Smith, A.G., 2004, A geologic time scale 2004: Cambridge, Cambridge University Press, 610 p.

Grafe, F., Stanek, K.P., Baumann, A., Maresch, W.V., Hames, W.E., Grevel, Ch., and Millán, G., 2001, Rb-Sr and ^{40}Ar/^{39}Ar mineral ages of granitoid intrusions in the Mabujina unit, Central Cuba: Thermal exhumation history of the Escambray massif: Journal of Geology, v. 109, p. 615–631, doi: 10.1086/321966.

Green, D.H., Lockwood, J.P., and Kiss, E., 1968, Eclogite and almandine-jadeite-quartz rock from the Guajira Peninsula, Colombia, South America: American Mineralogist, v. 53, p. 1320–1335.

Guppy, R.J.L., 1911, On the geology of Antigua and other West Indian islands with reference to the physical history of the Caribbean [sic] region: Geological Society of London, Quarterly Journal, v. 67, p. 681–700.

Harlow, G.E., 1994, Jadeitites, albitites, and related rocks from the Motagua fault zone, Guatemala: Journal of Metamorphic Geology, v. 12, p. 49–68.

Harlow, G.E., Sisson, V.B., Avé Lallemant, H.G., and Sorenson, S.S., Seitz, Russell, 2003, High-pressure metasomatic rocks along the Motagua Fault Zone, Guatemala: Ofioliti, v. 28, p. 115–120.

Hatten, C.W., Mattinson, J.M., Renne, P.R., Somin, M.L., Millán, G., Araqueliants, M.M., Kolesnikov, E.M., and Sumin, L.V., 1989, Rocas metamorficas de Alta Presión: nuevos datos acerca de sus edades, Primero Congreso Cubano de Geología, Havana, Cuba, p. 118.

Hauff, F., Hoernle, K., Tilton, G., Graham, D.W., and Kerr, A.C., 2000, Large volume recycling of oceanic lithosphere over short time scales: geochemical constraints from the Caribbean Large Igneous Province: Earth and Planetary Science Letters, v. 174, p. 247–263, doi: 10.1016/S0012-821X(99)00272-1.

Hebeda, E.H., Verdurmen, E.A.T., and Priem, H.N.A., 1984, K-Ar hornblende ages from the El Chacao Complex, north-central Venezuela, in Bonini, W., Hargraves, R., and Shagam R., eds., The Caribbean–South American plate boundary and regional tectonics: Geological Society of America Memoir 162, p. 413–414.

Hedberg, H.D., 1937, Stratigraphy of the Rio Querecual section of northeastern Venezuela: Geological Society of America Bulletin, v. 48, p. 1971–2024.

Hempton, M.R., and Barros, J.A., 1993, Mesozoic stratigraphy of Cuba: deposition architecture of a southeast facing continental margin, in Pindell, J.L., and Perkins, R.F., eds., Mesozoic and Early Cenozoic development of the Gulf of Mexico and Caribbean region—A context for hydrocarbon exploration: Proceedings, Gulf Coast Section, SEPM Foundation 13th Annual Research Conference: Houston, Texas, Society for Sedimentary Geology (SEPM), p. 193–209.

Henderson, W.G., 1979, Cretaceous to Eocene volcanic arc activity in the Andes of northern Ecuador: Journal of the Geological Society [London], v. 136, p. 367–378.

Higgs, R., 2000, The Chaudière and Nariva wildflysch of Central Trinidad: A modern sedimentological perspective: Geological Society of Trinidad and Tobago, Society of Petroleum Engineers (Trinidad and Tobago Section), Conference, Port of Spain, July 10–13, p. 17.

Higgs, R., and Pindell, J.L., 2001, Cenozoic composite-basin tectonics and sedimentation, Venezuela-Trinidad oil province: American Association of Petroleum Geologists Annual Meeting, Denver, Colorado, June 3–6, 2001, Program, p. A88.

Horne, G.S., Atwood, M.G., and King, A.P., 1974, Stratigraphy, sedimentology, and paleoenvironment of Esquias Formation of Honduras: AAPG Bulletin, v. 58, p. 176–188.

Hutson, F., Mann, P., and Renne, P., 1998, ^{40}Ar/^{39}Ar dating of single muscovite grains in Jurassic siliciclastic rocks (San Cayetano Formation): Constraints on the paleoposition of western Cuba: Geology, v. 26, p. 83–86, doi: 10.1130/0091-7613(1998)026<0083:AADOSM>2.3.CO;2.

Irving, E.M., 1975, Structural evolution of the northernmost Andes, Colombia: U.S. Geological Survey Professional Paper 846, 47 p.

Jackson, T.A., Duke, M.J.M., Smith, T.E., and Huang, C.H., 1988, The geochemistry of the metavolcanics in the Parlatuvier Formation, Tobago: Evidence of an island arc origin, in Transactions of the 11th Caribbean Geological Conference, 1986, Bridgetown, Barbados, p. 21.1–21.8.

Jaillard, E., 1993, The Cretaceous to early Palaeogene tectonic evolution of the central Andes and its relation to geodynamics, in Second International Symposium on Andean Geodynamics: Oxford, Institut Français de recherché scientifique pour le développement en cooperation (ORSTOM), p. 195–198.

Jaillard, E., 1994, Kimmeridgian to Paleocene tectonic and geodynamic evolution of the Peruvian (and Ecuadorian) margin, in Salfity, J., ed., Cretaceous tectonics of the Andes: Braunschweig and Wiesbaden, Vieweg Publishing, International Monograph Series, Earth Evolution Sciences, p. 101–167.

Jaillard, E., 1997, Síntesis estratigráfico y sedimentaria del Cretáceo y Paleógeno de la Cuenca Oriental del Ecuador, Informe Final del Convenio: Oxford, Institut Français de recherché scientifique pour le développement en cooperation (ORSTOM)–Petroproduccion, 164 p.

Jaillard, E., Soler, P., Carlier, G., and Mourier, T., 1990, Geodynamic evolution of the northern and central Andes during early to middle Mesozoic time: A Tethyan model: Journal of the Geological Society [London], v. 147, p. 1009–1022.

Jaillard, E., Ordoñez, M., Berrones, G., Bengtson, P., Bonhomme, M., Jiménez, N., and Zambrano, I., 1996, Sedimentary and tectonic evolution of southwestern Ecuador during Late Cretaceous and early Tertiary times: Journal of South American Earth Sciences, v. 9, p. 131–140, doi: 10.1016/0895-9811(96)00033-8.

Jaillard, E., Laubacher, G., Bengtson, P., Dhondt, A.V., and Bulot, L.G., 1999, Stratigraphy and evolution of the Cretaceous forearc Celica-Lancones basin of southwestern Ecuador: Journal of South American Earth Sciences, v. 12, p. 51–68, doi: 10.1016/S0895-9811(99)00006-1.

James, K.H., 2002, A simple synthesis and evolution of the Caribbean region, in Abstracts, 16th Caribbean Geological Conference, Barbados, June 16–21, 2002. Extended abstract: http://www.ig.utexas.edu/CaribPlate/forum/james/james_carib_model.pdf (Accessed: 16 May 2005).

Jarrard, R.D., 1986, Relations among subduction parameters: Reviews of Geophysics, v. 24, p. 217–284.

Johnson, C.A., 1990, Stratigraphy and structure of the San Lucas area, Michoacán and Guerrero states, southwestern Mexico [Ph.D. thesis]: Coral Gables, Florida, University of Miami, 220 p.

Jones, N.W., McKee, J.W., Anderson, T.H., and Silver, L.T., 1995, Jurassic volcanic rocks in northeastern Mexico: A possible remnant of a Cordillera magmatic arc, in Jacques, C., Gonzalez, C., and Roldán, J., eds., Studies on the Mesozoic of Sonora and adjacent areas: Geological Society of America Special Paper 301, p. 179–190.

Joyce, J., and Aronson, J., 1989, K-Ar ages for blueschist metamorphism on the Samaná Peninsula, Dominican Republic: Transactions, 10th Caribbean Geological Conference, Cartagena, Colombia, August 14–19, 1983, p. 454–458.

Kennerley, J.B., 1980, Outline of the geology of Ecuador: Overseas Geology and Mineral Resources (Institute of Geological Sciences), v. 55, 17 p.

Kerr, A.C., Marriner, G.F., Tarney, J., Nivia, A., Saunders, A.D., Thirlwall, M.F., and Sinton, C.W., 1997, Cretaceous basaltic terranes in western Colombia: Elemental, chronological and Sm-Nd isotopic constraints on petrogenesis: Journal of Petrology, v. 38, p. 677–702, doi: 10.1093/petrology/38.6.677.

Kerr, A.C., Tarney, J., Nivia, A., Marriner, G.F., and Saunders, A.D., 1998, The internal structure of oceanic plateaus: Inferences from obducted Cretaceous terranes in western Colombia and the Caribbean: Tectonophysics, v. 292, p. 173–188, doi: 10.1016/S0040-1951(98)00067-5.

Kerr, A.C., Iturralde Vinent, M.A., Saunders, A.D., Babbs, T.L., and Tarney, J., 1999, A new plate tectonic model of the Caribbean: Implications from a geochemical reconnaissance of Cuban Mesozoic volcanic rocks: Geological Society of America Bulletin, v. 111, p. 1581–1599, doi: 10.1130/0016-7606(1999)111<1581:ANPTMO>2.3.CO;2.

Kerr, A.C., Aspden, J.A., Tarney, J., and Pilatsig, L.F., 2002, The nature and provenance of accreted oceanic terranes in western Ecuador: geochemical and tectonic constraints: Journal of the Geological Society [London], v. 159, p. 577–594.

Klitgord, K.D., and Schouten, H., 1986, Plate kinematics of the Central Atlantic, in Vogt, P.R. and Tucholke, B.E., eds., The western Atlantic region: Boulder, Colorado, Geological Society of America, Geology of North America, v. M, p. 351–378.

Kohn, B.P., Shagam, R., Banks, P.O., and Burkley, L.A., 1984, Mesozoic-Pleistocene fission-track ages on rocks of the Venezuelan Andes and their tectonic implications, in Bonini, W., Hargraves, R., and Shagam R., eds., The Caribbean–South American plate boundary and regional tectonics: Geological Society of America Memoir 162, p. 365–384.

Krebs, M., Maresch, W.V., and Draper, G., 1999, P-T paths of subduction related high pressure rocks, Rio San Juan Complex, northern Dominican Republic: Journal of Conference Abstracts, v. 4, p. 706–707.

Krebs, M., Maresch, W.V., Schertl, H.-P., Baumann, A., Münker, C., Trapp, E., Gerya, T.V., and Draper, G., 2003, Geochronology and petrology of high pressure metamorphic rocks of the Rio San Juan Complex, northern Dominican Republic: Transactions, 18th Geowissenschaftliches Lateinamerika Kolloquium, Freiburg, Germany, 3–5 April 2003, p. 49.

Ladd, J.W., 1976, Relative motion of South America with respect to North America and Caribbean tectonics: Geological Society of America Bulletin, v. 87, p. 969–976, doi: 10.1130/0016-7606(1976)87<969:RMOSAW>2.0.CO;2.

Lapierre, H., Dupuis, V., de Lepinay, B.M., Bosch, D., Monie, P., Tardy, M., Maury, R.C., Hernandez, J., Polve, M., Yeghicheyan, D., and Cotten, J., 1999, Late Jurassic oceanic crust and Upper Cretaceous Caribbean Plateau picritic basalts exposed in the Duarte igneous complex, Hispaniola: Journal of Geology, v. 107, p. 193–207, doi: 10.1086/314341.

Lebrón, M.C., and Perfit, M.R., 1993, Stratigraphic and petrochemical data support subduction polarity reversal of the Cretaceous Caribbean island arc: Journal of Geology, v. 101, p. 389–396.

Lewis, J.F., and Draper, G., 1990, Geology and tectonic evolution of the northern Caribbean region, in Dengo, G., and Case, J.E., eds., The Caribbean region: Boulder, Colorado, Geological Society of America, Geology of North America, v. H, p. 77–140.

Lewis, J.F., Harper, C.T., Kemp, A.W., and Stipp, J.J., 1973, Potassium-Argon retention ages of some Cretaceous rocks form Jamaica: Geological Society of America Bulletin, v. 84, p. 335–340, doi: 10.1130/0016-7606(1973)84<335:PRAOSC>2.0.CO;2.

Litherland, M., Aspden, J.A., and Jemielitam, R.A., 1994, The metamorphic belts of Ecuador: London, British Geological Survey Overseas Memoir 11, 147 p.

Livaccari, R., Burke, K., and Şengör, A.M.C., 1981, Was the Laramide orogeny related to subduction of an oceanic plateau?: Nature, v. 289, p. 276–278, doi: 10.1038/289276a0.

Malfrère, J.-L., Bosch, D., Lapierre, H., Jaillard, E., Arculus, R., and Monie, P., 1999, The Raspas metamorphic complex (Southern Ecuador): Remnant of a Late Jurassic–Early Cretaceous accretionary prism; Geochemical constraints: Proceedings, Fourth International Symposium on Andean Geodynamics, Göttingen, Germany, September 1999: Paris, France, Institut de recherché pour le développement (IRD) p. 462–465.

Mann, P., and Burke, K., 1984, Neotectonics of the Caribbean: Reviews of Geophysics and Space Physics, v. 22, p. 309–362.

Manton, W.I., 1996, The Grenville of Honduras: Geological Society of America Abstracts with Programs, v. 28, no. 7, p. A-493.

Maresch, W.V., 1974, Plate tectonics origin of the Caribbean Mountain System of northern South America: Discussion and proposal: Geological Society of America Bulletin, v. 85, p. 669–682, doi: 10.1130/0016-7606(1974)85<669:PTOOTC>2.0.CO;2.

Maresch, W.V., Stöckhert, B., Baumann, A., Kaiser, C., Kluge, R., Kückhans-Lüder, G., Brix, M., and Thomson, S., 2000, Crustal history and plate tectonic development in the Southern Caribbean, in Geoscientific Cooperation with Latin America, 31st International Geological Congress, Rio de Janeiro 2000: Zeitschrift für Angewandte Geologie. v. 1, p. 283–290.

Maresch, W.V., Stanek, K.-P., Grafe, F., Idleman, B., Baumann, A., Krebs, M., Schertl, H.-P., and Draper, G., 2003, Age systematics of high-pressure metamorphism in the Caribbean: confronting existing models with new data: Abstracts, 5th Cuban Geological Congress, Havana, Cuba, March 25–27, 2003, p. 296–298.

Mattinson, J.M., Fink, L.K., and Hopson, C.A., 1980, Geochronologic and isotopic study of the La Desirade Island basement complex: Jurassic oceanic crust in the Lesser Antilles: Contributions to Mineralogy and Petrology, v. 71, p. 237–245.

Mattson, P.H., 1979, Subduction, buoyant breaking, flipping and strike-slip faulting in the northern Caribbean: Journal of Geology, v. 87, p. 293–304.

Maurrasse, F., 1990, Stratigraphic correlation for the circum-Caribbean region, in Dengo, G., and Case, J.E., eds., The Caribbean region: Boulder, Colorado, Geological Society of America, Geology of North America, v. H, Plates 4 and 5.

McBirney, A., Aoki, K.I., and Bass, M.N., 1967, Eclogites and jadeite from the Motagua fault zone, Guatemala: American Mineralogist, v. 52, p. 908–918.

McCourt, W.J., Aspden, J.A., and Brook, M., 1984, New geological and geochronological data from the Colombian Andes: Continental growth by multiple accretion: Journal of the Geological Society [London], v. 141, p. 831–845.

Meschede, M., and Frisch, M., 1998, A plate-tectonic model for the Mesozoic and early Cenozoic history of the Caribbean Plate: Tectonophysics, v. 296, p. 269–291, doi: 10.1016/S0040-1951(98)00157-7.

Millán, G., 1975, El complejo cristalino Mesozoico de Isla de Pinos; Su metamorfismo: La Habana, Cuba, Serie Geológica de CIDP, v. 23, p. 3–16.

Millán, G., 1988, La asociación glaucofana-pumpelleita en metagabroides de la faja metamórfica Cangre (The glaucophane-pumpellyite association in metagabbroids of the Cangre metamorphic band): Boletín de Geociencias, v. 3, no. 2, p. 35–36.

Mitchell, S., 2003, Timing and tectonic episodes based on new Late Cretaceous Caribbean rudist biostratigraphy: Abstracts, V Congreso Cubano de Geología y Minería, Havana, Cuba, 24–28 March 2003.

Montgomery, H., Pessagno, E.A., Lewis, J.F., and Schellekens, J., 1994, Paleogeography of Jurassic fragments in the Caribbean: Tectonics, v. 13, p. 725–732, doi: 10.1029/94TC00455.

Morgan, B.A., 1967, Geology of the Valencia area, Carabobo, Venezuela [Ph.D. thesis]: Princeton, Princeton University, 220 p.

Morgan, B.A., 1970, Petrology and mineralogy of eclogite and garnet amphibolite from Puerto Cabello, Venezuela: Journal of Petrology, v. 11, p. 101–145.

Mourier, T., Laj, C., Mégard, F., Roperch, P., Mitouard, P., and Farfan, A., 1988a, An accreted continental terrane in northwestern Peru: Earth and Planetary Science Letters, v. 88, p. 182–192, doi: 10.1016/0012-821X(88)90056-8.

Mourier, T., Mégard, F., Pardo, A., and Reyes, L., 1988b, L'evolution mesozoîque des Andes de Huancabamba (3°–8° S) et l'hypothèse de l'accretion du bloc Amotape-Tahuín: Bulletin de la Société Géologique de France, v. 8, p. 69.

Mourier, T., Bengtson, P., Bonhomme, M., Buge, E., Capetta, H., Crochet, J.-Y., Feist, M., Hirsch, K., Jaillard, E., Laubacher, G., Lefranc, J.-P., Moullade, M., Noblet, C., Pons, D., Rey, J., Sige, B., Tambareau, Y., and Taquet, P., 1988c, The upper Cretaceous–lower Tertiary marine to continental transition in the Bagua basin, northern Peru: Newsletters on Stratigraphy, v. 19, p. 143–177.

Muessig, K.W., 1978, The central Falcón igneous suite, Venezuela; alkaline basaltic intrusions of Oligocene-Miocene age, in Mac Gillavry, H.J., Beets, D.J., eds., Transactions, The 8th Caribbean geological conference: Geologie en Mijnbouw, v. 57, p. 261–266.

Müller, R.D., Royer, J.-Y., Cande, S.C., Roest, W.R., and Maschenkov, S., 1999, New constraints on the Late Cretaceous–Tertiary plate tectonic evolution of the Caribbean, in Mann, P., ed., Caribbean Basins: Amsterdam, Elsevier, Sedimentary Basins of the World, v. 4, p. 33–57.

Noble, S.R., Aspden, J.A., and Jemielitam, R., 1997, Northern Andean crustal evolution: New U-Pb geochronological constraints from Ecuador: Geological Society of America Bulletin, v. 109, p. 789–798, doi: 10.1130/0016-7606(1997)109<0789:NACENU>2.3.CO;2.

Orrego, A., Cepeda, H., and Rodriguez, G., 1980, Esquistos glaucofanicos en el area de Jambaló, Cauca, Colombia: Geologia Norandina, v. 1, p. 5–10.

Paulus, F.J., 1972, The geology of site 98 and Bahama Platform: Initial Reports of the Deep Sea Drilling Project, v. 15, p. 877–897.

Pecora, L., Jaillard, E., and Lapierre, H., 1999, Accretion paleogene et decrochement dextre d'un terrain oceanique dans le Nord du Perou: Comptes Rendus de l'Academie des Sciences, Serie II: Sciences de la Terre et des Planetes, v. 329, no. 6, p. 389–396.

Perfit, M.R., and McCulloch, M.T., 1982, Trace element, Nd- and Sr- isotope geochemistry of eclogites and blueschists from the Hispaniola–Puerto Rico subduction zone: Terra Cognita, v. 2, p. 321.

Pindell, J.L., 1985a, Plate tectonic evolution of the Gulf of Mexico and Caribbean region [Ph.D. thesis]: Durham, UK, University of Durham, 227 p.

Pindell, J.L., 1985b, Alleghenian reconstruction and the subsequent evolution of the Gulf of Mexico, Bahamas: proto-Caribbean Sea: Tectonics, v. 4, p. 1–39.

Pindell, J.L., 1990, Geological arguments suggesting a Pacific origin for the Caribbean plate, in Larue, D.K., and Draper, G., eds., Transactions of the 12th Caribbean Conference: St. Croix, 7–11 August, 1989, p. 1–4.

Pindell, J.L., 1993, Regional synopsis of Gulf of Mexico and Caribbean evolution, in Pindell, J.L., and Perkins, R.F., eds., Mesozoic and Early Cenozoic development of the Gulf of Mexico and Caribbean region—A context for hydrocarbon exploration, Proceedings, Gulf Coast Section, SEPM Foundation 13th Annual Research Conference: Houston, Texas, Society for Sedimentary Geology (SEPM), p. 251–274.

Pindell, J.L., 1994, Transtension in eastern Venezuela and Trinidad since 10 Ma [abs.]: Transactions, V Simposio Bolivariano de la Exploración Petrolera en las Cuencas Subandinas, Puerto la Cruz, Venezuela, p. 263.

Pindell, J.L., and Barrett, S.F., 1990, Geological evolution of the Caribbean region: A plate tectonic perspective, in Dengo, G., and Case, J.E., eds., The Caribbean region: Boulder, Colorado, Geological Society of America, Geology of North America, v. H, p. 405–432.

Pindell, J.L., and Dewey, J.F., 1982, Permo-Triassic reconstruction of western Pangea and the evolution of the Gulf of Mexico–Caribbean region: Tectonics, v. 1, p. 179–211.

Pindell, J.L., and Erikson, J.P., 1994, The Mesozoic passive margin of northern South America, in Salfity, J.A, ed., Cretaceous tectonics in the Andes: Braunschweig and Wiesbaden, Vieweg Publishing, International Monograph Series, Earth Evolution Sciences, p. 1–60.

Pindell, J.L., and Kennan, L., 2001a, Processes and events in the terrane assembly of Trinidad and eastern Venezuela, in Petroleum systems of deepwater basins: Global and Gulf of Mexico experience, Proceedings, Gulf Coast Section, SEPM, 21st Annual Research Conference, December 2–5: Houston, Texas, Society for Sedimentary Geology (SEPM), p. 159–192.

Pindell, J.L., and Kennan, L., 2001b, Kinematic evolution of the Gulf of Mexico and Caribbean, in Petroleum systems of deep-water basins: Global and Gulf of Mexico experience, Proceedings, Gulf Coast Section, SEPM, 21st Annual Research Conference, December 2–5: Houston, Texas, Society for Sedimentary Geology (SEPM), p. 193–220.

Pindell, J.L., and Kennan, L., 2002, Palinspastic paleogeographic evolution of eastern Venezuela and Trinidad: Abstracts, 16th Caribbean Geological Conference, Barbados, June 16–21, 2002, http://www.ig.utexas.edu/CaribPlate/reports/Barbados_June_2002_report.htm (Accessed 16 May 2005).

Pindell, J.L., and Tabbutt, K.D., 1995, Mesozoic-Cenozoic Andean paleogeography and regional controls on hydrocarbon systems, *in* Tankard, A.J., Suárez S., A.R., and Welsink, H.J., eds., Petroleum basins of South America: American Association of Petroleum Geologists Memoir 62, p. 101–128.

Pindell, J.L., Cande, S.C., Pitman, W.C., III, Rowley, D.B., Dewey, J.F., LaBrecque, J., and Haxby, W., 1988, A plate-kinematics framework for models of Caribbean evolution: Tectonophysics, v. 155, p. 121–138, doi: 10.1016/0040-1951(88)90262-4.

Pindell, J.L., Erikson, J.P., and Algar, S.T., 1991, The relationship between plate motions and the sedimentary basin development in northern South America: From a Mesozoic passive margin to a Cenozoic eastwardly-progressive transpressional orogen, *in* Gillezeau, K.A., ed., Transactions of the Second Geological Conference of the Geological Society of Trinidad and Tobago: San Fernando, Trinidad, p. 191–202.

Pindell, J.L., Higgs, R., and Dewey, J.F., 1998, Cenozoic palinspastic reconstruction, paleogeographic evolution, and hydrocarbon setting of the northern margin of South America, *in* Pindell, J.L. and Drake, C., eds., Paleogeographic evolution and non-glacial eustasy, North America: Society for Sedimentary Geology (SEPM) Special Publication 58, p. 45–86.

Pindell, J.L., Kennan, L., and Barrett, S.F., 2000, Kinematics: A key to unlocking plays, *in* Part 2, Regional plate kinematics: arm waving, or underutilized exploration tool: AAPG Explorer, July, http://www.aapg.org/explorer/geophysical_corner/2000/gpc07.html (Accessed 16 May 2005).

Pszczółkowski, A., 1999, The exposed passive margin of north America in western Cuba, *in* Mann, P., ed., Caribbean Basins: Amsterdam, Elsevier, Sedimentary Basins of the World, v. 4, p. 93–122.

Renne, P.R., Mattinson, J.M., Hatten, C.W., Somin, M., Onstott, T.C., Millán, G., and Linares, E., 1989, ^{40}Ar/^{39}Ar and U-Pb evidence for late Proterozoic (Grenville-age) continental crust in north-central Cuba and regional tectonic implications: Precambrian Research, v. 42, p. 325–341, doi: 10.1016/0301-9268(89)90017-X.

Restrepo, J.J., and Toussaint, J.F., 1974, Obducion Cretacea en el Occidente Colombia: Annales de la Facultad de Minas, Medellin, v. 58, p. 73–105.

Restrepo, J.J., and Toussaint, J.F., 1976, Edades radiometricas de algunas rocas de Antioquia, Colombia: Publicación Especial de la Universidad Nacional de Colombia, Medellin, v. 6, p. 1–18.

Reynaud, C., Jaillard, E., Lapierre, H., Mamberti, M., and Mascle, G.H., 1999, Oceanic plateau and island arcs of southwestern Ecuador; their place in the geodynamic evolution of northwestern South America: Tectonophysics, v. 307, p. 235–254, doi: 10.1016/S0040-1951(99)00099-2.

Romeuf, N., Münch, P., Soler, P., Jaillard, E., Pik, R., and Aguirre, L., 1997, Mise en évidence de deux lignées magmatiques dans le volcanisme du Jurassique inférieur de la zone subandine équatorienne: Comptes Rendus Academie des Sciences Paris Series 2, v. 324, p. 61–368.

Roperch, P., Megard, F., Laj, C., Mourier, T., Clube, T., and Noblet, C., 1987, Rotated oceanic blocks in western Ecuador: Geophysical Research Letters, v. 14, p. 558–561.

Rosencrantz, E., 1990, Structure and tectonics of the Yucatán Basin, Caribbean Sea, as determined from seismic reflection studies: Tectonics, v. 9, p. 1037–1059.

Rosencrantz, E., Ross, M.I., and Sclater, J.G., 1988, Age and spreading history of the Cayman Trough as determined from depth, heat flow, and magnetic anomalies: Journal of Geophysical Research, v. 93, p. 2141–2157.

Rosenfeld, J.H., 1993, Sedimentary rocks of the Santa Cruz Ophiolite, Guatemala—a Proto-Caribbean history, *in* Pindell, J.L., and Perkins, R.F., eds., Mesozoic and Early Cenozoic development of the Gulf of Mexico and Caribbean region—A context for hydrocarbon exploration, Proceedings, Gulf Coast Section, SEPM Foundation 13th Annual Research Conference: Houston, Texas, Society for Sedimentary Geology (SEPM) Foundation, p 173–180.

Salfity, J.A., and Marquillas, R.A., 1994, Tectonic and sedimentary evolution of the Cretaceous-Eocene Salta Group Basin, Argentina, *in* Salfity, J.A., ed., Cretaceous tectonics of the Andes: Braunschweig and Wiesbaden, Vieweg Publishing, International Monograph Series, Earth Evolution Sciences, p. 266–315.

Schaaf, P., Moran, Z.D.J., and Hernandez, B.M., de S., Solis, P.G.N., Tolson, G., and Koehler, H., 1995, Paleogene continental margin truncation in southwestern Mexico; geochronological evidence: Tectonics, v. 14, p. 1339–1350.

Sedlock, R.L., Ortega, G.F., and Speed, R.C., 1993, Tectonostratigraphic terranes and tectonic evolution of Mexico: Geological Society of America Special Paper 278, 153 p.

Sisson, V.B., Ertan, I.E., and Avé Lallemant, H.G., 1997, High-pressure (~2000 MPa) kyanite- and glaucophane-bearing pelitic schist and eclogite from Cordillera de la Costa belt, Venezuela: Journal of Petrology, v. 38, p. 65–83, doi: 10.1093/petrology/38.1.65.

Sisson, V.B., Harlow, G.E., Avé Lallemant, H.G., Hemming, S., and Sorenson, S., 2003, Two belts of jadeitite and other high pressure rocks in serpentinites, Motagua fault zone, Guatemala: Geological Society of America Abstracts with Programs, v. 35, no. 4, p. 75.

Skerlec, G.M., and Hargraves, R.B., 1980, Tectonic significance of paleomagnetic data from northern Venezuela: Journal of Geophysical Research B. v. 85, p. 5303–5315.

Smith, C.A., Sisson, V.B., Avé Lallemant, H.G., and Copeland, P., 1999, Two contrasting pressure-temperature-time paths in the Villa de Cura blueschist belt, Venezuela: Possible evidence for Late Cretaceous initiation of subduction in the Caribbean: Geological Society of America Bulletin, v. 111, p. 831–848, doi: 10.1130/0016-7606(1999)111<0831:TCPTTP>2.3.CO;2.

Snoke, W., 1991, An evaluation of the petrogenesis of the accreted Mesozoic island arc of the southern Caribbean, *in* Gillezeau, K.A., ed., Transactions, Second geological conference of the Geological Society of Trinidad and Tobago, v. 2, p. 222–230.

Snoke, A.W., and Noble, P.J., 2001, An ammonite-radiolarian assemblage, Tobago Volcanic Group, West Indies—Implications for the evolution of the Great Arc of the Caribbean: Geological Society of America Bulletin, v. 113, p. 256–264, doi: 10.1130/0016-7606(2001)113<0256:ARATVG>2.0.CO;2.

Snoke, A.W., Yule, J.D., Rowe, D.W., Wadge, G., and Sharp, W.D., 1990, Stratigraphic and structural relationships on Tobago and some tectonic implications, *in* Larue, D.K., and Draper, G., eds., Transactions of the 12th Caribbean Geological Conference: St. Croix, Aug. 7–11, 1989, p. 389–403.

Snoke, A.W., Rowe, D.W., Yule, J.D., and Wadge, G., 2001, Petrologic and structural history of Tobago, West Indies: A fragment of the accreted Mesozoic oceanic-arc of the southern Caribbean: Geological Society of America Special Paper 354, 56 p.

Somin, M., and Millán, G., 1972, Metamorfitscheskie kompleksy Pinosa, Eskambraja y oriente na Kubje y ich vozrast (The metamorphic complexes of Pinos, Escambray and Oriente in Cuba and their ages): Izvestia Akademii Nauk SSSR, Geology Series, v. 5, p. 48–57.

Somin, M., and Millán, G., 1977, Sobre la edad de las rocas metamorficas Cubanas (On the age of the Cuban metamorphic rocks): Informe Cientifico-Técnico, Academia de Ciencias de Cuba, v. 80, p. 11.

Somin, M., and Millán, G., 1981, Geology of the metamorphic complexes of Cuba: Moscow, Nauka, 219 p. (in Russian).

Somin, M.L., Arakeljanz, M.M., and Kolesnikov, E.M., 1992, Vozrast I tektoniceskoye znacenije vysokobariceskich metamorficeskich porod Kuby: Izvestija Akademii Nauk, Rossiiskaja Akademii Nauk, Geology Series, v. 3, p. 91–104.

Speed, R.C., 1985, Cenozoic collision of the Lesser-Antilles arc and continental South America and the origin of the El Pilar fault: Tectonics, v. 4, p. 41–69.

Speed, R.C., and Smith-Horowitz, P.L., 1998, The Tobago Terrane: International Geology Review, v. 40, p. 805–830.

Stanek, K.P., 2000, Geotectonic development of northwestern Caribbean—Outline of the Geology of Cuba (Geotektonische Entwicklung der nordwestlichen Karibik—Abriß der Geologie Kubas): Freiburger Forschungshefte, v. 476, 166 p.

Stanek, K.P., Cobiella, J., Maresch, W.V., Millán, G., Grafe, F., and Grevel, Ch., 2000, Geological development of Cuba, *in* Miller, H. and Hervé, F., eds., Geoscientific cooperation with Latin America: Zeitschrift für Angewandte Geologie, v. 1, p. 259–265.

Stöckhert, B., Maresch, W.V., Brix, M., Kaiser, C., Toetz, A., Kluge, R., and Kruckhansleuder, G., 1995, Crustal history of Margarita Island (Venezuela) in detail: Constraint on the Caribbean plate-tectonic scenario: Geology, v. 23, p. 787–790, doi: 10.1130/0091-7613(1995)023<0787:CHOMIV>2.3.CO;2.

Sutter, J., 1979, Late Cretaceous collisional tectonics along the Motagua fault zone, Guatemala: Geological Society of America Abstracts with Programs, v. 11, p. 525–526.

Tectonic Analysis, 1998, The Colombian hydrocarbon habitat: Integrated sedimentology, geochemistry, paleogeographic evolution, geodynamics, petroleum geology, and basin analysis: Unpublished report produced in collaboration with ECOPETROL, Bogotá, Colombia, 770 p.

Tectonic Analysis, 2002, Structural and sedimentological development of the greater Trinidad region: Unpublished report produced in collaboration with Petrotrin and the Ministry of Energy and Energy Industries, Trinidad and Tobago, 80 p.

Trenkamp, R., Kellogg, J.N., Freymueller, J.T., and Mora, H.P., 2002, Wide plate margin deformation, southern Central America and northwestern South America, CASA GPS observations: Journal of South American Earth Sciences, v. 15, p. 157–171.

van der Hilst, R., 1990, Tomography with P, PP, and pP delay-time data and the three-dimensional mantle structure below the Caribbean region [Ph.D. thesis]: University of Utrecht, Holland, 250 p.

van der Hilst, R., and Mann, P., 1994, Tectonic implications of tomographic images of subducted lithosphere beneath northwestern South America: Geology, v. 22, p. 451–454, doi: 10.1130/0091-7613(1994)022<0451:TIOTIO>2.3.CO;2.

van Houten, F.B., 1976, Late Cenozoic volcaniclastic deposits, Andean fore-deep, Colombia: Geological Society of America, v. 87, p. 481–495, doi: 10.1130/0016-7606(1976)87<481:LCVDAF>2.0.CO;2.

Vierbuchen, R.C., 1984, The geology of the El Pilar Fault Zone and adjacent areas in northeastern Venezuela, *in* Bonini, W.E., Hargraves, R.B., and Shagam, R., eds., The Caribbean–South American plate boundary and regional tectonics: Geological Society of America Memoir 162, p. 189–252.

Villamil, T., 1999, Campanian–Miocene tectonostratigraphy, depocenter evolution and basin development of Colombia and western Venezuela: Palaeogeography, Palaeoclimatology, Palaeoecology, v. 153, p. 239–275, doi: 10.1016/S0031-0182(99)00075-9.

Villamil, T., and Pindell, J.L., 1998, Mesozoic paleogeographic evolution of northern South America: Foundations for sequence stratigraphic studies in passive margin strata deposited during non-glacial times, *in* Pindell, J.L. and Drake, C., eds., Paleogeographic evolution and non-glacial eustasy, North America: Society for Sedimentary Geology (SEPM) Special Publication 58, p. 283–318.

Weber, J., Dixon, T., DeMets, C., Ambet, W., Jansma, P., Mattioli, G., Bilham, R., Saleh, J., and Peréz, O., 2001, A GPS estimate of the relative motion between the Caribbean and South American plates, and geological implications: Geology, v. 29, p. 75–78, doi: 10.1130/0091-7613(2001)029<0075:GEORMB>2.0.CO;2.

White, R.V., Tarney, J., Kerr, A.C., Saunders, A.D., Kempton, P.D., Pringle, M.S., and Klaver, G.T., 1999, Modification of an oceanic plateau, Aruba, Dutch Caribbean: Implications for the generation of continental crust: Lithos, v. 46, p. 43–68, doi: 10.1016/S0024-4937(98)00061-9.

Wilson, D.V., 1985, The deeper structure of the Central Andes and some geophysical constraints, in Pitcher, W.S., Atherton, M.P., Cobbing, E.J., and Beckinsale, R.D., eds., Magmatism at a plate edge: London, Blackie, p. 13–18.

Wood, L., 2000, Chronostratigraphy and tectonostratigraphy of the Columbus Basin, eastern Offshore Trinidad: American Association of Petroleum Geologists Bulletin, v. 84, p. 1905–1928.

MANUSCRIPT ACCEPTED BY THE SOCIETY 5 APRIL 2005

Geological Society of America
Special Paper 394
2005

Overview of the southeast Caribbean–South American plate boundary zone

Marino Ostos
Escuela de Geología, Minas, y Geofísica, Universidad Central de Venezuela, Caracas, Venezuela, and Estudios de Ingeniería Geológica Litos, C.A., Caracas, Venezuela
Franklin Yoris
Departamento de Ciencias de La Tierra, Universidad Simón Bolívar, Caracas, Venezuela, and Estudios de Ingeniería Geológica Litos, C.A., Caracas, Venezuela
Hans G. Avé Lallemant*
Department of Earth Science, Rice University, Houston, Texas 77005-1892, USA

ABSTRACT

Knowledge of the geologic evolution of the northern margin of South America has increased tremendously, inspired by the occurrence of huge hydrocarbon deposits. This margin originated in late Triassic time when the supercontinent of Pangea broke up and North and South America drifted apart. The passive margin accommodated a thick sequence of Jurassic to Tertiary sediments. During the latest Cretaceous to the Present, the Antilles volcanic arc, built upon the Caribbean plate, migrated southeastward and collided obliquely with South America. This collision resulted in the diachronous accretion of allochthonous terranes as well as diachronous formation of a fold and thrust belt. This belt was initiated in the west (Colombia) during the latest Cretaceous and progressively moved east and reached Trinidad only in Miocene time. In front of this thrust belt, diachronous foreland basins developed. The present paper reviews the geologic evolution of northern Venezuela and adjacent areas in the Caribbean Sea, based to a large extent on a huge amount of new data released by oil companies and data collected by universities.

Keywords: Sequence stratigraphy, passive margin, oblique collision, diachrony.

INTRODUCTION

Venezuela can be divided into five large physiographic provinces (Fig. 1) that are the result of Eocene to Recent tectonic processes active along the northern South American plate margin. These provinces are (1) mountain ranges, (2) foothill regions, (3) coastal plains, (4) interior plains, and (5) the Guiana Shield. The mountain ranges are (1a) the Venezuelan Andes and (1b) the Caribbean Mountain system (Perijá Mountains, San Luis and Baragua Mountains, and the Cordillera de la Costa).

Precambrian to Neogene formations occur in the mountain ranges, while the foothill regions are covered by Neogene molasse basins. The coastal plains occur north of the state of Falcón, near Barcelona (Anzoátegui), the Orinoco River delta, and north of the state of Sucre. The interior plains occur between the northern mountain ranges and the Guiana Shield and are underlain by the

*ave@rice.edu

Ostos, M., Yoris, F., and Avé Lallemant, H.G., 2005, Overview of the southeast Caribbean–South American plate boundary zone, *in* Avé Lallemant, H.G., and Sisson, V.B., eds., Caribbean–South American plate interactions, Venezuela: Geological Society of America Special Paper 394, p. 53–89, doi: 10.1130/2005.2394(02). For permission to copy, contact editing@geosociety.org. ©2005 Geological Society of America.

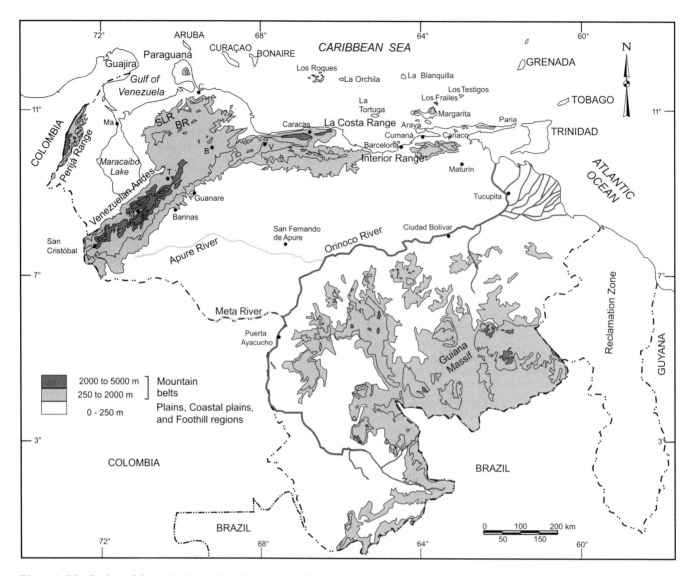

Figure 1. Distribution of the main Venezuelan physiographic provinces: mountain ranges including the Venezuelan Andes and the Caribbean Mountain system (Perijá, San Luis, Baragua, and La Costa ranges); foothills regions; coastal plains; plains between the Orinoco River and the mountain ranges; and Guiana massif or province. Contours at 250 m, and 1, 2, 3, 4, and 5 km. B—Barquisimeto; BR—Baragua Range; M—Mérida; Ma—Maracaibo; SLR—San Luis Range; T—Trujillo; V—Valencia.

Eastern and Barinas-Apure basins. The Lake Maracaibo region is physiographically a subprovince. It includes the foothill regions of the Perijá Mountains and the Venezuelan (Mérida) Andes, interior plains, mostly located between the foothills and Lake Maracaibo, the southernmost part of which extends into Colombia, and coastal plains around and toward the northern part of the lake. The southernmost physiographic province in Venezuela is the Guiana Shield or massif, which is located south of the Orinoco River. It is mostly covered by the Amazonian rain forest. The Guiana Shield is underlain by Precambrian rocks.

Precambrian

The Venezuelan Precambrian terranes crop out in the major mountain ranges and in the Guiana Shield. Those in the mountain ranges are allochthonous and were accreted during several collisional events between 570 and 245 Ma (Cambrian to Permian). Precambrian rocks also form part of the basement of the sedimentary basins south of the Apure fault (Feo-Codecido et al., 1984; Ostos, 1990, 1992; Yoris and Ostos, 1997).

The Guiana Shield is subdivided into four provinces: Imataca, Pastora, Cuchivero, and Roraima (Fig. 2). The Imataca province has yielded only Archean age dates (Santos et al., 2000; Voicu et al., 2001). It consists of metasedimentary rocks, granitic gneisses, and granitic intrusions that are metamorphosed to amphibolite and granulite facies (Dougan, 1972; Martín, 1975). They were folded during a tectonic event at 2.8 Ga and underwent partial melting. The province was intruded at 2.1 Ga by granitic magmas during the Transamazon orogeny (Hurley et al., 1976). Voicu et al. (2001) proposed that this greenstone sequence and the associated granitoid intrusions were formed between 2.25 and 2.08 Ga.

The Pastora province consists of low-grade metamorphic rocks ranging in age from 2.7 to 2.0 Ga. According to Martín (1974), this province consists of metasedimentary and felsic to mafic volcanic rocks that were locally intruded by gabbro and diabase dikes.

The Cuchivero province consists of metavolcanic and metasedimentary rocks intruded by felsic magmas. This terrane was built upon continental crust between 1.9 and 1.4 Ga.

The Roraima province consists of clastic sedimentary rocks interbedded with pyroclastics. It was deposited upon the Pastora province around 1.6 Ga (Priem et al., 1973).

The Precambrian basement in the basins north of the Guiana Shield cannot be assigned to any of these provinces as only a few wells have penetrated the basement.

The accretion of allochthonous terranes onto South America began during the early Paleozoic Caledonian orogeny (570–448 Ma); some of these rocks crop out near the cities of Mérida and San Cristóbal in western Venezuela. Later, during the Hercynian orogeny (385–245 Ma), allochthonous Precambrian blocks were juxtaposed onto South America (granites of the Sierra Nevada and Santa Marta massifs in Colombia; Fig. 2) (Case et al., 1973; Irving, 1975; Shagam, 1975; Restrepo and Toussaint, 1988; Pimentel de Bellizzia, 1992; Bartok, 1993).

The last collision started in the Late Cretaceous (Maastrichtian) along the western and northwestern corner of South America (Irving, 1975; Restrepo and Toussaint, 1988; Ostos, 1990, 1992; Dengo and Covey, 1993; Cooper et al., 1995; Lugo and Mann, 1995; Pindell and Tabbutt, 1995; Pindell et al., 1998; Yoris and Ostos, 1997; Villamil, 1999). This allochthon includes rocks of Precambrian (Ostos et al., 1989; Ostos, 1990, 1992) and lower Paleozoic ages (Avé Lallemant and Sisson, 1993) near Caracas (Federal District) and Valencia (Carabobo State).

Paleozoic

Allochthonous and autochthonous rocks of Paleozoic age are found in several regions in Venezuela. Feo-Codecido et al. (1984) noted that autochthonous terranes occur only in the subsurface of the Barinas-Apure and Eastern basins (Fig. 2) south of the Apure fault (Fig. 3). The Hato Viejo and Carrizal Formations are syn-rift red beds typical of Gondwana and Laurentia (Pimentel de Bellizzia, 1992). They are preserved only in deep structural depressions of the Venezuelan basins, such as the Espino graben.

The allochthonous terranes can be identified by the time of tectonic accretion to the northern margin of the South American plate. Accretion occurred during the early Paleozoic, late Paleozoic, and the late Mesozoic (Yoris and Ostos, 1997).

Granites (Burkley, 1976), shelf-slope clastics, and carbonates of Ordovician and Silurian age (González de Juana et al., 1980; Bartok, 1993) form part of the lower Paleozoic allochthons in the Venezuelan Andes mountain range. Another Ordovician metasedimentary sequence is found in the basement of the Maracaibo basin and in the Andes (Feo-Codecido et al., 1984; Bartok, 1993; Lugo and Mann, 1995). Devonian age allochthonous terranes crop out in the Perijá Mountains (Bowen, 1972; González de Juana et al., 1980; Kellogg, 1984).

Early and late Paleozoic collisional granites resulted from subduction underneath the northern margin of South America. Carboniferous granites are found in the subsurface of the Eastern, Barinas-Apure, and Maracaibo basins (Feo-Codecido et al., 1984; Bartok, 1993), and Permian granites occur in the El Baúl region (Martín, 1968). Sedimentary sequences of Carboniferous and Permian age crop out in the Perijá (Bowen, 1972) and Andes mountains (González de Juana et al., 1980).

Allochthonous terranes (Fig. 3) containing Devonian to Permian rocks (Urbani, 1982; Benjamini et al., 1987; Ostos, 1990, 1992) occur in the Caribbean Mountain system from the Guajira Peninsula (northwestern Venezuela) to the Paria Peninsula (northeastern Venezuela, including the subsurface basement of the Venezuela platform) (Talukdar and Bolívar, 1982, *in* Ysaccis, 1997; Kiser et al., 1984, *in* Ysaccis, 1997; Bellizzia, 1985) and the Cordillera de la Costa (Bellizzia, 1972; Bell, 1971; Stephan, 1977, 1982; Mascle et al., 1979; Avé Lallemant and Guth, 1990; Ostos, 1990, 1992; Yoris and Ostos, 1997; Sisson et al., this volume, Chapter 3).

Triassic-Jurassic

The Triassic is not present in Venezuela or, at least, no evidence of its presence has been found. The oldest part of the Jurassic system (208–181 Ma) is represented by the La Gé and Tinacoa Volcanics in the Perijá Mountains (Shagam, 1975) and the Guacamayas Volcanics in the El Baúl uplift (Martín, 1968). They are overlain by the La Quinta Formation and younger sequences related to the opening of the Proto-Caribbean Sea. They are the lateral equivalents of the Volcánicas de El Totumo in the Sierra de Perijá (Fig. 4).

In Venezuela, rifting produced several major structural lineaments that later influenced the evolution of the Venezuela sedimentary basins. Within continental Venezuela, the opening of the Proto-Caribbean caused the development of northeast-oriented graben (Fig. 5) such as the Apure-Mantecal (Feo-Codecido et al., 1984), Espino (Feo-Codecido et al., 1984; Motiscka, 1985), and Andes-Perijá mountains (Maze, 1984; Audemard, 1991), and the Maracaibo grabens (Audemard, 1991; Lugo and Mann, 1995; Parnaud et al., 1995a). It has been proposed that Jurassic rocks are present in the deepest parts of the Serranía del

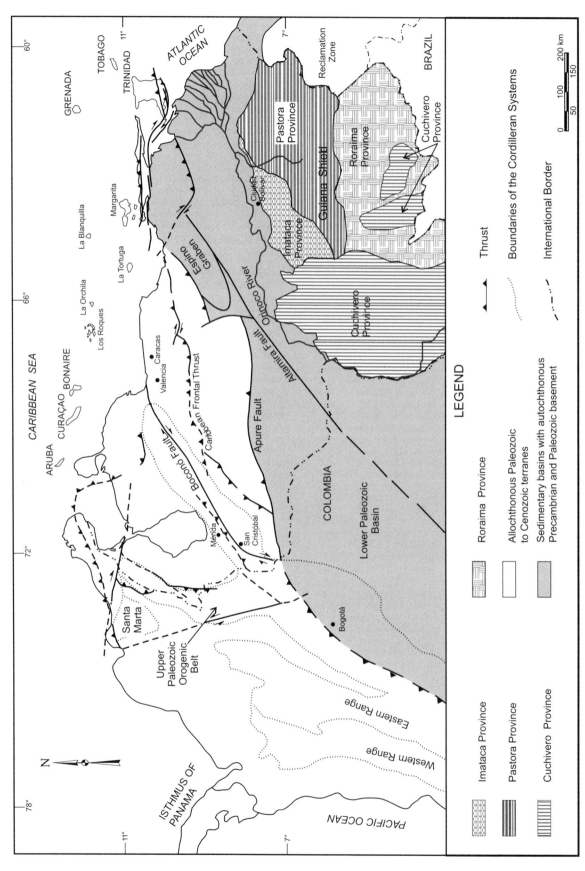

Figure 2. Map of northern South America showing the distribution of autochthonous terranes in the Guiana Shield including Imataca, Pastora, Cuchivero, and Roraima provinces. These have also been found in deep wells underneath the sedimentary cover north of the Apure fault. Modified from Yoris and Ostos (1997).

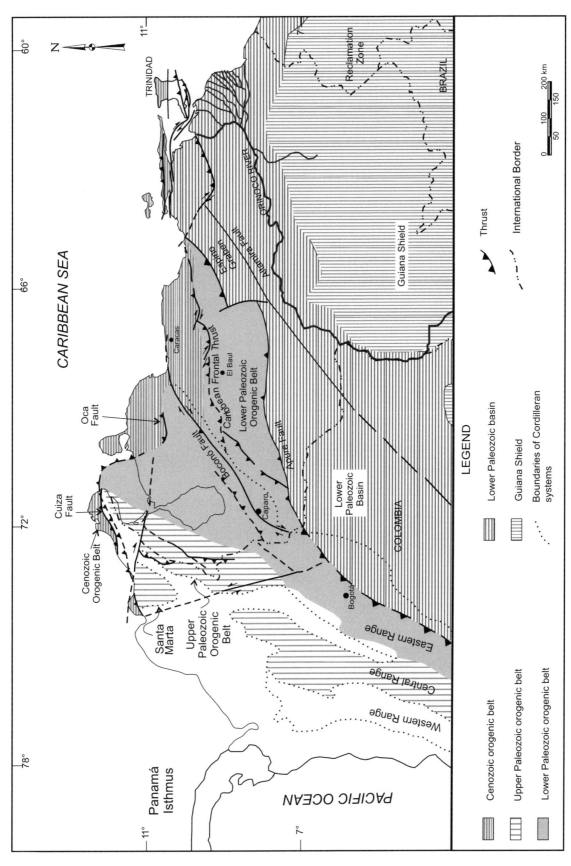

Figure 3. Map of northern South America showing the distribution of allochthonous terranes with Paleozoic rocks. These terranes were sequentially sutured during the Ordovician and Silurian, the Carboniferous, and the late Mesozoic to Recent. Modified from Yoris and Ostos (1997).

	ALLOCHTHONOUS			AUTOCHTHONOUS
Age	Upper Paleozoic Orogenic belt	Lower Paleozoic Orogenic belt	Cenozoic Orogenic belt	Lower Paleozoic basin
	Perijá and Guajira	Andes	La Costa Range	Guárico and Cojedes
Jurassic	Seco, Cojoro/COCINAS La Quinta Conglomerates	La Quinta	Pueblo Nuevo Las Brisas (*Zenda*) Macuro	Ipire
	El Totumo Macoita			
	La Gé Tinacoa Volcanics		?	?

Figure 4. Stratigraphic correlation chart of important Jurassic units in autochthonous and allochthonous terranes in Venezuela. In this and subsequent figures, the group rank is in all capital letters, formation rank is noted with initial capitalizations and lower-case letters, and member rank is in italics. Modified from Yoris and Ostos (1997).

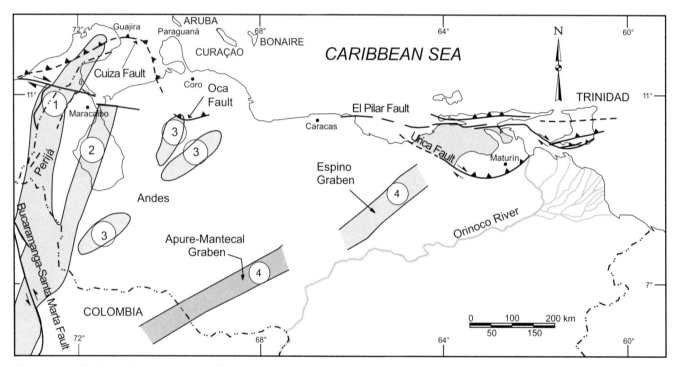

Figure 5. Distribution of Jurassic rocks in (1) the Perijá Range, (2) the basement of the Maracaibo basin, (3) the Andes, and (4) the Barinas-Apure and Eastern Venezuela basins (Apure-Mantecal and Espino graben). It has been proposed that the Jurassic rocks are involved in deep structures in the Serranía del Interior, east of the Úrica fault (Bartok, 1993; Passalacqua et al., 1995; Lugo and Mann, 1995). Modified from Yoris and Ostos (1997).

Interior of eastern Venezuela as part of the passive margin; they may occur in the autochthonous terrane, but they do not crop out (Parnaud et al., 1995b).

These grabens were filled during the Jurassic by red bed (continental) sediments, diverse volcanics, and occasional shallow marine clastics and limestones (Shagam, 1975; Feo-Codecido et al., 1984; González de Juana et al., 1980; Maze, 1984; Motiscka, 1985). They are preserved on the Guajira and Paraguaná Peninsulas (Cojoro and Cocinas Groups and Pueblo Nuevo Formation) and in western Venezuela (La Quinta Forma-

tion). They also occur west of the Úrica fault, in the subsurface of the Eastern Venezuela Basin (Altamira High, south of Guárico State, Ipire Formation; Motiscka, 1985). Recent interpretations of seismic reflection lines from northern Anzoátegui State, east of the Úrica fault, show thick "extensional regime" fills underlying beds assigned to Cretaceous sequences (Temblador Group); these pre-Cretaceous passive margin rocks are supposed to have been deposited in the Jurassic Espino grabens (D'Aubeterre, 2002) or other related basins of the same age (Cabarcas, 2001).

Metamorphosed limestones in the Cordillera de la Costa (Zenda Member of the Las Brisas Formation, Caracas Group) are Kimmeridgian in age (Urbani, 1969, 1973; González de Juana et al., 1980). Overlying metamorphic rocks of the Las Mercedes, Tacagua, and Antímano Formations could be of Jurassic age or younger (Navarro et al., 1988; Urbani et al., 1989b). Metamorphic rocks in the Araya-Paria Penínsulas of eastern Venezuela, such as those included in the Macuro and Uquire (?) Formations, seem also to be of Jurassic age (CVET, 1970; González de Juana et al., 1980; MEM, 1997).

Early Cretaceous

The correlation chart of the most important Lower Cretaceous units in Venezuela and the major sedimentary facies distribution are shown in Figures 6 and 7. In northwestern South America, the sedimentation was initially controlled by the Jurassic grabens as sandstones of variable thickness occurring in the Tambor Formation in Colombia, the Río Negro Formation in western Venezuela, and the Barranquín Formation in eastern Venezuela. In the southern Machiques trough, these sediments are more than 2 km thick and thin to just a few meters in some areas of the north flank of the Andes. In eastern Venezuela, they are also about 2 km thick (Smith et al., 1962; González de Juana et al., 1980; Yoris, 1985a; Audemard, 1991; Lugo and Mann, 1995).

In Albian-Aptian time, an epicontinental sea transgressed from the northwest (Stauffer, 1994) onto western Venezuela,

depositing calcareous sediments (Cogollo Group). Laterally, age equivalent clastic rocks were deposited in the south on the Guiana Shield (Aguardiente Formation).

In central Venezuela, there are some remnants of a calcareous shelf limestone (Macaira Limestone). This occurs dismembered along the mountain front of the Caribbean Mountain system in the State of Guárico (Beck and Furrer, 1977). More to the south and east, the oldest Cretaceous (clastic) sedimentary rocks are included in the Canoa Formation of the Temblador Group (González de Juana et al., 1980).

The paleoenvironment of the Sucre Group of eastern Venezuela resembles a passive "Atlantic"-type margin (Yoris, 1992a; Erikson, 1992, 1994). The oldest sedimentary rocks are quartz-rich clastics with some "shelf" limestones of the Barranquín Formation. The lower contact of the Barranquín is not exposed in eastern Venezuela; north of Aragua de Maturín (Monagas State), the exposed section is >1 km thick, but in the mountains near the Río Grande (Casanay-Caripito region, Sucre State; Yoris, 1985a), the thickness has been estimated to be >2 km. On the Chimana islands, north of Puerto La Cruz (Anzoátegui State) and Bahía de Santa Fe (Sucre State), a calcareous interval occurs within the Barranquín Formation, called the Morro Blanco Member, which is of Barremian age. Overlying the Barranquín Formation, there is an extensive and well-defined calcareous-clastic sequence (El Cantil and Chimana Formations). The El Cantil Formation is up to 1 km thick (Yoris, 1985a, 1988, 1992a), and the Chimana Formation has a thickness of >300 m (Yoris, 1985a, 1992b). The combined thickness of the

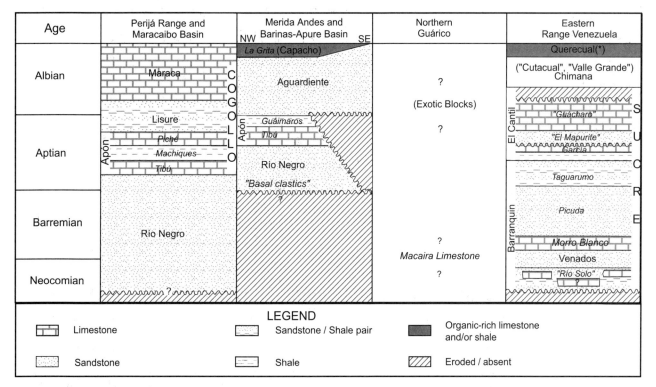

Figure 6. Stratigraphic correlation chart of the Early Cretaceous units of Venezuela. Informal units indicated between quotation marks. The asterisk indicates that the unit persists into the Late Cretaceous.

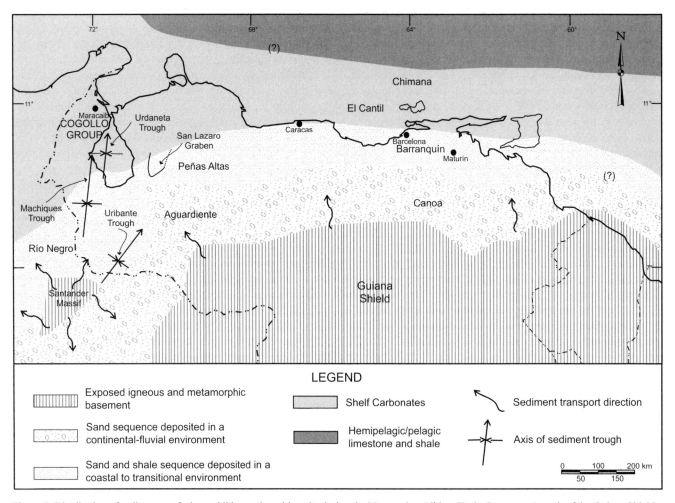

Figure 7. Distribution of sedimentary facies and lithostratigraphic units during the Neocomian-Albian (Early Cretaceous) north of the Guiana Shield.

El Cantil and Chimana Formations is several times greater than the average thickness of lateral equivalent rocks of the same age in western Venezuela (Cogollo Group).

The sources of the sediments of the Sucre Group are the Guiana Shield (Yoris, 1985b) and perhaps the Paleozoic to Jurassic rocks that were deposited along the northern "autochthonous" margin of the Guiana Shield. In contrast, petrographic data from the Río Negro Formation in western Venezuela indicate a "recycled orogenic" source (Hung and Ascanio, 1992).

The entire time span from the Neocomian (Barremian?) to Albian in eastern Venezuela is represented by a succession of fluvial-paralic and shallow marine (calcareous) environments. The sandy members of the Barranquín Formation (Venados and Picuda) may represent highstand systems tracts in third order sequences ("short-term" eustatic curve of Haq et al. [1987] and "third order" in the sense of Vail et al. [1991] and Brink et al. [1993]). The Morro Blanco (calcareous) and Taguarumo (sands, shales) may represent the marine transgressions that followed the highstand system tracts. We suggest here that the corresponding sequence boundaries should be included in the

definition of Morro Blanco and Taguarumo Members, instead of using the arbitrary, lithostratigraphic contact with Venados and Picuda sandy members, respectively. The maximum flooding surface after the transgression, represented by the Taguarumo Member, is the García Shale. The unconformity on top of the García Shale is interpreted as a sequence boundary–transgression surface (Yoris, 1992a) upon which the El Mapurite Member of the El Cantil Formation was deposited. Additional marine sequences are represented by the lower and upper parts of the Guácharo Member (Yoris, 1985a, 1988). The corresponding transgressive system tract–highstand system tract transitions of clastic units are represented in the middle Guácharo and Punceres beds (Yoris 1985a, 1988, 1992a). The Chimana Formation in the central core of the eastern Serranía may be considered as a complex, high frequency eustatically influenced sediment with low accommodation rate. The facies deepens to the north (Chimana Islands, Anzoátegui State) and northeast (Casanay region, Sucre State). This is why the facies described in the Venezuelan literature are so complex (e.g., Yoris, 1992b).

In the Machiques and Uribante troughs of western Venezuela, the Río Negro and Apón Formations are roughly similar to the Barranquín–El Cantil sediments, but the thicknesses are quite different. In the Eastern Range (Serranía del Interior Oriental) (Yoris 1985a, 1992a), the Barranquín–El Cantil Formations have a combined thickness of ~3 km while the Río Negro and Apón Formations in the Machiques trough (MEM, 1997) are a few tens of meters to almost 2.2 km thick.

The Machiques Member of the Apón Formation seems to be a maximum flooding surface. It is of the same age as the García Member in the Eastern Venezuela Basin. This correlation is tentative, because of the tectonic effect of the collision along the west Colombian margin. If this correlation is correct, the Río Negro and Apón Formations must be correlated with the Barranquín Formation and the García Member, and not with the Barranquín–El Cantil Formations. In this case, the maximum thickness for these Eastern Range units is close to 2.4 km (Yoris, 1985a, 1992a), similar to the equivalent rocks in the Machiques trough. The average thickness of the Río Negro–Apón in the Maracaibo basin and Perijá Mountains is close to 1 km (MEM, 1997) and in some places, such as on the Mérida Arch (particularly in the Guaruríes River region), it is only a few tens of meters thick and overlies the Paleozoic metamorphic basement rocks of the Mucuchachí Formation instead of the red beds of the La Quinta Formation. This implies that block faulting has occurred, basement has been eroded, and the basal clastics of the Cretaceous sequence are the youngest of this cycle in western Venezuela. These clastic sediments are included in the Apón Formation event instead of the Río Negro Formation as some authors in the past suggested (MEM, 1997). Thus, the Early Cretaceous basin in western Venezuela was controlled by block tectonics. The basin faults may be reactivated pre-Cretaceous extensional faults. These tectonics may be related to the collision of the Nazca plate with western Colombia, whereas the eastern Venezuela margin acted as a typical Atlantic passive margin.

The Chimana Formation in eastern Venezuela should be equivalent in age to the Lisure-Maraca or Aguardiente Formations in western Venezuela. It is important to recognize how the clastic sedimentation in the Albian is recorded in western and eastern Venezuela. Are the sediments related to a major geotectonic feature in the Proto-Caribbean crust, or are they related to a long-term climatic change before the worldwide Late Cretaceous transgression (Yoris, 1984, 1992a; Pindell and Tabbutt, 1995; Pindell et al., 1998; Villamil, 1998; Erlich et al., 1999a)? The conspicuous presence of feldspar in the sandstone of the Chimana Formation is thought to be the consequence of uplift of the Guiana Shield and reactivation of pre-Cretaceous faults along the northern South American plate boundary (Yoris, 1984, 1992a). This might be related to an island arc–oceanic plate collision, occurring northwest of the Guiana Shield (Navarro et al., 1988; Yoris, 1992a; Giunta et al., 2002). This geotectonic feature was outlined by Navarro (1983; see also Beck, 1985a, 1985b). It seems probable that both geotectonic and paleoclimatic factors impacted the Albian sedimentation along the

northern South American plate, prior to the global transgression in Late Cretaceous time.

Late Cretaceous

The correlation chart of the most important Upper Cretaceous units in Venezuela is shown in Figure 8. The Cenomanian to Maastrichtian distribution of the sedimentary facies on the northern margin of South America is shown in Figures 9 and 10.

An extensive diachronous, east to west transgression began at the end of the Albian. At this time, the sea covered southern Venezuela. This marine invasion coincides with the long term (ca. 107–77 Ma; Haq et al., 1987) worldwide transgressive pulse of the Late Cretaceous. In Venezuela, the transgression resulted in sedimentation of organic-rich limestones, shales, and cherts. These rocks are recognized as the Querecual–San Antonio (Guayuta Group), Mucaria, Navay, and La Luna Formations.

In western Venezuela, the Capacho and Escandalosa Formations are the lateral equivalents of the La Luna Formation in Perijá, Maracaibo, and Trujillo. Their age is Cenomanian-Turonian (Parnaud et al., 1995a). In these units, the organic carbon content is low and the siliciclastic proportion is very high, particularly in the sandstones of the Escandalosa Formation (Hevia et al., 1996). The upper member of the Capacho is the Guayacán Member, a thick carbonate deposited in a shallow marine environment underlying the La Luna–Navay Formations. Maximum anoxia may have occurred during the Turonian to the Santonian (Erlich, 1999; Erlich et al., 1999a, 1999b). Recent chemostratigraphic studies (V, Ni, Mo, Zn, and total organic carbon; Mata, 2001) identified a maximum anoxia peak in sections located in Táchira State. Based on our studies in the South Andean flank, Briceño et al. (1996a, 1996b; Briceño and Callejón, 2000) and Mata (2001) showed that several cycles can be recognized in the La Luna Formation that can be used as correlation tools and should represent up to third order eustatic pulses. On the basis of data, collected recently, we think that the anoxia maximum identified in the Las Delicias and La Ortiza Creek sections in Táchira State could be a second order, worldwide maximum flooding surface (Haq et al., 1987). Petrographic textures (Yoris et al., 1996a) and Zr-Hf chemostratigraphic indicators show that the silica content in the upper half of the La Luna Formation is related to a clastic influx and is not of a biogenetic origin (Mata, 2001). Therefore, the phosphatic-glauconitic quartz sandstone beds of the upper La Luna Formation (Tres Esquinas Member in Táchira and Mérida states) in the western Venezuelan basins could be considered as shelf-derived sediments, reworked by gravity flows and contour currents (Yoris et al., 1996a). The silica-rich limestone beds are the result of contamination of pelagic muds (silt-clay fractions) derived from land, and may not be the result of silica-test planktonic organisms concentrated by primary carbonate dissolution. Part of the phosphatic component could be derived from mass extinction on the shelf caused by local red tides of massive phytoplankton blooms (Erlich et al., 2000). Observed trends of paleocurrents (Yoris et al., 1996a) seem to be consistent with the

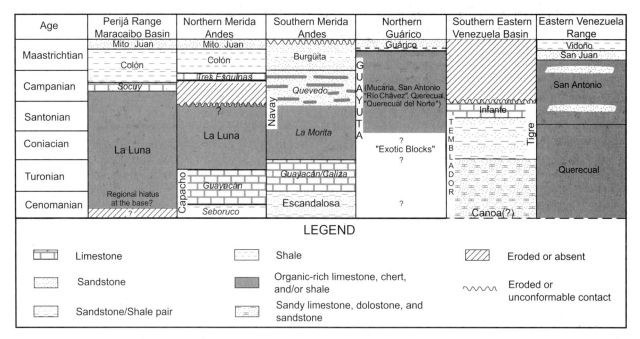

Figure 8. Stratigraphic correlation chart of the Late Cretaceous units of Venezuela. Guárico and Vidoño Formations continue into the Paleocene. Canoa and Querecual Formations were first deposited during the Albian (see Fig. 6). Modified from Yoris and Ostos (1997).

orientation of Colombian and western Venezuela basins during Cenomanian to Turonian time (Villamil, 1998; Villamil et al., 1999). Thus, the main source for the Guayuta Group may have been in the south (Guiana Shield) and the contour currents along the continental slope moved from east to west.

The rocks of the La Luna, Navay, and Querecual Formations are the main source rocks in the oil basins of Venezuela. The thickness of the La Luna Formation ranges from 50 to 300 m in western Venezuela. We found that the Navay Formation, on the southern flank of the Andes, is ~660 m thick and thickens to more than 800 m to the northeast in the El Curito Creek section in Barinas State.

Paleocurrent directions, corrected for tectonic transport, show a consistent northwest flow direction in the San Antonio–Mucaria Formations in the Serranía del Interior and Guárico mountain front (Yoris, 1992a). In the Serranía, along the Querecual River, 19 paleocurrent measurements indicate a main trend of N40°W to N70°W. Some of the measurements indicate a paleocurrent trend toward S80°E, based on the interpretation of rhomboidal ripple pattern, as seen along the Sabana de Piedras–Santa María road (Monagas State). Near the Guanapito Dam in the Guárico region, 39 measurements (migratory ripples, tool-marks, and flute casts) show a main trend of N10°W to N70°W.

In the La Luna Formation in the state of Táchira, along the Las Delicias–Rubio road (Yoris et al., 1996a), the paleocurrent directions (30 measurements of migratory ripples, tool marks, and flute casts) change to a west-southwest trend (S70°W to S80°W). This implies that the currents in the Late Cretaceous went from east to west, reorienting the sediment flux from the shield to a westerly trend. Evidence suggests that in the Maracaibo basin, the current

flux changed to the southwest, fitting the geometry of drowned areas of the northern margin of the South American plate.

Paleocurrent directions in eastern Venezuela have secondary modes in the NE and SE quadrants that probably indicate some upwelling (SE) or paleoclimatic (?)-paleobathymetric–induced reversals (NE). In the La Luna Formation, along the Gerarúíes River (Mérida State), 11 sedimentary structures have been analyzed: ten oscillation ripples and one turbidite-like structure (Tbcd of Bouma, 1962). Ripples have a wavelength of up to 60 cm and amplitude of 1.5–3.5. The NE-SW patterns are thought to have formed in upwelling related currents; NW-SE patterns are interpreted as contour currents. The cross-bedding direction of migration in the turbidite (unit Tc of Bouma, 1962) is S30°E, which is the most probable direction for an upwelling, storm-related turbidity current. In the Las Delicias section, a very similar structure (Tabc) has been recognized almost at the same stratigraphic level (2–3 m) from the base of the La Luna Formation. In the latter case, we found phosphatic nodules in unit Tb, and the direction of migration of the Tc interval was S72°W. Our interpretation is that it formed by a gravity-driven (storm related?) flow of sediment, coming from the shelf. Even without any correction for tectonic rotations of crustal blocks, in general, the directions found are consistent with the proposed paleogeography of the eastern and western margin of northern South America (Villamil, 1998; Villamil et al., 1999; Erlich et al., 1999b). Thus, during the Cenomanian to early Maastrichtian, turbidity and gravity-driven flow occurred. These rocks include phosphatic fragments from shallower regions of the shelf and sand derived from short-term lowstands during which huge quantities of shelf material were reworked and redeposited on shelf borders and in sub-

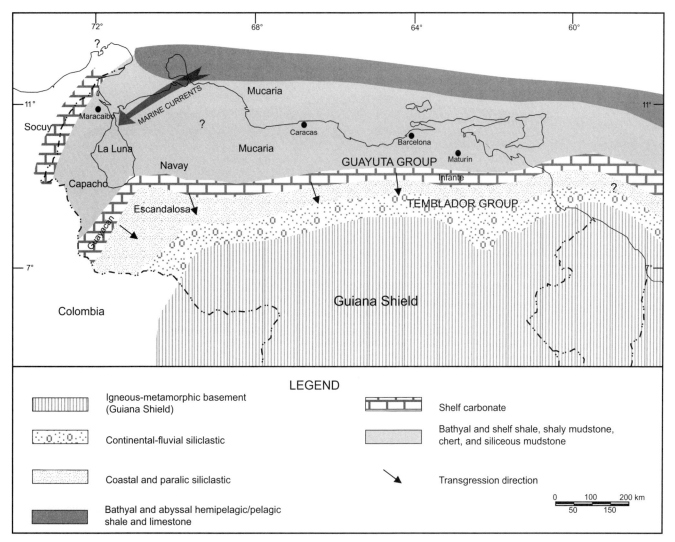

Figure 9. Sedimentary facies distribution during the Cenomanian-Campanian (Late Cretaceous) north of the Guiana Shield. Guayacán Limestone (Cenomanian) is younger than the Socuy Limestone (Campanian). During the Turonian to early Maastrichtian, there was transgression of the La Luna–Navay to the southeast. The same event is not as evident in north-central and eastern Venezuela. Modified from Yoris and Ostos (1997).

marine channels. For example, in the Cuite River, Apure State, three events of submarine sand deposition, 0.5–1 m thick, can be seen in the middle half of the La Luna–Navay facies. These are interbedded with siliceous limestones that we interpret as having formed at submarine conditions. These particularly clean sands did not generate the classic siliciclastic slope fans; instead, they were probably associated with low energy, contour currents and gravity flows induced by storms. Sand-silt sedimentation is particularly well developed during Santonian to early Maastrichtian times. The Ftanita (chert) de Táchira and Tres Esquinas Members have the largest number of this type of deposits as can be seen best along the Las Delicias–San Antonio (Táchira State) road.

In western Venezuela, the late Albian to Turonian lateral facies variations of the typical "La Luna" source rocks include pelagic and phosphatic limestones, dark shales, and shelly limestones. On the southeastern flank of the Táchira Andes, they grade laterally into sandy-clastic and glauconitic facies. The source rocks of western Venezuela are equivalent to the facies of the Mucaria Formation and Guayuta Group of north-central Venezuela. In the mountain front of Guárico, near the town of Valle de Morín, the "Querecual del Norte Facies" includes beds of calcareous, sandy turbidites interbedded with the typical "pelagic," black, laminated limestones (Bell, 1968). This is interpreted as the distal interfingering of the "Garr-apata-Guárico facies" turbidites with the oceanic, foredeep pelagic sediments of latest Cretaceous age (Maastrichtian) or, possibly, of earliest Paleocene. Due to the lack of precise chronostratigraphic determinations, the correlation is only speculative and needs further study. Nevertheless, the "Querecual del Norte Facies" seems to be older than the Mucaria Formation (northern Guárico State), based on the stratigraphic relation of the San Antonio–Querecual Formations in the Eastern Venezuela Basin. However, the

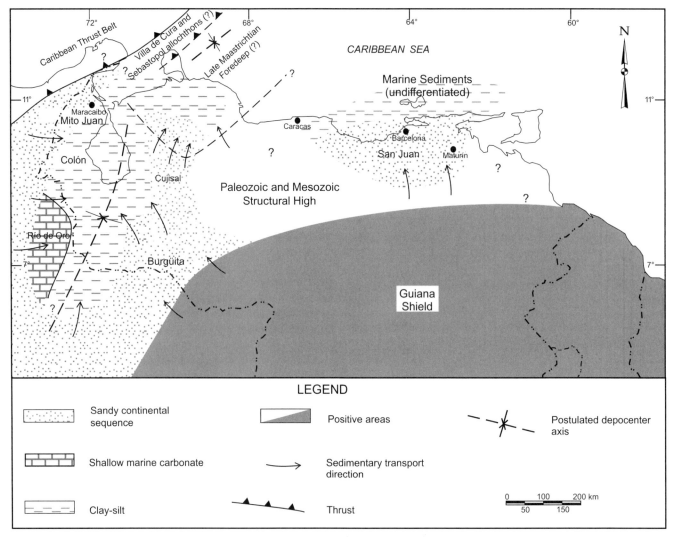

Figure 10. Sedimentary facies and lithostratigraphic distribution during the Maastrichtian (Late Cretaceous) north of the Guiana Shield. In western Venezuela, a depocenter was located subparallel to the Caribbean thrust belt. To the north, a Maastrichtian foredeep developed in front of the Villa de Cura–Sebastopol allochthons. Modified from Yoris and Ostos (1997).

Mucaria Formation in Cojedes should be older than the "Querecual del Norte Facies" if the model of west-to-east diachronous collision is accepted. This also implies that the Mucaria Formation in Cojedes State should be older than the "Mucaria Formation" in the fold and thrust belt of northern Guárico. Perhaps we should not correlate the siliceous-laminated mudstones with the "Mucaria," but with the "San Antonio–Río Chavez Formation." Clearly, we need more precise stratigraphic ages for all these units. These formations are conformably and diachronously overlain by the "Flysch of Guárico facies" and are the lateral equivalents of the upper part of Guayuta Group (San Antonio Formation) in eastern Venezuela.

The Guayuta Group is thickest (>1 km) at its type locality (Querecual River, Anzoátegui State). In the subsurface of the Eastern Basin where it is defined as the Canoa and Tigre Formations, which are part of the Temblador Group (Hedberg, 1950;

González de Juana et al., 1980; Erlich and Barrett, 1992; MEM, 1997), this unit changes toward the south, losing its source-rock characteristics and recording shallower environments, from shelf to coastline to continental.

The Late Cretaceous in Venezuela ends with Maastrichtian regressive units. In the Perijá Mountains and the Maracaibo basin, the La Luna Formation grades upward into glauconitic limestones (Socuy Member) and dark shales with thin sandstones of the Colón, Mito Juan, and Catatumbo Formations (Fig. 10). The Maastricht-ian-Paleocene boundary in the Lora River area, Táchira State, has been placed in the Catatumbo and Barco interval (Pocknall et al., 1997, 2001). On the northern flank of the Andes, the glauconitic-phosphatic Tres Esquinas Member may be the diachronous equivalent of the Socuy Member. Ford and Houbolt (1963) included the basal glauconitic limestone of the Socuy Member in its type section (Socuy river, Perijá Mountains) in the Tres Esquinas Member of the La Luna Formation. The basal age for the Socuy Member is Campanian (González de Juana et al., 1980; Erlich et al., 1999b), and the basal age for the Tres Esquinas Member is late Santonian (Erlich et al., 1999a, 1999b). On the southern flank of the Andes, the upper part of the source rocks becomes transitional with the Colón and Mito Juan.

The upper half of the La Luna Formation and the entire Navay, Mucaria, and San Antonio Formations are silica-enriched (significant silt-size quartz fraction plus authigenic chert). They also contain numerous sandstones (Navay and San Antonio Formations). This is indicative of regional highstand conditions after the Turonian maximum flooding but with many shorter-term sea-level retreats that moved sand from the Cretaceous passive margin. During this supposed highstand, we recognized along the Cuite River, in the Nula region of Apure State, an erosional hiatus beneath the basal (submarine) conglomeratic sandstones of the Maastrichtian Burgüita Formation. In several oil fields of western Venezuela, an unconformity may also exist at the base of the Burgüita Formation (Erlich et al., 1999b).

In north-central Venezuela, the Mucaria Formation is the lateral equivalent of the La Luna and Colón Formations. It grades upward into hemipelagic and turbidite sequences of the Guárico Formation. In eastern Venezuela, the black cherts and sandstones of the San Antonio Formation are overlain by the bathyal sandstones of the San Juan Formation. To the north and east, the San Juan Formation pinches out and the Guayuta Group underlies the basal late Maastrichtian dark shales of the Vidoño Formation. The San Juan Formation is correlative with the eustatic regressive Maastrichtian pulse of the global eustatic curve of Haq et al. (1987). It should be considered as a slope-fan complex of the third order lowstand system tract of the Late Cretaceous passive margin (Yoris, 1992a). This implies that in the southern flank of the Andes, western Venezuela, the sequence boundary underneath the San Juan Formation is correlative with the one observed at the base of Burgüita Formation. This kind of boundary has not been recognized in the northern flank of the Andes or in the Perijá. Supposedly, it is very close to the Colón–La Luna boundary, which is strongly affected by the deformation related to the collision of the Colombia island arc during the Late Cretaceous. The next transgressive system tract is supposed to begin at the end of the Maastrichtian and is represented by the Colón and Vidoño Formations in western and eastern Venezuela, respectively. North-central Venezuela lacks the "passive margin" equivalent to the Vidoño and Colón Formations, perhaps because the region is allochthonous and was located northwest of its present position. It might have been deformed by the southeast emplacement of the allochthonous belts of the Sebastopol microcontinent and the Villa de Cura, Paracotos, and Caucagua–El Tinaco belts. Nevertheless, the hemipelagic facies in the transition between Mucaria–San Antonio and Guárico Formations are age correlatives of basal Colón–Mito Juan and San Juan Formations.

Paleocene-Eocene of Western Venezuela

During the Late Cretaceous (Fig. 9) and early Paleocene, sedimentation in western Venezuela was influenced by the subduction of the Farallon plate (Pacific Ocean) under western Colombia (Stephan, 1977; Burke et al., 1984; Beck, 1985a; Restrepo and Toussaint, 1988; Ostos, 1990, 1992; Cooper et al., 1995; Lugo and Mann, 1995; Yoris and Ostos, 1997; Pindell et al., 1998; Hoernle et al., 2002). As the Caribbean plate and the deformation front migrated eastward, this generated successively younger depocenters toward the east (Figs. 11 and 12). The Perijá depocenter was the first one formed. It started probably in the late Maastrichtian, during deposition of the Colón Formation, and it continued to be active during the Paleocene (Guasare and Marcelina Formations in the north and Orocué Group in the south). Similarly, the oblique collision of the Lesser Antilles arc with the South American plate (Duncan and Hargraves, 1984; Speed, 1985; Erlich and Barrett, 1990; Lugo and Mann, 1995; Pindell and Tabbutt, 1995) generated from Paleocene to Eocene time successive tectonic thrust sheets (nappes) vergent to the south and southeast, with foredeep basins evolving in front of them. In the Maracaibo basin, these nappes were the source of the turbiditic sedimentation of the Trujillo and Morán Formations. However, the time-equivalent Guasare Formation was deposited in shallower environments (Parnaud et al., 1995a) (transitional to inner neritic; MEM, 1997) that were more distal from the Caribbean deformation front. It was deposited before the deposition of the coastal-marsh Marcelina Formation, as we discovered in the area along the Río Cachiri (north Perijá), but, in the west, it is a lateral equivalent of the Marcelina (Parnaud et al., 1995a; MEM, 1997).

During the Eocene, a complex sedimentary setting existed in the Maracaibo basin. It is characterized by local deltaic-estuarine, coastal-fluvial, and marine systems. The basin evolution was controlled by tectonic features such as the Perijá belt and the Lara nappes. The sedimentation of the Misoa and Pauji Formations was also strongly influenced by major faults. This is particularly true along the Icotea-Lama fault system (Audemard, 1991; Lugo and Mann, 1995; Escalona and Mann, 2002). For instance, there is seismic evidence in the north-central part of Lake Maracaibo that the preserved Eocene sedimentary unit west of the Icotea fault system is twice as thick as the preserved unit on the eastern block, due to Eocene reactivation (Link et al., 1994).

In the western part of Maracaibo basin, formations such as the Paleocene Barco–Los Cuervos and the middle late Eocene Mirador-Carbonera sequences represent two similar sedimentary pulses of fluvial-paralic environments (Yoris et al., 1996b). We were able to date the Los Cuervos Formation along the Rubio–San Antonio road (Táchira State) by palynological analysis as latest middle Eocene. This implies that the Mirador Formation in this area is not older than late Eocene; other authors have assigned the Mirador Formation to the early Eocene (Erlich et al., 1997), late Paleocene–early Eocene (Parnaud et al., 1995a), and early–middle Eocene (González de Juana et al., 1980). Brondijk (1967) mentioned that the Mirador Formation in locally preserved beds

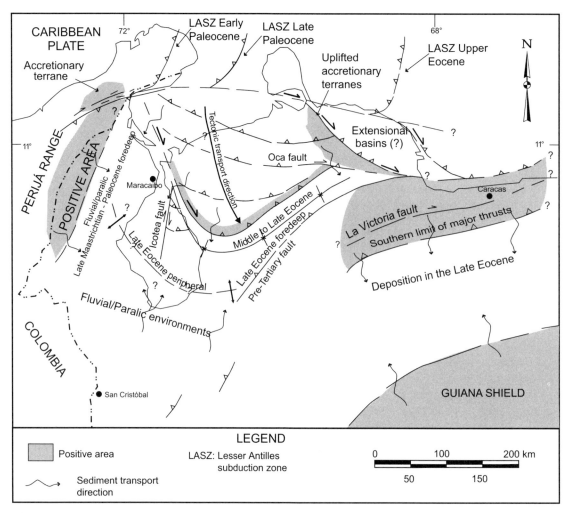

Figure 11. Diachronous tectonic evolution of the Paleocene-Eocene deformation front in northwestern South America related to interactions between the Caribbean and South American plates. LASZ—Lesser Antilles subduction zone.

might be of late Eocene age (MEM, 1997). This indicates that the lateral facies variations during Eocene time need more study.

The Orocué Group in Tachira State is bounded by two sequence boundaries. Thus, the Barco Formation is a transgressive system tract and the Los Cuervos Formation is a highstand system tract. This interpretation is speculative. The Mirador-Carbonera Formations may represent a second order transgressive system tract because the Mirador Formation may have been deposited in an estuarine environment (Toro, 1992; Paparoni, 1993; Toro et al., 1994). The Oligocene León Formation could be a second order maximum flooding surface. However, a tectonic influence cannot be ruled out, especially since we determined that in the Rubio–San Antonio road section the thickness of the combined Mirador–Carbonera–León Formations is close to 1 km. In the basin center, the Guasare, Trujillo, Misoa, Caús, and Paují Formations are marine lateral equivalents of the Catatumbo–Barco–Los Cuervos–Mirador (?) Formations, showing gradual deepening to the northeast. These formations represent sedimentary systems highly influenced by tectonism. For example, the Trujillo Formation is in part turbiditic,

resulting from the southward emplacement of the allochthonous Caribbean terranes. Consequently, maximum flooding surfaces and condensed sections in the Maracaibo basin, such as the Caús Formation, have been misinterpreted because of the similarity in the lithology of different transgressive systems (Higgs, 1997).

In the Barbacoas region, eastern Trujillo State, the depth of the Paleocene-Eocene sea was lower, but the region was also tectonically influenced during the deposition of the transitional, coastal-marine sedimentary rocks (the Paleocene–lower Eocene Humocaro–Quebrada Arriba and the middle Eocene Gobernador-Masparrito Formations). They represent two different tectonically influenced third order transgressive system tracts (Toro and Eichenseer, 1997); the maximum flooding surface and highstand system tracts are represented by the middle Eocene Paují (Maracaibo basin) and Pagüey (Apure-Barinas basin) Formations (Parnaud et al., 1995a). The Higuerones Member of the Pagüey Formation is of earliest late Eocene age (MEM, 1997). In Falcón State, the sedimentation started in the Eocene, occurring just south of the south-vergent deformation

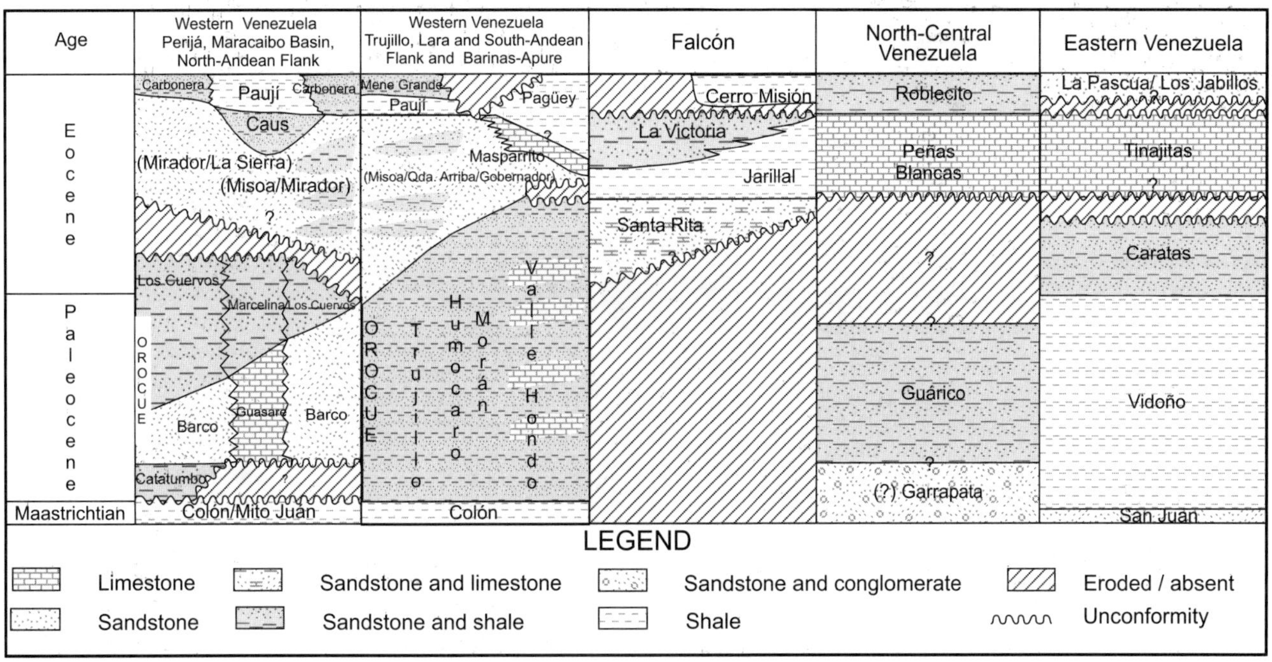

Figure 12. Stratigraphic correlation chart.

Age	Western Venezuela Perijá, Maracaibo Basin, North-Andean Flank	Western Venezuela Trujillo, Lara and South-Andean Flank and Barinas-Apure	Falcón	North-Central Venezuela	Eastern Venezuela
Eocene	Carbonera / Pauji / Carbonera / Caus / (Mirador/La Sierra) / (Misoa/Mirador) / ? / Los Cuervos / Marcelina/Los Cuervos	Mene Grande / Pauji / Masparrito / (Misoa/Qda. Arriba/Gobernador) / ? / Pagüey	Cerro Misión / La Victoria / Jarillal / Santa Rita	Roblecito / Peñas Blancas / ? / Guárico / ?	La Pascua/ Los Jabillos / Tinajitas / ? / Caratas / Vidoño
Paleocene	OROCUE / Barco / Guasare / Barco / Catatumbo / Colón/Mito Juan	OROCUE / Trujillo / Humocaro / Morán / Valle Hondo / Colón			(?) Garrapata
Maastrichtian	Colón/Mito Juan	Colón			San Juan

LEGEND

Limestone	Sandstone and limestone	Sandstone and conglomerate
Sandstone	Sandstone and shale	Shale
Eroded / absent	Unconformity	

Figure 12. Stratigraphic correlation chart for the Paleocene-Eocene of Venezuela. Note that the Colón Formation extends into the Campanian, and the Carbonera, Pauji, La Pascua, Roblecito, and Los Jabillos Formations extend into the Oligocene. The Guárico Formation extends into the Maastrichtian wherever the Garrapata Formation is absent.

front (La Victoria–Santa Rita and Jarillal Formations). This sedimentation was associated with extensional basin subsidence related to strike-slip faulting (Fig. 13). The "pull-apart" character of the Falcón basin has been discussed by Muessig (1984), Macellari (1995), and Audemard (1998).

Paleocene-Eocene of North-Central Venezuela

In north-central Venezuela, Paleocene sedimentary rocks of the Guárico Formation (including the olistoliths of limestone and other older rocks) may be an accretionary prism, formed in front of the Lesser Antilles volcanic arc. They may predate the diachronously migrating foredeeps of the Paleogene and Neogene. Alternatively, the Garrapata-Guárico foredeep might be the result of late Maastrichtian-Paleocene transpressive emplacement of the Villa de Cura belt and the Cordillera de la Costa belt. In the southern part of Guatopo, Guárico State, Beck (1985b) reports a late Maastrichtian–early Paleocene age for the deposition of flysch. In the Altagracia de Orituco–San Francisco de Macaira region, Paleogene taxa very similar to those in the Vidoño Formation of eastern Venezuela are found in hemipelagic shales of the Guárico Formation (Albertos, 1989). The source of these rocks was to the north and not to the south (Guiana Shield) as evidenced by the occurrence of fragments of magmatic arc and recycled orogenic materials (Albertos et al., 1989; Yoris, 1992a) and by paleocurrent indicators (Yoris and Albertos, 1989; Albertos et al., 1989; Yoris, 1992a).

The Paracotos Formation seems to have been deposited in the forearc-foredeep tectonic setting of the Tiará arc (Villa de Cura Group–Tiara–Dos Hermanas Formation; Navarro et al., 1988) and later, probably during Maastrichtian time (Shagam, 1960; Navarro et al., 1988), it was involved in the emplacement of the Villa de Cura complex (Van Berkel, 1988; Van Berkel et al., 1989; Yoris, 1992a). We do not consider it as the lateral equivalent of the Guárico Formation, metamorphosed during the southward emplacement of the Villa de Cura belt, as has been proposed previously (Maresch, 1974; González de Juana et al., 1980).

The Pampatar and Punta Carnero Formations of Margarita Island may be part of the Barbados prism accreted to the northern margin of the South American plate. Their source is the Lesser Antilles volcanic arc, as evidenced by their gravel and sand-sized fragments of volcanic rocks (Casas and Moreno, 1986; Yoris, 1992a; Casas et al., 1995). They were deposited in a forearc-foredeep environment during the middle Eocene. In addition, paleocurrent and petrographic data of the Maastrichtian (?) to Paleocene Garrapata-Guárico Formations (Yoris and Albertos, 1989; Yoris, 1992a) are consistent with the main source being a volcanic arc. This contradicts earlier suggestions by Kasper and Larue (1986) that the source of the sediments was the South American continent. Moreover, the Punta Carnero and Pampatar Formations are younger (middle Eocene [Bartonian]; Muñoz, 1970; Casas and Moreno, 1986) than the Guárico flysch facies, which is of Paleocene age (Albertos, 1989). Middle Eocene formations in north Guárico and Anzoátegui States are the Peñas Blancas and Tinajitas Members

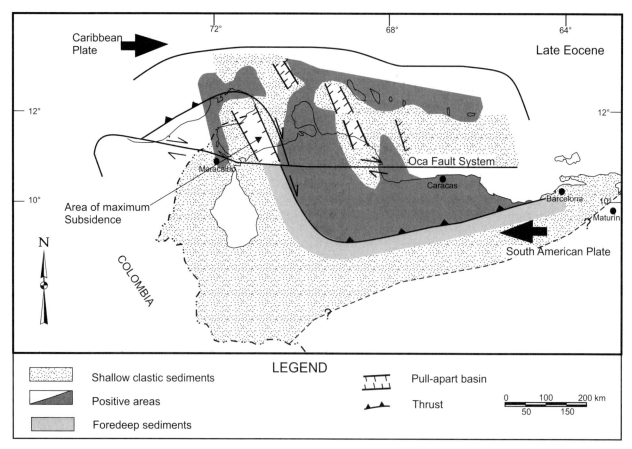

Figure 13. Generation of pull-apart basins in the northwestern Caribbean and South American plate boundary zone. The area of maximum subsidence was located north of Falcón during the late Eocene. Modified from Macellari (1995).

(Caratas Formation) (Galea, 1985). Both have a faunal assemblage of reworked macroforaminiferal taxa similar to the calcarenitic turbidites of the Punta Carnero Formation. The Peñas Blancas and Tinajitas are the age equivalents of the Pampatar and Punta Carnero and not the Guárico Formation, which is much older. Furthermore, the Guárico is petrographically and compositionally quite different from the Pampatar and Punta Carnero Formations. The Guárico Formation is associated with the (Paleocene) south-southeast–directed emplacement of Villa de Cura block onto the northern margin of the South American plate. The main sediment sources are located to the northwest, consisting of the Villa de Cura and Sebastopol complexes with components of the fold and thrust belt, while the Pampatar and Punta Carnero Formations are locally derived forearc sediments from the Lesser Antilles arc, which was transported transpressively to the east along the South American–Caribbean plate boundary (Yoris, 1992a).

Whereas the Caribbean plate moved to the east-southeast with respect to South America, the fold and thrust belt moved to the south-southeast. This resulted in southward migration of the foredeep into which the Guárico Formation was deposited. A new basin was formed during the late Eocene to Oligocene (?), in which the Roblecito Formation was deposited.

The loading of the nappes produced a lithospheric flexure in which sandy-clastics of the diachronous La Pascua Formation accumulated. The source of the Paleocene–middle Eocene formations of northeastern Venezuela (Vidoño and Caratas Formations) seems to have been the Guiana Shield. In Oligocene time, the bulk composition of sandstones in eastern Venezuela shows the influence of a northern source (Guzmán, 1995). This seems to be true for subsurface units in the eastern basins. But in outcrops near the town of Clarines in northern Anzoátegui State, southeast-directed paleocurrent indicators were found in turbiditic sandstones of the Caratas Formation, underlying the middle Eocene Peñas Blancas Formation (type locality). This suggests a probable source of uplifted areas to the northwest (Barbados prism?). We assume that no rotation has occurred during their emplacement to their present location.

Paleocene-Eocene of Eastern Venezuela

Paleocene and early Eocene sedimentation in eastern Venezuela was not influenced by the Caribbean deformation fronts. The Vidoño (hemipelagic marls, siltstones, and clays) and Caratas (quartz-rich sands) Formations accumulated on a continental (passive) margin.

The influence of the oblique collision of the Caribbean plate on the deposition of rocks in eastern Venezuela may have started in the middle Eocene, as recorded by sandy-glauconitic and macroforam-rich carbonates. Deposition of the Peñas Blancas and the Punta Carnero Formations as well as the Tinajitas Member of the Caratas Formation occurred in the foredeep margins (Yoris, 1992a; Casas et al., 1995; Yoris and Ostos, 1997). On Margarita Island, possible remnants of the Barbados accretionary prism are represented by the lithic (volcanic-rich) conglomerates and turbidites of the Pampatar and Punta Carnero Formations. They seem to be separated both in time and space from the Guárico and Roblecito Formations (see "Paleocene-Eocene of North-Central Venezuela"). The relationship between stratigraphic units and deformation fronts is shown in Figures 14 and 15. Figure 12 summarizes the Venezuelan Paleocene-Eocene stratigraphic nomenclature and whether each unit is a seal or reservoir rock. Due to the tectonic influence, it is risky to correlate global eustatic events with events observed in Venezuela. However, it seems that the maximum flooding surface (second order?) between the late Eocene (top of Caratas Formation) and late Maastrichtian (base of the San Juan Formation) occurs somewhere in the upper half of Vidoño Formation. The lack of complete, undeformed sections of this unit makes it difficult to correctly place the maximum flooding surface of second and higher orders. Possibly, the Caratas Formation is a second order highstand deposit with fewer "passive margin" characteristics because of its proximity to the Lesser Antilles subduction zone, which at the time was located north of Anzoátegui State.

The Tinajitas Member near Barcelona (northern Anzoátegui State) is of middle Eocene age (Galea, 1985). It clearly is correlative with the Peñas Blancas Formation of north central Venezuela and seems to occur between two sequence boundaries. The Peñas Blancas unconformably overlies the Guárico Formation turbidites in northern Guárico State, and, near Clarines, it overlies the shale-rich turbiditic beds of Caratas Formation. This facies is completely different from the classical "flysch" of the Guárico Formation. In the Barcelona region (northern Anzoátegui State; Yoris, 1992a), the base of the Tinajitas Member is also unconformable on siliciclastic beds of the Caratas Formation. In north-central Venezuela, the upper contact of the Peñas Blancas Formation is supposed to be unconformable with the deeper facies of the Roblecito Formation, which seems to be a submarine fan complex (Yoris, 1992a). In the Clarines area, distal, shaly facies and the laterally equivalent sandier Los Jabillos Formation are interpreted to be unconformable with the Tinajitas Member and with the top Caratas Formation siliciclastics facies elsewhere in the Serranía del Interior Mountain range. This implies that the top of the Peñas Blancas Formation and the Tinajitas Member of the Caratas Formation should be considered a regional sequence boundary, probably related to tectonic uplift and "in phase" with the middle Eocene, third order, eustatic regressions. This sequence boundary can be correlated with the base of Mirador Formation in western Venezuela (Yoris et al., 1996b).

The contact between the Masparrito and Pagüey Formations in the southern Andean flank is very similar to the contact of the Peñas Blancas and Roblecito Formations. This implies that an important event took place along the entire Venezuela margin between the middle and late Eocene. After a regional lowstand, sea level followed a rapid transgression, triggered by the bending of northern margin of the South American plate. This marine invasion diachronously advanced to the south and southeast. Most probably, the transgression during the deposition of the La Pascua Formation in the southern Guárico subbasin is equivalent to the event that began in the middle and late Eocene in northern Venezuela and in the Andes (Yoris, 1992a; Erlich and Barrett, 1992). The diachronous west-to-east tectonically induced transgressive system tracts of the middle to late Eocene are represented in the north Maracaibo basin by the Pauji Formation, in the south Maracaibo basin by the Mirador and Carbonera Formations, on the south Andean flank by the Pagüey Formation, in north-central Guárico by the lower Roblecito and the La Pascua, and in the northeastern mountain range by the lower Los Jabillos Formation.

Oligocene of Western and North-Central Venezuela

The correlation chart of the important late Eocene to Oligocene units is shown in Figure 16, and the Oligocene sedimentary regional framework for the western and north-central areas of Venezuela is shown in Figure 17. Oligocene sedimentary rocks in the Maracaibo basin are preserved on its flanks. To the west occur sandy clastics of the Carbonera and Ceibote Formations (El Fausto Group), to the south and east, the siliciclastics of the Carbonera and León Formations (Fig. 16), and in the center of the basin, the Icotea Formation.

Originally, the Icotea Formation (Fig. 16) was assigned an Oligocene age. It is preserved in grabens or depressions above the Eocene unconformity (González de Juana et al., 1980; Audemard, 1991; Parnaud et al., 1995a). Later, it was proposed that it contained lower Miocene sedimentary rocks as well (MEM, 1997). Also, sediments of the Miocene Lagunillas Formation are very similar in lithology and age. If we assume that the upper units of the Icotea were deposited in incised valleys on the Eocene discordance (Guzmán, 2000), they must have formed during the subsequent transgression (Emery and Myers, 2001). This transgression is of early Miocene age in the northern part of the Maracaibo basin and corresponds to the Lagunillas Formation. Consequently, the Icotea Formation needs to be redefined and more detailed work needs to be done.

The Falcón basin reached its maximum depth during the late Oligocene (28–23 Ma), associated with crustal thinning related to the emplacement of alkaline basalts (Muessig, 1984). The magmas intruded the turbidite beds of the Pecaya Formation of late Oligocene age (Fig. 16) at presumed paleodepths of 1000–1500 m (MEM, 1997). The Falcón area records a different tectonic setting from that of the Maracaibo, Barinas-Apure, and Eastern basins. Muessig (1984) and Macellari (1995) proposed that the Falcón

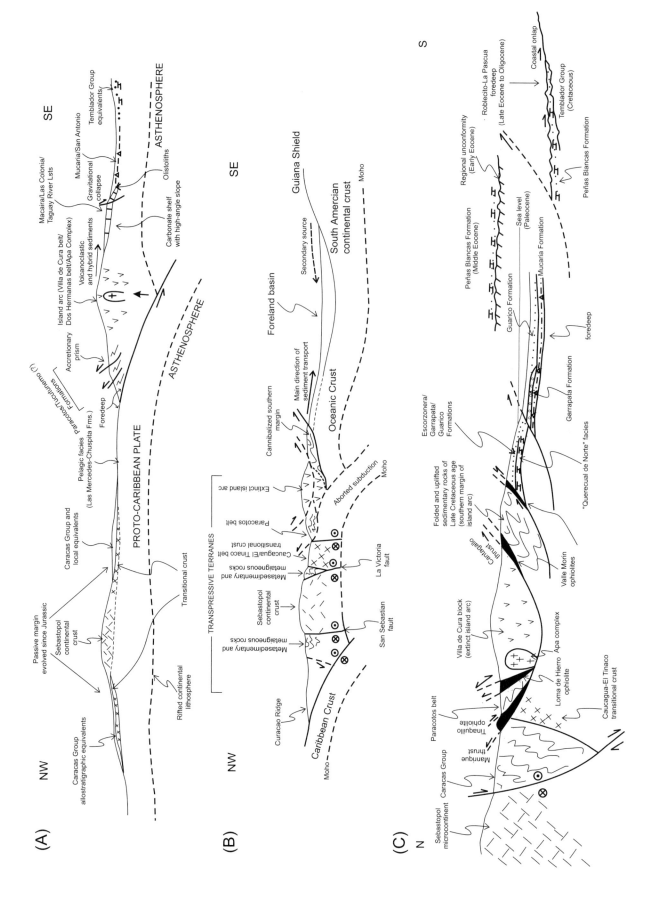

(A)

NW
SE

Caracas Group allostratigraphic equivalents

Passive margin evolved since Jurassic

Sebastopol continental crust

Caracas Group and local equivalents

Transitional crust

Pelagic facies (Las Mercedes-Chuspita Fms.)

Paracotos/Tucutunemo (?) Formations

Foredeep

Accretionary prism

Island arc (Villa de Cura belt/ Dos Hermanas belt/Apa Complex)

Volcanoclastic and hybrid sediments

Carbonate shelf with high-angle slope

Macaira/Las Colonia/ Taguay River Lsts

Mucaria/San Antonio

Gravitational collapse

Olistoliths

Temblador Group equivalents

PROTO-CARIBBEAN PLATE

ASTHENOSPHERE

ASTHENOSPHERE

Rifted continental lithosphere

(B)

NW
SE

Curacao Ridge

Moho

Caribbean Crust

San Sebastian fault

Metasedimentary and metaigneous rocks

Sebastopol continental crust

La Victoria fault

Metasedimentary and metaigneous rocks

Caucagua/El Tinaco belt transitional crust

Paracotos belt

Extinct island arc

Aborted subduction

Moho

Main direction of sediment transport

Cannibalized southern margin

Oceanic Crust

Foreland basin

Secondary source

Guiana Shield

South Amercian continental crust

Moho

TRANSPRESSIVE TERRANES

(C)

N
S

Sebastopol microcontinent

Caracas Group

Paracotos belt

Manrique thrust

Tinaquillo ophiolite

Villa de Cura block (extinct island arc)

Loma de Hierro ophiolite

Apa complex

Caucagua-El Tinaco transitional crust

Folded and uplifted sedimentary rocks of Late Cretaceous age (southern margin of island arc)

Escorzonera/ Garrapata/ Guarico Formations

Cantagallo thrust

Valle Morin ophiolites

"Querecual de Norte" facies

Garrapata Formation

Guarico Formation

Mucaria Formation

foredeep

Peñas Blancas Formation (Middle Eocene)

Regional unconformity (Early Eocene)

Roblecito-La Pascua foredeep (Late Eocene to Oligocene)

Sea level (Paleocene)

Coastal onlap

Temblador Group (Cretaceous)

Peñas Blancas Formation

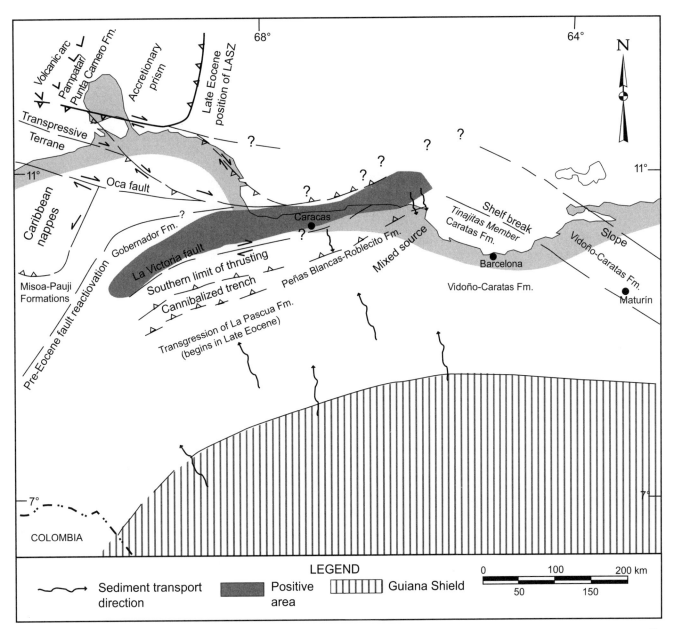

Figure 15. Distribution of deformation and stratigraphic units in central and northeastern Venezuela during the Eocene. LASZ—Lesser Antilles subduction zone.

Figure 14. Model for the tectonic framework of Cretaceous-Paleogene sedimentation around lithospheric blocks accreted to northern South America. Adapted from Navarro (1983), Navarro et al. (1988), Urbani et al. (1989), Yoris (1992a), and Giunta et al. (2002). Present location of tectonic blocks is given in Figure 24. This model is different from the model proposed by Avé Lallemant and Sisson (this volume, Chapter 7); the latter is more consistent with the model of Pindell et al. (this volume). (A) During the Cretaceous, an island arc formed due to subduction of the Proto-Caribbean plate. This happened probably far to the northwest of its present day position. The previously rifted margin that formed in the Jurassic (Sebastopol microcontinent) had symmetric passive margin sedimentation on both flanks. (B) During the Maastrichtian-Paleocene, the transpressive regime of the Caribbean plate collision created several belts in response to right-lateral strike-slip faulting. This occurred after the consumption of the Proto-Caribbean marginal basin. The Sebastopol microcontinent was incorporated in the Cordillera de la Costa and Caucagua–El Tinaco belts. In addition, the relict accretionary prism is now preserved as the Paracotos belt and the extinct island arc is seen in the Villa de Cura belt. The emplacement of the Villa de Cura belt caused a foreland basin in the Maastrichtian. Nomenclature is from Menéndez (1966). (C) During the Paleocene and late Eocene, shortening of the crustal terranes occurred. This caused redeposition of the Guárico foredeep resulting in the Garrapata and Escorzonera Formations. Afterward, in the early to (Luetian) middle Eocene, a regional unconformity predated the middle Eocene (Bartonian) sedimentation of the Peñas Blancas Formation as well as the Roblecito–La Pascua foredeep.

72

M. Ostos, F. Yoris, and H.G. Avé Lallemant

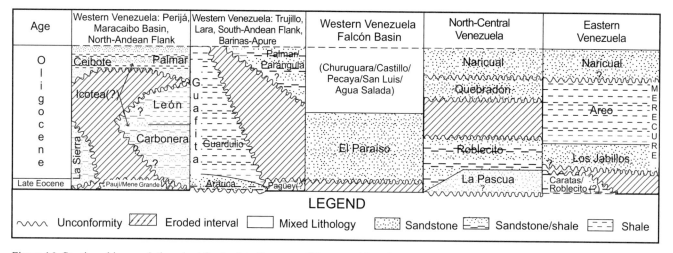

Figure 16. Stratigraphic correlation chart for the late Eocene to Oligocene. Note that the Pauji, Mene Grande, and Pagüey Formations extend into the middle Eocene, whereas the El Fausto Group and the Churuguara, Castillo, Pecaya, San Luis, Agua Salada, and Quebradon Formations extend into the Miocene. The Icotea Formation may be a lateral equivalent of the Carbonera-León and/or Ceibote-Palmar Formations.

basin is an extensional basin associated with major strike-slip faults related to the passage of the Caribbean plate (Fig. 18).

In north-central Venezuela, the Roblecito foredeep migrated to the east and southeast across the La Pascua sandstones. Because of diachrony, the ages of the "Roblecito Formation" of the Guárico mountain front must be greater than those of the "Roblecito Formation" along the Guárico subbasin to the south and southeast. The complete time span could be from late Eocene to Oligocene (Bell, 1968). If the formation of the Roblecito foredeep began in the late Eocene, the oldest beds of the La Pascua Formation have to be of the same age, because a "passive" southern margin of this foredeep is required (Yoris, 1992a). The exposed section of the Roblecito Formation in the Camatagua region (Aragua State) is the deepest facies of this initial sedimentation. The diachronous transgression resulted in younger, shallow facies beds of the La Pascua to the south. In one well in the Guárico subbasin, the facies were dated as early Oligocene by Arnstein et al. (1985). This indicates that the youngest age for the overlying Roblecito Formation in the Guárico subbasin should be late Oligocene. This is best explained by diachrony, because the upper Eocene beds of the Roblecito Formation were folded, uplifted, and cannibalized during the southeast migration of the foredeep in Oligocene times.

Oligocene of Eastern Venezuela

Latest Eocene and Oligocene sedimentation in the eastern Serranía del Interior is represented by the Merecure Group, consisting of the Los Jabillos, Areo, and Naricual Formations (Fig. 16). The Los Jabillos Formation was deposited in diverse, sandy, clastic (transgressive) environments. The Areo Formation consists of fine-grained marine and glauconitic clastic rocks, implying that it represents the maximum transgression of the Oli-

gocene in northeastern Venezuela. The Naricual Formation consists of shallow marine and coastal-fluvial pelitic and sandy clastics (Socas, 1991; Yoris, 1992a; MEM, 1997). At its type section (Naricual Coal Mines, in northern Anzoátegui State), the Naricual Formation overlies the Areo and Los Jabillos Formations discordantly. We established that this discordance can be followed on seismic lines northward to the Clarines region, in Anzoátegui State. The same boundary relation has been cited by Carnevali (1988), Fasola and Paredes de Ramos (1991), and Erlich and Barrett (1992). This sequence boundary correlates with the 30 Ma late Oligocene eustatic fall of the Global Sea Level Curve of Haq et al. (1987). The presence of coal in the Naricual beds points to a relatively extensive and peneplained surface that developed in northeastern Venezuela before the demise of the late Oligocene–early Miocene foredeep. The upper part of Naricual Formation has been interpreted as being transitional to the deeper environments of the Carapita Formation (Yoris, 1992a). This implies that Naricual Formation should be considered as a third order, eustatic and tectonically controlled, transgressive system tract overlying an important regional sequence boundary. Figure 19 shows the relationship among the stratigraphic units and the deformation fronts. The Naricual Formation had two sediment sources (similar to the Quebradón Formation): one was in the north, where these beds bordered the fold and thrust belt, and the other was the Guiana Shield in the south (Yoris, 1992a; Erlich and Barrett, 1992). It is possible that the southernmost beds of the Merecure Formation are part of the transgressive system tract resulting from the initiation of the foreland basin of eastern Venezuela during the early Miocene. They really are lateral equivalents of the Oficina and Carapita Formations and not the Merecure Group of the northeastern mountain range, which is mainly Oligocene in age (lowermost beds of Los Jabillos Formation are supposed to be of late Eocene age; Yoris and Navarro, 1989; Yoris, 1992a).

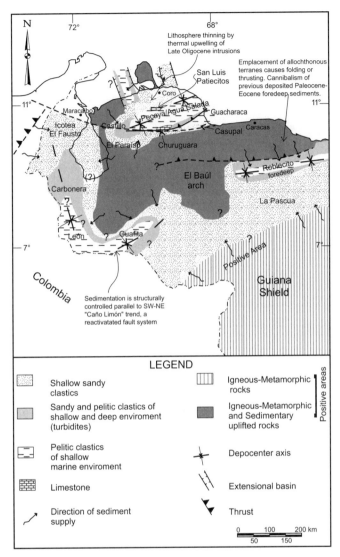

Figure 17. Regional sedimentary framework in western Venezuela (Maracaibo, Falcón, Barinas-Apure, and Guárico basins) during the Oligocene. The major depocenters are located in the Táchira (León Formation), Falcón (Pecaya and Agua Salada Formations) and Guárico (Roblecito Formation). Modified from Yoris and Ostos (1997).

Neogene and Quaternary

The stratigraphic summary of the Neogene and Pleistocene units is shown in Figure 20. The regional sedimentary framework was characterized by important orogenic events that resulted in uplift of the Perijá, the Andes, and the Caribbean Mountains (Fig. 21). The uplift was the result of the collision of the Panama arc with South America in the west and by the continuous oblique collision of the Caribbean plate with South America in eastern Venezuela. During the late Oligocene–early Miocene, the northern part of the Falcón basin, the Maracaibo basin, and the Andean and Caribbean foreland basins were formed. The former two received sediments mainly from the south, from the uplifted terrains of

Caribbean nappes in the states of Lara and Trujillo, and from the uplifted sedimentary terrains to the northwest, such as the Mérida Andes and Sierra de Perijá. The Barinas-Apure basin received sediments mostly from the rising Colombian and Venezuelan Andes in the north. The southern areas of the Eastern Venezuelan Basin received sediments from the north as well (see Fig. 21).

In eastern Venezuela, basin subsidence resulted from the oblique collision. The oldest of the sedimentary pile (in the sub-surface) may be a time surface (sequence boundary) close to the Oligocene-Miocene boundary (25.5 Ma; Di Croce, 1995). In the northern Monagas subbasin, the peak uplift rates of the fold and thrust belt and, thus, the peak subsidence rate of the foredeep, occurred in the middle Miocene. However, the main depocenter moved to the east from Pliocene to Recent times (Jácome et al., 2003). By Pliocene time (Fig. 21), the Cordillera de la Costa belt was juxtaposed to the entire Venezuelan margin. In addition, the Andes and the present-day distribution of the petroleum basins were established (Fig. 22).

In western Venezuela, the erosion of the emergent Andes resulted in the sedimentation of molasse deposits locally as thick as 5 km (Guayabo Group, La Villa, La Puerta, and El Milagro Formations; Fig. 20). In the Perijá Mountains, the El Fausto Group was deposited in Oligocene time (Parnaud et al., 1995a). In the Andes, it is age equivalent to the lower part of the Guayabo Group (MEM, 1997). The oldest apatite fission-track age in the Los Andes is 24 Ma (Shagam et al., 1984) and could be the oldest age of the first beds of the sandy-conglomeratic Palmar and Parángula Formations deposited on both flanks of the rising Venezuelan Andes. The Guafita Formation (Fig. 16; Barinas-Apure basin) is the distal equivalent of the continental environments on the southern flank of the Andes (Ortega et al., 1987). This is consistent with the Oligocene age of the León Formation. The overlying beds in the Chama River section are defined by Arminio and Allen (1990) as the "Caracol Member" of the León Formation. The "Chama formation" (informal name; MEM, 1997) consists of the remaining clastics underlying the Isnotú Formation. These rocks were formerly assigned to the Palmar Formation (Creole Petroleum Corporation, 1953–1962). A late Oligocene age for the oldest, basal beds of Guayabo Group needs to be considered. The La Rosa and Lagunillas Formations were deposited in distal environments with respect to the transitional-continental areas of the El Fausto and Guayabo Groups during early to middle Miocene times (Fig. 20).

The La Rosa Formation has great economic importance. It contains the characteristic "middle shale" interval and has lateral sandy equivalents. They are important reservoirs and have been productive since 1917 (Rivero, 1956; Young et al., 1956). Its thickness is variable (70–1100 m) because the unit was deposited on an irregular fault-controlled erosion surface. Its age is early Miocene (MEM, 1997). It represents a "third order sequence" transgressive system tract (T6 sequence of Parnaud et al., 1995a), and some "incised valley" fills are attributed to this formation (Guzmán, 2000). The "La Rosa Shale" may be the maximum flooding surface during the transgression (Parnaud et al., 1995a; Chedid et al., 1999, 2000).

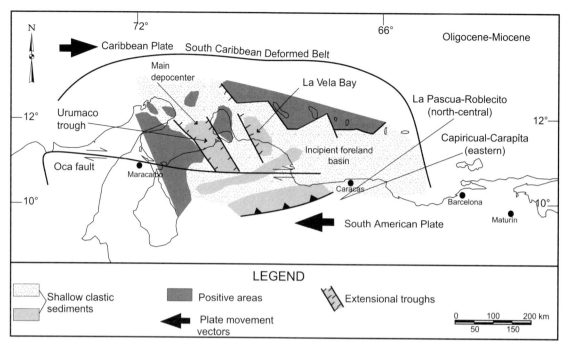

Figure 18. Development of the Falcón pull-apart basin and generation of extensive structural highs northeast of the Maracaibo basin and northern Falcón. Toward the south and east, a foreland basin formed during the late Eocene to Oligocene. This is where the La Pascua–Roblecito Formations were deposited from the early to middle Miocene followed by the Carapita-Capirical Formations.

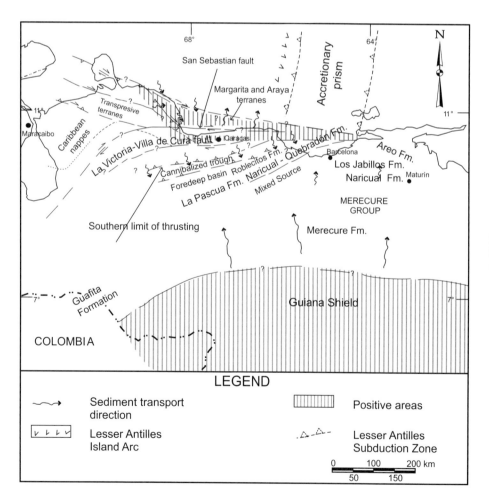

Figure 19. Tectonic framework and sedimentation in central and eastern Venezuela during the Oligocene.

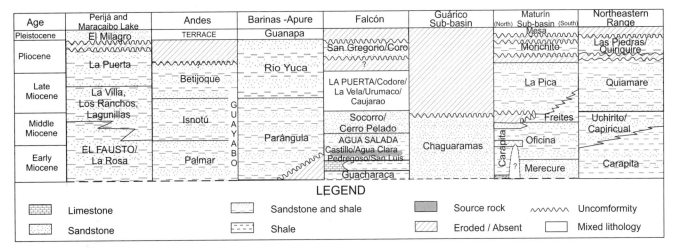

Age	Perijá and Maracaibo Lake	Andes	Barinas -Apure	Falcón	Guárico Sub-basin	Maturín (North) Sub-basin (South)	Northeastern Range
Pleistocene	El Milagro	TERRACE	Guanapa			Mesa	Las Piedras/ Quiriquire
Pliocene	La Puerta		Río Yuca	San Gregorio/Coro ?		Morichito	
Late Miocene	La Villa, Los Ranchos, Lagunillas	Betijoque		LA PUERTA/Codore/ La Vela/Urumaco/ Caujarao		La Pica	Quiamare
Middle Miocene		Isnotú	Parángula	Socorro/ Cerro Pelado	Chaguaramas	Freites / Oficina	Uchirito/ Capiricual
Early Miocene	EL FAUSTO/ La Rosa	Palmar		AGUA SALADA Castillo/Agua Clara Pedregoso/San Luis Guacharaca		Carapita / Merecure ?	Carapita

(column labeled vertically: GUAYABO; MEM)

LEGEND

▦	Limestone	▭	Sandstone and shale	▨	Source rock	∿∿∿ Uncomformity
▧	Sandstone	▭	Shale	▨	Eroded / Absent	☐ Mixed lithology

Figure 20. Stratigraphic correlation chart for the Venezuelan Neogene. Note that El Fausto Group as well as the Palmar, Guacharaca, Chaguaramas, and Merecure Formations extend into the late Oligocene.

The middle to late Miocene Lagunillas Formation is a very important oil reservoir that overlies the La Rosa Formation (Rivero, 1956; González de Juana et al., 1980). It was deposited in a transitional, shallow, coastal to continental environment. In the central parts of the Maracaibo basin, it can be thicker than 1 km. In the Barinas-Apure basin, the Parángula and Río Yuca Formations (continental environment) are age equivalents of the La Rosa and Lagunillas Formations and Guayabo Group (MEM, 1997).

In the Falcón region, two epicontinental environments existed, such as deep-marine turbidites (e.g., Pecaya Formation), shallow clastics (e.g., Cerro Pelado Formation), and carbonates (e.g., San Luis Formation). Sedimentation in the basin ceased in the Pliocene, contemporaneously with the basin inversion (Audemard, 1998). The youngest sediments of the basin are conglomerates and marine clastics of the La Vela Formation and the continental Coro Conglomerate of Pliocene-Pleistocene age (Fig. 20).

In north-central Venezuela, most deposits (upper Quebradón and Quiamare Formations, Fig. 20) are fluvial and continental (Fig. 21). The thickness of these units increases considerably toward the east and south.

In the states of Guárico and western Anzoátegui, south of the Guárico Mountain front, in the subbasins of Guárico and Maturín (including the eastern Serranía del Interior), there are transitional deltaic to shallow-marine environments represented by the Merecure and Oficina Formations (Figs. 20 and 21). These are important petroleum reservoirs (Young et al., 1956; González de Juana et al., 1980).

To the east, in the Maturín subbasin, the depositional environment gradually became deeper, as shown by the Capiricual and Carapita Formations (Figs. 20 and 21). The Chapapotal Member of Carapita Formation is turbiditic and is also of great importance for the petroleum industry as it is a seal as well as a reservoir (CVET, 1970; González de Juana et al., 1980; González and Márquez, 1985; Parnaud et al., 1995b; MEM, 1997). In the Orocual oil field (Monagas State), non-turbiditic lower sands

are also reservoirs (Stifano, 1993; Baquero, 1998). The Carapita Formation is mostly a seal (Yoris and Ostos, 1997). The Capiricual Formation is a shallow, lateral equivalent of the Carapita Formation; however, sudden increases in depth (turbiditic sandstones and dark shales, submarine channels and dark shales) can be seen in its type region. Paleocurrent indicators show sediment transport coming from the south, north, and west. Pebbles and cobbles in the Capiricual conglomerate (northern Anzoátegui) are black chert from the Guayuta Group, indicating that Cretaceous rocks were exposed not only in the north but also in the south (perhaps along a peripheral bulge; Fig. 23). This facies is also seen in the type section of the Carapita Formation (Carapita River, Anzoátegui State), but here it was derived from the north (Yoris, 1992a). The rocks were formed by grain flow (Yoris and Navarro, 1989; Yoris, 1992a). The middle Miocene Chapapotal Member of the Carapita Formation in the north Monagas oil fields has been considered as turbiditic; this formation, as a whole, seems to be a complex of submarine slope and basin fans coming mainly from the north and shallower environments derived from the "passive" south margin of the early–middle Miocene foredeep.

To the south, in the Oficina fields and the Orinoco River, the "heavy oil" belt and younger, diachronous elements of Neogene age are found. They are related to the evolution of the foreland basin (Audemard et al., 1985; Roure et al., 1994). The basal unit, usually discordant over the Upper Cretaceous Temblador Group, is the sandy Merecure Formation (Fig. 22). Overlying are the fluvial-paralic sedimentary rocks and coals of the Oficina Formation. This unit has been subdivided into ~21 members (De Sisto, 1960; González de Juana et al., 1980), each representing a parasequence or a set of parasequences. This complex sequence is the result of the collision of the Caribbean and South American plates, causing local growth faults and changes of eustatic sea level and rates of accommodation. Local climate changes controlled coal accumulations. The coastline during Oficina time

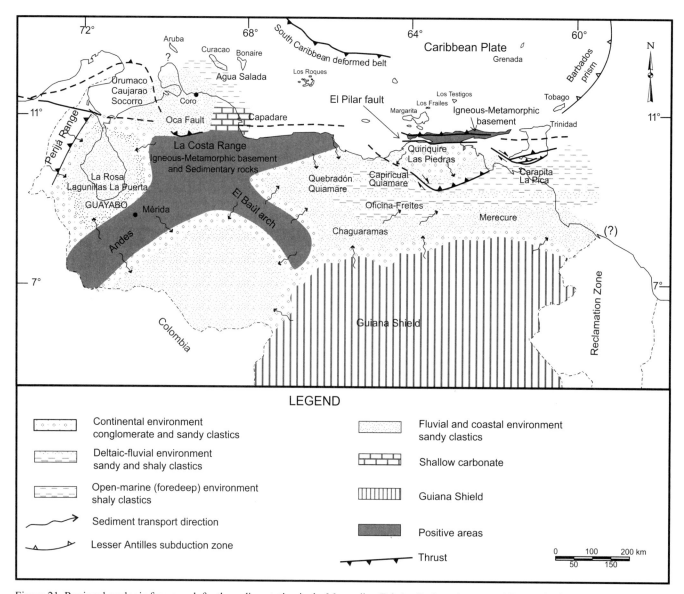

Figure 21. Regional geologic framework for the sedimentation in the Maracaibo, Falcón, Barinas-Apure, and Eastern basins during the Miocene-Pliocene. The greatest accumulations of continental sediments occurred on the flanks of the Andes and Cordillera de la Costa ranges. Some of the most important oil reservoirs of Venezuela formed at this time, such as the La Rosa, Lagunillas, Isnotú (Guayabo Group), Carapita, Oficina, Chaguaramas, and Merecure Formations.

trended from east-west to almost north-south. The width of the channels in the Oficina Member also varied from hundreds of meters to several kilometers like the present-day Orinoco upper delta plain. In Monagas State, the main trend of the channels seems to have been east-west to east-northeast–west-southwest, instead of north-south along the peripheral bulge (Fig. 23) (see also Pindell et al., 1998). The Miocene equivalent of this unit in the Guárico subbasin and Orinoco heavy oil belt is the Chaguaramas Formation. Near San José de Guaribe, in Guárico State, the Chaguaramas has examples of lacustrine environments

To the northeast, the Maturín subbasin is filled with shallower facies sediments of the Uchirito and Quiamare Formations. The Quiamare Formation was deposited in a variety of environments: lagoon, fluvial channels, and alluvial fans (González de Juana et al., 1980; Vivas and Macsotay, 1989). It is several kilometers thick in eastern Anzoátegui. On the southern flank of the basin, the shales of the Freites Formation overlie the Oficina Formation. These shales are overlain by the deltaic cycles of La Pica Formation and the Pliocene molasse of the Morichito, Las Piedras, and Quiriquire Formations. The sedimentary cycle ends with the Pleistocene Mesa Formation.

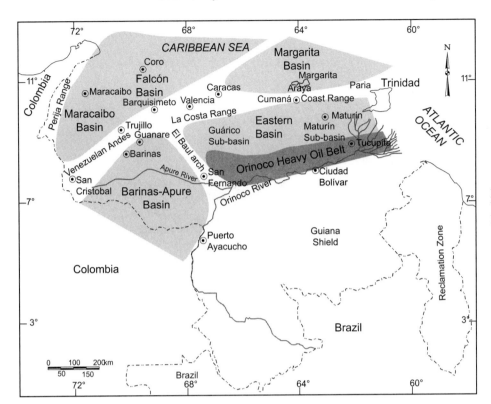

Figure 22. Petroliferous basins of Venezuela. Adapted from Pérez de Mejía et al. (1980).

CENOZOIC ALLOCHTHONS

During the Tertiary, several allochthonous belts were emplaced onto the South American continent. These belts are elongate and trend approximately east-west. They are, from north to south: the South Caribbean deformed belt, Leeward Antilles volcanic arc, Venezuelan platform, and Caribbean Mountains system. Convergence between the Caribbean and South American plates was highly right oblique to the South American continental margin. Thus, southward thrusting was diachronous: in the west, it started in Paleocene time, while thrusting in the east started in Miocene time.

South Caribbean Deformed Belt

The South Caribbean Deformed belt (Case et al., 1984) consists of moderately deformed Cretaceous and Tertiary sedimentary rocks (Fig. 24). The deformation is the result of Tertiary subduction of the Caribbean plate beneath South America. The belt is well established from Colombia in the west to the Los Roques Trough (Fig. 24) in the east (e.g., Mascle et al., 1979; Ladd et al., 1984). East of the Los Roques Trough and north of La Blanquilla Island, seismic reflection lines (Biju-Duval et al., 1982) suggest a similar, but somewhat ill-defined, south-dipping subduction zone.

Leeward Antilles Volcanic Arc

The Leeward Antilles arc crops out from west to east on the Los Monjes Archipelago, on the Dutch Leeward Islands (Aruba, Curaçao, and Bonaire), on the Venezuelan Leeward Antilles (Los Roques Archipelago, La Orchila, La Blanquilla, Los Hermanos Archipelago), and on Margarita, Los Frailes Archipelago, and Los Testigos Archipelago (Figs. 1 and 24). Many of these islands have a basement of volcanic and volcaniclstic rocks, some of which were metamorphosed at low grade and intruded by granitic plutons. Cenozoic rocks consist of detrital rocks and reefal limestone. Numerous K-Ar ages have been determined from the basement; however, some of them show uncertainties, which are intrinsic to the method and due to Ar loss or gain.

Basement Rocks

Basalt, gabbro, and mafic volcaniclastic rocks are generally metamorphosed at low grades. On Aruba (Helmers and Beets, 1977), Bonaire (Beets, 1972; Beets et al., 1984), and Curaçao (Beets, 1977), the rocks are metamorphosed at zeolite to prehnite-pumpellyite facies conditions. On Los Monjes (Bellizzia et al., 1969; Bellizzia, 1972) and Los Roques (Schubert and Motiscka, 1972), greenschist facies conditions were reached. On La Orchila (González de Juana et al., 1980; Schubert and Motiscka, 1972) and Margarita Island (La Rinconada Formation; Maresch, 1975;

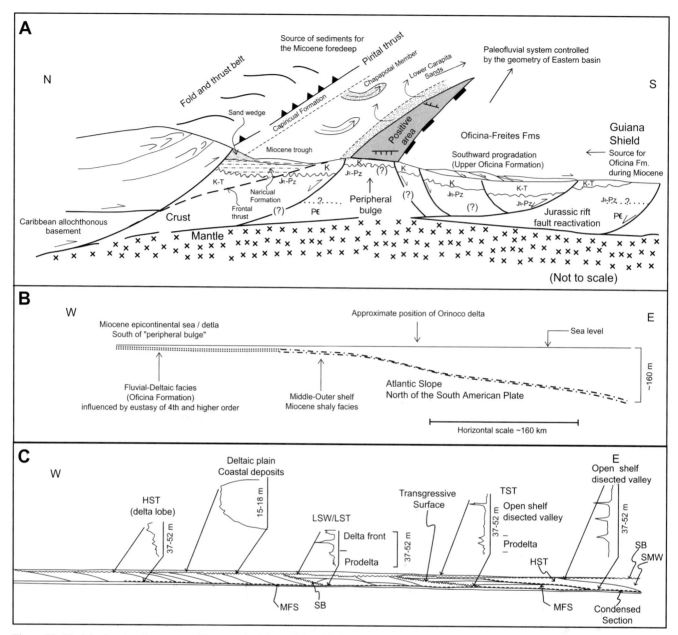

Figure 23. Models showing the topographic control of the peripheral bulge on Miocene sedimentation in northeastern Venezuela. (A) Miocene trough fed from fold and thrust belt in the north and the peripheral bulge in the south. This basin geometry forced drainage to the east with some prograding units coming from the north. (B) Schematic cross section through the Eastern Venezuela Basin during the Miocene south of the peripheral bulge. (C) Schematic cross section for fourth order stratigraphic sequences for the "R" and "S" sands in the Oficina Formation. HST—highstand systems tract; LSW—lowstand wedge; MFS—maximum flooding surface; SB—sequence boundary; SMW—shelf margin wedge; TST—transgressive system tract.

Stöckhert et al., 1995), the metamorphism reached amphibolite facies conditions (with a late overprint of greenschist facies).

On the basis of their geochemical composition, these mafic rocks were thought to have formed at a mid-oceanic ridge (Maresch, 1975; Beets et al., 1984), a primitive island arc (Beets et al., 1984), or an oceanic plateau intruded by island arc magmas (Duncan and Hargraves, 1984; Sinton et al., 1998; White et al., 1999).

Some of these rocks have been dated radiometrically or by fossils in intercalated or overlying sedimentary rocks. These rocks have yielded ages of 116 and 114 Ma on Los Monjes (K-Ar; Santamaría and Schubert, 1974), Turonian on Aruba (ammonites; MacDonald, 1968), Albian on Curaçao (ammonites; Beets, 1977; Beets et al., 1977), Albian to Coniacian on Bonaire (fossils; Beets et al., 1984), and 130–127 Ma on Los Roques (K-Ar; Santamaría and Schubert, 1972).

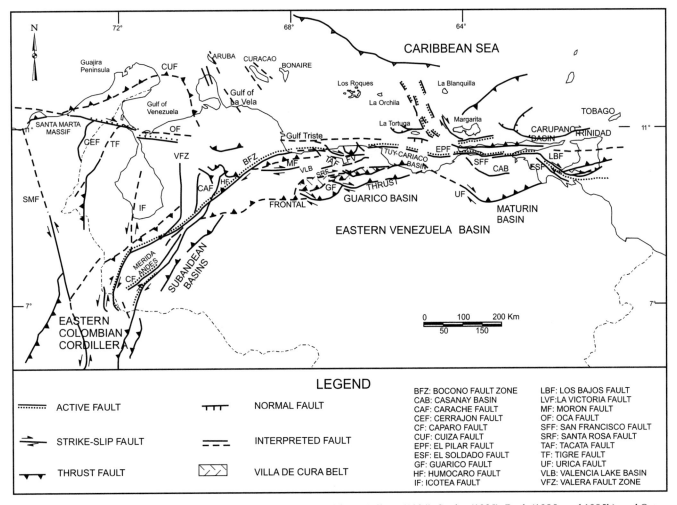

Figure 24. Major tectonic features of northern South America. Adapted from Kellogg (1984), Soulas (1985), Beck (1985a and 1985b), and Ostos (1990).

Younger Igneous Sequence

The basement is intruded by granitic to gabbroic rocks of calcalkaline affinities on Aruba (Helmers and Beets, 1977; Beets et al., 1984), Los Roques (Schubert and Motiscka, 1972), La Orchila (Schubert and Motiscka, 1972), La Blanquilla (Schubert and Motiscka, 1973), Los Hermanos (Schubert and Motiscka, 1973), Margarita (Stöckhert et al., 1995), Los Frailes (Motiscka, 1972; Chevalier, 1987), and Los Testigos (Schubert and Motiscka, 1973). On the last two archipelagos, young basaltic rocks occur as well.

The ages of the younger igneous sequence are 90–67 Ma on Aruba (K-Ar, biotite, hornblende, and Rb-Sr, biotite, and whole rock; Priem et al., 1966; Santamaría and Schubert, 1974; Beets et al., 1984), 66 and 65 Ma on Los Roques (K-Ar, amphibole and biotite; Santamaría and Schubert, 1974), 64–62 Ma on La Blanquilla (K-Ar, biotite and feldspar; Santamaría and Schubert, 1974), 71–67 Ma on Los Hermanos (K-Ar, hornblende; Santa-maría and Schubert, 1974), 115–70 Ma on Margarita Island (K-Ar, amphibole; Santamaría and Schubert, 1974; U-Pb, zircon; Stöckhert et al., 1995),

66 Ma on Los Frailes (K-Ar, whole rock; Santamaría and Schubert, 1974), and 47–44 Ma on Los Testigos (K-Ar, hornblende and feldspar; Santamaría and Schubert, 1974). White et al. (1999) determined Ar-Ar ages in a range between 81.8 and 84.9 Ma for this younger igneous sequence. The ages of these igneous sequences are discussed in Sisson et al. (this volume, Chapter 3).

Although more and better-constrained radiometric age determinations are necessary, there seems to be a possibility that the igneous activity of the Leeward Antilles arc is shut off progressively from Late Cretaceous in the west to middle Eocene in the east.

Venezuelan Platform

Extensive geological and geophysical research has been carried out on the Venezuelan platform by the oil industry. The platform is located between the South Caribbean Deformed belt and the reverse fault north of Los Testigos in the north, and in

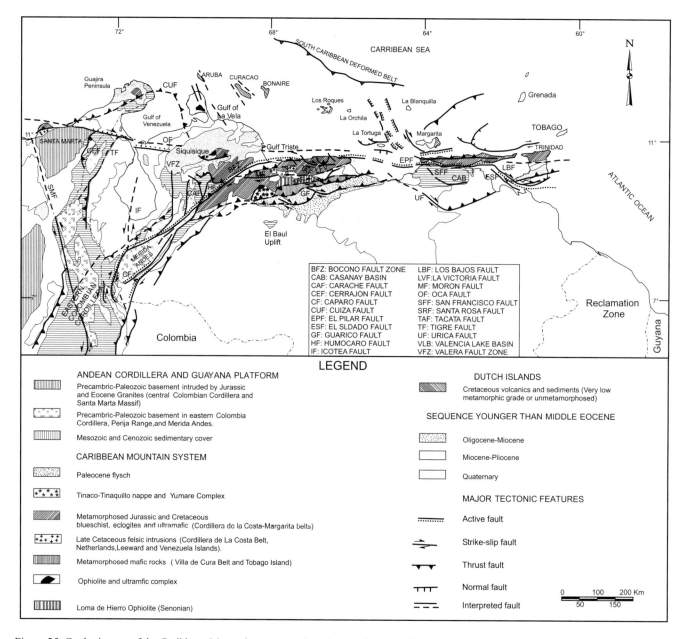

Figure 25. Geologic map of the Caribbean Mountain system and northern Andean Cordillera. Adapted from Stephan et al. (1980), Ostos (1990), and Ysaccis (1997).

the south by the Caribbean Mountain system (Fig. 25). The best-studied areas are Golfo de La Vela, Golfo Triste, Cariaco basin, and Carúpano basin.

Golfo de la Vela

The Golfo de la Vela is located north of the city of Coro and west of the Paraguaná Peninsula (Fig. 25). It is underlain by Oligocene to Miocene and younger sediments (Kiser et al., 1984; Boesi and Goddard, 1991), which unconformably overlie a metasedimentary and meta-igneous basement. Radiometric ages of the basement are 114–83.5 Ma (K-Ar; González de Juana et

al., 1980; Kiser et al., 1984, *in* Ysaccis, 1997; see Sisson et al., this volume, Chapter 3).

Golfo Triste

The Golfo Triste is located north of the city of Valencia and east of the Baragua Range (Fig. 25). It is underlain by a lower Eocene (?) flysch, which is unconformably overlain by upper Oligocene to lower Miocene shallow-water deposits (González de Juana et al., 1980; Kiser et al., 1984, *in* Ysaccis, 1997). Together with the Bonaire and Falcón basins, it belongs to an Oligocene and younger pull-apart basin (Muessig, 1984).

Cariaco Basin

The Cariaco basin is located north and northwest of the city of Barcelona (Fig. 25). The oldest rocks in this basin are Eocene flysch, which lies underneath Oligocene carbonates, and Miocene shallow-water deposits, all overlying unconformably a metamorphic complex and meta-andesites of Late Cretaceous age (K-Ar whole-rock ages of 73.3–65.4 Ma; Talukdar and Bolívar, 1982, *in* Ysaccis, 1997). The Cariaco basin is thought to be a pull-apart basin as well (Schubert, 1982; Ysaccis, 1997).

Carúpano Basin

The Carúpano basin is located north of the Paria Peninsula (Fig. 25). The basement of the Carúpano basin consists of basalts and quartz wackes of low metamorphic grade of the high pressure–low temperature (HP-LT) type (Talukdar, 1983, *in* Ysaccis, 1997). The basalts have both mid-oceanic-ridge basalt (MORB) and primitive island arc (PIA) affinities. Two samples of the PIA basalts were dated by whole rock K-Ar at 102.2 and 87 Ma (Talukdar, 1983, *in* Ysaccis, 1997; see Sisson et al., this volume, Chapter 3). Near the Los Testigos Islands, basaltic andesites occur with an island arc affinity; two samples were dated and yielded ages of 38.6 and 33.5 Ma (whole-rock K-Ar; Talukdar, 1983, *in* Ysaccis, 1997; Sisson et al., this volume, Chapter 3). The metasedimentary rocks have Barremian to Santonian fossils (Castro and Mederos, 1985). Younger sandstones overlie the igneous and metamorphic rocks; they may have been derived from an older eroding orogenic belt (Talukdar, 1983, *in* Ysaccis, 1997). The Carúpano basin was deformed considerably in Neogene time (Ysaccis, 1997).

The southern portion of the Venezuelan platform is characteristically offset by a main east-west strike-slip fault (Figs. 24 and 25). It is relatively young and displaces the previous tectonic contact between the Cordillera de la Costa and the Cordillera de la Costa–Margarita terranes (Stephan, 1982, 1985; Ostos, 1990, 1992). This east-west discontinuity is known as the San Sebastian fault (also sometimes referred to as the Morón fault; Schubert, 1984). It is a major dextral strike-slip fault, which to the east in the area of the Cariaco basin steps to the right and continues as the El Pilar fault. Near the village of El Pilar, the fault steps to the left. Near Puerto Cabello in the west, the San Sebastian fault is thought to merge into the southwest-trending Boconó fault (Figs. 24 and 25). In a recent study, Pérez et al. (2001) stated that the rate of dextral motion on the fault is 20–21 mm/yr with respect to stable South America; vectors of movement just to the north of the El Pilar fault give 20–21 mm/yr.

Central Caribbean Mountain System

Menéndez (1966) divided the Caribbean Mountain system into four belts: (1) the Cordillera de la Costa belt, (2) the Caucagua–El Tinaco belt, (3) the Paracotos belt, and (4) the Villa de Cura belt (Fig. 25).

Cordillera de la Costa Belt

The Cordillera de la Costa belt in north-central Venezuela lies south of the dextral San Sebastian and north of the La Victoria strike-slip faults (Menéndez, 1966). The belt consists of granitic rocks of the Sebastopol complex, metasedimentary rocks of the Caracas Group, the Tacagua Formation, and ultramafic rocks.

The Sebastopol complex consists of granitic gneisses metamorphosed in the greenschist facies. It has been proposed that it is a microcontinental fragment of the South American plate, left behind during rifting (Navarro et al., 1988; Giunta et al., 2002; Fig. 13). It is considered as basement upon which the Caracas Group was deposited (Smith, 1952; Morgan, 1967, 1969; Wehrmann, 1972). A Precambrian age has been proposed (González de Juana et al., 1980; Pimentel et al., 1985), and it has been correlated with the igneous-metamorphic rocks of the Guiana Shield (e.g., Dengo, 1953).

The Caracas Group consists of four lithotectonic slices, which were named from bottom to top: Peña de Mora, Las Brisas, Antímano, and Las Mercedes Formations (Aguerrevere and Zuloaga, 1938; Dengo, 1951; Wehrmann, 1972). Slices of ultramafic rocks occur throughout the belt. The Peña de Mora Formation consists of quartz-feldspar augengneiss, biotite gneiss, mica schists, and minor amphibolite and marble (Wehrmann, 1972; Urbani and Quesada, 1972). Several new U-Pb ages indicate that the gneisses, as well as undeformed granites, crystallized in the Cambrian and Ordovician (Avé Lallement and Sisson, 1993; Sisson et al., this volume, Chapter 3). The Las Brisas Formation consists of mica schists (sometimes with graphite, garnet, or feldspar) and marble (e.g., González de Juana et al., 1980; Bellizzia, 1985). The sedimentary age may be Late Jurassic (Kimmeridgian) based on sparse fossils (Díaz de Gamero, 1969; Urbani, 1969). The Antímano Formation consists of graphitic marble and schist and amphibolite, blueschist, and eclogite (e.g., Dengo, 1951; Wehrmann, 1972; Bellizzia, 1985). The high-pressure metamorphic rocks are overprinted at greenschist-facies conditions (Talukdar and Loureiro, 1982; Avé Lallement and Sisson, 1993; Sisson et al., 1997). Metamorphic cooling ages are Eocene to Oligocene ($^{40}Ar/^{39}Ar$; Sisson et al., this volume, Chapter 3).

The Las Mercedes Formation consists of graphitic, calcareous mica schists and phyllites, and graphitic marbles. Fossils can constrain the age of these rocks only to the Mesozoic (MacKenzie, 1966).

The Caracas Group is defined in north central Venezuela near Caracas. To the east, the metamorphic rocks of the Araya and Paria Peninsulas are correlative with the rocks of the Caracas Group, and to the west, rocks on the Guajira Peninsula are correlative with the Caracas Group rocks.

In the past, it was assumed that the Caracas Group was one stratigraphic package. The occurrence of knockers of eclogite and blueschists and of serpentinites in one of the "formations" clearly indicates that this assumption is wrong. These rocks have undergone such severe deformation (e.g., isoclinal folding) that even within one "formation," a stratigraphy cannot be recognized (e.g., Avé Lallement and Sisson, this volume, Chapter 7). Notwithstanding, the assumption that the metasedimentary rocks of the Caracas Group are mostly Jurassic and Cretaceous and that they were deposited on the passive continental margin of South America may still be correct.

Caucagua–El Tinaco Belt

The Caucagua–El Tinaco belt is bounded to the north by the Victoria fault and to the south by the Santa Rosa fault, as shown in Figure 25 (Menéndez, 1966, Schubert, 1984). The belt consists of the Paleozoic metamorphic Tinaco complex. It is overlain by metasedimentary rocks that contain blocks of limestone with a Permian fossil assemblage similar to the fauna of the Palmarito Formation in the Venezuelan Andes (Benjamini et al., 1987). These rocks are interbedded with alkalic metavolcanics (Tucutunemo Formation; Beck, 1985b) and Cretaceous metasedimentary and metavolcanic rocks (Konigsmark, 1958, 1965; Shagam, 1960; Menéndez, 1965). The Tinaquillo peridotite complex, probably of Jurassic age (Ostos et al., this volume, Chapter 8), occurs along the contact of this belt and the Cordillera de la Costa belt (Ostos et al., this volume, Chapter 8).

The most important constituent of the Tinaco complex is the Aguadita Gneiss, consisting of quartz-feldspar gneisses and amphibolites. Several K-Ar and Rb-Sr ages have been determined (see Sisson et al., this volume, Chapter 3) ranging from 945 to 112.4 Ma. A new amphibole ^{40}Ar/^{39}Ar determination yielded 146 Ma (Sisson et al., this volume, Chapter 3).

The most important formation overlying the Tinaco complex is the Tucutunemo Formation. It consists of a lower volcanic member dated as 73.5 Ma (Beck, 1986), a clastic middle member, and a calcareous upper member. Benjamini et al. (1987) recognized a Permian fauna in the calcareous rocks, but these rocks may have been redeposited.

Paracotos Belt

The Paracotos belt consists entirely of the Paracotos Formation (Shagam, 1960). It consists of coarse- to fine-grained clastic rocks and limestone of possibly Campanian to Maastrichtian age (Shagam, 1960; Beck, 1985a, 1986). At the contact with the Caucagua–El Tinaco, slices of serpentinite and disrupted ophiolite occur (Loma de Hierro peridotite; Beck, 1985b). Serpentinites occur at the contact with the Villa de Cura belt as well. The Paracotos belt is bounded to the south by the Agua Fría thrust fault.

Villa de Cura Belt

The Villa de Cura belt has generally been divided into the Villa Group, the Dos Hermanas Formation, and ultramafic-mafic rocks. Figure 25 shows the location of this belt, which may be a tectonic klippe (e.g., Bellizzia and Dengo, 1990; Pérez de Armas, this volume) thrust southward across the Cordillera de la Costa, Caucagua–El Tinaco, and Paracotos belts or it is an imbricate thrust sheet (Lugo, 2000, personal commun.).

The Villa de Cura Group underwent HP-LT metamorphism. Shagam (1960) divided the group into four formations (from the base to the top: El Caño, El Chino, El Carmen, and Santa Isabel Formations). Navarro (1983) divided it into three units (from base to top: Granofels, Metalava, and Metatuff units). Smith et al. (1999) divided it into four tectonometamorphic slices on the basis of metamorphic grade (from base to top: pumpellyte-actinolite, glaucophane-lawsonite, glaucophane-epidote, and barroisite subbelts). Several serpentinite bodies occur in these belts.

On the basis of chemical compositions, in particular of trace elements, Ostos and Sisson (this volume) and Unger et al. (this volume) decided that the Villa de Cura complex formed in a volcanic island arc (see also Beets et al., 1984). The age of metamorphism is from 96.4 to 79.8 Ma (^{40}Ar/^{39}Ar; Smith et al., 1999; see Sisson et al., this volume, Chapter 3).

The Dos Hermanas Formation consists of volcanic rocks (Piburn, 1968) metamorphosed at prehnite-pumpellyite facies conditions (Navarro, 1983). On the basis of chemical composition, Girard (1981) and Ostos and Sisson (this volume), suggested that these rocks were derived from a volcanic island arc as well. The age of these rocks are not well constrained; Beck (1985a) published two whole-rock K-Ar ages (52.2 and 34.7 Ma) and Loubet et al. (1985) analyzed plagioclase of two samples by K-Ar (119.0 and 112.0 Ma).

Eastern Caribbean Mountain System

Toward the east, near the Cariaco basin, the Caucagua–El Tinaco and the Paracotos belts seem to disappear (Fig. 25). It has been suggested that HP-LT metamorphic rocks in drill cores from the Cariaco basin are related to the Villa de Cura belt (Talukdar and Bolívar, 1982). However, east of the Cariaco basin on Margarita Island and on the Araya and Paria Peninsulas, no such rocks have been recognized.

Margarita Island

Margarita Island is underlain by serpentinites, the La Rinconada amphibolites, and the Juan Griego and Los Robles schists, intruded by several phases of granitic rocks (Taylor, 1960; Maresch, 1971, 1973; Chevalier, 1987) and by basaltic dikes. Maresch (1973) suggested that the Rinconada amphibole gneisses were formed at the mid-oceanic ridge (see also Bocchio et al., 1990) that formed the proto-Caribbean seafloor. These gneisses contain large lenses of eclogite.

The Juan Griego Group consists of quartz-feldspar gneisses, graphitic schists, marbles, and eclogite lenses. It has been correlated with the Las Brisas Formation of the Caracas Group (Chevalier, 1987). The occurrence of eclogite in both the Rinconada and Juan Griego suggests that these assemblages were juxtaposed at ~40–50 km depth in a subduction zone.

Serpentinites occur in large sheets and are clearly in tectonic contact with the schists and gneisses. Originally, these serpentinites were harzburgitic.

The Los Robles Group consists of phyllites, marbles, schists, quartzites, and metaconglomerate. Fossils indicate a Cenomanian age for these rocks (González de Juana et al., 1980). The rocks were metamorphosed in the greenschist facies; no high-pressure minerals have been identified.

Several varieties of granites occur, some of which were deformed at high-pressure conditions. Some may have been oceanic plagiogranites; others are clearly related to the Leeward Antilles island arcs.

Radiometric Ages

U-Pb dating suggests that the protolith age of the Juan Griego gneisses is Paleozoic (ca. 315 Ma; Stöckhert et al., 1995). Pretectonic granites have U-Pb ages of 114 Ma. A posttectonic granite has an 86 Ma age (Stöckhert et al., 1995). Several new $^{40}Ar/^{39}Ar$ ages for amphiboles and white mica indicate that a greenschist facies overprint occurred between 90 and 80 Ma (Stöckhert et al., 1995; Sisson et al., this volume, Chapter 3; $^{40}Ar/^{39}Ar$ amphibole and white mica cooling ages range to ca. 50 Ma). Posttectonic basalt dikes dated by the $^{40}Ar/^{39}Ar$ method are 52–47 Ma (Stöckhert et al., 1995).

Araya and Paria Peninsulas

Schubert (1971, 1972), González de Juana et al. (1972), Seijas (1972), and Vierbuchen (1984) mapped the area north of the El Pilar fault. It is underlain by metamorphic rocks divided in four formations: Manicuare, Laguna Chica (or El Copey; Chevalier, 1987), Carúpano, and Tunapui Formations. Each formation is a lithotectonic unit separated by thrust faults (Schubert, 1972; Beltrán and Giraldo, 1989; Avé Lallemant, 1991).

The Manicuare Formation is the highest structural panel and consists of mica schists with kyanite and staurolite. White mica was dated at 84.5 Ma ($^{40}Ar/^{39}Ar$; Avé Lallemant, 1997).

The Laguna Chica Formation underlies the Manicuare Formation. It consists of low-grade schists, quartzites, and serpentinites.

The Carúpano Formation consists of graphitic, calcareous phyllites and schists and graphitic marbles. Vierbuchen (1984) correlated it with the Albian-Aptian Tinapui Formation.

The Tinapui Formation consists of phyllites, quartzites, and conglomerates of very low metamorphic grade. Albian and Aptian ammonites were found in this lowermost unit (Vierbuchen, 1984).

These formations are similar to and may thus be correlated with the Caracas Group rocks. However, no eclogites or blueschists were recognized in the Araya Peninsula, although the presence of kyanite and staurolite suggests that the Manicuare rocks were deeply buried (pressures were at least 0.5 GPa; Spear, 1993).

Western Caribbean Mountain System

In several areas west of the Boconó Fault (Fig. 24), rock assemblages have been mapped that may be related to the Caribbean Mountain system of north central Venezuela. These areas are near Siquisique and on the Guajira and Paraguaná Peninsulas (Figs. 24 and 25).

Siquisique

Gabbros, pillow lavas, serpentinites, cherts, limestones, and shales, intruded by basalt dikes, are exposed near the village of Siquisique, as shown on Figure 25 (Stephan et al., 1980; Bartok et al., 1985). This assemblage has been interpreted as a dismembered ophiolite. An ammonite fauna in the shales is identified as Jurassic in age (Bajocian to early Bathonian; Bartok et al., 1985). The Siquisique ophiolite may be part of the proto-Caribbean lithosphere formed during Jurassic rifting of the North and South American plates. It was thrust southward in Paleogene time when the plates converged again (Stephan et al., 1980).

Paraguaná Peninsula

The Paraguaná Peninsula is underlain by a Paleozoic-Mesozoic igneous-metamorphic complex, which has been correlated with the Cordillera de la Costa belt in north-central Venezuela (González de Juana et al., 1980; Stephan, 1985). Mafic and ultramafic rocks occur here too. The oldest rocks are granites, dated at 265 and 262 Ma (U-Pb titanite; Martín, 1968). Overlying them nonconformably are graphitic schists and phyllites, sandstone, chert, and limestone metamorphosed at greenschist facies conditions. Ammonites indicate that the sedimentary rocks are of Jurassic age (MacDonald, 1968).

The mafic-ultramafic rocks occur in a zoned complex, as intrusive gabbros, and as volcanic rocks. Whole rock K-Ar ages are 129–118 Ma.

La Guajira Peninsula

The peninsula is underlain by three lithotectonic units. The oldest consists of Precambrian and lower Paleozoic metamorphic rocks. The second association consists of schists, which Bellizzia (1985) correlated with the Caracas Group in north-central Venezuela. High-grade metamorphic rocks (schists and gneisses with garnet, biotite, and hornblende) were correlated with the Caucagua–El Tinaco belt (Bellizzia, 1985).

SUMMARY AND CONCLUSIONS

During the Paleozoic, the northern margin of South America experienced at least two contractional, accretionary events. These may be equivalent to the Taconic and Alleghenian orogenic phases in eastern North America. However, little is known about them, as most Paleozoic structures were destroyed during the Cretaceous-Cenozoic orogenic event.

From Early Jurassic to mid-Cretaceous time, North and South America drifted apart. Jurassic red beds (volcanic and volcaniclastic rocks) were deposited in NE-trending grabens perpendicular to the divergence vector. Northern South America became a passive, Atlantic-type margin upon which thick Cretaceous sedimentary sequences were deposited.

The Cretaceous-Cenozoic orogenic belt of northern South America appears, upon casual observation, to be a classical fold and thrust belt with a non-metamorphic foreland belt and a high-grade metamorphic hinterland intruded by granitic plutons. However, the foreland fold and thrust belt formed diachronously from latest Cretaceous time in the west to the present in the east, whereas the metamorphism took place from mid to Late Cretaceous time. Furthermore, the granitic "plutons" in the orogen are of Cambro-Ordovician age. Thus, the metamorphic belts are highly allochthonous. Tectonic transport directions were variable.

The Cretaceous-Cenozoic orogenic belt was formed as the result of strongly right-oblique collision of the Caribbean plate and the Leeward Antilles volcanic arc with South America. The east-southeast–trending convergence rate vector was partitioned into a south- to south-southeast–trending component that resulted in the fold and thrust belt, and an east-west component expressed by displacements along extensive right-lateral strike-slip faults.

Two types of sedimentary basins formed during the Cenozoic transpression in the plate boundary zone: foreland basins south of the thrust front and pull-apart basins in the north related to the extensive east-west–trending strike-slip faults. Knowledge of these two basin types and of the Cretaceous passive-margin basins has increased greatly, mainly because of their rich hydrocarbon occurrences.

ACKNOWLEDGMENTS

We are very grateful for the help from the staff of Litos, Inc. We thank Jinny Sisson, Bob Erlich, and Keith James for their thorough reviews.

REFERENCES CITED

Aguerrevere, S.E., and Zuloaga, G., 1938, Nomenclatura de las formaciones de la parte central de la Cordillera de la Costa: Caracas, Boletín de Geología y Minas, v. 2, no. 2–4, p. 281–284.

Albertos, M.A., 1989, Estudio geológico de las secciones: Altagracia de Orituco-Agua Blanca y Gamelotal–San Francisco de Macaira (Estados Guárico y Miranda): Análisis petrográfico y estadístico de la Formación Guárico [Tesis de Grado]: Caracas, Universidad Central de Venezuela, 274 p.

Albertos, M.A., Yoris, F.G., and Urbani, F., 1989, Estudio geológico y análisis petrográfico-estadístico de la Formación Guárico y sus equivalentes en las secciones Altagracia de Orituco–Agua Blanca y Gamelotal–San Francisco de Macaira (Estados Guárico y Miranda), in Bellizzia, N.P., González, L., and Ríos, J.H., Memoria, VII Congreso Geológico Venezolano: Caracas, Sociedad Venezolana de Geólogos, v. 1, p. 289–314.

Arminio, J., and Allen, G., 1990, Estratigrafía litológica y secuencial de la sección Terciaria de Río Chama en el flanco norte de los Andes centrales, Venezuela, in Memoria, Congreso Venezolano de Geofísica: Caracas, Sociedad Venezolana de Geofísicos, v. 5, p. 244–251.

Arnstein, R., Cabrera, E., Russomanno, F., and Sánchez, H., 1985, Revisión estratigráfica de la Cuenca de Venezuela Oriental, in Espejo, A., Ríos, J.H., and Bellizzia, N.P., eds., Memoria, VI Congreso Geológico Venezolano: Caracas, Sociedad Venezolana de Geólogos, v. 1, p. 41–69.

Audemard, F.A., 1998, Basin tertiaire de Falcón, Venezuela Nord-Occidental: Synthèse stratigraphique et inversion tectonique Mio-Quaternaire: Port of Spain (Trinidad), in Transactions, XIV Caribbean Geological Conference: v. 2, p. 570–583.

Audemard, F.E., 1991, Tectonics of western Venezuela [Ph.D. Thesis]: Houston, Rice University, 245 p.

Audemard, F.E., Azpiritxaga, I., Baumann, P., Isea, A., and Latreille, M., 1985, Marco geológico del terciario en la faja petrolífera del Orinoco de Venezuela, in Espejo, A., Ríos, J.H., and Bellizzia, N.P., eds, Memoria, VI Congreso Geológico Venezolano: Caracas, Sociedad Venezolana de Geólogos, v. 1, p. 70–108.

Avé Lallemant, H.G., 1991, The Caribbean–South America plate boundary, Araya Peninsula, Eastern Venezuela, in Larue, D.K., and Draper, G., eds.: Transactions of the 12th Caribbean Geological Conference, St. Croix, U.S. Virgin Islands: Miami Geological Society, p. 461–471.

Avé Lallemant, H.G., 1997, Transpression, displacement partitioning, and exhumation in the eastern Caribbean–South America plate boundary zone: Tectonics, v. 16, p. 272–289, doi: 10.1029/96TC03725.

Avé Lallemant, H.G., and Guth, L.R., 1990, Role of extensional tectonics in exhumation of eclogites and blueschists in an oblique subduction setting: Northeastern Venezuela: Geology, v. 18, p. 950–953, doi: 10.1130/0091-7613(1990)018<0950:ROETIE>2.3.CO;2.

Avé Lallemant, H.G., and Sisson, V.B., 1993, Caribbean–South America plate interactions: Constraints from the Cordillera de la Costa belt, Venezuela, in Pindell, J.L., and Perkins, B.F, eds., Mesozoic and early Cenozoic development of the Gulf of Mexico and Caribbean region—A context for hydrocarbon exploration, Proceedings, Gulf Coast Section, SEPM Foundation 13th Annual Research Conference: Houston, Texas, Society for Sedimentary Geology (SEPM) Foundation, p. 211–219.

Baquero, M., 1998, Caracterización estática y dinámica de las areniscas basales de la Formación Carapita, Campo Orocual, Estado Monagas: Caracas, Departamento de Geología, Facultad de Ingeniería, Universidad Central de Venezuela, v. 2, 242 p.

Bartok, P., 1993, Pre-breakup geology of the Gulf of Mexico–Caribbean: Its relation to Triassic and Jurassic rift systems of the region: Tectonics, v. 12, p. 441–459.

Bartok, P.E., Renz, O., and Westermann, G.E.G., 1985, The Siquisique Ophiolite, Northern Lara State, Venezuela: A discussion on their Middle Jurassic ammonites and tectonic implications: Geological Society of America Bulletin, v. 96, p. 1050–1055, doi: 10.1130/0016-7606(1985)96<1050:TSONLS>2.0.CO;2.

Beck, C., 1985a, Caribbean colliding, Andean drifting, and the Mesozoic-Cenozoic evolution of the Caribbean, in Espejo, A., Ríos, J.H., Bellizzia, N.P., and de Pardo, A.S., eds., Memoria, VI Congreso Geológico Venezolano: Caracas, Sociedad Venezolana de Geólogos, v. X, p. 6575–6614.

Beck, C., 1985b, La Chaîne Caraibe au méridien de Caracas: geologie, tectogenèse, place dans l'evolution geodynamique Mesozoique-Cenozoique des Caraibes Meridionales [Ph.D. Thesis]: Lille, France, Université de Sciences et Techniques de Lille, 2 volumes, 462 p.

Beck, C., 1986, Geologie de la Chaîne Caraibe au meridien de Caracas, Venezuela: Société Géologique du Nord Publication 14, 462 p.

Beck, C., and Furrer, M., 1977, Sobre la existencia de sedimentos marinos no metamorfizados del Neocomiense en el noreste del Estado Guárico, Venezuela septentrional, in Espejo, A., Zozaya, D., Key, C., and Vasquez, E., eds., Memoria, V Congreso Geológico Venezolano: Caracas, Sociedad Venezolana de Geólogos, v. I, p. 135–147.

Beets, D.J., 1972, Lithology and stratigraphy of the Cretaceous and Danian successions of Curaçao: Publicatie van de Natuurwetenschappelijke Studiekring Nederlandsche Antillen, v. 70, p. 135.

Beets, D.J., 1977, Cretaceous and early Tertiary of Curaçao, Guide to field excursions, in Transactions, 8th Caribbean Geological Conference: Amsterdam, Gemeentelijke Universiteit Amsterdam (GUA) Papers of Geology, v. 10, p. 7–17.

Beets, D.J., Klaver, G.T., and Mac Gillavry, H.J., 1977, Geology of the Cretaceous and early Tertiary of Bonaire, Guide to the field excursions, in Transactions, 8th Caribbean Geological Conference: Amsterdam, Gemeentelijke Universiteit Amsterdam (GUA) Papers of Geology, v. 10, p. 18–28.

Beets, D.J., Maresch, W., Klaver, G.T., Mottana, A., Bocchio, R., Beunk, F., and Monen, H., 1984, Magmatic rocks series and high-pressure metamorphism and constraints on the tectonic history of the Southern Caribbean, in Bonini, W.E., Hargraves, R.B., and Shagam, R., eds., The Caribbean–South American plate boundary and regional tectonics: Geological Society of America Memoir 162, p. 95–130.

Beltrán, C., and Giraldo, C., 1989, Aspectos neotectónicos de la región nororiental de Venezuela, in Bellizzia, N.P., González, L., and Ríos, J.H., eds., Memoria, VII Congreso Geológico Venezolano: Caracas, Sociedad Venezolana de Geólogos, v. 3, p. 999–1022.

Bell, J.S., 1968, Geología del área de Camatagua, Estado Aragua, Venezuela: Caracas, Boletín de Geología, v. 9, no. 18, p. 291–440.

Bell, J.S., 1971, Tectonic evolution of the central part of the Venezuelan Coast Range, *in* Donnelly, T.W., ed., Caribbean geophysical, tectonic, and petrologic studies: Geological Society of America Memoir 130, p. 107–118.

Bellizzia, A., 1972, Sistema montañoso del Caribe, borde sur de la placa Caribe: Es una cordillera alóctona?, *in* Petzall, C., ed., Memoria, VI Conferencia Geológica del Caribe: Caracas, Impreso por Cromotip, p. 247–258.

Bellizzia, A., 1986, Sistema montañoso del Caribe—una cordillera alóctona en la parte norte de América del Sur, *in* Bellizzia, N.P., and Iturralde, J.M., eds., Memoria, VI Congreso Geológico Venezolano: Caracas, Sociedad Venezolana de Geólogos, v. X, p. 6657–6836.

Bellizzia, A., and Dengo, G., 1990, The Caribbean Mountain system, northern South America; A summary, *in* Dengo, G., and Case, J. E., eds., The Caribbean region: Geological Society of America, The Geology of North America, v. H, p. 167–175.

Bellizzia, A., Carmona, C., and Graterol, M., 1969, Reconocimiento geológico de las Islas Los Monjes del Sur; Archipiélago de Los Monjes, Venezuela: Caracas, Boletín de Geología, v. 10, no. 20, p. 225–234.

Benjamini, C., Shagam, R., and Menendez, A., 1987, (Late?) Paleozoic age for the "Cretaceous" Tucutunemo Formation, northern Venezuela: Stratigraphy and tectonic implications: Geology, v. 15, p. 922–926, doi: 10.1130/0091-7613(1987)15<922:LPAFTC>2.0.CO;2.

Biju-Duval, B., Mascle, A., Rosales, H., and Young, G., 1982, Episutural Oligo-Miocene basins along the North Venezuelan Margin, *in* Watkins, J.G., and Drake, C.I., eds., Studies in continental margin geology: American Association of Petroleum Geologists Memoir 34, p. 347–358.

Bocchio, R., De Capitani, L., Liborio, G., Maresh, W.V., and Mottana, A., 1990, The eclogite-bearing series of Isla de Margarita, Venezuela: Geochemistry of metabasic lithologies in the La Rinconada and Juan Griego Groups: Lithos, v. 25, p. 55–69, doi: 10.1016/0024-4937(90)90006-M.

Boesi, T., and Goddard, D., 1991, A new geological model related to the distribution of hydrocarbon source rocks in the Falcón basin, northwestern Venezuela, *in* Biddle, K.T., ed., Active margin basins: American Association of Petroleum Geologists Memoir 52, p. 303–319.

Bouma, A.H., 1962, Sedimentology of some flysch deposits: A graphic approach to facies interpretation: Amsterdam, Elsevier, 168 p.

Bowen, J.M., 1972, Estratigrafía del precretácico en la parte norte de la Sierra de Perijá, *in* Petzall, C., Bellizzia, A., and Bellizzia, C.M., eds., Memoria, IV Congreso Geológico Venezolano: Caracas, Boletín de Geología, Publicación Especial Geológica, v. 5, p. 729–761.

Briceño, H., and Callejón, A., 2000, Chemostratigraphic correlation of the source rock in the La Luna K-T(!) petroleum system in southeastern Venezuela, *in* Paleogeography and hydrocarbon potential of the La Luna Formation and Cretaceous anoxic systems: Memoir, Society of Economic Paleontologists and Mineralogists Research Conference, p. 34–41.

Briceño, H., Callejón, A., and Lander, R., 1996a, Caracterización de quimiofacies en rocas Cretácicas del área sur del Estado Táchira, Venezuela Occidental, *in* Memoria, V Congreso de Geoquímica Orgánica, Cancún, México (abs.): Caracas, Asociación Latinoamericana de Geoquímica Orgánica (ALAGO), p. 153.

Briceño, H., Callejón, A., Lander, R., Galea, F., Ostos, M., and Yoris, F., 1996b, Chemostratigraphy: Applications in the Tachira Depression, Tachira State, Venezuela: AAPG Bulletin, v. 80, p. 1276.

Brink, G., Keenan, H., and Brown, L., 1993, Deposition of fourth-order, postrift sequences and sequence sets, Lower Cretaceous (lower Valanginian to lower Aptian), Pletmos basin, southern offshore, South Africa, *in* Weimer, P., and Posamentier, H., eds., Siliciclastic sequence stratigraphy: Recent developments and applications: American Association of Petroleum Geologists Memoir 58, p. 43–70.

Brondijk, J.F., 1967, Contribuciones de la Asociación Venezolana de Geología, Minerolgía y Petrología (AVGMP), Maracaibo Basin Eocene Nomenclature Committee III, The Misoa and Trujillo Formations: Caracas, AVGMP Boletín Informativa, v. 1, no. 1, p. 1–19.

Burke, K., Cooper, C., Dewey, J.F., Mann, P., and Pindell, J.L., 1984, Caribbean tectonics and relative plate motions, *in* Bonini, W.E., Hargraves, R.B., and Shagam, R., eds., The Caribbean–South American plate boundary and regional tectonics: Geological Society of America Memoir 162, p. 31–63.

Burkley, L.A., 1976, Geochronology of the central Venezuelan Andes [Ph.D. Thesis]: Cleveland, Ohio, Case Western University, 150 p.

Cabarcas, C., 2001, Integración del modelo exploratorio del convenio Sanvi-Güere a la interpretación VIPA ["Visión País"] realizada al oeste de la subcuenca de Maturín [Estado Monagas] [Tesis de Grado]: Caracas, Universidad Simón Bolívar, 80 p.

Carnevali, J., 1988, Venezuela nor-oriental: Exploración del frente de montañas, *in* Bellizzia, A., Leslie, A., and Bass, I., eds., Memoria, III Simposio Bolivariano: Caracas, Boletín de la Sociedad Venezolana de Geólogos, v. 1, p. 69–89.

Casas, J., and Moreno, J., 1986, Estudio petrográfico y estadístico de la secuencia flysch Eocena de la isla de Margarita [Trabajo Especial de Grado]: Caracas, Universidad Central de Venezuela, 177 p.

Casas, J., Moreno, J., and Yoris, F.G., 1995, Análisis tectono-sedimentario de la Formación Pampatar (Eoceno Medio), Isla de Margarita (Venezuela): Buenos Aires, Asociación Paleontología de Argentina, Publicación Especial 3, Paleogeno de América del Sur, p. 27–33.

Case, J.E., Barnes, J., Paris, G., Gonzalez, H., and Vina, A., 1973, Trans-Andean geophysical profile, southern Colombia: Geological Society of America Bulletin, v. 84, no. 9, p. 2895–2903, doi: 10.1130/0016-7606(1973)84<2895:TGPSC>2.0.CO;2.

Case, J.E., Holcombe, T.L., and Martin, R.G., 1984, Map of geologic provinces in the Caribbean region, *in* Bonini, W.E., Hargraves, R.B., and Shagam, R., eds., The Caribbean–South American plate boundary and regional tectonics: Geological Society of America Memoir 162, p. 1–30.

Castro, M., and Mederos, A., 1985, Litoestratigrafía de la Cuenca de Carúpano, *in* Espejo, A., Ríos, J.H., and Bellizzia, N.P., eds., Memoria, VI Congreso Geológico Venezolano: Caracas, Sociedad Venezolana de Geólogos, v. 1, p. 201–225.

Chedid, R., Abreu, A., and Yoris, F., 1999, Increasing oil production in a mature oil field by using a model within a multidisciplinary concept in the Bolivar Coastal Field, Venezuela: Alberta, Canadian Society of Petroleum Geologists and Petroleum Society Joint Convention, 1999, June 14–18, CD Memoir.

Chedid, R., Abreu, A., and Yoris, F., 2000, Detecting non drained sand bodies in a mature oil field, Tia Juana, Zulia State, Venezuela: Calgary, XVI World Petroleum Congress, June 11–15, CD Memoir.

Chevalier, Y., 1987, Les zones internes de la Chaîne Sud-Caraibe sur le transect Île de Margarita–Péninsula d'Araya (Venezuela) [Thèse de Doctorat]: Brest, France, L'Université de Bretagne Occidentale, 464 p.

Cooper, M.A., Addison, F.T., Alvarez, R., Hayward, A.B., Howe, S., Pulhman, A.J., and Taborda, A., 1995, Basin development and tectonic history of the Llanos basin, Eastern Cordillera, and Middle Magdalena Valley, Colombia: AAPG Bulletin, v. 79, p. 1421–1443.

Creole Petroleum Corporation, 1953–1962, Mapas de Geología de Superficie: Hoja F3 de Venezuela Occidental: Caracas, Ministerio de Energía y Minas.

CVET (Comisión Venezolana de Estratigrafía y Terminología), 1970, Léxico estratigráfico de Venezuela: Caracas, Boletín de Geología, Publicación Especial, v. 4, 756 p.

D'Aubeterre, M.G., 2002, Integración del modelo exploratorio del convenio Guárico Oriental a la interpretación VIPA ["Visión País"] realizada al este de la subcuenca de Guárico [Tésis de grado]: Caracas, Universidad Simón Bolívar, 104 p.

De Sisto, J., 1960, Correlation of the Santa Ines Group in northeastern Anzoátegui: Caracas, Asociación Venezolana de Geología, Minas y Petróleo; Boletín Informativo, v. 3, no. 5, p. 138–143 and p. 144–146.

Dengo, C., and Covey, M.C., 1993, Structure of the eastern Cordillera of Colombia: Implications for traps, styles, and regional tectonics: AAPG Bulletin, v. 77, p. 1315–1337.

Dengo, G., 1951, Geología de la región de Caracas: Caracas, Boletín de Geología, v. 1, no. 1, p. 39–115.

Dengo, G., 1953, Geology of the Caracas region: Geological Society of America Bulletin, v. 64, p. 7–40.

Díaz de Gamero, M.L., 1969, Identificación de los pelecípodos de la Formación Las Brisas: Caracas, Asociación Venezolana de Geología, Minería y Petróleo, Boletín Informativo, v. 13, no. 2, p. 455–464.

Di Croce, J., 1995, Eastern Venezuela Basin: Sequence stratigraphy and structural evolution [Ph.D. Thesis]: Houston, Rice University, 225 p.

Dougan, T.W., 1972, Origen y metamorfismo de los gneises de Imataca y Los Indios, rocas precámbricas de la región de Los Indios–El Pilar, Estado Bolívar, Venezuela, *in* Petzall, C., Bellizzia, A., and Bellizzia, C., eds., Memoria, IV Congreso Geológico Venezolano: Caracas, Boletín de Geología, Publicación Especial 5, no. 3, p.1337–1548.

Duncan, R., and Hargraves, R., 1984, Plate-tectonic evolution of the Caribbean region in the mantle reference frame, *in* Bonini, W.E., Hargraves, R.B., and Shagam, R., eds., The Caribbean–South American plate boundary and regional tectonics: Geological Society of America Memoir 162, p. 81–93.

Emery, D., and Myers, K.J., 2001, Sequence stratigraphy: Oxford, Blackwell Science, 4th reprint, 297 p.

Erikson, J.P., 1992, Northeastern Venezuela's Jurassic through Eocene passive margin, Hispaniola's Neogene Cibao basin, and their histories and causes of evolution [Ph.D. Thesis]: Hanover, New Hampshire, Dartmouth College, 472 p.

Erikson, J.P., 1994, A Lower Cretaceous shelf and delta in Eastern Venezuela, *in* Pérez de Mejia, D., ed., Memoria, V Simposio Bolivariano, Exploración Petrolera en las Cuencas Subandinas (Puerto La Cruz, Venezuela): Caracas, Sociedad Venezolana de Geólogos, p. 174–189.

Erlich, R., 1999, Depositional environments, geochemistry, and paleoceanography of upper Cretaceous organic carbon-rich strata, Costa Rica and Western Venezuela [Ph.D. thesis]: Amsterdam, Vrije Universiteit, 140 p.

Erlich, R., and Barret, S., 1990, Cenozoic plate tectonic history of the northern Venezuela-Trinidad area: Tectonics, v. 9, p. 161–184.

Erlich, R., and Barrett, S., 1992, Petroleum geology of the Eastern Venezuela foreland basin, *in* Macqueen, R. and Leckie, D., eds., Foreland basins and fold belts: American Association of Petroleum Geologists Memoir 55, p. 341–362.

Erlich, R., Pocknall, D., Yeilding, C., and Lorente, M., 1997, Chronostratigraphy, depositional environments, and reservoir potential of Eocene rocks, southern and central Mérida Andes (Maracaibo and Barinas–Apure basins), western Venezuela, *in* Shanley, K.W., and Perkins, B., eds., Shallow marine and non-marine reservoirs, Proceedings, Gulf Coast Section Society for Sedimentary Geology (SEPM) 18th Annual Research Conference: Houston, Texas, SEPM Foundation, p. 93–106.

Erlich, R., Palmer-Koleman, S., and Lorente, M., 1999a, Geochemical characterization of oceanographic and climatic changes recorded in upper Albian to lower Maastrichtian strata, western Venezuela: Cretaceous Research, v. 20, p. 547–581, doi: 10.1006/cres.1999.0167.

Erlich, R., Macsotay, O., Nederbragt, A., and Lorente, M., 1999b, Palaeoecology, palaeogeography and depositional environments of Upper Cretaceous rocks of western Venezuela: Palaeogeography, Palaeoclimatology, Palaeoecology, v. 153, p. 203–238, doi: 10.1016/S0031-0182(99)00072-3.

Erlich, R., Macsotay, O., Nederbragt, A., and Lorente, M., 2000, Birth and death of the late Cretaceous "La Luna Sea," and origin of the Tres Esquinas phosphorites: Journal of South American Earth Sciences, v. 13, p. 21–45, doi: 10.1016/S0895-9811(00)00016-X.

Escalona, A., and Mann, P., 2002, Three-dimensional structural architecture and evolutionary history of an Eocene pull-apart basin, Maracaibo basin, Venezuela: Towards an integrated understanding of Caribbean tectonics and stratigraphy (abs.): http://www.ig.utexas.edu/CaribPlate/reports/Texas_workshop.htm#abstracts (Accessed April 2003).

Fasola, A., and Paredes de Ramos, I., 1991, Late Cretaceous palynological assemblages from El Furrial area wells: Revista Técnica Instituto Tecnológico Venezolano de Petróleo, v. 2, no. 1, p. 3–14.

Feo-Codecido, G., Smith, F.D., Aboud, N., and de Di Giacomo, E., 1984, Basement and Paleozoic rocks of the Venezuela Llanos basins, *in* Bonini, W.E., Hargraves, R.B., and Shagam, R., eds., The Caribbean–South American plate boundary and regional tectonics: Geological Society of America Memoir 162, p.175–188.

Ford, A., and Houbolt, J.J., 1963, Las microfacies del Cretáceo de Venezuela Occidental: Brill, Leiden, The Netherlands, International Sedimentary and Petrographic Series, v. 6, p. 1–59.

Galea, F., 1985, Bioestratigrafía y ambiente sedimentario del Grupo Santa Anita del Cretáceo Superior-Eoceno, Venezuela nor-oriental, *in* Espejo, A., Ríos, J.H., and Bellizzia, N.P., eds., Memoria, VI Congreso Geológico Venezolano: Caracas, Sociedad Venezolana de Geólogos, v. 1, p. 703–721.

Girard, D., 1981, Petrologie de quelques séries spilitiques mésozoiques du domaine caraibe et des ensembles magmatiques de l'île de Tobago [Thèse Doct. 3th Cycle]: Brest, France, L'Université de Bretagne Occidentale, 229 p.

Giunta, G., Beccaluva, L., Coltorti, M., Siena, F., and Vaccaro, C., 2002, The southern margin of the Caribbean plate in Venezuela: tectono-magmatic setting of the ophiolitic units and kinematic evolution: Lithos, v. 63, p. 19–40, doi: 10.1016/S0024-4937(02)00120-2.

González, S.L., and Márquez, P., 1985, Reevaluación de la extensión noreste de Jusepín, *in* Espejo, A., Ríos, J.H., and Bellizzia, N.P., eds., Memoria, VI Congreso Geológico Venezolano: Caracas, Sociedad Venezolana de Geólogos, v. 5, p. 3037–3085.

González de Juana, C., Muñoz, N.G., and Vignali, M., 1972, Reconocimiento geológico de la Península de Paria, Venezuela, *in* Petzall, C., Bellizzia, A., and Bellizzia, C., eds., Memoria, IV Congreso Geológico Venezolano: Caracas, Boletín de Geología, Publicación Especial v. 3, p. 1549–1586.

González de Juana, C., Iturralde, J.M., and Picard, X., 1980, Geología de Venezuela y de sus cuencas petrolíferas: Caracas, Ediciones Foninves, 1031 p.

Guzmán, J., 1995, Procedencia de los sedimentos entre el Cretácico Tardío y el Mioceno Temprano, flanco norte de la cuenca oriental de Venezuela [Tesis M.Sc.]: Caracas, Universidad Central de Venezuela, 261 p.

Guzmán, J., 2000, Sistemas deltaicos Perijá–La Rosa y Perijá-Lagunillas en el contexto paleogeográfico de la conexión marina Maracaibo-Falcón durante el Mioceno temprano y medio, *in* Truskowski, I., ed., Memoria, VII Simposio Bolivariano, Exploración Petrolera en las Cuencas Subandinas: Caracas, Sociedad Venezolana de Geólogos, p. 83–108.

Haq, B., Hardenbol, J., and Vail, P., 1987, Chronology of fluctuating sea levels since the Triassic: Science, v. 235, p. 1156–1167.

Hedberg, H.D., 1950, Geology of the Eastern Venezuela Basin (Anzoátegui–Monagas–Sucre–Eastern Guárico portion): AAPG Bulletin, v. 61, p. 1173–1215.

Helmers, H., and Beets, D.J., 1977, Cretaceous of Aruba, Guide to field excursions, *in* MacGillavry, H.J., and Beets, D., eds., Transactions, 8th Caribbean Geological Conference: Amsterdam, Gemeentelijke Universiteit Amsterdam (GUA) Papers of Geology, v. 10, p. 29–35.

Hevia, A., Yoris, F., Pérez, A., Pérez, J., Contreras, O., Ascanio, E., Vivas, M., and Lander, R., 1996, Aguardiente and Escandalosa formations, potential Cretaceous reservoirs in the southwestern Táchira area, Venezuela: AAPG Bulletin, v. 80, no. 8, p. 1301.

Higgs, R., 1997, Sequence stratigraphy and sedimentology of the Misoa Formation (Eocene), Lake Maracaibo, Venezuela, *in* Memoria, Congreso Latinoamericano de Sedimentología (Porlamar, Venezuela): Caracas, Sociedad Venezolana de Geólogos, v. 1, p. 325–334.

Hoernle, K., van den Bogaard, P., Werner, R., Lissinna, B., Hauff, F., Alvarado, G., and Garbe-Schönberg, D., 2002, Missing history (16–71 Ma) of the Galapagos hotspot: Implications for the tectonic and biological evolution of the Americas: Geology, v. 30, no. 9, p. 795–798, doi: 10.1130/0091-7613(2002)030<0795:MHMOTG>2.0.CO;2.

Hung, O., and Ascanio, E., 1992, Ambientes sedimentarios y tectónicos de la secuencia Cretácico-Terciaria en la región de Zea-Mesa Bolívar, El Vigía-Estanques, Estado Mérida [Trabajo Especial de Grado]: Caracas, Universidad Central de Venezuela, 181 p.

Hurley, P., Melchier, G.C., Pinson, W.H., and Fairbairn, H.W., 1976, Progress report on early Archean rocks in Liberia, Sierra Leona and Guayana and their general stratigraphic setting, *in* Windley, B.F., ed., The early history of the Earth: Proceedings, North Atlantic Treaty Organisation Advanced Study Institute: New York, John Wiley and Sons, p. 511–521.

Irving, E.M., 1975, Structural evolution of the northernmost Andes: U.S. Geological Survey Professional Paper 846, 47 p.

Jácome, M.I., Kusznir, N., Audemard, F., and Flint, S., 2002, Tectono-stratigraphic evolution of the Maturín foreland basin, eastern Venezuela: Tectonics, v. 22, no. 5, p. 1046, doi: 10.1029/2002TC001381.

Kasper, D.C., and Larue, D.K., 1986, Paleogeographic and tectonic implications of quartzose sandstones of Barbados: Tectonics, v. 5, no. 6, p. 837–854.

Kellogg, J.N., 1984, Cenozoic tectonic history of the Sierra de Perijá, Venezuela-Colombia, and adjacent basins, *in* Bonini, W.E., Hargraves, R.B., and Shagam, R., eds., The Caribbean–South American plate boundary and regional tectonics: Geological Society of America Memoir 162, p. 239–262.

Kiser, D., Escalona, N., Portilla, A., Monsalve, O., Ramírez, P.E., and Colina, G., 1984, Plataforma continental Venezolana, La Vela–Golfo Triste: Caracas, Petróleo de Venezuela, S.A., Coordinación de Exploración, Grupo Interfilial, v. II, p. 75.

Konigsmark, T.A., 1958, Geology of the northern Guárico–Lake Valencia área, Venezuela: Asociación Venezolana de Geología, Minería, y Petróleo, Caracas, Boletín Informativo, v. 1, no. 5, p. 151–165.

Konigsmark, T.A., 1965, Geología del area Guárico septentrional–Lago de Valencia, Venezuela: Caracas, Boletín de Geología, v. 6, no. 11, p. 209–285.

Ladd, J.W., Truchman, M., Talwani, M., Stuffa, P.L., Buhl, P., Houtz, R., Mauffret, A., and Westbrook, G., 1984, Seismic reflection profiles across the southern margin of the Caribbean, *in* Bonini, W.E., Hargraves, R.B., and Shagam, R., eds., The Caribbean–South American plate boundary and regional tectonics: Geological Society of America Memoir 162, p. 153–160.

Link, M.H., Taylor, C.K., Bueno, E., and Mitchum, R.M., 1994, Structure, stratigraphy and sequence stratigraphy, Maraven's Block I: A seismic perspective, Maracaibo basin, *in* Memoria, VII Congreso Venezolano de Geofísica: Caracas, Sociedad Venezolana de Geofísicos, p. 401–408.

Loubet, M., Montigny, R., Chachati, B., Duarte, N., Lambret, B., Martin, C., and Thuizat, R., 1985, Geochemical and geochronological constraints on the geodynamic development of the Caribbean Chain of Venezuela, *in* Mascle, A., ed., Symposium Geodynamique des Caraibes: Paris, Edition Technip, p. 553–566.

Lugo, J., and Mann, P., 1995, Jurassic-Eocene tectonic evolution of Maracaibo basin, Venezuela, *in* Tankard, A., Suárez, R., and Welsink, H.J., eds., Petroleum basins of South America: American Association of Petroleum Geologists Memoir 62, p. 699–725.

Mac Donald, W.D., 1968, Estratigrafía, estructura y metamorfismo, rocas del Jurásico Superior, Península de Paraguaná, Venezuela: Caracas, Boletín de Geología, v. 9, no. 18, p. 441–458.

Macellari, C.E., 1995, Cenozoic sedimentation and tectonics of the southwestern Caribbean pull-apart basin, Venezuela and Colombia, *in* Tankard, A., Suárez, R., and Welsink, H.J., eds., Petroleum basins of South America: American Association of Petroleum Geologists Memoir 62, p. 757–780.

MacKenzie, D.B., 1966, Geología de la región norte-central de Cojedes: Caracas, Boletín de Geología, v. 8, no. 15, p. 3–72.

Maresch, W.V., 1971, The metamorphism and structure of northeastern Margarita Island, Venezuela [Ph.D. Thesis]: Princeton, New Jersey, Princeton University, 278 p.

Maresch, W.V., 1973, Metamorfismo y estructura de Margarita nor-oriental, Venezuela: Caracas, Boletín de Geología, v. 12, no. 2, p. 3–172.

Maresch, W.V., 1974, Plate tectonics origins of the Caribbean Mountains system of northern South America: Discussion and Proposal: Geological Society of America Bulletin, v. 85, no. 5, p. 669–682, doi: 10.1130/0016-7606(1974)85<669:PTOOTC>2.0.CO;2.

Maresch, W.V., 1975, The geology of northeastern Margarita Island, Venezuela: A contribution to the study of Caribbean plate margins: Geologische Rundschau, v. 64, p. 846–883.

Martín, B.C., 1968, Edades isotópicas de rocas Venezolanas: Caracas, Boletín de Geología, v. 19, p. 356–380.

Martín, B.C., 1974, Paleotectónica del Escudo de Guayana, *in* Memoria, IX Conferencia Geológica Inter-Guayanas: Caracas, Boletín de Geología, Publicación Especial, v. 6, p. 251–305.

Martín, B.C., 1975, Excursión geológica No. 6, Puerto Ordaz-La Vergareña, *in* Memoria, II Congreso Latinoamericano de Geología: Caracas, Boletín de Geología, Publicación Especial 7, p. 371–388.

Mascle, A., Biju-Duval, B., Letouzey, J., Bellizzia, A., Auboin, J., Blanchet, R., Stephan, J.F., and Beck, C., 1979, Estructura y evolución de los márgenes este y sur del Caribe: Bulletin du BRGM (Bureau de recherches géologiques et minières), deuxième serie, section IV, no. 3–4, p. 171–184.

Mata, L., 2001, Estudio quimioestratigráfico de la Formación La Luna, Estado Táchira [Trabajo Especial de Grado]: Caracas, Universidad Central de Venezuela, 163 p.

Maze, W.B., 1984, Jurassic La Quinta Formation in the Sierra de Perijá, northwestern Venezuela: Geology and tectonic environment of red beds and volcanic rocks, *in* Bonini, W.E., Hargraves, R.B., and Shagam, R., eds., The Caribbean–South American plate boundary and regional tectonics: Geological Society of America Memoir 162, p. 287–294.

MEM (Ministerio de Energía y Minas), 1997, Léxico estratigráfico de Venezuela: Caracas, Boletín de Geología, Publicación Especial, v. 12, no. 2, 828 p.

Menéndez, A., 1965, Geología del area de El Tinaco, centro del Estado Cojedes, Venezuela: Caracas, Boletín de Geología, v. 6, no. 12, p. 417–543.

Menéndez, A., 1966, Tectónica de la parte central de las Montañas Occidentales del Caribe, Venezuela: Caracas, Boletín de Geología, v. 8, no. 15, p. 116–139.

Morgan, B.A., 1967, Geology of the Valencia area, Carabobo, Venezuela [Ph. D. Thesis]: Princeton, New Jersey, Princeton University, 220 p.

Morgan, B.A., 1969, Geología de la región de Valencia, Carabobo, Venezuela: Caracas, Boletín de Geología, v. 20, p. 3–136.

Motiscka, P., 1972, Geología del Archipiélago de Los Frailes, *in* Petzall, C., ed., Memoria, VI Conferencia Geológica del Caribe: Caracas, Impreso por Cromotip, p. 69–73.

Motiscka, P., 1985, Volcanismo Mesozoico en el subsuelo de la faja petrolífera del Orinoco, Estado Guárico, Venezuela, *in* Ríos, J.H., and Pimental de Bellizzia, N., eds., Memoria, VI Congreso Geológico Venezolano: Caracas, Sociedad Venezolana de Geólogos, v. 3, p. 1929–1943.

Muessig, K.W., 1984, Paleomagnetic data on the basic igneous intrusions of the central Falcón basin, Venezuela, *in* Bonini, W.E., Hargraves, R.B., and Shagam, R., eds., The Caribbean–South American plate boundary and regional tectonics: Geological Society of America Memoir 162, p. 231–238.

Navarro, E., 1983, Petrología, petrogénesis de las rocas metavolcánicas del Grupo Villa de Cura: Caracas, Geos, v. 28, p. 170–317.

Navarro, E., Ostos, M., and Yoris, F.G., 1988, Revisión y redefinición de unidades litoestratigráficas y síntesis de un modelo tectónico para la evolución de la parte norte-central de Venezuela durante el Jurásico–medio Paleogeno: Acta Cientifica Venezolana, v. 39, no. 5–6, p. 427–436.

Ortega, J.F., van Erve, A., and Monroy, Z., 1987, Formación Guafita: Nueva unidad litoestratigráfica del Terciario en el subsuelo de la Cuenca Barinas-Apure, Venezuela suroccidental: Caracas, Boletín de la Sociedad Venezolana de Geólogos, v. 31, p. 9–35.

Ostos, M., 1990, Tectonic evolution of the south-central Caribbean based on geochemical and structural data [Ph.D. Thesis]: Houston, Rice University, 411 p.

Ostos, M., 1992, Tectonic evolution of the south-central Caribbean based on geochemical data: Caracas, Geos, v. 30, p. 1–294.

Ostos, M., Navarro, E., and Urbani, F., 1989, Edad Rb/Sr del augengneis de Peña de Mora, Cordillera de la Costa, *in* Pimentel de Bellizzia, N., González, L., and Ríos, J.H., eds., Memoria, VII Congreso Geológico Venezolano: Caracas, Sociedad Venezolana de Geólogos, v. 1, p. 125–136.

Paparoni, G., 1993, Análisis y caracterización de litofacies pertenecientes a parasecuencias de edad Eoceno (ambientes de transición), Formación Mirador de Venezuela occidental [Trabajo Especial de Grado]: Caracas, Universidad Central de Venezuela, 163 p.

Parnaud, F., Gou, Y., Pascual, J.C., Capello, M.A., Truskowski, Y., Passalacqua, H., and Roure, F., 1995a, Stratigraphic synthesis of western Venezuela, *in* Tankard, A., Suárez, R., and Welsink, H.J, eds., Petroleum basins of South America: American Association of Petroleum Geologists Memoir 62, p. 681–698.

Parnaud, F., Gou, Y., Pascual, J.C., Capello, M.A., Truskowski, Y., Passalacqua, H., and Roure, F., 1995b, Petroleum geology of the central part of the Eastern Venezuela Basin, *in* Tankard, A., Suárez, R., and Welsink, H.J. eds., Petroleum basins of South America: American Association Petroleum of Geologists Memoir 62, p. 741–756.

Passalacqua, H., Fernández, F., Gou, Y., and Roure, F., 1995, Crustal architecture and strain partitioning in the eastern Venezuela ranges, *in* Tankard, A., Suárez, R., and Welsink, H.J., eds., Petroleum basins of South America: American Association Petroleum of Geologists Memoir 62, p. 667–680.

Pérez de Mejía, D., Kiser, G.D., Maximowitsch, B., and Young, G., 1980, Geología de Venezuela, *in* Felder, B., Brie, A., Gartner, J., Hepp, V., Hrabie, M., Kervella, M., Mons, F., Mowat, G., Neville, N., Plomb, J., Sadras, W., Tejada, A., Trassard, J., Vidal, J., and Zinat, D., eds., Evaluación de formaciones en Venezuela, 1st edition: Caracas, Schlumberger Surenco S.A., 287 p.

Pérez, O., Bilham, R., Bendick, R., Velandia, J.R., Hernández, N., Moncayo, C., Hoyer, M., and Kozuch, M., 2001, Velocity field across the southern Caribbean plate boundary and estimates of Caribbean–South-American plate motion using GPS geodesy 1994–2000: Geophysical Research Letters, v. 28, no. 15, p. 2987–2990, doi: 10.1029/2001GL013183.

Piburn, M.D., 1968, Metamorfismo y estructura del Grupo de Villa de Cura, Venezuela septentrional: Caracas, Boletín de Geología, v. 9, no. 18, p. 184–290.

Pimentel de Bellizzia, N., 1992, Paleozoico Inferior: Una sintesis del noroeste de América del Sur (Venezuela, Colombia y Ecuador), *in* Gutierrez-Marco, J.C., Saavedra, J., Rabano, I., and Liso Rubio, M.J., eds., Paleozoico inferior de Ibero América: Mérida, Extremadura, España, Conferencia Internacional sobre el Paleozoico Inferior de Ibero-América, p. 203–224.

Pimentel de Bellizzia, N., Gaudette, H., and Olsewsky, W., 1985, Nuevas dataciones en el "basamento" de la Cadena Caribe, *in* Espejo, A., Ríos, J.H., Pimentel de Bellizzia, N., and de Pardo, A.S., eds., Memoria, VI Congreso Geológico Venezolano: Caracas, Sociedad Venezolana de Geólogos, v. 3, p. 1979–1994.

Pindell, J.L., and Tabbutt, K.D., 1995, Mesozoic-Cenozoic Andean paleogeographic and regional controls on hydrocarbon systems, *in* Tankard, A.J., Suárez, S., and Welsink, H.J., eds., Petroleum basins of South America: American Association of Petroleum Geologists Memoir 62, p. 101–128.

Pindell, J.L., Higgs, R., and Dewey, J.F., 1998, Cenozoic palinspastic reconstruction, paleogeographic evolution, and hydrocarbon setting of the northern margin of South America, *in* Pindell, J.L., and Drake, C., eds., Paleogeographic evolution and non-glacial eustasy, Northern South America: Society for Sedimentary Geology (SEPM) Special Publication 58, p. 45–85.

Pocknall, D., Erlich, R., Stein, J., Bergen, J., and Lorente, M., 1997, A Cretaceous-Tertiary boundary section at Rio Lora, Mérida Andes, western Venezuela: Cartagena, Colombia, Memoria, VI Simposio Bolivariano "Exploración Petrolera en las Cuencas Subandinas," p. 552–564.

Pocknall, D., Erlich, R., Stein, J., and Lorente, M., 2001, The palynofloral succession across the Cretaceous to Paleocene transition zone, Mérida

Andes, western Venezuela, *in* Goodman, D.K., and Clarke, R.T., eds., Proceedings of the IX International Palynological Congress, Houston, Texas: American Association of Stratigraphic Palynologists Foundation, p. 171–179.

Priem, H.N.A., Boelrijk, N.A.I.M., Verschure, R.H., Hebeda, E.H., and Lagaay, R.A., 1966, Isotopic ages of the quartz-diorite batholith on the island of Aruba, Netherlands Antilles: Geology en Mijnbouw, v. 45, p. 188–190.

Priem, H.N.A., Boelrijk, N.A.I.M., Hebeda, E.H., and Verschure, R.H., 1973, Age of Precambrian Roraima Formation in north-eastern South America: Evidence from isotopic dating of Roraima pyroclastic volcanic rock in Suriname: Geological Society of America Bulletin, v. 84, no. 5, p. 1677–1684, doi: 10.1130/0016-7606(1973)84<1677:AOTPRF>2.0.CO;2.

Restrepo, J.J., and Toussaint, J.F., 1988, Terranes and continental accretion in the Colombian Andes: Episodes, v. 11, no. 3, p. 189–193.

Rivero, F., 1956, Léxico estratigráfico de Venezuela: Caracas, Boletín de Geología, Publicación Especial, 1, 728 p.

Roure, F., Carnevali, J.O., Gou, Y., and Subieta, T., 1994, Geometry and kinematics of the North Monagas thrust belt (Venezuela): Marine and Petroleum Geology, v. 11, no. 3, p. 347–362, doi: 10.1016/0264-8172(94)90054-X.

Santamaría, F., and Schubert, C., 1974, Geochemistry and geochronology of the southern Caribbean–northern Venezuela plate boundary: Geological Society of America Bulletin, v. 85, p. 1085–1098, doi: 10.1130/0016-7606(1974)85<1085:GAGOTS>2.0.CO;2.

Santos, J.O.S., Hartmann, L.A., Gaudette, H.E., Groves, D.I., Mcnaughton, N.J., and Fletcher, I.I., 2000, A new understanding of the provinces of the Amazon craton based on integration of field mapping and U-Pb and Sm-Nd geochronology: Gondwana Research, v. 3, p. 453–488.

Schubert, C., 1971, Metamorphic rocks of the Araya Peninsula, eastern Venezuela: Geologische Rundschau, v. 60, p. 1571–1600.

Schubert, C., 1972, Geología de Península de Araya, Estado Sucre, *in* Petzall, C., Bellizzia, A., and Bellizzia, C.M., eds., Memoria, IV Congreso Geológico Venezolano: Caracas, Boletín de Geología, Publicación Especial, v. 5, no. 3, p. 1823–1886.

Schubert, C., 1982, Origin of the Cariaco basin, southern Caribbean Sea: Marine Geology, v. 47, p. 345–360, doi: 10.1016/0025-3227(82)90076-7.

Schubert, C., 1984, Basin formation along the Bocono–Moron–El Pilar fault system, Venezuela: Journal of Geophysical Research, v. 89, p. 5711–5718.

Schubert, C., and Motiscka, P., 1972, Geological reconnaissance of the Venezuelan Islands in the Caribbean Sea, between Los Roques and Los Testigos: Porlamar, Venezuela, Memoria, VI Conferencia Geológica del Caribe, p. 81–82.

Schubert, C., and Motiscka, P., 1973, Reconocimiento geológico de las Islas Venezolanas en el Mar Caribe, entre Los Roques y Los Testigos (Dependencias Federales): Caracas, Acta Científica Venezolana, v. 24, p. 19–31.

Seijas, F., 1972, Geología de la región de Carúpano, *in* Petzall, C., Bellizzia, A., and Bellizzia, C.M., eds., Memoria, IV Congreso Geológico Venezolano: Caracas, Boletín de Geología, Publicación Especial, v. 5, no. 3, p. 1887–1923.

Shagam, R., 1960, Geology of central Aragua State, Venezuela: Geological Society of America Bulletin, v. 71, p. 249–302.

Shagam, R., 1975, The northern termination of the Andes, *in* Nairn, A.E.M., and Stehli, F.G., eds., The ocean basins and margins, vol. 3, Gulf of Mexico and the Caribbean: New York, Plenum Press, v. 5, no. 3, p. 325–420.

Shagam, R., Kohn, B.P., Banks, P.O., Dasch, L.E., Vargas, R., Rodriguez, G.I., and Pimentel, N., 1984, Tectonic implications of Cretaceous-Pliocene fission-track ages from rocks of the circum-Maracaibo basin region of western Venezuela and eastern Colombia, *in* Bonini, W.E., Hargraves, R.B., and Shagam, R., eds., The Caribbean–South American plate boundary and regional tectonics: Geological Society of America Memoir 162, p. 385–412.

Sinton, C.W., Duncan, R.A., Storey, M., Lewis, J., and Estrada, J.J., 1998, An oceanic flood basalt province within the Caribbean plate: Earth and Planetary Science Letters, v. 155, p. 221–235, doi: 10.1016/S0012-821X(97)00214-8.

Sisson, V.B., Ertan, I.E., and Avé Lallemant, H.G., 1997, High pressure (~2000 MPa) glaucophane–bearing pelitic schist and eclogites from Cordillera de la Costa belt, Venezuela: Journal of Petrology, v. 38, p. 65–83, doi: 10.1093/petrology/38.1.65.

Smith, C.A., Sisson, V.B., Avé Lallemant, H.G., and Copeland, P., 1999, Two contrasting pressure-temperature-time paths in the Villa de Cura blueschist belt, Venezuela: Possible evidence for late Cretaceous initiation of subduction in the Caribbean: Geological Society of America Bulletin, v. 111, no. 6, p. 831–848, doi: 10.1130/0016-7606(1999)111<0831:TCPTTP>2.3.CO;2.

Smith, F.D., Jr., and Personal Técnico de las compañías Shell de Venezuela, Creole Petroleum Corporation, Mene Grande Oil Company, Ministerio de Minas e Hidrocarburos, Mobil Oil Company de Venezuela, Richmond Exploration and Texas Petroleum Company, 1962, Cuadro de correlación de las unidades estratigráficas en Venezuela y Trinidad, *in* Congreso Venezolano Petroleo I, Aspectos de la Industria Petrolera en Venezuela: Caracas, Sociedad Venezolano de Ingenieros de Petróleo (SVIP), 850 p.

Smith, R.J., 1952, Geología de la región Los Teques–Cúa, Venezuela: Caracas, Boletín de Geología, v. 2, no. 6, p. 333–406.

Socas, M., 1991, Estudio sedimentológico de la Formación Naricual, Estado Anzoátegui [Trabajo Especial de Grado]: Caracas, Universidad Central de Venezuela, 287 p.

Soulas, J.P., 1985, Neotectónica y tectónica activa en Venezuela y regiones vecinas, *in* Espejo, A., Ríos, J.H., and Bellizzia, N.P., eds., Memoria, VI Congreso Geológico Venezolano: Caracas, Sociedad Venezolana de Geólogos, v. 10, p. 6639–6656.

Spear, F.S., 1993, Metamorphic phase equilibria and pressure-temperature-time paths: Mineralogical Society of America Monograph, 799 p.

Speed, R.C., 1985, Cenozoic collision of the lesser Antilles arc and continental South America; the origin of the El Pilar fault: Tectonics, v. 4, p. 41–69.

Stauffer, K., 1994, Depositional model of the Cogollo Group, Maracaibo basin, Venezuela, *in* Memoria, V Simposio Bolivariano, Exploración Petrolera en las Cuencas Subandinas (Puerto La Cruz, Venezuela): Caracas, Sociedad Venezolana de Geólogos, p. 174–189.

Stephan, J.F., 1977, El contacto cadena Caribe-Andes Meridenos entre Carora y el Tocuyo (Estado Lara, Venezuela), *in* Memoria, V Congreso Geológico Venezolano: Caracas, Sociedad Venezolana de Geólogos, v. 2, p. 789–816.

Stephan, J.F., 1982, Evolution géodynamique du domain Caraibe; Andes et Chaîne Caraibe sur la Transversale de Barquisimeto (Venezuela) [Thèse d'Etat]: Brest, France, L'Université de Bretagne Occidentale, 512 p.

Stephan, J.F., 1985, Andes et chaîne Caraibe sur la transversale de Barquisimeto (Venezuela): Evolution géodynamique: Symposium Geodynamique des Caraibes, Edition Technip, p. 505–529.

Stephan, J.F., Beck, C., Bellizzia, A., and Blanchet, R., 1980, La chaîne Caraibe du Pacifique á l'Atlantique: Transactions, 26th Congrés Géologique International, Paris, p. 39–59.

Stifano, M.P., 1993, Estratigrafia de la Formación Carapita en su sección tipo y en la sección del pozo ORS-52: Caracas, Universidad Central de Venezuela, 2 volumes, 195 p.

Stöckhert, B., Maresch, W.V., Brix, M., Kaistr, C., Tortz, A., Kluge, R., and Krïckhans-Lueder, G., 1995, Crustal history of Margarita Island (Venezuela) in detail: Constraints on the Caribbean plate-tectonic scenario: Geology, v. 23, no. 9, p. 787–790, doi: 10.1130/0091-7613(1995)023<0787:CHOMIV>2.3.CO;2.

Talukdar, S., 1983, Petrological study of volcanic and sedimentary rocks from offshore wells of the north of Paria area: Instituto Tecnológico Venezolano del Petróleo, Informe Técnico INT-00877, 126 p.

Talukdar, S., and Bolívar, E., 1982, Petroleum geology of Tuy-Cariaco basin, eastern Venezuela continental shelf: a preliminary appraisal: Caracas, Instituto Tecnológico Venezolano del Petróleo, Informe Técnico, INT-00661, 78 p.

Talukdar, S., and Loureiro, D., 1982, Geología de una zona ubicada en el segmento norcentral de la Cordillera de la Costa, Venezuela: Metamorfismo y deformación; Evolución del margen septentrional de Suramérica en el marco de la tectónica de placas: Caracas, Geos, v. 27, p. 15–76.

Taylor, G.C., 1960, Geología de la Isla de Margarita, Venezuela: Caracas, Memoria, III Congreso Geológico Venezolano, Boletín de Geología, Publicación Especial, v. 3, no. 2, p. 838–893.

Toro, M., 1992, Estratigrafía y arquitectura de facies fluvio-deltaicas en la zona de San Pedro del Río, Lobatera, Estado Táchira [Trabajo Especial de Grado]: Caracas, Universidad Central de Venezuela, 163 p.

Toro, M., and Eichenseer, H., 1997, Sedimentología y estratigrafía secuencial de las formaciones Gobernador y Masparrito en el Flanco sur Andino, *in* Memoria, I Congreso Latinoamericano de Sedimentología: Caracas, Sociedad Venezolana de Geólogos, v. 1, p. 309–314.

Toro, M., Paparoni, G., Yoris, F., Falcón, R., and Taheri, M., 1994, Ambientes sedimentarios y distribución de porosidad y permeabilidad en las formaciones Mirador y Carbonera en la región de Lobatera, Edo. Táchira, Venezuela, *in* Memoria, V Simposio Bolivariano, Exploración Petrolera en las Cuencas Subandinas: Caracas, Sociedad Venezolana de Geólogos, p. 207–209.

Urbani, F., 1969, Primera localidad fosilífera del Miembro Zenda de la Formación Las Brisas: Cueva El Indio, La Guarita, Estado Miranda: Caracas, Asociación Venezolana de Geología, Minas y Petróleo, Boletín Informativo, v. 12, no. 2, p. 447–453.

Urbani, F., 1973, Notas sobre el hallazgo de fósiles en rocas metamórficas de la parte central de la Cordillera de la Costa: Caracas, Asociación Venezolana de Geología, Minas y Petróleo, Boletín Informativo, v. 16, no. 4–6, p. 41–54.

Urbani, F., 1982, Comentarios sobre algunas edades de las rocas de la parte central de la Cordillera de la Costa: Caracas, Geos, v. 27, p. 77–84.

Urbani, F., and Quesada, E.A., 1972, Migmatitas y rocas asociadas del área de la Sabana, Cordillera de la Costa: Caracas, Memoria, IV Congreso Geológico Venezolano, Boletín de Geología, Publicación Especial, v. 5, no. 4, p. 2375–2400.

Urbani, F., Chirinos, A., and Marquina, M., 1989a, Reconocimiento geológico de la región de Guatopo, Miranda, *in* Bellizzia, N., González, L., and Ríos, J.H., eds., Memoria, VII Congreso Geológico Venezolano: Caracas, Sociedad Venezolana de Geólogos, v. 1, p. 199–222.

Urbani, F., Yoris, F., Szcerban, E., Renz, O., and Jung, P., 1989b, Una localidad fosilífera en la Fase Tacagua, Cordillera de la Costa: Caracas, Geos, v. 29, p. 274–275.

Vail, P., Audemard, F., Bowman, S.A., Eisner, P.N., and Perez-Cruz, C., 1991, The stratigraphic signature of tectonics, eustasy and sedimentology–an overview, *in* Einsele, G., Ricken, W., and Seilacher, A., eds., Cycles and events in stratigraphy, Part II: Larger cycles and sequences: Berlin, Springer-Verlag, p. 617–659.

Van Berkel, D., 1988, Geología del área ubicada entre las poblaciones de Tácata y Altagracia de La Montaña, Estado Miranda [Trabajo Especial de Grado]: Caracas, Universidad Central de Venezuela, 152 p.

Van Berkel, D., Ostos, M., and Yoris, F., 1989, Geología del área ubicada entre las poblaciones de Tácata y Altagracia de la Montaña, Estado Miranda: Caracas, Geos, v. 29, p. 97–107.

Vierbuchen, R.C., 1984, The geology of the El Pilar fault zone and adjacent areas in northeastern Venezuela, *in* Bonini, W.E., Hargraves, R.B., and Shagam, R., eds., The Caribbean–South American plate boundary and regional tectonics: Geological Society of America Memoir 162, p. 189–212.

Villamil, T., 1998, A new sequence stratigraphic model for basinal Cretaceous facies of Colombia, *in* Pindell, J.L., and Drake, C., eds., Paleogeographic evolution and non-glacial eustasy, Northern South America: Society for Sedimentary Geology (SEPM) Special Publication 58, p. 161–216.

Villamil, T., 1999, Campanian-Miocene tectonostratigraphy, depocenter evolution and basin development of Colombia and western Venezuela: Palaeogeography, Palaeoclimatology, Palaeoecology, v. 153, p. 239–275, doi: 10.1016/S0031-0182(99)00075-9.

Villamil, T., Arango, C., and Hay, W., 1999, Plate tectonic paleoceanographic hypothesis for Cretaceous source rocks and cherts of northern South America: Geological Society of America Special Paper 332, p. 191–201.

Vivas, V., and Macsotay, O., 1989, Miembro El Pilar de la Formación Quiamare: Ejemplo de molasa orogénica neogena de Venezuela nororiental: Caracas, Geos, v. 29, p. 108–125.

Voicu, G., Bardoux, M., and Stevenson, R., 2001, Lithostratigraphy, geochronology and gold metallogeny in the northern Guiana Shield, South America: A review: Ore Geology Reviews, v. 18, p. 211–236, doi: 10.1016/S0169-1368(01)00030-0.

Wehrmann, M., 1972, Geología de la región de Guatire–Colonia Tovar: Caracas, Memoria, IV Congreso Geológico Venezolano, Boletín de Geología, Publicación Especial, v. 5, no. 4, p. 2093–2119.

White, R.V., Tarney, J., Kerr, A.C., Saunders, A.D., Kempton, P.D., Pringle, M.S., and Klaver, G.T., 1999, Modification of an oceanic plateau, Aruba, Dutch Caribbean: Implications for the generation of continental crust: Lithos, v. 46, p. 43–68, doi: 10.1016/S0024-4937(98)00061-9.

Yoris, F.G., 1984, Revisión de la estratigrafía regional del Cretácico Inferior en la franja San Antonio de Maturín–Aragua de Maturín–Caripito–Bolivita–Campo Alegre (estados Monagas y Sucre) y análisis petrográfico-estadístico de areniscas al oeste del Río San Juan [Tesis M.Sc.]: Caracas, Universidad Central de Venezuela, 428 p.

Yoris, F.G., 1985a, Revisión de la estratigrafía del Cretáceo Inferior al sur y este de la Serranía del Interior, Venezuela nororiental, *in* Espejo, A., Ríos, J.H., and Bellizzia, N.P., eds., Memoria, VI Congreso Geológico Venezolano: Caracas, Sociedad Venezolana de Geólogos, v. 2, p. 1343–1393.

Yoris, F.G., 1985b, Análisis petrográfico-estadístico de areniscas del Grupo Sucre (franja oeste del Río San Juan; Estados Sucre y Monagas), Venezuela nororiental, *in* Espejo, A., Ríos, J.H., and Bellizzia, N.P., eds., Memoria, VI Congreso Geológico Venezolano: Caracas, Sociedad Venezolana de Geólogos, v. 2, p. 1307–1342.

Yoris, F.G., 1988, Localidades tipo y secciones de referencia para los miembros de la Formación El Cantil en la Serranía del Interior, Venezuela nororiental: Caracas, Boletín de la Sociedad Venezolana de Geólogos, v. 34, p. 52–70.

Yoris, F.G., 1992a, Análisis de secuencias clásticas por métodos petrográficos y estadísticos [Doctoral Thesis]: Caracas, Universidad Central de Venezuela, 4 volumes, 1045 p.

Yoris, F.G., 1992b, Localidades tipo para los miembros de la Formación Chimana en la Serranía del Interior, Venezuela nororiental: Caracas, Geos, v. 30, p. 295–324.

Yoris, F.G., and Albertos, M.A., 1989, Medidas de paleocorrientes en la secuencia de la Formación Guárico y sus equivalentes en las secciones: Altagracia de Orituco–Guatopo y Gamelotal–San Francisco de Macaira, estados Guárico y Miranda: Caracas, Geos, v. 29, p. 152–159.

Yoris, F.G., and Navarro, E., 1989, Consideraciones sobre la Formación Los Jabillos y sus equivalentes en la Serranía del Interior, Venezuela nororiental: Caracas, Geos, v. 29, p. 139–151.

Yoris, F.G., and Ostos, M., 1997, Petroleum Geology of Venezuela, *in* 1997 Well Evaluation Conference, Chapter 1: Caracas, Schlumberger Surenco, C.A., p. 1–44.

Yoris, F.G., Ostos, M., Boujana, M., Perez, J., Booth, G., Packer, S., Galea, F., and Lander, R., 1996a, Detailed lithostratigraphy and age determinations of La Luna Formation in two sections of SW Tachira State, Venezuela (abs.): AAPG Bulletin, v. 80, p. 1346.

Yoris, F.G., Ostos, M., Boujana, M., Contreras, O., and Lander, R., 1996b, Mirador Formation in SW Tachira State, Venezuela: Potential reservoir for the Paleogene Sequence (abs.): AAPG Bulletin, v. 80, p. 1346.

Young, G., Bellizzia, A., Renz, H.H., Johnson, F., Robie, R., and Mas Vall, J., 1956, Geología de las cuencas sedimentarias de Venezuela y de sus campos petrolíferos: Caracas, Boletín de Geología, Publicación Especial, v. 2, 140 p.

Ysaccis, R., 1997, Tertiary evolution of the northeastern Venezuela offshore [Ph.D. Thesis]: Houston, Texas, Rice University, 285 p.

MANUSCRIPT ACCEPTED BY THE SOCIETY 5 APRIL 2005

Geological Society of America
Special Paper 394
2005

Overview of radiometric ages in three allochthonous belts of northern Venezuela: Old ones, new ones, and their impact on regional geology

Virginia B. Sisson
Hans G. Avé Lallemant
Department of Earth Science, MS-126, Rice University, Houston, Texas 77252-1892, USA
Marino Ostos
Escuela de Geología, Minas, y Geofísica, Universidad Central de Venezuela, Caracas, Venezuela,
and Estudios de Ingeniería Geologica Litos, C.A., Caracas, Venezuela
Ann E. Blythe
Department of Earth Sciences, University of Southern California, Los Angeles, California 90089-0740, USA
Lawrence W. Snee
U.S. Geological Survey, MS 974, P.O. Box 25046, Denver Federal Center, Denver, Colorado, 80225, USA
Peter Copeland
Department of Geosciences, University of Houston, Houston, Texas 77204-3399, USA
James E. Wright
Raymond A. Donelick
Department of Earth Sciences, MS-126, Rice University, Houston, Texas 77252-1892, USA
Lawrence R. Guth
Department Geo/Physical Sciences, Fitchburg State College, Fitchburg, Massachusetts 01420-2697, USA

ABSTRACT

The margin of northern Venezuela is a complex zone representing the orogenic events from basement formation to subsequent subduction and exhumation during transpressional collision. This boundary zone has six east-west–trending belts that each record a different segment of its development. This geologic complexity requires radiometric ages to unravel, and we herein provide 48 new ages including U-Pb (4), Rb-Sr (2), $^{40}Ar/^{39}Ar$ (24), zircon and apatite fission-track (17), and ^{14}C (1) ages to constrain the evolution of three of these belts. These three belts are the Cordillera de la Costa, Caucagua–El Tinaco, and Serranía del Interior belts.

In the Cordillera de la Costa belt, U-Pb geochronologic data indicate portions of the basement igneous and metaigneous rocks formed in the Cambro-Ordovician (513–471 Ma). New $^{40}Ar/^{39}Ar$ data from Margarita Island indicate that some of the subduction complex was rapidly cooled and exhumed, whereas other portions indicate slower cooling. This contrasts with new $^{40}Ar/^{39}Ar$ data from the Puerto Cabello

E-mails: j_sisson@netzero.com; ave@rice.edu; ORmarino@cs.com; blythe@earth.usc.edu; lsnee@usgs.gov; copeland@uh.edu; Wright now at Department of Geology, University of Georgia, Athens, Georgia 30602, USA, jwright@gly.uga.edu; Donelick now at Apatite to Zircon, Inc., 1075 Matson Road, Viola, Idaho 83872-9709, USA, donelick@apatite.com

Sisson, V.B., Avé Lallemant, H.G., Ostos, M., Blythe, A.E., Snee, L.W., Copeland, P., Wright, J.E., Donelick, R.A., and Guth, L.R., 2005, Overview of radiometric ages in three allochthonous belts of northern Venezuela: Old ones, new ones, and their impact on regional geology, *in* Avé Lallemant, H.G., and Sisson, V.B., eds., Caribbean–South American plate interactions, Venezuela: Geological Society of America Special Paper 394, p. 91–117, doi: 10.1130/2005.2394(03). For permission to copy, contact editing@geosociety.org. ©2005 Geological Society of America.

portion of the subduction complex that has Eocene to Oligocene (42–28 Ma) cooling ages. New fission-track data imply the entire Cordillera de la Costa belt from Puerto Cabello to La Guaira (~150 km) was uplifted at the same time.

In the Caucagua–El Tinaco belt, the oldest $^{40}Ar/^{39}Ar$ amphibole ages from the Tinaquillo ultramafic complex are Jurassic (190 Ma). Additional amphibole $^{40}Ar/^{39}Ar$ cooling ages are older than previously recorded in either the Tinaco or Tinaquillo complex. One amphibole $^{40}Ar/^{39}Ar$ cooling age for the Tinaco complex is similar to previous U-Pb results.

New apatite fission-track results from the Serranía del Interior foreland fold and thrust belt are synchronous with exhumation in the Cordillera de la Costa belt. In addition, several zircon fission-track ages in the Serranía del Interior belt are older than their fossil ages, indicating a Cretaceous minimum provenance age for Miocene beds.

Significant new findings from these geochronologic studies include (1) several igneous and metaigneous bodies that may be correlated with orogenic events in the Appalachians occur within the subduction mélange; (2) the Tinaquillo complex may record Jurassic rifting; (3) Cretaceous source rocks for the Serranía del Interior sedimentary strata; (4) exhumation of the subduction complex is segmented because two regions have significantly different cooling histories, with Margarita Island exhumed in the Cretaceous, whereas to the west, the Puerto Cabello region has widespread Paleogene cooling and exhumation ages; and (5) earthquake activity in 1812 caused uplift as recorded by exposure of Recent corals.

Keywords: geochronology, exhumation, rift, fold and thrust belt, subduction mélange.

INTRODUCTION

The geochronologic data currently available for igneous and metamorphic rocks in the allochthonous belts of northern Venezuela are inadequate to fully characterize the evolution of these rocks either along or cross-strike of the Caribbean Mountain system. Nevertheless, the existing data are quite useful for interpreting the origin, evolution, and exhumation of some individual belts in this region. This chapter is a summary of geochronologic data, both previously published and our new analyses. The authors collected much of the unpublished data in the 1990s in the course of collaborative studies (e.g., Avé Lallemant and Guth, 1990; Avé Lallemant and Sisson, 1993; Sisson et al., 1997; Avé Lallemant, 1997). Additional geologic and tectonostratigraphic features associated with each belt are detailed in the various chapters of this volume.

The Caribbean Mountain system is a complex east-west–trending boundary zone between the Caribbean and South American plates. This boundary zone is found offshore in the Leeward Antilles and onshore in the Caribbean Mountain system; it has six east-west–trending belts (Fig. 1; Maresch, 1974; Case et al., 1984; Bellizzia and Dengo, 1990). These belts include (1) the Leeward Antilles island arc, composed of Late Cretaceous through Paleogene volcanic rocks; (2) the Cordillera de la Costa belt, consisting of a mélange with eclogite-facies rocks, mica schists, and Paleozoic granites metamorphosed in a Late Cretaceous subduction zone; (3) the Caucagua–El Tinaco belt, which consists of Paleozoic high-grade metamorphic and igneous rocks with Jurassic ultramafic complexes; (4) the Paracotos belt of weakly metamorphosed and deformed sedimentary rocks

of Maastrichtian to late Eocene age and ophiolite fragments; (5) the Villa de Cura belt, a sequence of mid-Cretaceous blueschist-facies metavolcanic and metavolcaniclastic rocks; and (6) the Serranía del Interior foreland fold and thrust belt, with deformed Cretaceous and Paleogene strata and less deformed Neogene sedimentary rocks that were involved with south vergent thrusting during the Eocene and Miocene.

Most plate tectonic models for the evolution of the Caribbean plate assume a Pacific (Farallon) origin of the plate (e.g., Pindell and Barrett, 1990; Pindell, 1993; Pindell et al., this volume). According to these models, after the breakup of Pangea in the late Triassic or early Jurassic, a west-facing magmatic arc developed along the west margin of North, Central, and South America. Beneath the Central American segment, Pacific (Farallon) oceanic lithosphere was subducted to the east under the Proto-Caribbean crust, which in turn had been formed by spreading between North and South America. Most models of Caribbean plate motion invoke a mid- to Late Cretaceous subduction polarity reversal, as first proposed by Burke et al. (1978), Mattson (1978), and Pindell (1985). Others (e.g., Malfait and Dinkelman, 1972; Duncan and Hargraves, 1984; Burke, 1988) argue that the thick Caribbean crust choked the subducting slab and caused a subduction polarity reversal around 80–70 Ma. This polarity change caused the Farallon (Caribbean) plate and the "Great Arc of the Caribbean" (Burke, 1988) to migrate northeastward with respect to North and South America. Most of the recent data agrees with a mid- to Late Cretaceous timing for the subduction reversal (e.g., Smith et al., 1999; Harlow et al., 2004; Pindell et al., this volume). The relatively northeastward movement continued until the Eocene. From this time to the Present, the

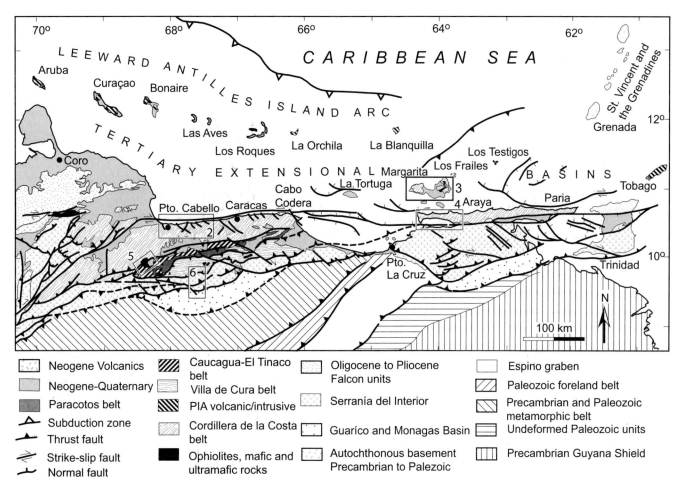

Figure 1. Geologic map of northern Venezuela showing the belts with igneous and metaigneous rocks. The various inset boxes show the locations of the detailed geologic maps given in subsequent figures. PIA—primitive island arc volcanics and intrusives. Map is adapted from Ysaccis (1997) with contributions from A.W. Bally, J. di Croce, E. Hung, H.G. Avé Lallemant, and V.B. Sisson.

Caribbean plate has moved slowly east or southeastward relative to North and South America.

This multistage tectonic history suggests that there should be a mixture of protolith ages for the various belts. In addition, the age of the youngest tectonic events should become younger to the east along strike in response to the eastward movement of the Caribbean plate since the Eocene. We will also use our radiometric data to identify various exhumation histories or pressure-temperature-time (*P-T-t*) paths in the different belts.

Geologic Setting

We concentrated our efforts on three of the six tectonic belts in northern Venezuela: these are the Cordillera de la Costa belt, which includes the region near Puerto Cabello, Margarita Island, and Araya Peninsula; the Caucagua–El Tinaco belt, which includes the Tinaquillo ultramafic complex; and the central Serranía del Interior fold and thrust belt near Camatagua and Alta Gracia. Brief descriptions of these three belts follow.

Cordillera de la Costa Belt

The Cordillera de la Costa belt is a subduction mélange of mid- to Late Cretaceous age with a wide variety of lithologies including eclogite, blueschist, mica schist, marble, serpentinite, and metamorphosed volcanic rocks (Figs. 2, 3, and 4). It also includes metamorphosed felsic igneous rocks. The protoliths of these rocks are often assumed to be continental slope deposits of Late Jurassic and Cretaceous age (e.g., Menendez, 1966; Urbani, 1969). We have subdivided the Cordillera de la Costa near Puerto Cabello into two subbelts with dissimilar metamorphic histories; both of these subbelts are lithologically similar and contain Paleozoic metamorphosed felsic igneous rocks. The main difference between these two is that the northern subbelt contains knockers or lenses of eclogite and blueschist, whereas there are no mafic inclusions in the southern subbelt (e.g., Avé Lallemant and Sisson, 1993; Sisson et al., 1997; Sorensen et al., this volume). The eclogite inclusions and blocks record peak temperature conditions of 550 to >600 °C at pressures of 2000–2200 MPa during subduction metamorphism (Sisson et al., 1997).

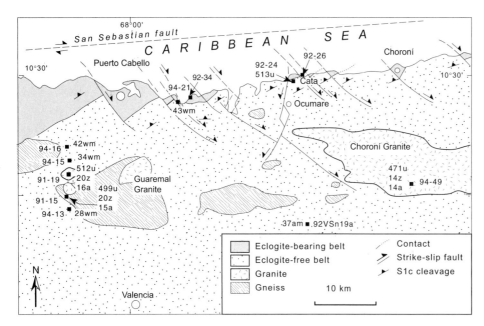

Figure 2. Geologic and sample location map for the Cordillera de la Costa belt. Sample numbers have been shortened. All dates are Ma. Abbreviations used for the different geochronologic methods: u—U-Pb zircon; am—⁴⁰Ar/³⁹Ar amphibole; wm—⁴⁰Ar/³⁹Ar white mica; z—zircon fission-track; a—apatite fission-track. Map is adapted from Bellizzia et al. (1976) with the Cordillera de la Costa belt subdivided into a northern eclogite-bearing mélange subbelt and a southern eclogite-free schist subbelt.

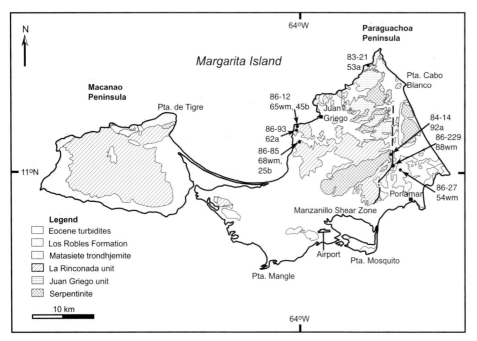

Figure 3. Geologic and sample location map for Margarita Island. Ages given are all ⁴⁰Ar/³⁹Ar data with either plateau or isochron ages as described in the text. Mineral abbreviations: a—amphibole; b—biotite; wm—white mica. Map adapted from Guth (1991).

To the east of Puerto Cabello, the northern subbelt continues on Margarita Island (Fig. 3), which consists of three metamorphic units as well as metaigneous and igneous lithologies (e.g., Maresch, 1975; Avé Lallemant and Guth, 1990; Guth, 1991; Stöckhert et al., 1995; Avé Lallemant, 1997). In addition, there are large serpentinite bodies (Abujaber and Kimberley, 1992). The metamorphic units include the Juan Griego Group, the La Rinconada Group, and the Los Robles Group. Paleogene to Quaternary sedimentary rocks such as the Paleogene Pampatar Formation and Eocene Punta Carnero Group overlie all these units. The Juan Griego Group is a metasedimentary sequence with quartzo-feldspathic units, marbles, and metaquartzites, and includes numerous eclogite and amphibolite knockers and lenses. The La Rinconada Group is mainly a mafic sequence metamorphosed at eclogite facies conditions. The peak metamorphic conditions were 500–600 °C at pressures of 1000–1400 MPa (Stöckhert et al., 1995). The Los Robles Group is a low-grade metasedimentary sequence with quartz-chlorite phyllites, marble, dolomitic marble, calcareous phyllites, and metaconglomerates. It does not contain any eclogite knockers or amphibolites.

South of Margarita Island is the Araya and Paria Peninsula (Fig. 4), which is also known as the Carúpano region (Avé

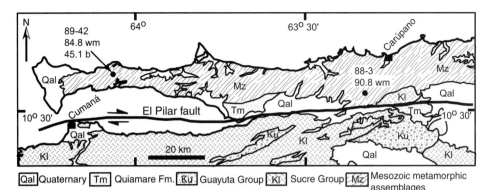

Figure 4. Geologic and sample location map for Araya Peninsula. Ages given are all $^{40}Ar/^{39}Ar$ white mica (wm) data as described in the text. Qal—Quaternary; Kl—Lower Cretaceous; Ku—Upper Cretaceous; Mz—Mesozoic; Tm—Tertiary Miocene. Map simplified from Bellizzia et al. (1976).

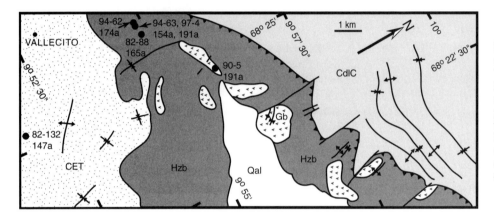

Figure 5. Geologic and sample map of a portion of the Tinaquillo and El Tinaco complexes. Sample numbers have been shortened. Ages given are all $^{40}Ar/^{39}Ar$ amphibole data with either plateau or isochron ages as described in the text. CdlC—Cordillera de la Costa belt; Hzb—harzburgite; Gb—gabbro; CET—Caucagua–El Tinaco belt; Qal—Quaternary alluvium. Map adapted from Ostos (1984, 1990).

Lallemant, 1997). The Carúpano region consists of several metamorphic assemblages that may correlate with the schists in the southern subbelt near Puerto Cabello. These range in metamorphic grade from amphibolite facies in the Manicuare assemblage to lower greenschist grade in the Laguna Chica, Carúpano, and Tunapui assemblages. Two of these belts, the Manicuare and Tunapui, were sampled for this study (Fig. 4). The metamorphic conditions for the Manicuare assemblage reached temperatures of 500–550 °C at pressures of 500–700 MPa (Avé Lallemant, 1997).

Caucagua–El Tinaco Belt

The Caucagua–El Tinaco belt, or terrane, consists of two major units: the Tinaco complex and the Tinaquillo peridotite complex (Fig. 5) (Ostos et al., this volume, Chapter 8). Within the area of Figure 5, the Tinaco complex is predominantly hornblende-plagioclase gneiss that was intruded by trondhjemite sills and dikes. However, Seyler et al. (1998) also found garnet-pyroxene gneisses that record granulite facies metamorphic conditions in this area and refer to it as the Tinaquillo crustal formation. They document peak metamorphic temperatures of 800 °C at pressures of 500–600 MPa.

The contact between the Tinaco and Tinaquillo complexes is a ductile shear zone. The Tinaquillo complex is mostly an ultramafic sequence that includes harzburgite, dunite, pyrox-enite, and metagabbro (MacKenzie, 1960; Ostos, 1984; Seyler and Mattson, 1989, 1993; Seyler et al., 1998; Ostos et al., this volume, Chapter 8). It may have formed by either oceanic or continental rifting (Ostos et al., this volume, Chapter 8). Both the Tinaquillo and Tinaco complexes were thrust northward over low-grade metasedimentary rocks of the Cordillera de la Costa belt that locally includes graphitic phyllite, calcareous quartzite, and marble.

Serranía del Interior Foreland Fold and Thrust Belt

The Serranía del Interior foreland fold and thrust belt is constructed from Upper Cretaceous to Cenozoic sedimentary rocks (Fig. 6). Upper Cretaceous rocks may have been deposited on an Atlantic-type passive margin during the drift phase (González de Juana et al., 1980; Case et al., 1984; di Croce, 1995; Ostos et al., this volume, Chapter 2; Pérez de Armas, this volume). González de Juana et al. (1980) summarizes the stratigraphic information for the region. For this study, we sampled from the Cretaceous Garapata, Mucaria, and Guárico Formations. Subsequent deposition of Paleogene flysch indicates initial collision of the Leeward Antilles arc with South America (Beck, 1978, 1985; Ostos et al., this volume, Chapter 2). In central Venezuela, these orogenic deposits are of Oligocene and Neogene age. The samples for this study are from the Quebradón and Quiamare Formations.

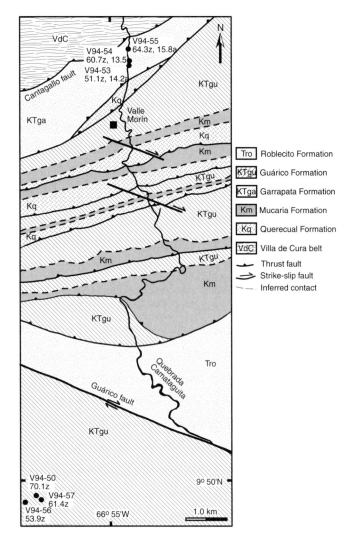

Figure 6. Geologic and sample map of a portion of the central Serranía del Interior foreland fold and thrust belt. Note that samples V94-59, V94-60, and V94-61 are to the west along strike from this map region. Mineral abbreviations: a—apatite; z—zircon. Map adapted from Bell (1968) and Pérez de Armas (this volume).

METHODS

To address the various tectonic problems in northern Venezuela, we used several methods on many samples. These include U-Pb, Rb-Sr, and $^{40}Ar/^{39}Ar$ isotopic analysis, fission-track analysis, and ^{14}C analysis. Brief descriptions of these techniques follow with full tables and associated figures.

Sampling

Samples were collected during nine field seasons in the three belts. The belts were chosen based on tectonic setting, lithology, and mineral assemblage. Care was taken to get the freshest possible samples. In some locations, it was not possible to avoid the effects of tropical weathering. The altered portions were then eliminated

before mineral separation. Sample locations are shown in various figures for each region and tabulated in Appendix Table A1.

Mineral Chemistry

Mineral chemistry and cathodoluminescence (CL) were determined using a Cameca SX-50 electron microprobe at Rice University, Houston, Texas. Operating conditions were 15 keV and 15 nA for amphibole with a beam diameter of 5 μm. Calibration was done on natural and synthetic mineral and oxide standards, and all corrections were performed using PAP reduction procedures (Pouchou and Pichoir, 1987).

U-Pb Analyses

U-Pb isotope data for four samples were determined using well-established techniques on a Finnigan MAT 262 mass spectrometer at Rice University. Mineral separates for U-Pb geochronology were prepared using standard techniques; these minerals were nonmagnetic at 1.7 A with a 20° forward and a 2°–7° side tilt on a Frantz magnetic separator. They were subsequently sorted into size-fractions and handpicked to >99% purity. Three size fractions of zircon were processed for each sample. The samples were analyzed before the CL study; thus, it was not known that these samples needed additional processing such as air abrasion prior to analysis. Thus, only one size fraction for one sample was additionally processed by air abrasion to remove rim material. The zircon data all give discordant ages and suggest either an inherited component or subsequent resetting of the age by a metamorphic event.

Rb-Sr Analyses

Whole-rock Rb-Sr isochrons were determined for two lithologies, one in the Cordillera de la Costa belt and the other in the Caucagua–El Tinaco belt. Teledyne Isotopes of New Jersey (now Teledyne Brown Engineering) performed the analyses using standard techniques. Isochrons were calculated using least square regression techniques after York (1968) with a decay constant of $1.42 \times 10^{-11} yr^{-1}$. Several other lithologies were also analyzed but gave meaningless results because of significant plagioclase alteration.

$^{40}Ar/^{39}Ar$ Analyses

Mineral separates for $^{40}Ar/^{39}Ar$ analyses were prepared by standard techniques and analyzed at two different facilities at the University of Houston and U.S. Geological Survey in Denver. All separates were >99% pure. Samples analyzed at the University of Houston were irradiated at Texas A&M University for ~30 h. Analyses were performed by the standard step-heating technique on a MAP 215-50 rare-gas mass spectrometer in the University of Houston Argon Thermochronology Laboratory. Neutron fluence was monitored with a standard mineral (Fish Canyon Tuff sanidine, 27.9 Ma; Steven et al., 1967; Hurford and Hammerschmidt, 1985; Cebula et al., 1986). Interfering reactions were accounted for by analyzing optical grade CaF_2 and synthetic glass with K_2O content of 18 wt%. Samples analyzed at the U.S. Geologic Survey in Denver were irradiated in the TRIGA reactor. Analyses were preformed by standard step-heating techniques on a Mass Analyzer Products 215 rare gas mass spectrometer located in the Denver Argon Lab as described by Snee (2002). Neutron fluence for these samples was monitored with hornblende MMhb-1, 520.4 Ma (Samson and Alexander, 1987). Many of our samples do not meet the criteria for "true" plateau ages with three or more fractions constituting more than 60% of the ^{39}Ar released within 2σ of each other. Thus, many of these results are weighted average plateau ages. The analytical data for all the $^{40}Ar/^{39}Ar$ analyses are in GSA Data Repository Tables DR1–DR4[1].

Fission-Track Analyses

Apatite and zircon were separated from rock samples using conventional heavy liquid and magnetic separation techniques (Naeser, 1979) and analyzed at two different facilities (University of Southern California and Rice University). The samples were then mounted in epoxy and polished along with an external muscovite detector. The samples analyzed at Rice University were irradiated in the Texas A&M University Radiation Center. The rest of the samples were irradiated using the Cornell University TRIGA reactor. Both numbers of tracks as well as track length distributions were measured. The standard fission-track age equation was used with a weighted mean zeta calibration factor based on the Durango apatite age standards (Hurford and Green, 1983).

For two samples, the apatite fission-track age and length data were grouped into kinetic classes using a calibrated parameter (Dpar), the mean etch pit diameter parallel to the crystallographic c-axis (Donelick, 1993; Burtner et al., 1994; Donelick, 1995; Carlson et al., 1999; Ketcham et al., 1999). These data were then used to model thermal history using AFTSolve (©1996–2000 Donelick Analytical, Inc., and Richard A. Ketcham), which implements various laboratory calibrations for fission tracks in apatite in response to heating and/or cooling histories. Full details concerning these calibrations and the various uses of AFTSolve are available in Carlson et al. (1999), Donelick et al. (1999), Ketcham et al. (1999), and Ketcham et al. (2000). A temperature history was deemed acceptable or good when both the model fission-track age and the model fission-track length distribution matched their measured counterparts with a level of confidence of 0.05 and 0.50, respectively.

[1]GSA Data Repository item 2005144, Tables DR1–DR4, analytical data for all the $^{40}Ar/^{39}Ar$ analyses, is available on the Web at http://www.geosociety.org/pubs/ft2005.htm. Requests for data repository items may also be sent to editing@geosociety.org.

Carbon-14 Analysis

Two sedentary fossil corals situated far above present sea level were collected along the Caribbean coast of northern Venezuela between Puerto Cabello and Caracas. Sample V92-26 was collected near Cata, and sample V92-34 came from Punta Yapascua (Fig. 2). They were collected for ^{14}C dating to obtain uplift rates.

Sample V92-26 came from a site 6.3 ft (2 m) above the level of live corals. However, it was completely replaced by calcite and, thus, useless for dating purposes. Fossil coral V92-34 was sampled on April 30, 1992. It consisted of 100% aragonite, and was thus datable. It occurred in growth position ~12 ft above sea level and 16 ft above the highest level of living corals, so we assume a minimum uplift of 16 ft (5.3 m). The site is situated near the east-west–trending right-lateral San Sebastian strike-slip fault (sometimes called the Morón fault).

First, an aliquot of the coral was processed at the stable isotope facility at Rice University, which determined $\delta C^{13} = 0.67\%$ relative to Peedee belemnite. Next, Beta Analytic Inc. Laboratory, in Miami, Florida, pretreated another aliquot with dilute HCl acid to remove outer layers. This was followed by dispersal in hot acid, multiple rinses to neutrality, and combustion in a closed system. Finally, the sample was put through benzene synthesis and accelerator mass spectrometry to determine its age.

RESULTS

U-Pb Geochronology

The igneous and metaigneous rocks in the Cordillera de la Costa belt are mapped as crosscutting units and thus their age should help bracket the age of high-pressure metamorphism and subduction. Four samples in the Cordillera de la Costa belt were analyzed (Table 1; Fig. 2). Three samples were from the Paleozoic intrusive complex. Two of these were from igneous bodies: the Guaremal granite (91VSn15) between Puerto Cabello and Valencia and the Choroní granite (V94-49) between Choroní and Victoria. The third sample is an augen gneiss (91VSn19) with garnet–biotite–K-feldspar–plagioclase–quartz, located near the Guaremal granite. Previous geologic mapping suggests that the Guaremal granite intruded the augen gneiss. The fourth sample comes from a folded trondhjemitic dike in quartzofeldspathic schists within 400 m of eclogite inclusions or blocks near Ocumare de la Costa.

The morphology of the zircon grains range from elongate to equant with a variety of internal structures when imaged by CL (Fig. 7). In some of the samples, the zircon grains have entirely straight-edged oscillatory zoning (91VSn15). In other samples, there are zircon grains with dark subhedral cores overgrown with regions of oscillatory zoning (91VSn19). This same sample also has cores with straight-edged oscillatory zoning surrounded by a simple unzoned rim. The zoning visible with CL can also be patchy as in the core of V94-49. A few grains exhibit late U enrichment (dark veins in V94-49). CL imaging of all samples shows that none of these had a simple, one-stage magmatic history.

TABLE 1. U-PB ISOTOPIC DATA FOR THE CORDILLERA DE LA COSTA BELT

Sample#	U (ppm)	^{206}Pb* (ppm)	Measured ratios†			Atomic ratios			Apparent ages§ (Ma)		
			$\frac{^{206}Pb}{^{204}Pb}$	$\frac{^{207}Pb}{^{206}Pb}$	$\frac{^{208}Pb}{^{206}Pb}$	$\frac{^{206}Pb*}{^{238}U}$	$\frac{^{207}Pb*}{^{235}U}$	$\frac{^{207}Pb*}{^{206}Pb*}$	$\frac{^{206}Pb*}{^{238}U}$	$\frac{^{207}Pb*}{^{235}U}$	$\frac{^{207}Pb*}{^{206}Pb*}$
V92-24 +150A	918	57.87	650	0.07996	0.24925	0.07340(37)	0.58300(336)	0.05761(17)	456.6	466.4	514.7 ± 6.3
V92-24 +150	940	58.71	1008	0.07192	0.21715	0.07268(36)	0.57625(309)	0.05751(11)	452.3	462.1	511.0 ± 4.3
V92-24 150–210	1048	66.57	1100	0.07077	0.22076	0.07394(37)	0.58676(312)	0.05756(10)	459.8	468.8	512.9 ± 3.9
V92-24 –210	947	60.16	1805	0.06553	0.21221	0.07398(37)	0.58636(302)	0.05748(7)	460.1	468.5	510.0 ± 2.7
V94-49 +150	573	41.03	1253	0.07455	0.17217	0.08333(42)	0.72423(378)	0.06303(9)	516.0	553.2	709.3 ± 3.2
V94-49 150–210	628	43.37	1733	0.06814	0.17356	0.08039(40)	0.66266(343)	0.05978(8)	498.5	516.2	595.7 ± 2.8
V94-49 210–325	745	50.18	1626	0.06734	0.18664	0.07841(39)	0.63157(326)	0.05842(8)	486.6	497.1	545.5 ± 2.9
V94-49 –325	946	62.58	1497	0.06779	0.19800	0.07701(38)	0.61689(320)	0.05809(8)	478.3	487.9	533.3 ± 3.0
91VSn19 +100	732	33.55	1559	0.06486	0.12578	0.05333(27)	0.40818(210)	0.05551(7)	334.9	347.6	432.9 ± 2.8
91VSn19 +150	738	31.57	588	0.07998	0.16877	0.04977(25)	0.37877(227)	0.05519(18)	313.1	326.1	419.9 ± 7.3
91VSn19 150–210	574	26.97	378	0.09418	0.20297	0.05467(27)	0.41931(296)	0.05562(28)	343.1	355.6	437.4 ± 11.1
91VSn19 210–325	523	25.55	907	0.07193	0.14545	0.05689(28)	0.43830(239)	0.05587(12)	356.7	369.1	447.3 ± 4.9
91VSn15 150–210	546	24.45	312	0.10418	0.24130	0.05210(26)	0.41337(318)	0.05754(34)	327.4	351.3	512.4 ± 12.9
91VSn15 210–325	516	22.62	509	0.08540	0.19378	0.05106(26)	0.40024(248)	0.05685(21)	321.0	341.8	485.8 ± 8.1
91VSn15 –325	514	21.82	475	0.08749	0.18868	0.04943(25)	0.38777(246)	0.05689(22)	311.0	332.7	487.3 ± 8.5

\# Sample weights between 1 and 6 mg; numbers after sample numbers refer to size fractions in mesh; A—air abraded fraction.

*Denotes radiogenic Pb, corrected for common Pb using the isotopic composition of ^{206}Pb/^{204}Pb = 18.6 and ^{207}Pb/^{204}Pb = 15.6. Sample dissolution and ion exchange chemistry modified from Krogh (1973). U and Pb concentrations determined by isotope dilution via the addition of a mixed ^{208}Pb–^{235}U tracer added to a solution aliquot (HCL) of each sample.

†Isotopic compositions corrected for mass fractionation (0.11% per A.M.U.).

§Ages calculated using the following constants: decay constants for ^{235}U and ^{238}U = 9.8485 E-10 and 1.55125 E-10 yr^{-1}, respectively; ^{238}U/^{235}U = 137.88. Error analysis for individual zircon fractions follows Mattinson (1987).

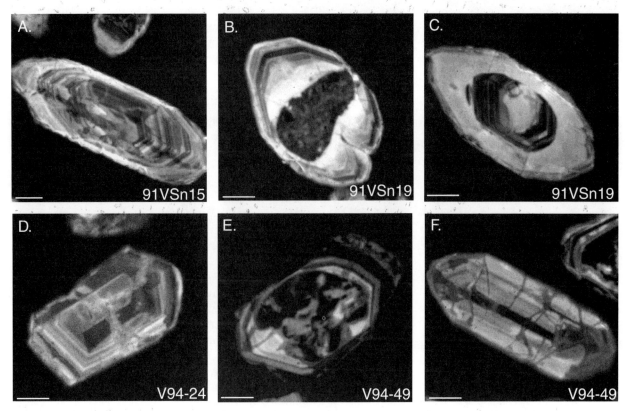

Figure 7. Cathodoluminescence (CL) images of zircon grains analyzed for geochronology. Changes in intensity of CL shown as grayscale changes representative of chemical variations, crystallization of the zircon, as well as late fractures. Scale bar in all images is 20 μm. (A) Sample 91VSn15 from an augengneiss on the highway between Puerto Cabello and Valencia. (B and C) Sample 91VSn19 from the Guaremal granite on the highway between Puerto Cabello and Valencia. (D) Sample V94-24 from a cross-cutting intrusive trondhjemitic dike near Ocumare. (E and F) Sample V94-49 from the Choroní granite.

Table 1 and Figure 8 shows that all of the samples are discordant and only sample V92-24 gives a relatively uncomplicated result. Although all four analyses for V92-24 are significantly discordant, all zircon fractions have the same ^{207}Pb*/^{206}Pb* dates within analytical error (Table 1). The weighted mean of these dates is 511.3 ± 1.8 Ma with a mean square of weighted deviates = 0.93. We interpret this to be the age of this sample.

Four zircon fractions from sample V94-49, the Choroní granite (Table 1), are all discordant but do form a linear array on concordia (Fig. 8). On the concordia diagram (Fig. 8), the four fractions give a lower concordia intercept of 471 ± 23 Ma and a very poorly resolved upper concordia intercept of 1791 ± 740 Ma. There are two possible interpretations of this data. Either the granite has a crystallization age of 471 ± 23 Ma that includes an older inherited Precambrian zircon component or the sample is Precambrian in age and the zircons were severely affected by a metamorphic (?) event at ca. 471 Ma. Because of the evidence that some of the zircons contain irregular cores (Fig. 7E), we prefer the interpretation that the Choroní granite has a crystallization age of ca. 471 Ma.

Four zircon fractions from the Guaremal gneiss (91VSn-19; Table 1) plot as a linear array on concordia with an upper concordia intercept of 501 ± 25 Ma and a lower concordia intercept

of 148 ± 32 Ma. Again, two possibilities exist for the interpretation of the available zircon data. Either the Guaremal gneiss has a crystallization age of ca. 500 Ma and underwent an episodic Pb loss disturbance (metamorphism) reflected by the lower intercept or it has a crystallization age of ca. 150 Ma with an older inherited component. We tentatively favor that this sample has a crystallization age of ca. 500 Ma because CL imaging of zircons (Fig. 7C) shows a delicately zoned core overgrown by unzoned zircon. Unzoned overgrowths are often produced during high-grade metamorphism.

The analyses from the Guaremal granite (Table 1; Fig. 8) are not sufficient to yield an interpretation of the age of this sample.

Rb-Sr Geochronology

The basement units in the Cordillera de la Costa and Caucagua–El Tinaco belts include the Peña de Mora Formation and the La Aguadita Gneiss. Three samples of the Peña de Mora Formation (two from Avila National Park and one from near Chichiriviche) were analyzed and resulted in an initial ^{87}Sr/^{86}Sr of 0.71103 ± 0.00734 with a crystallization age of 1560 ± 83 Ma. These samples were collected over a large region and may not record a single intrusive. Four samples of variable lithology from

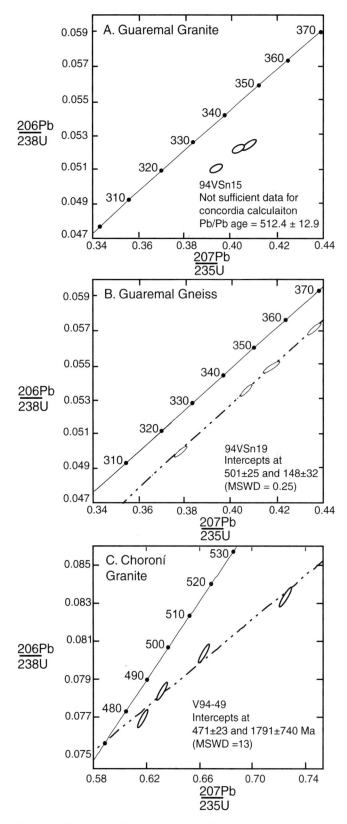

the El Tinaco complex (La Aguadita Gneiss) were analyzed. These resulted in an initial $^{87}Sr/^{86}Sr$ of 0.70475 ± 0.00197 with a crystallization age of 945 ± 178 Ma. This determination may be suspect because of widespread alteration of feldspar in the gneissic rocks. There is also the possibility of a complex thermal history for this region (see Ostos and Sisson, this volume). In addition, the variability in the lithologies may indicate that the rocks are not cogenetic. Both of these results should be reanalyzed with U-Pb or other geochronologic techniques. Since the quality of the data is suspect, we do not present either the data or isochrons. Several other samples of the La Guacamaya metadiorite and Todasona complex were analyzed but resulted in meaningless ages (Ostos, 1990).

$^{40}Ar/^{39}Ar$ Geochronology

Cordillera de la Costa Belt

To constrain the metamorphic cooling history and regional distribution of ages, four white mica and one amphibole separates from the Puerto Cabello region were analyzed (Figs. 2, 9, and 10). Four of these samples were micaceous schists typically with garnet, feldspar, and quartz. Rarely did they contain biotite. One sample was near an eclogite inclusion. The white mica cooling ages yielded information about the regional thermal history following peak metamorphism. These all yielded plateau ages ranging from 28.0 Ma in the south to 41.4 Ma in the north (Fig. 9; Table DR1 [see footnote 1]). These seem to fall on a distinct trend that becomes younger to the south. R.C. Speed (1992, personal commun.) also reported a white mica cooling age with a plateau of 32.9 ± 0.3 Ma for a sample of the Caracas Group collected to the southeast of Caracas. Five other samples from the Caracas Group yielded poor spectra with ages between 45 and 37 Ma. This age trend is supported by one amphibole $^{40}Ar/^{39}Ar$ weighted average plateau date of 37.4 Ma from actinolite schist north of Maracay (Fig. 10; Table DR2 [see footnote 1]). We attempted to date three other amphibole separates from this region, but they did not yield interpretable plateau or isochron ages. Additional amphibole analyses are in progress to better resolve this apparent trend in ages.

Margarita and Araya

Ten samples from Margarita Island and two samples from Araya Peninsula represent a diverse array of lithologies and minerals analyzed, including amphibole, biotite, and white mica (Figs. 3–4 and 11–15; Table DR3 [see footnote 1]). The units sampled on Margarita Island include the high-pressure units, La Rinconada and Juan Griego, and the low-grade Los Robles Formation. Araya Peninsula lacks any high-pressure units and so two different metamorphic units, amphibolite facies Manicuare and greenschist facies Carúpano assemblages, were sampled (Fig. 4). Some of the questions to be addressed with radiometric data include (1) is there an age difference between the two high-pressure units and the lower grade Los Robles Formation, (2) was the metamorphism on Margarita Island synchronous with that on Araya Peninsula, (3) are there any regional trends in age relation-

Figure 8. Concordia diagrams of zircon fractions for three samples from the Cordillera de la Costa belt. Data point error ellipses represent two-sigma variation.

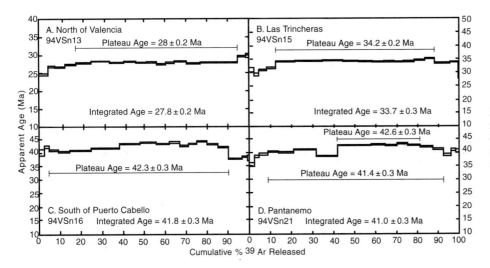

Figure 9. White mica $^{40}Ar/^{39}Ar$ incremental step heating spectra from Cordillera de la Costa belt, Venezuela. Both integrated age for the entire spectrum and plateau age are given.

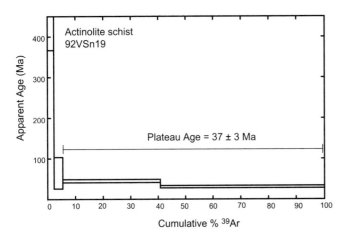

Figure 10. Amphibole $^{40}Ar/^{39}Ar$ incremental step heating spectra from Cordillera de la Costa belt, Venezuela. The analysis only includes four release steps; thus, only the weighted average age is indicated.

ships, and (4) what is the difference in age between minerals with different closure temperature? These results will be discussed by comparing data from each mineral analyzed.

Amphibole is only present in the two high-pressure units from Margarita Island. Three amphibole separates from eclogite of the Juan Griego unit and garnet-amphibolite from both the La Rinconada and Juan Griego units were analyzed. These yield plateau ages between 92.4 and 52.1 Ma with many steps that are not included in these plateaus (Fig. 11). There may be a north-south trend with the oldest age in the south (sample IM84-14) and the youngest age from the north coast (sample VM83-21). However, this trend could also reflect amphibole composition as separates of all samples have a different type of amphibole (Table 2). The oldest age is from an actinolite (IM84-14), whereas the youngest age is a barroisite (VM83-21). Since the amphibole composition may affect the closure temperature, the age spread could simply

reflect amphibole composition. There does not seem to be a difference in the age of the two high-pressure units, the Juan Griego and La Rinconada.

A biotite separate from a metaconglomerate (sample VM86-12) in the La Rinconada unit yielded an isochron age of 44.9 ± 1.7 Ma for nine steps (Fig. 12). The age spectrum for this sample was very disturbed, as indicated by the $^{39}Ar/^{37}Ar$ ratio, and appears to represent alteration degassing. The white mica separate from this same sample yielded an integrated age of 65.0 ± 0.2 Ma with Ar loss for the low temperature release (Fig. 13).

Another biotite separate from the La Rinconada unit did not yield an interpretable plateau age because there was significant Ar loss probably related to late stage alteration of the biotite (Fig. 14). The total gas age is 24.9 ± 0.9 Ma. A third biotite separate from a garnet-staurolite schist on Araya Peninsula had a similar loss pattern with a poorly defined plateau near 50 Ma. This sample (VS89-42) has a total gas age of 45.1 ± 0.3 Ma. Thus, most of the biotite in this region is not suitable for further analysis.

Two white mica separates from the Los Robles Formation have a range of have a range of ages similar to the amphibole ages between 88.5 (sample M86-229) and 53.5 Ma (sample IM86-27) (Fig. 13). A white mica from the La Rinconada unit has an integrated age of 68.3 Ma (Fig. 13). Unlike the amphibole ages, there are no regional variations in the white mica ages. There is overlap in the ages between the high-pressure units and the lower grade Los Robles Formation.

A white mica separate (sample VS89-42) from a garnet staurolite schist on Araya Peninsula yielded a plateau age of 84.8 ± 0.2 Ma (Fig. 15). A white mica separate (sample VE88-3) yielded an integrated age of 90.8 ± 0.4 Ma. This spectra looks like a mixture of components (Fig. 15).

Caucagua–El Tinaco Belt

Determination of the age of ultramafic complexes is inherently difficult because they often lack suitable mineral assem-

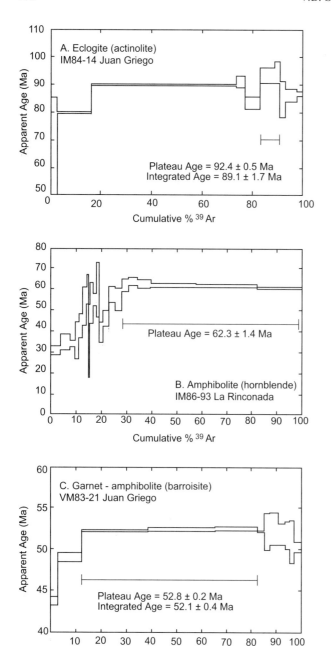

Figure 11. Amphibole $^{40}Ar/^{39}Ar$ incremental step heating spectra from three high-pressure blocks in the Juan Griego and La Rinconada units on Margarita Island. The plateau age is given for each spectra.

blages. Associated with the Tinaquillo ultramafic complex are several amphibole-bearing units including undeformed and deformed gabbros, associated pegmatite, and late amphibole veins (hornblendite). Amphibole separates from seven samples were collected from these variably deformed metaigneous rocks of the Tinaquillo complex as well as one granulite from the Tinaco complex (Figs. 5, 16, and 17). The $^{40}Ar/^{39}Ar$ data from these separates yield a range in ages from 190.6 to 124.2 Ma

(Figs. 16 and 17; Table DR3 [see footnote 1]). Three of the samples give plateau ages as well as isochron dates (Fig. 17). There is no correlation between the age obtained and the location at which the samples were collected. In fact, three samples collected within 100 m of each other (V94-62, V94-63, and V97-4) span from 190.6 to 153.9Ma. There is also no obvious relationship between either the amount of deformation or the distance from major shear zones with age, as undeformed hornblendite veins range from 190.6 to 154.7 Ma. The scatter in the results may be explained by low-potassium content (Table 2), excess argon, or mineral purity.

Fission-Track Geochronology

The rates and timing of the final exhumation of orogenic belts is typically constrained with zircon and apatite fission-track geochronology. In addition, fission-track analysis can help constrain the provenance, burial, and subsequent thermal history of sedimentary units. Previous studies in the region were only able to obtain zircon from the Cordillera de la Costa belt and apatite from the Serranía del Interior belt (Kohn et al., 1984; Pérez de Armas, this volume), so we collected both apatite and zircon to understand the relationships between exhumation and regional tectonics.

Cordillera de la Costa Belt

Three samples were analyzed for both zircon and apatite from granite and augen gneiss of the Cordillera de la Costa belt (Table 3). Two samples are of the Guaremal granite and augen gneiss near Valencia and the other sample is from the Choroní granite (Fig. 2). The three-apatite ages are almost identical within error and ranged from 16.3 ± 1.6 to 14.1 ± 1.7 Ma. Two of the zircon ages from near Valencia were identical (19.8 ± 1.2 Ma), whereas the zircon from the Choroní granite was younger, at 13.6 ± 1.4 Ma.

One of the fundamental aspects of fission-track data is that it can be used to construct temperature-time cooling histories (Fig. 18). All samples have a unimodal distribution around ~12 μm. Cooling paths for two of these samples (Fig. 18) indicate an initial moderate cooling rate after passing through zircon closure temperature with cooling rate decreasing until ca. 7 Ma. There is a slight change in cooling rate at 15–20 Ma.

Serranía del Interior Fold and Thrust Belt

Three new apatite and nine new zircon fission-track analyses were acquired from samples representing five different formations in the Valle Morín–Camatagua region in the Serranía del Interior fold and thrust belt (Fig. 6; Table 4). This is the same region investigated by Pérez de Armas (this volume). The three apatite results range from 13.5 to 15.8 Ma with an average of 14.5 Ma, almost identical to results of Pérez de Armas (this volume). For example, in the Garapata Formation north of Valle Morín, the pooled apatite ages are within statistical error in these two studies. There is no trend in either apatite or zircon fission-track ages from north to south along this transect.

TABLE 2. REPRESENTATIVE ANALYSES OF AMPHIBOLE FROM MARGARITA ISLAND
AND TINAQUILLO COMPLEX

Sample	IM84-14	IM86-93	VM83-21	VTO82-88	Ti90-5
location	Margarita	Margarita	Margarita	Tinaquillo	Tinaquillo
lithology	eclogite	amphibolite	grt-amph	hornblendite	hornblendite
amph	act	hbl	bar	hbl	tsch
SiO_2	54.46	45.75	47.26	45.36	43.35
TiO_2	0.16	0.42	0.52	2.82	1.17
Al_2O_3	6.12	12.66	12.05	12.46	15.59
Fe_2O_3	0.00	0.00	0.00	0.00	0.00
FeO	4.03	8.28	8.13	5.81	8.49
MnO	4.30	9.78	8.45	1.98	0.85
MgO	0.03	0.23	0.22	0.09	0.09
CaO	9.63	10.30	7.68	10.48	11.42
Na2O	2.53	1.47	3.73	3.45	2.78
K_2O	0.24	0.40	0.29	0.28	0.18
H_2O	2.18	2.08	2.09	2.15	2.15
Total	101.07	101.13	100.86	101.66	101.75
Si	7.500	6.597	6.767	6.321	6.049
Al^{IV}	0.500	1.403	1.233	1.679	1.951
Al^{VI}	0.493	0.749	0.800	0.367	0.613
Ti	0.016	0.045	0.056	0.296	0.123
Fe^{3+}	0.418	0.898	0.876	0.610	0.892
Fe^{2+}	0.496	1.179	1.012	0.231	0.099
Mn	0.003	0.027	0.026	0.011	0.011
Mg	3.575	2.101	2.230	3.487	3.262
Ca	1.420	1.591	1.178	1.565	1.708
Na	0.674	0.411	1.036	0.932	0.752
K	0.042	0.073	0.054	0.050	0.032
OH	2.000	2.000	2.000	2.000	2.000

Note: Cations calculated for 23 anions. Fe^{3+} was estimated by calculating total cations to 13, exclusive of K, Na, Ca. H_2O content was calculated. Abbreviations: act—actinolite; amph—amphibolite; grt—garnet; hbl—hornblende; bar—barroisite, tsch—tschermakite.

The zircon fission-track ages range from 85.1 to 51.1 Ma. Most of the ages fall within the range expected for the sedimentary protolith. This implies that these are unroofing ages for these units. Two of the ages (V94-59 and V94-61) are older than their sedimentary age, which implies an earlier unroofing event; thus, these ages are inherited from their source area.

Carbon-14 Geochronology

The final uplift of orogenic belts can occasionally be constrained with geochronology of geomorphic features such as exposed corals and marine terraces. We analyzed one coral (V92-34) that yielded an uncorrected age of 500 ± 60 radiocarbon years. The age is reported as radiocarbon years before 1950 AD. The quoted errors represent one standard deviation from counting statistics of standard, background, and sample. The final adjusted age was normalized to $\delta C^{13} = -25‰$, which yields an age of 500 ± 60 yr B.P. However, this date has to be adjusted for the age of the

Caribbean waters (Hughen et al., 1996). According to R.B. Dunbar (2002, personal commun.), the real age of the coral is between 200 and 50 yr B.P. and, thus, formed between 1800 and 1950 AD.

DISCUSSION

The initial history of the Venezuelan margin can be partially determined by protolith ages for the various belts (Table 5). The fragmentary fossil evidence indicates that the various belts were deposited over a wide age range from Jurassic to Paleogene. Table 6 summarizes the old and new age determinations for the igneous and metamorphic rocks for three belts in northern Venezuela (see Appendix Tables A2–A5 for additional data); these are the Cordillera de la Costa, Villa de Cura, and Caucagua–El Tinaco belts. Two of these belts, the Cordillera de la Costa and Villa de Cura, formed in response to subduction of Proto-Caribbean crust underneath the Great Arc of the Caribbean. The third belt, the Caucagua–El Tinaco, records early events in the Proto-Caribbean basin.

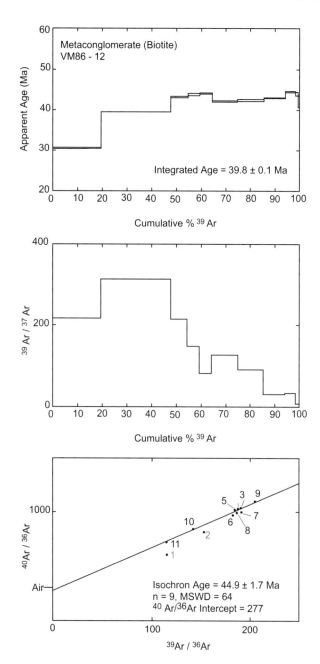

Figure 12. Biotite Ar data for a metaconglomerate on Margarita Island. Top panel is an Ar release spectrum. Middle panel is $^{39}Ar_K/^{37}Ar_{Ca}$ value for each heating step (equal to 2× the K/Ca ratio). Bottom panel is an isochron diagram. The black numbers are included in the calculated isochron and the gray numbers (steps 1 and 2) were not included.

Table 6 shows the diversity of events recorded in each belt as each geochronologic technique captures a different part of the tectonic history. Much of the old geochronologic data is either K-Ar or Rb-Sr data acquired in the 1960s with some additional data collected through the 1970s and 1980s (Appendix Tables A2–A5). Much of this early data is suspect for several reasons: (1) it is not consistent for any region, (2) it used unreliable minerals such as clinozoisite,

(3) it is often poorly documented, and (4) it typically records a wide age range for the different belts. There are a few modern studies that employ more reliable geochronologic data (e.g., Stöckhert et al., 1995; Speed et al., 1997; Seyler et al., 1998).

Most of our new age determinations for northern South America can be related to various phases of orogeny that affected the Caribbean–South American plate boundary: formation of basement, Jurassic rifting, Cretaceous subduction, and Late Cretaceous to Tertiary exhumation as outlined by previous geochronologic studies (see Appendix Tables A2–A5). In the following, we discuss the implications of the new geochronologic data with respect to these events.

Basement: Its Formation and Subsequent Deformation

The basement rocks in northern Venezuela occur as intrusives, fragments, and blocks within the subduction mélange. Previous work in northern Venezuela recognized Paleozoic intrusives in the Cordillera de la Costa belt, the Dragon gneiss on Araya Peninsula, and the El Amaparo body in the Paraguana Peninsula (e.g., González de Juana et al., 1980; Feo-Codecido et al., 1984; Bartok, 1993; Speed et al., 1997). Much of the previous data relied on K-Ar or Rb-Sr whole rock analysis (see Appendix Tables A2, A3, and A5). Elsewhere in Venezuela, basement is exposed in the Perija and Merida Andes, Santander massif, and Guyana Shield (e.g., Bartok, 1993; Ostos et al., this volume, Chapter 2). Below, we discuss new data related to basement in the Cordillera de la Costa belt.

The Peña de Mora Formation has a low-quality Rb-Sr age of early-middle Proterozoic. Thus, it probably represents the basement upon which the Jurassic-Cretaceous Caracas Group was deposited. It could also represent a fragment of an older terrane incorporated into the region. This age is older than that for the La Aguadita Gneiss of the Tinaco complex. Both of these may represent a northern extension of the Precambrian Guyana Shield.

The intrusive and metaigneous rocks in the Puerto Cabello region all have Cambro-Ordovician intrusive ages. One sample from the Choroní granite has a Precambrian inherited component; this may be similar to the age for the Peña de Mora Formation. It may indicate a component from the Guyana Shield such as the Cuchivero or Roraima Provinces (see Ostos et al., this volume, Chapter 2). The Guaremal gneiss has been affected by later metamorphism in the Jurassic. This is similar to the age for the La Aguadita Gneiss in the Caucagua–El Tinaco belt. Thus, these bodies were part of northern South America prior to subduction metamorphism that affected the Cordillera de la Costa belt.

If these igneous bodies are truly intrusive rocks, as they have been mapped, this implies that the entire region has an older protolith than the regional metamorphism. Of particular importance is the trondhjemitic dike (sample V92-24) that looks like it was folded and foliated prior to or during regional metamorphism and that occurs near eclogite blocks. This may mean that remnants of an older continental margin persist with large, intact blocks of the subduction mélange. This does not agree with most previous

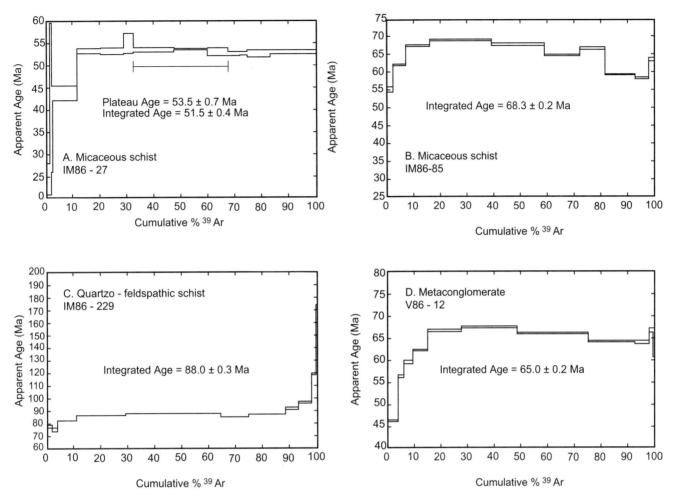

Figure 13. White mica ^{40}Ar/^{39}Ar incremental step heating spectra from micaceous schist, quartzofeldspathic schist, and metaconglomerate on Margarita Island. Either the plateau or integrated age is given for each sample.

interpretations that have assumed that the protolith for the metamorphic rocks was deposited on the passive northern continental margin of South America during Late Jurassic and Early Cretaceous time (e.g., Bellizzia, 1986; also see Table 5).

This suite of Cambro-Ordovician igneous and metaigneous rocks may be correlative with a buried orogenic system accreted onto the Guyana Shield (e.g., Bartok, 1993). These rocks are exposed in the southern Mérida and Perijá Andes and have ages between 680–500 Ma; examples include the Avispa (660 Ma) and Santander massifs (680 Ma; González de Juana et al., 1980; Feo-Codecido et al., 1984). There are also Paleozoic strata preserved below a sub-Cretaceous unconformity (Feo-Codecido et al., 1984). This orogenic system may be related to Pan-African or Brasiliano events between 650–540 Ma. This was followed by rifting of a block or blocks from Laurentia at 540–535 Ma into an already open Iapetus Ocean to establish the main passive-margin sequence in the Appalachians. The Ordovician plutonism may be correlated with the Taconic event in the Appalachians.

On Paria Peninsula, the Dragon augen gneiss has U-Pb concordia with an upper intercept of 587 ± Ma and a lower intercept of 321 ± 29 Ma (Speed et al., 1997). They interpret the lower intercept age as the crystallization age for this metaigneous body and correlate the igneous intrusion with the collision of Pangea with North America to form the Ouachita and Alleghanian allochthons. If the older intercept ages represent inherited cores, they could come from rocks correlative with metaigneous and igneous rocks in the Puerto Cabello region. The gneiss was then mylonitized in the Miocene as recorded by white mica ^{40}Ar/^{39}Ar ages of 21 Ma (Speed et al., 1997).

Jurassic Rifting: Caucagua–El Tinaco Belt

All of our amphibole ^{40}Ar/^{39}Ar cooling ages are older than previously reported in the Tinaquillo complex (see Appendix Table A4). The La Aguadita Gneiss of the Tinaco Complex records a large range of K-Ar ages from 235 to 112 Ma (Appendix Table A4). It is unclear if these ages reflect peak metamor-

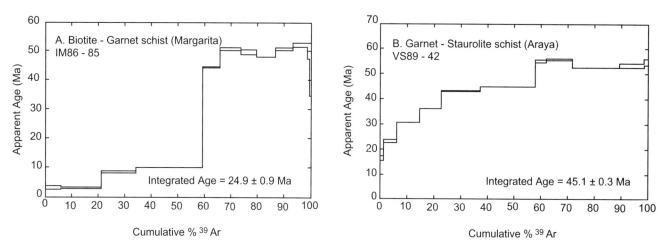

Figure 14. Biotite ^{40}Ar/^{39}Ar incremental step heating spectra from schists from Margarita Island and Araya Peninsula. Neither of these has an interpretable plateau age due to later Ar loss or excess Ar.

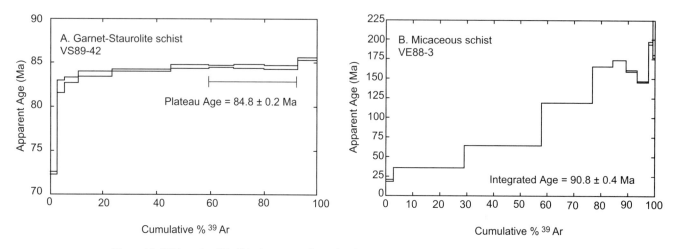

Figure 15. White mica ^{40}Ar/^{39}Ar incremental step heating spectra from schists from Araya Peninsula.

phism during the Triassic or Cretaceous or if they record exhumation or cooling. More recent geochronologic data gives one U-Pb age of 150 Ma (Seyler et al., 1998) and one Nd-Sm age of 94.7 ± 3.3 Ma (Lar, 1992). Our oldest age results of ca. 190 Ma may indicate that initial emplacement of the complex occurred in the Jurassic concurrent with rifting in the Caribbean and Atlantic and Mesozoic breakup of Pangea (see Ostos et al., this volume, Chapter 8). Elsewhere in Venezuela, there are Jurassic grabens (e.g., La Quinta and Espino) with volcanic rocks and volcaniclastic sediments that may correlate with the emplacement of the Tinaquillo complex.

In the adjacent El Tinaco complex, our amphibole ^{40}Ar/^{39}Ar cooling age of 146 Ma is close to the U-Pb zircon age of 150 Ma for a felsic dike that cross-cuts pyroxenite-amphibolite dikes in the Tinaquillo complex (Seyler et al., 1998). This is older than a U-Pb geochronologic result for a peraluminous gneiss of the

Tinaco complex that has a lower intercept age of ca. 125 Ma with a poorly defined upper intercept of 1.1 Ga. This sample records metamorphic conditions of ~780 °C at 620 MPa. Seyler et al. (1998) suggest this lower intercept age may record anatexis during uplift of the region.

The juxtaposition of the Tinaquillo complex and Caucagua–El Tinaco complex formed at ca. 90 Ma as recorded by an Nd-Sm age on a mafic granulite (Seyler et al., 1998). This is much younger than any of our ^{40}Ar/^{39}Ar amphibole ages from the Tinaquillo or El Tinaco complex. The ^{40}Ar/^{39}Ar (age range of 190–146 Ma) and U-Pb (150 Ma) data are suggestive but not conclusive that the granulite facies metamorphism of the Tinaco complex occurred ~40 m.y. after the initial diapiric ascent of the mantle asthenosphere associated with Jurassic rifting. The region probably remained at amphibolite facies conditions until after ca. 90 Ma as recorded by the Nd-Sm geochronologic results.

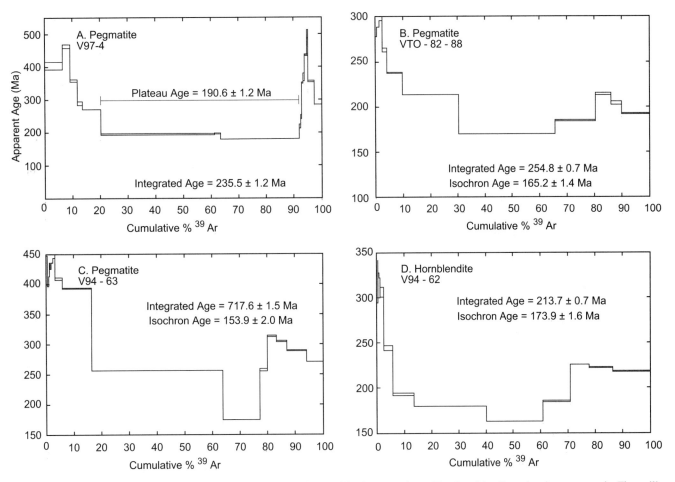

Figure 16. Amphibole ^{40}Ar/^{39}Ar incremental step heating spectra from gabbroic pegmatite and late hornblendite veins that crosscut the Tinaquillo complex, Venezuela. Both integrated age for the entire spectrum and plateau are given in A; both integrated and isochron ages are given in B, C, and D. See Table DR3 (see text footnote 1) for details about the isochron interpretation.

Cretaceous Orogeny: Provenance of the Serranía del Interior Sedimentary Rocks

Just south of the contact between the Villa de Cura blueschist belt and the Serranía del Interior foreland fold and thrust belt along Valle Morín both apatite and zircon fission-track ages were determined (V94-53, V94-54, and V94-55; Table 4). The apatite ages are between 15.8 and 13.5 Ma, similar to apatite fission-track ages that Pérez de Armas (this volume) acquired, probably indicating Miocene uplift and exhumation.

In easternmost north central Serranía, Pérez de Armas (this volume) found not only Miocene, but also Eocene apatite fission-track ages. To the east, Locke and Garver (this volume) reported only Miocene and early Oligocene apatite ages and attributed their older ages to uplift and exhumation as a result of convergence between North and South America that initiated ca. 50 Ma (Pindell et al., this volume).

The zircon fission-track ages of the rocks from Valle Morín (V94-53, V94-54, and V94-55) and other samples in the more southern part of the Serranía are quite different, ranging from 85 to 51 Ma (Table 4). Two samples (V94-60 and V94-61) have zircon ages (85 and 63 Ma) much older than their Miocene stratigraphic age. All other zircon ages overlap with the stratigraphic ages of the rocks. Because of the uncertainties of these zircon ages, two interpretations are allowable.

First, the zircon ages may indicate the age of the source area. This would mean that somewhere not far away felsic plutonic or more likely volcanic rocks of Late Cretaceous to early Eocene age were being eroded. This idea seems to be difficult to accept, because to our knowledge there are no igneous rocks of this age nearby, and the "Great Arc of the Caribbean" was ~1000 km to the west (Pindell et al., 1988).

The second possibility is that these ages represent exhumation ages. According to Pindell et al. (this volume), convergence between North and South America began in Maastrichtian time (72 Ma). This convergence may have resulted in subduction of the Proto-Caribbean plate underneath South America and uplift of the South American continental margin. Assuming exhumation and erosion rates to be ~1 mm/yr., a geothermal gradient of 25 °C/km, and a closure temperature of fission tracks in zircon

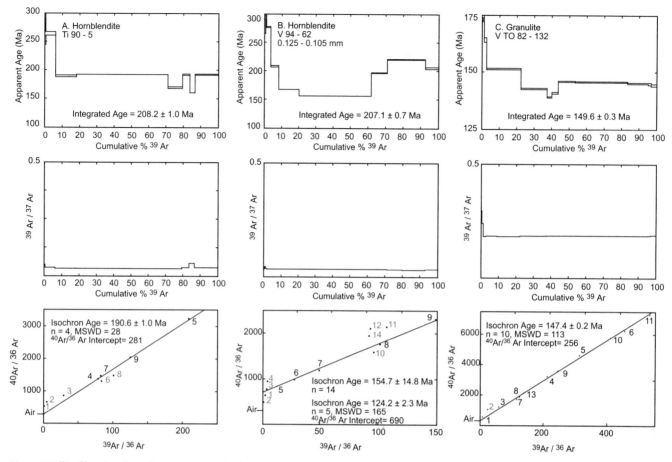

Figure 17. $^{40}Ar/^{39}Ar$ data from three representative hornblende separates from (A and B) late hornblendite veins that crosscut the Tinaquillo complex and (C) the El Tinaco complex, Venezuela. Top figure for each is Ar release spectrum. Middle figure is $^{39}Ar_K/^{37}Ar_{Ca}$ value for each heating step (equal to 2× the K/Ca ratio). Bottom figure is an isochron diagram. The black numbers are included in the calculated isochrons and the gray numbers were not included. Steps not included in calculations are 1–3, 6, and 8 in A, 1–4, 10–12, and 14 in B, and 2 in C.

of ~240 °C, then it can be estimated that ~10 km of sediments had to be removed in a time span of 10 m.y. Subsequently, the sediments may have been transported to the east and deposited in the Eastern Venezuela basin, causing the large negative gravity anomaly in the basin.

Exhumation of High-Pressure Rocks

The two high-pressure subduction belts (Villa de Cura Group and Cordillera de la Costa–Margarita belt) have similar peak metamorphic ages of ca. 95 Ma (Table 6) (Stöckhert et al., 1995; Smith et al., 1999). This implies that these probably formed in the same subduction system despite the differences in protolith and metamorphic conditions between these two belts. The subduction zone was active until at least ca. 80 Ma as recorded by white mica Ar-Ar ages for three lower temperature zones in the Villa de Cura Group (Smith et al., 1999) (Table 6) and post-tectonic island arc magmatism recorded by the intrusion of the Salado granite at 86 Ma on Margarita Island (Stöckhert et al., 1995). We interpret the young ages for the Las Hermanas Formation (Table 6), which

is adjacent to the Villa de Cura Group, to be the result of poor analyses. Instead, we propose that the age of 104 Ma represents the timing of volcanism for this segment of the Great Arc of the Caribbean prior to subduction zone metamorphism. The exhumation rates for the Cordillera de la Costa belt are poorly constrained by previous geochronologic data (Appendix Table A2). There is a wide range of K-Ar ages from 98 to 40 Ma for a variety of minerals and lithologies on Margarita Island (Appendix Table A3). Most of these are difficult to interpret.

On Margarita Island, Stöckhert et al. (1995) proposed rapid cooling between eclogite facies metamorphism and intrusion of post-metamorphic trondhjemite, and between trondhjemite and white mica $^{40}Ar/^{39}Ar$ cooling ages (see Appendix Table A3). This interpretation is consistent with the close agreement between some of the amphibole and white mica ages analyzed for this study. Also, one $^{40}Ar/^{39}Ar$ analysis of actinolite yielded an age of 92.4 ± 0.5 Ma related to cooling after peak metamorphism. This agrees well with timing of peak eclogite facies metamorphism constrained by U-Pb ages of ca. 110 and 86 Ma on pre-tectonic and post-tectonic felsic intrusions on Margarita Island (Stöck-

TABLE 3. FISSION-TRACK DATA FOR THE CORDILLERA DE LA COSTA BELT

Sample	Elevation (m)	No. of grains	Standard track density ×10^5	Spontaneous track density ×10^5	Induced track density ×10^5	$P(\chi^2)$ (%)	U (ppm)	FT age ±1σ (Ma)	Mean track length (mm)	Standard deviation (mm)
Mineral										
apatite										
91VSn15	50	18	3.251	0.410	5.244	16.20	83	16.3 ± 1.6	12.8 ± 0.2	2.65
91VSn19	45	20	3.509	0.421	5.839	25.61	81	15.0 ± 1.4	12.9 ± 0.2	2.35
V94-49	1150	20	15.14	0.836	14.39	75		14.1 ± 1.7	12.1 ± 0.5	1.76
zircon										
91VSn15	50	20	0.676	34.25	7.893	24.59	712	19.8 ± 1.2		
91VSn19	45	20	0.678	28.66	6.630	25.37	601	19.8 ± 1.2		
V94-49	1150	11	2.10	28.50	72.83	82		13.6 ± 1.4		

Note: Standard and induced track densities measured on mica external detectors and spontaneous track density on internal mineral surfaces. Ages for 91VSn15 and 91VSn19 determined by Raymond A. Donelick using zeta = 119 ± 4 (apatite) and 135 ± 4 (zircon) for dosimeter glass CN-1. Ages for V94-49 determined by Ann E. Blythe using zeta = 320 ± 9 (apatite) and 335 ± 20 (zircon) for dosimeter glass SRM962a (e.g., Hurford and Green, 1983). All ages are pooled ages.

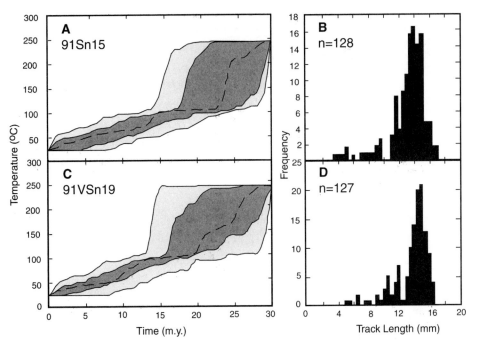

Figure 18. Fission-track data and interpretation for apatite for Guaremal granite (91VSn15) and from augen gneiss (sample 91VSn19). (A and C) Time-temperature history estimated using methods of Ketcham et al. (1999). The dashed line is the best fit to the data. The dark shaded region shows the good model envelope (level of confidence of 0.05) and the light shaded region outlines the acceptable model envelope (level of confidence of 0.50). (B and D) Fission-track length distribution.

hert et al., 1995). Furthermore, if we assume that the Los Robles Formation was metamorphosed at relatively low pressure, then the close agreement in white mica ^{40}Ar/^{39}Ar ages between the greenschist facies metamorphism and cooling of the high-pressure suite would imply a significant pressure decrease during rapid exhumation of the complex.

Several of the amphibole and white mica ^{40}Ar/^{39}Ar ages reported here, however, are significantly younger than the range of white mica Ar ages documented by Stöckhert et al. (1995). Our younger ages are similar to many K-Ar ages reported in previous studies (see Appendix Table A3).

It is possible that there were regionally variable cooling rates. This can be documented with minerals with different closure temperatures, such as white mica and biotite (~350 vs. ~300 °C). Their relative ages are quite dependent on cooling

rates. The pair of white mica and biotite ^{40}Ar/^{39}Ar ages from a metaconglomerate in the La Rinconada unit (sample V86-12) record relatively slow cooling rates of ~2.3 °C/m.y. between 66 Ma to 45 Ma. This is distinctly different from the 13–6 °C/m.y. cooling rates documented elsewhere in the complex by Stöckhert et al. (1995). Regional differences in cooling rates provide a plausible explanation for some but not all of the observed spread in amphibole and white mica ages. It is difficult to make any further interpretations, as previous studies do not have sufficient location or mineral composition data to verify spatial, cooling, or compositional trends.

Another significant finding is that the garnet-staurolite schist (sample VS89-42) from Araya Peninsula has a white mica ^{40}Ar/^{39}Ar age similar to those of Margarita Island. This supports the hypothesis that these two metamorphic belts may

TABLE 4. FISSION-TRACK DATA FOR THE SERRANÍA DEL INTERIOR BELT

Sample	No. of grains	Standard track density ×10⁶ cm⁻²	Spontaneous track density ×10⁶ cm⁻²	Induced track density ×10⁶ cm⁻²	P(χ²) (%)	FT age ±1σ Ma
apatite						
V-94-53	20	1.53	0.96	16.59	86	14.2 ± 2.0
V-94-54	16	1.53	1.05	19.22	47	13.5 ± 1.8
V-94-55	18	1.54	0.53	8.27	92	15.8 ± 2.8
zircon						
V-94-50	30	0.21	68.54	34.47	Fail	70.1 ± 9.7
V-94-53	14	0.21	53.19	35.39	Fail	51.1 ± 6.4
V-94-54	26	0.21	58.72	33.17	Fail	60.7 ± 7.5
V-94-55	40	0.21	43.26	22.51	Fail	64.3 ± 6.2
V-94-56	8	0.21	78.58	48.01	Fail	53.9 ± 13.3
V-94-59	26	0.20	45.51	20.00	Fail	73.4 ± 8.9
V-94-60	9	0.20	82.15	30.48	Fail	85.1 ± 19.7
V-94-61	4	0.20	39.06	20.56	Fail	62.8 ± 16.8

Note: All samples were analyzed by Ann E. Blythe. Apatite was mounted in epoxy and zircon in teflon. Apatite mounts were etched in 7% HNO_3 at 18 °C for 22 s; zircons were etched in KOH:NaOH at 210 °C for 12 to 24 h. An "external detector" (e.g., Naeser, 1979), consisting of low-U (<5 ppb) Brazil Ruby muscovite, was used for each sample. Following irradiation, muscovite was etched in 48% HF at 18 °C for 30 min. A Kinitek stage and software written by Dumitru (1993) was used for analyses. Standard and induced track densities were determined on external detectors (geometry factor = 0.5), and fossil track densities were determined on internal mineral surfaces. Ages were calculated using zeta 320 ± 9 for dosimeter NBS 962 for apatites and a zeta of 335 ± 20 for zircons (e.g., Hurford and Green, 1983). All ages are central ages, with the conventional method (Green, 1981) used to determine errors on sample ages. The chi-square test estimated the probability that individual grain ages for each sample belong to a single population with a Poisson distribution (Galbraith, 1981).

TABLE 5. METAMORPHIC PROTOLITH AGES FOR NORTHERN VENEZUELA

Lithotectonic Unit	Protolith age	Sedimentary environment	Lithology	Reference
Cordillera de la Costa				
Las Brisas Fm.	Jurassic–Cretaceous	shallow marine	marble	Wolcott (1943)
	Kimmeridgian	shallow marine	biohermic marble	Urbani (1969)
Las Mercedes Fm.	Mesozoic	shallow marine	marble	MacKenzie (1960)
	Mesozoic	shallow marine	biohermic marble	Spena et al. (1977)
Nirgua Fm.	Neocomian	shallow marine	marble	Bellizzia (1972)
Los Robles Fm.	Cenomanian	?	marble	Vignali (1976)
Caucagua–El Tinaco Belt				
Urape Fm.	Late Cretaceous	pelagic		Sellier de Civrieux (1953)
Chuspita Fm.	Albian	outer shelf	metaconglomerate	Macsotay (1972)
Tucutunemo Fm.	Permian	platform	calcareous conglomerate	Benjamini et al. (1987)
Paracotos Belt				
Paracotos Fm.	Turonian–Maastrichtian	?	limestone olistolith	Sellier de Civrieux (1953)
Paracotos Fm.	Cenomian	pelagic	limestone olistolith	Smith (1952)
Paracotos Fm.	Campanian–Maastrichtian	pelagic	limestone olistolith	Konigsmark (1965)
Paracotos Fm.	Late Cretaceous–Paleogene	shallow water	limestone lens	Oxburgh (1965)
Paracotos Fm.	Campanian–Maastrichtian	pelagic	limestone lens	Oxburgh (1965)
Paracotos Fm.	Maastrichtian	?	limestone lens	Shagam (1960)
Villa de Cura Belt				
Villa de Cura Group	Aptian–Albian	shallow water		Johnson (1965)

be related despite the differences in lithology and metamorphic grade. Miocene deformation and recrystallization, as possibly indicated by the disturbed Ar spectra, probably affected all of the samples on Araya Peninsula.

Farther to the west, near Puerto Cabello, there is a significant change in the cooling and exhumation history as the Miocene $^{40}Ar/^{39}Ar$ white mica ages imply that this region was not exhumed until after this time. This is in stark contrast to the Margarita Island region that was exhumed shortly after Cretaceous subduction. It is not clear why there is this difference in late stage history for these two segments of the same subduction complex.

The final stages of exhumation of the Cordillera de la Costa belt can be estimated from zircon and apatite ages. The new zircon fission-track ages reported here for the Guaremal granite and augen gneiss are very similar to the late Miocene ages (average = 19.7 Ma) of Kohn et al. (1984) for zircon in the Cordillera de la Costa belt. One sample of the Choroní granite yields a slightly younger age of 13.6 Ma, which is somewhat problematic because it is younger than the apatite fission-track age from the same sample. Our study extends the region with late Miocene ages by 60 km to the west. The consistency within the zircon ages indicates that the entire Cordillera de la Costa belt from Puerto Cabello to La Guaira (~150 km) was uplifted at the same time.

TABLE 6. SUMMARY OF GEOCHRONOLOGIC DATA FOR IGNEOUS AND METAMORPHIC ROCKS OF NORTHERN VENEZUELA

Location	Protolith	P-T	U-Pb	Rb-Sr	Amphibole	Mica	Fission track
Cordillera de la Costa belt							
Puerto Cabello eclogite[1]	b, f, m, um, gn	550–600 °C 2000–2200 MPa			37 ± 3	42–28 (ms) 33 ± 3 (k-bi)	
Guaremal gneiss	gr, gn	?	501 511	79 ± 5			19 (z), 15 (a)
Cata dike	gr						126 ± 15 (t), 24–14 (z),
Choroní granite	gr, gn	?	471			30 ± 2 (k-bi)	
Tovar gneiss	gn	?					14 (a) 16 (z)
Peña de Mora gneiss	gn	?					24–17 (z)
Margarita Island							
La Rinconada and Juan Griego Fm.	b, f, m, um	500–600 °C[2] 1000–1400 MPa			92.4 ± 0.5[3]	86.5 ± 0.2[3]	53–50 (z)[2]
pre-tectonic intrusive	gn		114–105[2]				
post-tectonic intrusive	gr		86[2]				11–9 (z)[2]
Araya Peninsula[4]	f	500–550 °C 500–700 MPa				84.5 ± 0.2[3]	
Dragon gneiss[5]	gn	?	312			23 ± 0.2	
Basement of the Carúpano Basin[6]	b, fv	fv, hydrothermal b, unaltered b, low grade			39–34 (w) 102–87 (w) Jr or K (?)		
Villa de Cura belt							
barroisite zone[7]	b, f, c	400–500 °C			96.3 ± 0.4	89–91	
glaucophane-epidote zone[7]	b, f, c	500–700 MPa 300–375 °C				79.8 ± 0.4	
Las Hermanas Fm.	b	600–700 MPa 200–300 °C 100–200 MPa			104 (w)[8]		
Cantagallo Metagabbro[8]	g				67–65 (w) 107–91 (k)		
Chacao Complex[8]	um, g	800 °C[9]	150 felsic dike[9]		190–185[3]	59–50 (k-fs)	49–42 (z)[10], 6 (a)
Tinaquillo and El Tinaco complexes[9]	um, g	500–600 MPa	125 anatexis 90–87 shearing		145 125 (gabbro)		

Note: Error estimates are given only for single ages and when reported. Amphibole and mica ages are all Ar-Ar data except where noted by the following abbreviations: k—K/Ar data; w—whole rock K/Ar. Abbreviations used for protoliths: b—basalts; c—chert; f—felsic sediments and conglomerates; fv—felsic volcanics; g—gabbros; gn—felsic gneiss; gr—felsic intrusive; k-bi—K-Ar age on biotite; k-fs—K-Ar age on feldspar; m—marble; ms—muscovite; um—ultramafic. Fission track ages: z—zircon; a—apatite. P-T—pressure-temperature. Data sources indicated by superscript numbers: 1—Santamaria and Schubert (1974), Morgan (1967), Kohn et al. (1984), Avé Lallemant and Sisson (1993), Sisson et al. (1997), and this study; 2—Stöckert et al. (1995); 3—this study; 4—Avé Lallemant (1997); 5—Speed et al. (1997); 6—Ysaccis (1997); 7—Smith et al. (1999); 8—Beck (1978), Hebeda et al. (1984), Loubet et al. (1985), and Chevalier (1987); 9—Seyler et al., 1998; 10—Kohn et al. (1984).

However, our apatite fission-track age (14–16 Ma) reported here for the Cordillera de la Costa belt is older than the 6.1 ± 1.3 Ma Tinaco trondhjemite (Kohn et al., 1984) and younger than the zircon fission-track ages. There is insufficient apatite data for the Cordillera de la Costa belt to constrain the along strike exhumation as Kohn et al. (1984) do not report any apatite data for this region. Pérez (this volume) reports apatite fission-track ages of 26.9–17.2 Ma at the northern end of his transect, which is approximately due south of Puerto Cabello–Valencia. He does not report cooling histories for these samples. The differences in apatite fission-track data from the Cordillera de la Costa, Caucagua–El Tinaco, and Serranía del Interior belts suggest regional variations in final exhumation with the Caucagua–El Tinaco belt being the final belt that was uplifted.

Quaternary Uplift

Recent coral was collected ~5.3 m above its original life position. If the uplift of the coral occurred by steady-state fault creep, the minimal rate of uplift was between ~25 and 105 mm/yr. Both these rates are absurdly high.

It is more likely that the uplift is related to a major earthquake on the seismically very active San Sebastian fault. According to F.A. (Frank) Audemard (2002), eight major earthquakes occurred in northern Venezuela between 1641 and 1894. The only earthquake that occurred offshore between Puerto Cabello and Caracas had a magnitude M_s = 6.2–6.3 and happened on March 26, 1812. The age of the uplifted coral (50–200 B.P.) is consistent with the occurrence of the 1812 earthquake. Thus, the final 5 m of exhumation is probably related to instantaneous uplift of this region in 1812. According to empirical relationships between earthquake magnitude and surface displacement, this is within error for surface displacement (Wells and Coppersmith, 1994).

SUMMARY

The new ages reported here for three belts in northern Venezuela range from Cambro-Ordovician igneous and metamorphic rocks to an ~200 yr old coral (Table 6). In the northern Cordillera de la Costa belt, U-Pb geochronologic data indicate portions of the basement igneous and metaigneous rocks near Puerto Cabello formed in the Cambro-Ordovician (513–471 Ma). One of these bodies has an inherited component possibly from either the Roraima or Cuchivero provinces in the Guyana Shield. New $^{40}Ar/^{39}Ar$ data from both the high-pressure suites and the greenschist facies suite on Margarita Island indicate some of the subduction complex was rapidly cooled and exhumed, whereas other portions indicate slower cooling. Also, this was synchronous with garnet-staurolite–grade metamorphism on Araya Peninsula. This contrasts with new $^{40}Ar/^{39}Ar$ data from the Puerto Cabello portion of the subduction complex that has Eocene to Oligocene (42–28 Ma) cooling ages. Thus, different segments of the subduction complex were probably exhumed at different rates in response to the transpressional nature of Caribbean–South American plate interactions. New zircon fission-track data imply that the entire Cordillera de la Costa belt from Puerto Cabello to La Guaira (~150 km) was uplifted at the same time.

In the next belt to the south, the Caucagua–El Tinaco belt, the oldest $^{40}Ar/^{39}Ar$ amphibole ages from the Tinaquillo ultramafic complex are Jurassic (190 Ma). Our additional amphibole $^{40}Ar/^{39}Ar$ cooling ages are older than previously recorded in either the El Tinaco or Tinaquillo complexes. One amphibole $^{40}Ar/^{39}Ar$ cooling age for the Tinaco complex is similar to previous U-Pb results. This is also similar to a U-Pb lower intercept age of 148 Ma for the Guaremal gneiss in the Cordillera de la Costa belt. Thus, the ultramafic complex was emplaced simultaneously with rifting and formation of a sequence of grabens during Mesozoic breakup of Pangea. At ca. 90 Ma, the Tinaquillo and El Tinaco complexes were juxtaposed along a ductile shear zone.

New apatite fission-track results from the southernmost Serranía del Interior foreland fold and thrust belt are slightly older than those from the Cordillera de la Costa belt. This may suggest regional differences in the final exhumation across these three belts. In addition, several zircon fission-track ages in the Serranía del Interior belt are older than their fossil ages, indicating a Cretaceous provenance for Miocene beds.

In summary, this wide span of ages records a variety of tectonic events from Jurassic rifting to Cretaceous collision, subduction, and exhumation, followed by Tertiary thrusting and further exhumation. New findings include several igneous and metaigneous rocks within a subduction mélange that may be correlated with orogenic events in the Appalachians, Cretaceous provenance for the Serranía del Interior sedimentary strata, and widespread Miocene cooling and exhumation. The final tectonic activity recorded is recent earthquake displacement related to the San Sebastian fault.

ACKNOWLEDGMENTS

We thank many who assisted with various geochronologic and other analyses. These include Jen-Ping Wen for U-Pb geochronology, David A. Macaroni and Robert B. Dunbar who assisted in the XRD and stable isotope analysis of the Recent coral sample, Milton Pierson for electron microprobe analyses, and Steve Harlan, Ross Yeoman, Libby Prueher, Mark Gordon, Chad Smith, and Leanne McIntyre for $^{40}Ar/^{39}Ar$ analyses. Funding came from numerous sources including National Science Foundation grants EAR-9019243, EAR-9304377, and EAR-9706521, American Chemical Society Petroleum Research Fund grant #27788-AC2, and Consejo de Investigacionces Cientificas de Venezulea (CONICIT). Financial and logistical support also came from Amoco (in particular, Bob Erlich and Jon Blickwede), Conoco (in particular, Bill Schmidt, Larry Standlee, and Keith James) and Mobil. Will Maze, Jim Mattinson, Paul Layer, and Dan Miggins provided helpful reviews.

TABLE A1. SAMPLE LOCATION AND OTHER INFORMATION

Sample	Location	Lithology/Mineral	Latitude	Longitude	Technique	Analyst	Age (Ma)	
Cordillera de la Costa belt								
91VSn15	highway to Valencia	augen gneiss	10°21'42"N	68°05'31"W	U/Pb	JW	512.4 ± 12.9	
91VSn19	highway to Valencia	metagranite	10°19'38"N	68°05'32"W	U/Pb	JW	501 ± 25	
V-92-24	Cata	trondhjemite dike	10°29'43"N	67°00'35"W	U/Pb	JW	511.3 ± 1.8	
V-94-49	Choroní	granite	10°18'20"N	67°36'58"W	U/Pb	JW	471 ± 23	
92VSn19	highway to Cata	actinolite schist	10°21'20"N	67°36'57"W	Ar	PC	37 ± 3	
94VSn13	highway to Valencia	schist/wm	10°19'28"N	68°05'28"W	Ar	PC	28 ± 0.2	
94VSn15	highway to Valencia	schist/wm	10°18'92"N	68°05'23"W	Ar	PC	34.2 ± 0.2	
94VSn16	highway to Valencia	schist/wm	10°20'58"N	68°06'32"W	Ar	PC	42.3 ± 0.3	
94VSn21	Pantanemo	schist/wm	10°28'14"N	67°55'44"W	Ar	PC	42.6 ± 0.3	
91VSn15	highway to Valencia	augen gneiss/ap & zrc	10°21'42"N	68°05'31"W	FT	RD	20 zrc, 15 ap	
91VSn19	highway to Valencia	metagranite/ap & zrc	10°19'38"N	68°05'32"W	FT	RD	20 zrc, 16 ap	
V-94-49	Choroní	granite/ap & zrc	10°21'20"N	67°36'00"W	FT	AB	14 zrc, 14 ap	
CH-86-1	S of Chichiriviche	metagranite	10°33'29"N	67°23'48"W	Rb/Sr	TI	1560 ± 83	
PM86-1	El Avila National Park	metagranite	10°34'05"N	66°59'89"W	Rb/Sr	TI	1560 ± 83	
PM86-2	El Avila National Park	metagranite	10°33'92"N	66°59'53"W	Rb/Sr	TI	1560 ± 83	
IM84-14	Margarita	eclogite/am	11°01'45"N	63°52'12"W	Ar	LS	92.4 ± 0.5	
IM86-27	Margarita	ms schist/wm	10°59'49"N	63°51'22"W	Ar	LS	53.5 ± 0.5	
IM86-85	Margarita	bi grt schist/bi	11°05'18"N	64°00'29"W	Ar	LS	24.9 ± 0.9	
IM86-85	Margarita	ms schist/wm	11°05'18"N	64°00'29"W	Ar	LS	68.3 ± 0.2	
IM86-93	Margarita	amphibolite/am	11°03'48"N	64°00'16"W	Ar	LS	62.3 ± 1.4	
IM86-229	Margarita	qtz-fs schist/wm	11°00'20"N	63°52'29"W	Ar	LS	86.0 ± 0.3	
VM86-12	Margarita	metaconglomerate/wm	11°04'00"N	64°00'10"W	Ar	LS	62.3 ± 0.2	
VM86-12	Margarita	metaconglomerate/bi	11°04'00"N	64°00'10"W	Ar	LS	44.9 ± 0.7	
VM83-21	Margarita	grt-amp/am	11°09'22"N	63°53'50"W	Ar	LS	52.8 ± 0.2	
VE88-3	Araya	ms schist/wm	10°33'30"N	63°25'05"W	Ar	LS	90.8 ± 0.4	
VS89-42	Araya	grt stl schist/bi	10°37'30"N	64°07'42"W	Ar	LS	45.1 ± 0.3	
VS89-42	Araya	grt stl schist/wm	10°37'30"N	64°07'42"W	Ar	LS	84.8 ± 0.2	
							Adjusted age	¹⁴C age
V-92-34	Cata	recent coral	10°27'86"N	67°44'96"W	C¹⁴	Beta	500 ± 60	80 ± 60
Caucagua–El Tinaco belt								
VTO82-88	Tinaquillo	gabbroic pegmatite	9°54'58"	66°26'19"	Ar	LS	165.2 ± 1.4	
VTO82-132	Tinaco complex	granulite/amphibolite	9°51'32"	66°25'53"	Ar	LS	147.4 ± 0.3	
Ti90-5	Tinaquillo	hornblendite vein	9°55'49"	66°24'28"	Ar	LS	190.6 ± 1.0	
V94-62coarse	Tinaquillo	hornblendite vein	9°54'46"	66°26'12"	Ar	LS	173.9 ± 1.6	
V94-62fine	Tinaquillo	hornblendite vein	9°54'46"	66°26'12"	Ar	LS	154.7 ± 0.3	
V94-63	Tinaquillo	gabbroic pegmatite	9°54'48"	66°26'14"	Ar	LS	153.9 ± 2.0	
V97-4	Tinaquillo	gabbroic pegmatite	9°54'48"	66°26'14"	Ar	PC	190.6 ± 1.2	
RT-87-1	Tinaco complex	gneiss	n.d.	n.d.	Rb/Sr	TI	945 ± 178	
RT-87-2	Tinaco complex	gneiss	n.d.	n.d.	Rb/Sr	TI	945 ± 178	
RT-87-4	Tinaco complex	gneiss	n.d.	n.d.	Rb/Sr	TI	945 ± 178	
RT-87-5	Tinaco complex	gneiss	n.d.	n.d.	Rb/Sr	TI	945 ± 178	
Serranía del Interior								
V94-50	Emb. de Camatagua	Guárico/zrc	9°49'14"	66°56'38"	FT	AB	70.1 ± 9.7	
V94-53	Valle Morín	Garrapata/zrc	9°56'18"	66°54'57"	FT	AB	51.1 ± 6.4	
V94-54	Valle Morín	Garrapata/zrc	9°56'18"	66°54'50"	FT	AB	60.7 ± 7.5	
V94-55	Valle Morín	Garrapata/zrc	9°56'18"	66°56'23"	FT	AB	64.3 ± 6.2	
V94-56	Emb. de Camatagua	Guárico/zrc	9°48'47"	66°57'00"	FT	AB	53.9 ± 13.3	
V94-57	Emb. de Camatagua	Guárico/zrc	9°49'18"	66°56'30"	FT	AB	61.4 ± 8.6	
V94-59	E of Palmarito	Quebradon/zrc	9°44'27"	66°35'31"	FT	AB	73.4 ± 8.9	
V94-60	N of Taguay	Mucaria/zrc	9°49'17"	66°38'56"	FT	AB	85.1 ± 19.7	
V94-61	Altagracia de Orituco	Quiamare/zrc	9°51'52"	66°21'14"	FT	AB	62.8 ± 16.8	
V94-53	Emb. de Camatagua	Garrapata/ap	9°56'18"	66°54'57"	FT	AB	14.2 ± 2.0	
V94-54	Valle Morín	Garrapata/ap	9°56'18"	66°54'50"	FT	AB	13.5 ± 1.8	
V94-55	Valle Morín	Garrapata/ap	9°56'18"	66°56'23"	FT	AB	15.8 ± 2.8	

Note: n.d.—not determined. All ages are in Ma except for the coral analysis. Mineral abbreviations: am—amphibole; ap—apatite; bi—biotite; fsp—feldspar; grt—garnet; ms—muscovite; qtz—quartz; stl—staurolite; wm—white mica; zrc—zircon. Analysts: AB—Ann Blythe; Beta—Beta Analytical Inc.; PC—Peter Copeland; RD—Ray Donelick; LS—Larry Snee; TI—Teledyne; JW—Jim Wright. Emb.—Embalse (reservoir).

TABLE A2. PREVIOUS GEOCHRONOLOGIC RESULTS FROM THE CORDILLERA DE LA COSTA BELT

Rock Type	Method	Mineral	Age (Ma)	
Sebastopol				
Metagranite				
Metagranite	K/Ar	Muscovite	41 ± 2	1
Granitic gneiss	Rb/Sr	Whole rock	420	2
Granitic gneiss	Rb/Sr	Whole rock	359	2
Paragneiss	Rb/Sr	Whole rock	350–260	3
Guaremal Metagranite				
Orthogneiss	K/Ar	Biotite	33 ± 3	4
Orthogneiss	Rb/Sr	Biotite	79 ± 5	4
Orthogneiss	K/Ar	Biotite	32 ± 2	5
Orthogneiss	K/Ar	Biotite	33 ± 2	5
Orthogneiss	K/Ar	Apatite	6.1 ± 1.3	5
Orthogneiss	Rb/Sr	Whole rock	402 ± 6	6
Orthogneiss	Rb/Sr	Whole rock	264 ± 4	7
Avila Metagranite				
Orthogneiss	Rb/Sr	Whole rock	220 ± 20	8
Gneiss	FT	Apatite	18.9 ± 1.9	9
Gneiss	FT	Apatite	23.9 ± 1.9	9
Gneiss	FT	Apatite	17.4 ± 2.1	9
Gneiss	FT	Apatite	18.8 ± 2.1	9
Gneiss	FT	Apatite	18.4 ± 1.9	9
Gneiss	FT	Apatite	17.5 ± 1.7	9
Avila Metasediments				
Biotite gneiss	Rb/Sr	Whole rock	714–1475	10
Choroni Granite				
Metagranite	K/Ar	Biotite	30.0 ± 1.9	5
Metagranite	K/Ar	Biotite	30.0 ± 1.8	5
Metagranite	FT	Apatite	24.1 ± 3.0	9
Metagranite	FT	Apatite	22.3 ± 2.3	9
Metagranite	FT	Apatite	17.5 ± 1.9	9
Metagranite	FT	Apatite	21.9 ± 2.9	9
Metagranite	FT	Titanite	126 ± 15	9
Colonia Tovar				
Granite	FT	Apatite	16.4 ± 2.1	9
Oritapo				
Metadiorite	K/Ar	Biotite	76.0 ± 3.9	5
Metadiorite	K/Ar	Biotite	77.0 ± 4.0	5
Puerto Cabello				
Garnet amphibolite	K/Ar	Amphibole	32.4 ± 1.2	10
Oricao				
Garnet amphibolite	K/Ar	Amphibole	735 ± 30	10
Cabo Codera				
Garnet amphibolite	K/Ar	Amphibole	155 ± 7	10
Garnet amphibolite	K/Ar	Amphibole	753 ± 31	10

Note: FT—fission-track analysis. References: 1—Olmeta (1968); 2—Hurley and Hess (1968); 3—Pimental et al. (1985); 4—Morgan (1967); 5—Santamaria and Schubert (1974); 6—Urbani (1983); 7—Urbani (1988); 8—Kovach et al. (1977); 9—Kohn et al. (1984); 10—Loubet et al. (1985).

TABLE A3. PREVIOUS GEOCHRONOLOGIC RESULTS FROM MAGARITA ISLAND, PARIA PENINSULA, AND ARAYA PENINSULA

Rock Type		Mineral	Age (Ma)	
Margarita Island				
Trondhjemite	K/Ar	Amphibole	71.0 ± 5	1
Granite	K/Ar	Amphibole	72.0 ± 6	2
Trondhjemite	K/Ar	Hornblende	70.0 ± 6	2
Pegmatite	K/Ar	Feldspar	32.0 ± 2	2
Amphibole gneiss	K/Ar	Amphibole	47.0 ± 4	3
Amphibolite gneiss	K/Ar	Clinozoisite	43 ± 31	3
Amphibolite gneiss	K/Ar	Muscovite	40.1 ± 2.5	3
Amphibolite gneiss	K/Ar	Clinozoisite	57.5 ± 15	3
Amphibolite gneiss	K/Ar	Chloritized amphibole	37.0 ± 19	3
Amphibolite gneiss	K/Ar	Muscovite	50.5 ± 15	3
Amphibolite gneiss	K/Ar	Clinozoisite	44.5 ± 3.5	3
Amphibolite gneiss	K/Ar	Chloritized amphibole	45.5 ± 7.5	3
Amphibolite gneiss	K/Ar	Muscovite	51.0 ± 1.5	3
Amphibolite gneiss	K/Ar	Chlorite	56.5 ± 26	3
Amphibolite gneiss	K/Ar.	Clinozoisite	98.0 ± 30	3
Amphibolite gneiss	K/Ar	Muscovite	59.5 ± 2	3
Granodiorite	K/Ar	Muscovite	67.5 ± 2	3
Granodiorite	K/Ar	Muscovite	54.0 ± 2	3
Orthogneiss	K/Ar	Mica	62.5 ± 3.1	4
Orthogneiss	K/Ar	Mica	57.1 ± 2.9	4
Amphibolite	K/Ar	Mica	84.7 ± 4.2	4
Amphibolite	K/Ar	Mica	79.3 ± 3.8	4
Augengneiss	U/Pb	Zircon	315 ± 35	5
Trondhjemite	U/Pb	Zircon	114–105	5
Granite	U/Pb	Zircon	86	5
Garnet amphibolite	Ar/Ar	White mica	90–80	5
Gabbro	Ar/Ar	Amphibole	66 Ma	5
Greenschist	Ar/Ar	White mica	55–50	5
Granite and trondhjemite	FT	Zircon	53–50	5
Basaltic dikes	Ar/Ar	Amphibole	52–47	5
Araya Peninsula				
Augen gneiss	K/Ar	Amphibole	128 ± 11	2
Augen gneiss	K/Ar	Whole rock	53 ± 3	2
Paria Peninsula				
Augen gneiss	U/Pb	Zircon	321 ± 29	6
Greenschist	Ar/Ar	White mica	21	6

Note: FT—fission-track analysis. References: 1—Olmeta (1968); 2—Santamaria and Schubert (1974); 3—Loubet et al. (1985); 4—Chevalier (1987); 5—Stöckhert et al. (1995); 6—Speed et al. (1997).

TABLE A4. PREVIOUS GEOCHRONOLOGIC RESULTS FROM THE CAUCAGUA–EL TINACO BELT

Rock type	Method	Mineral	Age (Ma)	Reference
Tinaco Complex				
(La Aguadita Gneiss)				
Biotite gneiss	K/Ar	Biotite	112.4 ± 3.0	1
Biotite gneiss	K/Ar	Hornblende	117.5 ± 3.0	1
Hornblende gneiss	K/Ar	Hornblende	204.0 ± 12	1
Hornblende gneiss	K/Ar	Actinolite (?)	210.0 ± 10	1
Hornblende gneiss	K/Ar	Hornblende	235.8 ± 13	2
Hornblende gneiss	K/Ar	Plagioclase	192.1 ± 15	2
Gneiss	FT	Apatite	49.0 ± 5.8	3
Diorite	FT	Apatite	41.9 ± 4.9	3
Diorite	FT	Apatite	43.4 ± 5.6	3
Trondhjemite	FT	Apatite	6.1 ± 1.3	3
Felsic granulite	U/Pb	Zircon	125 ± 1	4
Mafic granulite	Nd/Sm	Grt-Hbl-whole rock	87.1 ± 3.1	4
Tinaquillo Complex				
Granulite	U/Pb	Zircon	150 ± 2	4
Garnet gabbro	Nd/Sm	Garnet-whole rock	94.7 ± 3.3	5

Note: FT—fission track analysis. Mineral abbreviations: Grt—garnet; Hbl—hornblende. References: 1—Martin (1968); 2—Hess (1966) *in* Urbani (1982); 3—Kohn et al. (1984); 4—Seyler et al. (1998); 5—Lar (1992).

TABLE A5. PREVIOUS GEOCHRONOLOGIC RESULTS FROM OFFSHORE VENEZUELA

Rock type	Method	Mineral	Age (Ma)	Reference
Tuy-Cariaco basin				
Metavolcanic	K/Ar	whole rock	65.4	1
Metavolcanic	K/Ar	whole rock	69.4	1
Metaandesite	K/Ar	whole rock	78.3 ± 3.9	1
Carúpano basin				
Amphibolite gneiss	K/Ar	whole rock	38.6 ± 2	2
Amphibolite gneiss	K/Ar	whole rock	33.5 ± 1.8	2
Amphibolite gneiss	K/Ar	whole rock	87.0 ± 9	2
Amphibolite gneiss	K/Ar	whole rock	102.2 ± 10	2
Gulf of Venezuela				
Granite	K/Ar	whole rock (?)	304	3
Granite	K/Ar	whole rock	138 ± 6.9	3
Gulf of La Vela				
Quartz–sericite phyllite	K/Ar	whole rock	83.5	4
Metagabbro	K/Ar	feldspar	114	4

Note: References: 1—Talukdar and Bolívar (1983) *in* Ysaccis (1997); 2—Talukdar (1983) *in* Ysaccis (1997); 3—Feo-Codecido et al. (1984); 4—Kiser et al. (1984).

REFERENCES CITED

Abujaber, N.S., and Kimberley, M.M., 1992, Origin of ultramafic-hosted magnesite on Margarita Island, Venezuela: Mineralium Deposita, v. 27, p. 234–241.

Audemard, F.A., 2002, Ruptura de los grandes sismos históricos Venezolanos de los siglos XIX y XX revelados por la sismicidad contemporánea: XI Congresso Venezolano de Geofísica, Sociedad Venezolana de Ingenerio Geofísicos, extended abstract on CD-Rom, 9 p.

Avé Lallemant, H.G., 1997, Transpression, displacement partitioning, and exhumation in the eastern Caribbean–South American plate boundary zone: Tectonics, v. 16, p. 272–289, doi: 10.1029/96TC03725.

Avé Lallemant, H.G., and Guth, L.R., 1990, Role of extensional tectonics in exhumation of eclogites and blueschists in an oblique subduction setting: Northwestern Venezuela: Geology, v. 18, p. 950–953, doi: 10.1130/0091-7613(1990)018<0950:ROETIE>2.3.CO;2.

Avé Lallemant, H.G., and Sisson, V.B., 1993, Caribbean–South American plate interactions: Constraints from the Cordillera de la Costa Belt, Venezuela, *in* Pindell, J.L., and Perkins, B.F., eds., Mesozoic and Early Cenozoic development of the Gulf of Mexico and Caribbean region: Austin, Texas, Transactions of the 13th Annual Research Conference, Gulf Coast Section, Society of Economic Paleontologists and Mineralogists Foundation, p. 211–219.

Bartok, P., 1993, Pre-breakup geology of the Gulf of Mexico–Caribbean: Its relation to Triassic and Jurassic rift systems of the region: Tectonics, v. 12, p. 441–459.

Beck, C.M., 1978, Polyphase Tertiary tectonics of the interior range in the central part of the western Caribbean chain, Guárico State, northern Venezuela: Geologie en Mijnbouw, v. 57, p. 99–104.

Beck, C.M., 1985, La chaîne Caraïbe au meridien de Caracas: Géologie, tectonogénèse, place dans l'évolution géodinamique Mésozoique-Cénozoique des Caraïbes Meridionales [Ph.D. dissertation]: Lille, France, Université de Sciences et Techniques de Lille, 462 p.

Bell, J.S., 1968, Geología de la region de Camatagua, Estado Aragua, Venezuela: Boletín de Geología, Venezuela Ministerio de Minas e Hidrocarburos, v. IX, p. 292–440.

Bellizzia, A., 1972, Sistema Montañoso del Caribe, bordre sur de la placa Caribe, es una cordillera alóctona?: Memorias VI Conferencia de Geología Caribe, Porlamar, v. 1971, p. 247–258.

Bellizzia, A., 1986, Sistema montañoso del Caribe—Una cordillera allóctona en la parte norte de América del Sur: VI Congreso Geológico Venezolano, Memorias, v. X, p. 6657–6836.

Bellizzia, A., and Dengo, G., 1990, The Caribbean Mountains system, northern South America; A summary, *in* Dengo, G., and Case, J.E., eds., The Caribbean region: Geological Society of America, The Geology of North America, v. H, p. 167–175.

Bellizzia, A., Pimental, N., and Bajo, R., 1976, Mapa geológico estructural de Venezuela: Caracas, Foninves, scale 1:500,000.

Benjamini, C., Shagam, R., and Menendez, V.A., 1987, (Late?) Paleozoic age for the "Cretaceous" Tucutunemo Formation, northern Venezuela: Stratigraphy and tectonic implications: Geology, v. 15, p. 922–926, doi: 10.1130/0091-7613(1987)15<922:LPAFTC>2.0.CO;2.

Burke, K., 1988, Tectonic evolution of the Caribbean: Annual Review of Earth and Planetary Sciences, v. 16, p. 201–230, doi: 10.1146/annurev.ea.16.050188.001221.

Burke, K., Fox, P.J., and Şengör, A.M.C., 1978, Buoyant ocean floor and the evolution of the Caribbean: Journal of Geophysical Research, v. 83, p. 3949–3954.

Burtner, R.L., Nigrini, A., and Donelick, R.A., 1994, Thermochronology of Lower Cretaceous source rocks in the Idaho-Wyoming thrust belt: AAPG Bulletin, v. 78, p. 1613–1636.

Carlson, W.D., Donelick, R.A., and Ketcham, R.A., 1999, Variability of apatite fission-track annealing kinetics I: Experimental results: American Mineralogist, v. 84, p. 1213–1223.

Case, J.E., Holcombe, T.L., and Martin, R.G., 1984, Map showing major geologic provinces of the Caribbean region, *in* Bonini, W.E., Hargraves, R.B., and Shagam, R., eds., The Caribbean–South American plate boundary and regional tectonics: Boulder, Geological Society of America Memoir 162, p. 1–30.

Cebula, G.T., Kunk, M.J., Mehnert, H.H., Naeser, C.W., Obradovich, J.D., and Sutter, J.F., 1986, The Fish Canyon Tuff, a potential standard for the $^{40}Ar/^{39}Ar$ and fission-track dating methods: Terra Cognita, v. 6, p. 139.

Chevalier, Y., 1987, Les zones internes de la chaine sub-Caraïbe sur le transect ile de Margarita-peninsula d'Araya (Venezuela) [Ph.D. Dissertation]: France, L'Université de Bretagne Occidentale, 464 p.

di Croce, J., 1995, Eastern Venezuela basin: Sequence stratigraphy and structural evolution [Ph.D. Dissertation]: Rice University, 225 p.

Donelick, R.A., 1993, A method of fission-track analysis utilizing bulk chemical etching of apatite: U.S. Patent no. 5,267,274.

Donelick, R.A., 1995, A method of fission-track analysis utilizing bulk chemical etching of apatite: Australian Patent no. 658,800.

Donelick, R.A., Ketcham, R.A., and Carlson, W.D., 1999, Variability of apatite fission-track annealing kinetics II: Crystallographic orientation effects: American Mineralogist, v. 84, p. 1224–1234.

Dumitru, T.A., 1993, A new computer-automated microscope stage system for fission-track analysis: Nuclear Tracks and Radiation Measurements, v. 21, p. 575–580, doi: 10.1016/1359-0189(93)90198-I.

Duncan, R.A., and Hargraves, R.B., 1984, Plate tectonic evolution of the Caribbean region in the mantle reference frame, *in* Bonini, W.E., Hargraves, R.B., and Shagam, R., eds., The Caribbean–South American plate boundary and regional tectonics: Boulder, Geological Society of America Memoir 162, p. 81–93.

Feo-Codecido, G., Smith, F.D., Aboud, N., and de Di Giacomo, E., 1984, Basement and Paleozoic rocks of the Venezuela Llanos basins, *in* Bonini, W.E., Hargraves, R.B., and Shagam, R., eds., The Caribbean–South American plate boundary and regional tectonics: Boulder, Geological Society of America Memoir 162, p. 175–188.

Galbraith, R.F., 1981, On statistical models for fission-track counts: Journal of the International Association for Mathematical Geology, v. 13, p. 471–478, doi: 10.1007/BF01034498.

González de Juana, C., Iturralde, J.M., and Picard, X., 1980, Geología de Venezuela y de sus Cuencas Petrolíferas: Caracas, Ediciones Foninves, 1031 p.

Green, P.F., 1981, A new look at statistics in fission-track dating: Nuclear Tracks, v. 5, p. 77–86, doi: 10.1016/0191-278X(81)90029-9.

Guth, L.R., 1991, Kinematic analysis of the deformational structures on eastern Isla de Margarita [Ph.D. Dissertation]: Houston, Rice University, 582 p.

Harlow, G.E., Hemming, S.R., Avé Lallemant, H.G., Sisson, V.B., and Sorensen, S.S., 2004, Two HP-LT serpentinite-matrix mélange belts, Motagua fault zone, Guatemala: A record of Aptian and Maastrichtian collisions: Geology, v. 32, p. 17–20, doi: 10.1130/G19990.1.

Hebeda, E.H., Verdurmen, E.A.Th., and Priem, H.N.A., 1984, K-Ar hornblende ages from the El Chacao complex, north-central Venezuela, *in* Bonini, W.E., Hargraves, R.B., and Shagam, R., eds., The Caribbean–South American plate boundary and regional tectonics: Boulder, Geological Society of America Memoir 162, p. 413–414.

Hess, H.H., editor, 1966, Caribbean Geological Investigations: Geological Society of America Memoir 98, 310 p.

Hughen, K.A., Overpeck, J.T., Peterson, L.C., and Anderson, R.F., 1996, The nature of varved sedimentation in the Cariaco basin, *in* Kemp, A.E.S., ed., Palaeoclimatology and palaeoceanography from laminated sediments: London, Geological Society Special Publication 116, p. 171–183.

Hurford, A.J., and Green, P.F., 1983, The zeta age calibration of fission-track dating: Isotope Geoscience, v. 1, p. 285–317.

Hurford, A.J., and Hammerschmidt, K., 1985, $^{40}Ar/^{39}Ar$ and K-Ar dating of the Bishop and Fish Canyon Tuffs: Calibration ages for fission-track dat-

ing standards: Chemical Geology, v. 58, p. 23–32, doi: 10.1016/0009-2541(85)90176-7.

Hurley, P., and Hess, H.H., 1968, Basement gneiss, Cordillera de la Costa, Venezuela: 16th Annual Progress Report: U.S. Atomic Energy Commission, Contract AT (30–1)-1391, MIT Press, Cambridge, 81 p.

Johnson, J.H., 1965, Three lower Cretaceous algae new to the Americas: Journal of Paleontology, v. 39, p. 719–720.

Ketcham, R.A., Donelick, R.A., and Carlson, W.D., 1999, Variability of apatite fission-track annealing kinetics III: Extrapolation to geological time scales: American Mineralogist, v. 84, p. 1235–1255.

Ketcham, R.A., Donelick, R.A., and Donelick, M.B., 2000, AFTSolve: A program for multi-kinetic modeling of apatite fission-track data: Geological Materials Research, v. 2, no. 1, 32 p.

Kiser, D., Escalona, N., Portilla, A., Monsalve, O., Ramirez, P.E., and Colina, G., 1984, Plataforma Continental Venezolanan, La Vela–Golfo Triste: Petroleos de Venezuela, Coordinación de Exploración, Grupo Interfilial, v. 2, 75 p.

Kohn, B.P., Shagam, R., and Subieta, T., 1984, Results and preliminary implications of sixteen fission-track ages from rocks of the western Caribbean Mountains, Venezuela, *in* Bonini, W.E., Hargraves, R.B., and Shagam, R., eds., The Caribbean–South American plate boundary and regional tectonics: Boulder, Geological Society of America Memoir 162, p. 415–421.

Konigsmark, T.A., 1965, Geología del area de Gaurico septentrional–Lago de Valencia, Venezuela: Caracas, Boletín de Geología, v. 6, p. 209–285.

Kovach, A., Hurley, P., and Fairbairn, H., 1977, Rb-Sr whole rock dating of metamorphic events in the Iglesias Group, Venezuelan Andes: Unpublished report, Cambridge, Massachusetts Institute of Technology, 15 p.

Krogh, T.E., 1973, A low-contamination method for hydrothermal decomposition of zircon and extraction of U and Pb for isotopic age determinations: Geochimica et Cosmochimica Acta, v. 37, p. 485–494, doi: 10.1016/0016-7037(73)90213-5.

Lar, A.U., 1992, Etude Géochimique de Massif Basiques et Ultrabasiques (Apa, Todasana, Tinaquillo) de la Chaîne Tertaire Caraïbe du Venezuela: Genèse de magmas matelliques et interaction Manteau-Croûte [Ph.D. Dissertation]: Toulouse, Université de Paul Sabatier, 232 p.

Loubet, M., Montigny, R., Chachati, B., Duarte, N., Lambret, B., Martin, C., and Thuizat, R., 1985, Geochemical and geochronological constraints on the geodynamic development of the Caribbean Chain of Venezuela, *in* Mascle, A., ed., Symposium Géodynamique des Caraibes: Paris, Février, p. 553–566.

MacKenzie, D.B., 1960, High-temperature alpine-type peridotite from Venezuela: Geological Society of America Bulletin, v. 71, p. 303–318.

Macsotay, O., 1972, Observaciones sobre la edad y paleoecologia de algunas formaciones de la region de Barquisimeto, Estado Lara, Venezuela: Caracas, IV Congreso Geología de Venezuela Memoría, tomo III, p. 1673–1689.

Malfait, B.T., and Dinkelman, M.G., 1972, Circum-Caribbean tectonic and igneous activity and the evolution of the Caribbean plate: Geological Society of America Bulletin, v. 83, p. 251–272.

Maresch, W.V., 1974, Plate tectonics origin of the Caribbean Mountain system of northern South America: Discussion and proposal: Geological Society of America Bulletin, v. 85, p. 669–682, doi: 10.1130/0016-7606(1974)85<669:PTOOTC>2.0.CO;2.

Maresch, W.V., 1975, The geology of northeastern Margarita Island, Venezuela: A contribution to the study of Caribbean plate margins: Geologische Rundschau, v. 64, p. 846–883.

Martin, B.C., 1968, Edades isotópicas de rocas Venezolanas: Caracas, Boletín Geos, v. 9, no. 19, p. 356–380.

Mattinson, J.M., 1987, U-Pb ages of zircons; a basic examination of error propagation: Chemical Geology, Isotope Geoscience Section, v. 66, p. 151–162, doi: 10.1016/0168-9622(87)90037-6.

Mattson, P.H., 1978, Subduction, buoyant braking, flipping and strike slip faulting in the northern Caribbean: Journal of Geology, v. 8, p. 293–304.

Menendez, A., 1966, Tectónica de la parte central de las Montañas Occidentales del Caribe: Caracas, Boletín Geos, v. 8, no. 15, p. 116–139.

Morgan, B.A., 1967, Geology of the Valencia area, Carabobo, Venezuela [Ph.D. Dissertation]: Princeton, New Jersey, Princeton University, 220 p.

Naeser, C.W., 1979, Fission-track dating and geologic annealing of fission-tracks, *in* Jäger, E., and Hunziker, J.C., eds., Lectures in isotope geology: Heidelberg, Springer-Verlag, p. 154–169.

Olmeta, M.A., 1968, Determinación de edades radiométricas en rocas de Venezuela y su procedimiento por método K-Ar: Caracas, Boletín Geos, v. 10, no. 9, p. 339–344.

Ostos, M., 1984, Structural interpretation of the Tinaquillo peridotite and its country rock, Cojedes State, Venezuela [M.S. thesis]: Houston, Rice University, 135 p.

Ostos, M., 1990, Tectonic evolution of the south-central Caribbean based on geochemical data [Ph.D. Dissertation]: Houston, Rice University, 441 p.

Oxburgh, E.R., 1965, Geología de la region oriental del Estado Carabobo, Venezuela: Caracas, Boletín de Geología, v. 6, p. 103–208.

Pimental, B.N., Gaudette, H., and Olsewsky, W., 1985, Nuevas dataciones en el "basamento" de la Cadena Caribe: Caracas, Memorias VI Congreso Geologia Venezolana, v. 2, p. 1979–1994.

Pindell, J.L., 1985, Alleghenian reconstruction and subsequent evolution of the Gulf of Mexico, Bahamas, and Proto-Caribbean: Tectonics, v. 4, p. 1–39.

Pindell, J.L., 1993, Regional synopsis of Gulf of Mexico and Caribbean evolution, *in* Pindell, J.L., and Perkins, B.F., eds., Mesozoic and early Cenozoic development of the Gulf of Mexico and Caribbean region—A context for hydrocarbon exploration, Proceedings, Gulf Coast Section, SEPM Foundation 13th Annual Research Conference: Houston, Texas, Society for Sedimentary Geology (SEPM) Foundation, p. 251–274.

Pindell, J.L., and Barrett, S.F., 1990, Geological evolution of the Caribbean region; A plate-tectonic perspective, *in* Dengo, G., and Case, J.E., eds., The Caribbean region: Boulder, Colorado, Geological Society of America, Geology of North America, v. H, p. 405–432.

Pindell, J.L., Cande, S.C., Pitman, W.C., III, Rowley, D.B., Dewey, J.F., Labrecque, J., and Haxby, W., 1988, A plate-kinematic framework for models of Caribbean evolution: Tectonophysics, v. 155, p. 121–138, doi: 10.1016/0040-1951(88)90262-4.

Pouchou, J.L., and Pichoir, F., 1987, PAP procedure for improved quantitative microanalysis, *in* Armstrong, J.T., ed., Microbeam analysis: San Francisco, San Francisco Press, p. 88–97.

Samson, S.D., and Alexander, E.C., 1987, Calibration of interlaboratory $^{40}Ar/^{39}Ar$ dating standard MMhb-1: Isotope Geoscience, v. 66, p. 27–34, doi: 10.1016/0168-9622(87)90025-X.

Santamaría, F., and Schubert, C., 1974, Geochemistry and geochronology of the southern Caribbean–northern Venezuela plate boundary: Geological Society of America Bulletin, v. 85, p. 1085–1098, doi: 10.1130/0016-7606(1974)85<1085:GAGOTS>2.0.CO;2.

Sellier de Civrieux, J.M., 1953, Informe paleontológico sobre muestras del Grupo Paracotos en la region Caucagua: Informe inedito Ministerio de Energia y Minas, v. 12, no. I, 53 p.

Seyler, M., and Mattson, P.H., 1989, Petrology and thermal evolution of the Tinaquillo peridotite (Venezuela): Journal of Geophysical Research, v. 94, p. 7629–7660.

Seyler, M., and Mattson, P.H., 1993, Gabbroic and pyroxenite layers in the Tinaquillo, Venezuela, peridotite: Succession of melt intrusions in a rising mantle diapir: Journal of Geology, v. 101, p. 501–511.

Seyler, M., Paquette, J.-L., Ceuleneer, G., Kienast, J.-R., and Loubet, M., 1998, Magmatic underplating, metamorphic evolution and ductile shearing in a Mesozoic lower crustal–upper mantle unit (Tinaquillo, Venezuela) of the Caribbean belt: Journal of Geology, v. 106, p. 35–58.

Shagam, R., 1960, Geology of the central Aragua State, Venezuela: Geological Society of America Bulletin, v. 71, p. 249–302.

Sisson, V.B., Ertan, I.E., and Avé Lallemant, H.G., 1997, High pressure (~2000 MPa) kyanite- and glaucophane-bearing pelitic schist and eclogite from Cordillera de la Costa belt, Venezuela: Journal of Petrology, v. 38, p. 65–83, doi: 10.1093/petrology/38.1.65.

Smith, C.A., Sisson, V.B., Avé Lallemant, H.G., and Copeland, P., 1999, Two contrasting pressure-temperature-time paths in the Villa de Cura blueschist belt, Venezuela: Possible evidence for Late Cretaceous initiation of subduction in the Caribbean: Geological Society of America Bulletin, v. 111, no. 6, p. 831–848, doi: 10.1130/0016-7606(1999)111<0831:TCPTTP>2.3.CO;2.

Smith, R.J., 1952, Geología de la region Los Teques-Cúa, Venezuela: Caracas, Boletín de Geología, v. 2, p. 333–406.

Snee, L.W., 2002, Argon thermochronology of mineral deposits: A review of analytical methods, formulations, and selected applications of the U.S. Geological Survey, Denver, Colorado: U.S. Geological Survey Bulletin 2194, 39 p.

Speed, R.C., Sharp, W.D., and Foland, K.A., 1997, Late Paleozoic granitoid gneisses of the Northeastern Venezuela and the North America–Gondwana collision zone: Journal of Geology, v. 105, p. 457–470.

Spena, F., Furrer, M., and Urbani, F., 1977, Fósiles en las rocas metamórficas de la region de Birongo-Capaya, Barlovento, Estado Miranda: Caracas, Boletín de Geología, v. 19, p. 169–176.

Steven, T.A., Mehnert, H.H., and Obradovich, J.D., 1967, Age of volcanic activity in the San Juan Mountains, Colorado: U.S. Geological Survey Professional Paper 575D, p. 47–55.

Stöckhert, B., Maresch, W.V., Brix, M., Kaiser, C., Toetz, A., Kluge, R., and Kruckhaus-Lueder, G., 1995, Crustal history of Margarita Island (Venezuela) in detail: Constraints on the Caribbean plate-tectonic scenario: Geology, v. 23, no. 9, p. 787–790, doi: 10.1130/0091-7613(1995)023<0787:CHOMIV>2.3.CO;2.

Talukdar, S., 1983, Petrological study of volcanic and sedimentary rocks from offshore wells of the north of Paria area: Instituto Tecnológico Venezolano del Petróleo, Informe Técnico INT-00877, 126 p.

Talukdar, S., and Bolívar, E., 1982, Petroleum geology of Tuy-Cariaco basin, eastern Venezuela continental shelf: a preliminary appraisal: Caracas, Instituto Tecnológico Venezolano del Petróleo, Informe Técnico, INT-00661, 78 p.

Urbani, F., 1969, Primera localidad fosilifera del Miembro Zenda de la Formación Las Brisas Cueva El Indio, La Guirita, Estado Mirando: Caracas, Asociación Venezolana de Geología, Minas, y Petroleo, Boletín Informativo, v. 12, no. 12, p. 447–453.

Urbani, F., 1982, Comentarios sobre algunas edades de las rocas de la parte central de la Cordillera de la Costa: Caracas, Geos, v. 27, p. 77–84.

Urbani, F., 1983, Las rocas graniticas de area de las Trincheras-Mariara, Estado Carabobo: Geología y edad: Científica Venezolana, v. 34, suppl. 1, p. 93.

Urbani, F., 1988, Algunos complejos de rocas metaigneous en la Cordillera de la Costa: Revista de la Facultad de Ingeniería (Universidad Central de Venezuela, Caracas), v. 3, no. 2, p. 22–39.

Vignali, M., 1976, The stratigraphy and structure of the metamorphic eastern Cordillera, Venezuela (Araya–Paria Peninsula and Margarita Island) [Ph.D. Dissertation]: Zurich, Eidgenoessische Technischen Hochschule, 129 p.

Wells, D.L., and Coppersmith, K.J., 1994, New empirical relationships among magnitude, rupture length, rupture area, and surface displacements: Bulletin of the Seismological Society of America, v. 84, p. 974–1002.

Wolcott, P.P., 1943, Fossils from metamorphic rocks of Coast Range of Venezuela: AAPG Bulletin, v. 27, p. 1632.

York, D., 1968, Least-square fitting of a straight line with correlated errors: Earth and Planetary Science Letters, v. 5, p. 320–324.

Ysaccis, R., 1997, Tertiary evolution of the northeastern Venezuela offshore [Ph.D. Dissertation]: Houston, Rice University, 285 p.

MANUSCRIPT ACCEPTED BY THE SOCIETY 5 APRIL 2005

Geological Society of America
Special Paper 394
2005

Geochemistry and tectonic setting of igneous and metaigneous rocks of northern Venezuela

Marino Ostos*

Escuela de Geología, Minas, y Geofísica, Universidad Central de Venezuela, Caracas, Venezuela, and Estudios de Ingenieria Geologica Litos, C.A., Caracas, Venezuela

Virginia B. Sisson*

Department of Earth Science, MS-126, Rice University, Houston, Texas 77252-1892, USA

ABSTRACT

Northern Venezuela consists of a complex series of dismembered east-west–trending deformed belts that define the southern edge of the Caribbean plate. This contribution uses petrologic and geochemical data to define the tectono-magmatic affiliation of some of the belts. These include (1) mid-oceanic-ridge basalts (MORB) included within a mélange composed primarily of passive margin sediments in the Cordillera de la Costa belt, (2) Jurassic sublithospheric mantle and MORB in the Tinaco-Tinaquillo belt, (3) island-arc tholeiites of the Villa de Cura belt, and (4) oceanic island basalts and island-arc intrusive rocks on Gran Roque island, part of the Venezuelan and Dutch Leeward Antilles. Two of the belts (Cordillera de la Costa and Villa de Cura) were metamorphosed in subduction zones then exhumed and thrust onto the margin of Venezuela. The other two belts (Tinaco-Tinaquillo and Leeward Antilles) were obducted onto the edge of Venezuela. These different units record the complex evolution of the Caribbean plate: initial rifting, which formed the proto-Caribbean seafloor (MORB) and Great Arc of the Caribbean, followed by a reversal in subduction polarity caused by the overthickened crust of the Caribbean large igneous province, followed in turn by exhumation and/or obduction of the units and their subsequent emplacement onto northern Venezuela. In the Venezuelan islands, island arc activity continued through the Tertiary.

Keywords: Caribbean, geochemistry, protolith, metabasalt, tectono-magmatic affiliation.

*E-mails: ORmarino@cs.com, j_sisson@netzero.com

Ostos, M., and Sisson, V.B., 2005, Geochemistry and tectonic setting of igneous and metaigneous rocks of northern Venezuela, *in* Avé Lallemant, H.G., and Sisson, V.B., eds., Caribbean–South American plate interactions, Venezuela: Geological Society of America Special Paper 394, p. 119–156, doi: 10.1130/2005.2394(04).

INTRODUCTION

The northern, eastern, and southern margins of the Caribbean plate are marked by the presence of numerous igneous and metaigneous rocks. These include island-arc lavas and intrusive rocks, ocean island basalts, and mid-oceanic ridge basalts that were emplaced throughout the Paleozoic and Mesozoic. Some Early to Late Cretaceous volcanic suites, such as in the Dominican Republic, consist of basalts and rhyolites that formed in a primitive island arc setting (PIA of Donnelly and Rogers, 1978; Donnelly et al., 1990; Lebrón and Perfit, 1994; Jolly et al. 2001). In contrast, younger post-Albian age lavas are mostly calc-alkaline andesites (Donnelly et al., 1990). In other regions, such as Puerto Rico, the oldest lavas are remnants of mid-oceanic-ridge basalt (MORB) (Jolly et al., 1998). Recent geochemical investigations have described Late Cretaceous to Paleocene ocean island suites and assigned them to an oceanic plateau, the Caribbean Large Igneous Province (CLIP; e.g., Donnelly et al., 1973; Beets et al.,

1984; Donnelly et al., 1990; Kerr et al., 1996; Hauff et al., 1997; Lapierre et al., 1997, 2000). In northwestern South America, Late Jurassic to Early Cretaceous remnants of oceanic terranes occur in Columbia and Ecuador (e.g., Sinton et al., 1997; Kerr et al., 1997; Mamberti et al., 2003). In Hispaniola, Pindell and Barrett (1990) and Lapierre et al. (2000) suggest that the Early Cretaceous arc collided with the buoyant Caribbean oceanic plateau. Fragments of mid-oceanic ridge and associated mantle are found in northern Venezuela (Seyler et al., 1998; Ostos et al., this volume, Chapter 8). The relationships among the different suites of arc rocks, accreted fragments of the Caribbean plateau, and MORB are poorly known in the southern Caribbean.

In northern Venezuela, relicts of all three of these igneous protolith types are exposed in the Caribbean Mountain system. This region is a complex east-west–trending boundary zone between the Caribbean and South American plates. Six east-west–trending belts (Fig. 1; Maresch, 1974; Bellizzia and Dengo, 1990) include (1) the Leeward Antilles island arc, composed of

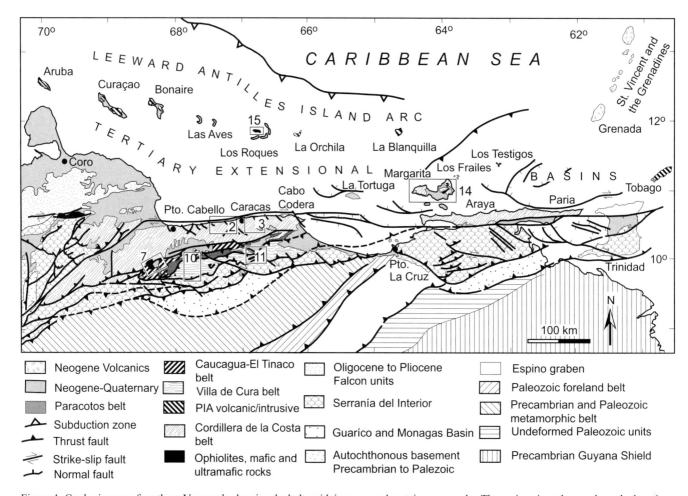

Figure 1. Geologic map of northern Venezuela showing the belts with igneous and metaigneous rocks. The various inset boxes show the locations of the detailed geologic maps given in subsequent figures. Figures 2 and 3 represent the Cordillera de la Costa belt. The Tinaquillo–El Tinaco belt (Fig. 7) is described in Ostos et al. (this volume, Chapter 8). Figures 10 and 11 show the Villa de Cura belt (see also Unger et al., this volume). Figures 14 and 15 cover the Venezuelan islands. PIA—Primitive island arc volcanics and intrusives. Adapted from Ysaccis (1997) with contributions from A.W. Bally, J. di Croce, E. Hung, H.G. Avé Lallemant, and V.B. Sisson.

Late Cretaceous through Paleogene volcanic rocks (Beets et al., 1984; Pindell, 1994); (2) the Cordillera de la Costa belt, which consists of a mélange with eclogite-facies rocks, mica schists, and Paleozoic granites metamorphosed in a Late Cretaceous subduction zone (Avé Lallemant and Sisson, 1993; Stöckhert et al., 1995; Sisson et al., 1997; Sorensen et al., this volume); (3) the Caucagua–El Tinaco belt, composed of Paleozoic high-grade metamorphic and igneous rocks (Menéndez, 1965; Bellizzia and Dengo, 1990; Seyler et al., 1998; Ostos et al., this volume, Chapter 2); (4) the Paracotos belt, which consists of weakly metamorphosed and deformed sedimentary rocks of Maastrichtian to upper Eocene age and ophiolite fragments (Bellizzia and Dengo, 1990; Pindell, 1994); (5) the Villa de Cura belt, composed of mid-Cretaceous blueschist-facies metavolcanic and metavolcaniclastic rocks (Shagam, 1960; Seiders, 1962; Oxburgh, 1966; Navarro, 1983; Smith et al., 1999; Unger et al., this volume); and (6) the Serranía del Interior foreland fold and thrust belt, which consists of Upper Cretaceous to Paleogene age flysch and Neogene sedimentary rocks that show south vergent thrusting in the Eocene and Miocene (Beck, 1978; Locke and Garver, this volume; Pérez de Armas, this volume; Hung, this volume). Igneous and metaigneous rocks occur in four of the belts: the Leeward Antilles, the Cordillera de la Costa, Caucagua–El Tinaco, and Villa de Cura (e.g., Donnelly and Rogers, 1978). Although these are predominantly mafic compositions and/or mineral assemblages, they also include a range of intermediate to felsic rocks.

Several models have been proposed for the development of the Caribbean Mountain system (e.g., Maresch, 1974; Pindell et al., 1988; Burke, 1988; Pindell and Barrett, 1990; Bellizzia and Dengo, 1990; Avé Lallemant, 1991, 1997; Pindell, 1993, 1994; Pindell et al., this volume). They arrive at significantly different conclusions about the protoliths of the belts. The goal of this study is to ascertain the tectonic setting for several of these belts using geochemical discriminant diagrams for igneous and metaigneous rocks.

Plate Tectonic Setting

Most plate tectonic modelers for the evolution of the Caribbean plate assume it originated as part of the Pacific (Farallon) plate (e.g., Pindell, 1994; Pindell et al., this volume). After the breakup of Pangea in the late Triassic or Early Jurassic, a west-facing magmatic arc developed along the western margin of the Americas. Beneath the Central American segment, Pacific (Farallon) oceanic lithosphere was subducted to the east under the Proto-Caribbean crust, which in turn had been formed by spreading between North and South America. Most models of Caribbean plate motion invoke a mid- to Late Cretaceous subduction polarity reversal, as proposed by Burke et al. (1978) and Mattson (1978). Pindell (1994) suggested that the reversal to westward subduction occurred in response to a sudden increase in spreading rates in the Atlantic, and placed an age of ca. 100 Ma on the event. Others argue that the thick Caribbean crust choked subduction and caused the subduction polarity reversal

ca. 80–70 Ma (e.g., Malfait and Dinkelman, 1972; Duncan and Hargraves, 1984; Burke, 1988). The polarity change caused the Farallon (Caribbean) plate and the "Great Arc of the Caribbean" (Burke, 1988) to migrate northeastward with respect to North and South America (e.g., Pindell, 1994). Proto-Caribbean lithosphere began to be subducted under the Caribbean plate. The relatively northeastward movement continued until the Eocene, when the Caribbean plate collided with the Bahaman platform (Duncan and Hargraves, 1984; Pindell, 1994). From this time to the present, the Caribbean plate has moved slowly east or southeastward relative to North and South America. Many of the early events produced suites of igneous rocks that range from MORBs to ocean island basalts (OIB) to island arc volcanics and volcaniclastics. Some regions were subsequently metamorphosed under seafloor hydrothermal to eclogite facies conditions.

ANALYTICAL METHODS

The samples analyzed in this study were collected along several geologic transects examined by Ostos (1990; Fig. 1). Enrique Navarro and Daniel Loureiro obtained additional samples for these regions. Only samples with fresh amphibole and/or pyroxene were analyzed. In addition, care was taken to avoid samples with secondary veins, fractures, and weathered rinds.

Chemical analyses were obtained by X-ray fluorescence spectrometry (XRF), inductively coupled plasma (ICP), and instrumental neutron activation analysis (INAA) techniques (Tables 1–5). The majority of the samples were analyzed using XRF equipment at Universidad Central de Venezuela. Additional data was acquired at Ministerio de Energía y Minas de Venezuela and at X-ray Assay Laboratories in Ontario, Canada. Ostos (1990) has additional analytical details. Major elements and select trace elements, including Ni, Cr, Zr, Y, Nb, Rb and Sr, were analyzed. Analytical precision is ~2%–4%. Duplicate analyses are essentially identical. Loss on ignition (LOI) values were only measured in a few representative samples. Rare earth element (REE) and Sr isotopic analyses were all done at X-ray Assay Laboratories.

Since these samples represent a variety of metamorphic grades, Appendix Tables A1–A6 give mineral assemblages of selected samples. These represent point counts of ~1000 points per thin section. Ostos (1990) contains additional mineral assemblage data for other samples from these transects.

RESULTS

In general, the use of only major element geochemistry in low- to high-grade metaigneous rocks is problematic to establishing their tectonic affinities because significant element mobility can take place during seafloor hydrothermal activity, weathering, and subsequent metamorphism (e.g., Pearce, 1982). Most of the element mobility probably occurs during seafloor alteration (e.g., Staudigel et al., 1996; Alt, 1999; Alt and Teagle, 2000). However, there is also ample evidence

TABLE 1. GEOCHEMISTRY OF MAFIC ROCKS FROM THE CORDILLERA DE LA COSTA BELT, VENEZUELA

Sample	VO83-5	VO83-5C	VO83-5DA	VO83-9	VO83-9B	VO83-10	DF-234A1	DF-234A2	DF-323B	DF-412B
Region	Chichiriviche–La Victoria transect						El Limon and Tacagua rivers			
Formation	Nirgua	Nirgua	Nirgua	Antimano	Antimano	Antimano	Antimano	Antimano	Antimano	Antimano
SiO_2	49.62	55.84	47.64	48.43	50.56	50.34	41.80	42.54	43.26	44.33
Al_2O_3	13.68	13.31	15.09	15.37	15.40	15.19	17.06	17.94	14.30	17.83
TiO_2	1.26	1.15	0.60	1.55	1.41	1.23	0.20	0.24	3.02	0.98
Fe_2O_3	13.70	11.55	11.07	10.71	10.11	10.34	16.53	13.79	17.72	10.49
MnO	0.17	0.15	0.14	0.28	0.25	0.31	0.13	0.26	0.26	0.25
MgO	7.52	6.89	7.74	10.80	10.93	11.02	12.68	15.56	4.96	14.68
CaO	11.60	9.00	11.00	7.34	5.58	5.89	8.60	9.73	11.90	8.23
Na_2O	2.04	1.06	2.87	2.99	4.36	3.98	2.33	0.85	3.12	2.39
K_2O	0.35	0.12	0.05	0.38	1.06	0.96	0.27	0.25	0.78	0.69
P_2O_5	0.10	0.11	0.20	0.20	0.19	0.23	0.01	0.01	1.30	0.16
LOI	n.d.	1.89	1.98	n.d.	n.d.	n.d.	n.d.	n.d.	n.d.	n.d.
Total	100.04	101.07	98.38	98.05	99.85	99.49	99.61	101.17	100.62	100.03
Cr	136	88	116	252	199	200	150	201	99	120
Ni	65	67	56	67	42	75	66	71	47	48
Zr	55	48	67	33	48	4	50	58	51	56
Y	21	19	24	22	20	18	27	224	28	25
Nb	7.71	6.66	7.86	5.27	5.45	1.00	7.14	6.41	6.09	5.99
Rb	38	52	43	11	14	16	17	23	21	24
Sr	413	372	407	81	119	174	91	135	103	116
La				7.3		6.5				
Ce				18.4		18.4				
Nd				14.1		14.1				
Sm				3.5		3.7				
Eu				1.17		0.99				
Tb				1.05		1.15				
Yb				3.58		3.98				
Lu				0.59		0.66				

Continued

TABLE 1. GEOCHEMISTRY OF MAFIC ROCKS FROM THE CORDILLERA DE LA COSTA BELT, VENEZUELA (continued)

Sample	DF-512	DF-512B	DF-517	DF-689B	DF-1123B	DF-1226	DF-2227B	DF-2229	DF-2252	DF-3012	DF-3220
Region	El Limon and Tacagua rivers (continued)										
Formation	Antimano	Antimano	Antimano	Antimano	Antimano	Antimano	Antimano	Antimano	Nirgua	Nirgua	Nirgua
SiO_2	48.70	48.41	47.64	45.64	48.43	47.02	47.64	47.64	48.41	48.37	50.28
Al_2O_3	12.73	12.82	13.12	12.66	15.24	14.41	13.12	13.12	16.24	12.73	13.92
TiO_2	0.95	1.36	1.25	0.89	1.79	1.11	1.68	1.62	1.02	4.30	1.50
Fe_2O_3	15.82	11.77	16.76	14.96	16.36	14.09	16.05	16.64	9.43	12.97	11.15
MnO	0.17	0.22	0.17	0.17	0.35	0.19	0.26	0.22	0.25	0.18	0.28
MgO	7.85	9.77	6.67	12.30	8.94	10.53	7.53	7.10	14.01	8.39	9.19
CaO	7.84	9.37	10.38	7.25	5.88	6.91	9.00	10.31	8.49	7.30	6.50
Na_2O	3.10	3.15	1.28	2.33	3.44	2.21	2.51	2.15	2.18	4.49	4.10
K_2O	0.03	0.25	0.08	0.87	0.90	0.68	0.05	0.09	0.30	0.23	0.40
P_2O_5	0.14	0.17	0.16	0.15	0.19	0.16	0.16	0.16	0.01	0.16	0.65
LOI	n.d.	n.d.	n.d.	n.d.	n.d.	n.d.	n.d.	n.d.	n.d.	n.d.	n.d.
Total	97.33	97.29	97.51	97.22	101.52	97.31	98.00	99.05	100.34	99.12	97.97
Cr	79	89	100	207	104	108	118	117	90	103	88
Ni	27	17	43	99	45	61	37	41	56	69	35
Zr	39	45	32	52	72	96	106	136	132	122	96
Y	16	21	17	30	48	38	44	38	30	38	32
Nb	7.38	5.20	5.27	6.08	17.73	8.16	9.00	9.19	9.39	10.61	9.59
Rb	12	16	22	30	38	36	54	71	56	8	9
Sr	135	187	102	142	475	31	229	259	674	99	94
La								6.7			
Ce								26.0			
Nd								15.1			
Sm								3.8			
Eu								1.24			
Tb								1.15			
Yb								4.24			
Lu								0.74			

Continued

TABLE 1. GEOCHEMISTRY OF MAFIC ROCKS FROM THE CORDILLERA DE LA COSTA BELT, VENEZUELA (continued)

Sample	DF-3233	DF-3248	DF-3303	DF-3309B	DF-3406	DF9092	DF91288	DF9131	DF9134	DF9135	DF9147
Region	El Limon and Tacagua rivers (continued)					El Avila National Park					
Formation	Nirgua	Nirgua	Nirgua	Nirgua	Nirgua	Nirgua	Nirgua	Nirgua	Nirgua	Nirgua	Nirgua
SiO_2	42.26	47.59	47.64	50.77	51.73	49.10	53.38	49.83	52.02	51.15	53.71
Al_2O_3	14.30	17.67	13.52	15.65	15.79	16.67	14.90	13.91	13.52	12.50	12.05
TiO_2	3.70	1.39	1.68	1.14	1.10	0.18	1.12	0.47	0.95	0.91	1.18
Fe_2O_3	18.19	10.37	18.40	10.26	9.25	5.14	9.09	13.45	12.00	11.93	11.27
MnO	0.26	0.30	0.34	0.25	0.28	0.09	0.11	0.15	0.09	0.13	0.23
MgO	4.90	7.40	8.28	9.88	8.16	9.51	7.89	7.53	6.35	9.23	8.12
CaO	12.11	8.84	6.20	3.10	6.04	14.00	12.15	10.50	11.00	10.83	10.70
Na_2O	3.10	2.75	2.87	2.19	3.50	2.26	2.32	2.00	1.46	2.34	2.83
K_2O	0.41	1.76	0.50	0.52	1.22	0.14	0.16	0.28	0.06	0.12	0.29
P_2O_5	1.50	0.41	0.15	0.52	0.46	n.d.	n.d.	n.d.	n.d.	n.d.	n.d.
LOI	n.d.	n.d.	n.d.	n.d.	n.d.	0.01	0.17	0.07	0.08	0.21	0.36
Total	100.73	98.48	99.58	94.28	97.53	97.10	101.29	98.19	97.53	99.35	100.74
Cr	120	189	923	14	180	214	132	234	144	65	99
Ni	56	45	234	36	61	81	61	89	59	50	45
Zr	3	52	69	62	32	42	75	48	54	118	180
Y	35	26	24	28	19	15	23	17	26	27	33
Nb	6.00	15.25	5.39	5.43	6.77	6.29	5.33	5.87	8.25	7.44	12.30
Rb	27	18	28	31	24	30	9	16	35	23	34
Sr	103	133	210	424	516	194	71	144	255	250	499
La								6.5			
Ce								18.4			
Nd								11.0			
Sm								2.6			
Eu								0.86			
Tb								0.67			
Yb								3.22			
Lu								0.54			

Continued

TABLE 1. GEOCHEMISTRY OF MAFIC ROCKS FROM THE CORDILLERA DE LA COSTA BELT, VENEZUELA (continued)

Sample	DF9150	DF9150B	DF9153	DF9156	DF9159	DF9162	VO83-302	VO83-302B	VO83-305B	VO83-307	VO83-308
Region	El Avila National Park (continued)						Isla de Margarita				
Formation	Nirgua	Nirgua	Nirgua	Nirgua	Nirgua	Nirgua	Rinconada	Rinconada	Juan Griego	Juan Griego	Juan Griego
SiO_2	49.21	49.10	47.18	49.10	49.43	50.06	49.76	53.02	50.00	13.34	43.26
Al_2O_3	12.12	14.30	14.01	14.70	15.95	12.52	10.71	13.61	17.00	16.61	17.03
TiO_2	0.65	0.47	0.59	0.53	0.99	1.18	0.30	0.30	1.21	0.98	0.91
Fe_2O_3	10.29	12.97	12.02	12.25	9.95	11.95	9.41	7.91	12.52	13.45	12.97
MnO	0.14	0.14	0.14	0.15	0.27	0.23	0.13	0.12	0.12	0.15	0.16
MgO	10.90	9.67	7.58	8.87	8.02	10.47	14.53	10.17	3.74	4.54	6.93
CaO	12.07	9.50	13.20	9.80	9.59	9.60	7.66	9.49	9.50	9.46	12.64
Na_2O	2.01	2.80	1.32	3.40	1.62	2.87	0.56	3.41	4.24	4.45	3.23
K_2O	0.14	0.12	0.07	0.07	0.64	0.24	0.05	1.04	0.22	1.08	0.25
P_2O_5	0.41	0.05	0.06	0.03	0.03	0.19	0.07	0.07	0.22	0.15	0.00
LOI	n.d.	n.d.	n.d.	n.d.	n.d.	n.d.	5.12	0.75	0.14	6.12	1.38
Total	97.94	99.12	96.17	98.90	96.49	99.31	98.30	98.89	98.91	100.33	98.75
Cr	200	235	42	191	321	221	1000	85	6	619	240
Ni	70	97	68	89	79	106	380	126	17	132	37
Zr	37	36	2	57	40	43	3	60	1	21	30
Y	14	16	20	16	18	13	9	26	18	14	13
Nb	5.45	5.99	1.00	6.54	5.95	6.01	1.00	13.97	2.00	7.47	7.45
Rb	14	17	14	12	18	24	12	7	11	7	11
Sr	132	180	102	124	185	314	519	166	225	199	297
La				2.3					7.9		6.6
Ce				8.6					20.6		16.3
Nd				7.0					13.1		13.1
Sm				2.0					3.5		2.8
Eu				0.65					1.41		0.92
Tb				0.67					0.86		0.67
Yb				3.16					3.10		2.80
Lu				0.53					0.50		0.46

Continued

TABLE 1. GEOCHEMISTRY OF MAFIC ROCKS FROM THE CORDILLERA DE LA COSTA BELT, VENEZUELA (continued)

Sample	VO83-308B	VO83-309	VO83-310	VO83-311	VO83-313B	VO83-315	VO83-316	VO83-317	VO83-318	VO83-319	VO83-321
Region	Isla de Margarita (continued)										
Formation	Juan Griego	Rinconada	Rinconada	Rinconada	Rinconada	Rinconada	Rinconada	Juan Griego	Rinconada	Rinconada	Rinconada
SiO_2	46.58	47.64	49.10	47.64	49.10	51.33	49.83	47.06	47.00	48.13	49.53
Al_2O_3	14.54	16.00	15.37	17.00	14.95	15.37	15.78	16.20	16.20	16.62	15.68
TiO_2	0.64	0.70	0.64	0.75	1.04	0.65	0.58	0.31	1.13	1.06	1.20
Fe_2O_3	8.70	12.26	11.07	11.78	9.41	10.12	8.46	9.65	10.84	9.41	10.13
MnO	0.11	0.15	0.14	0.11	0.15	0.12	0.08	0.11	0.11	0.13	0.15
MgO	12.14	5.71	7.52	4.54	8.42	6.79	7.73	9.78	6.79	6.60	7.71
CaO	8.00	10.17	10.00	10.00	10.45	11.58	12.50	11.79	11.54	12.10	10.55
Na_2O	3.12	2.76	3.88	3.98	3.55	2.87	2.87	2.22	3.25	3.23	3.31
K_2O	0.32	0.16	0.19	0.50	0.20	0.16	0.08	0.66	0.12	0.18	0.15
P_2O_5	0.09	0.09	0.12	0.12	0.05	0.10	0.00	0.01	0.13	0.12	0.10
LOI	4.02	2.76	1.65	1.99	1.35	1.07	1.41	2.70	1.70	1.56	n.d.
Total	96.26	98.60	99.68	98.85	95.67	100.16	99.38	100.49	98.81	99.33	97.51
Cr	12	41	180	2	190	11	897	57	58	54	64
Ni	36	32	59	18	28	12	328	67	33	37	41
Zr	8	45	3	5	21	24	21	30	27	21	27
Y	21	19	19	18	21	21	23	28	16	15	21
Nb	1.00	7.98	1.00	1.00	5.19	6.44	5.09	6.22	6.77	7.09	7.28
Rb	14	8	11	15	6	9	9	5	5	7	2
Sr	468	276	190	180	234	201	43	199	199	78	154
La						4.4			4.9		
Ce						13.0			14.1		
Nd						9.1			8.0		
Sm						1.8			2.5		
Eu						0.63			0.95		
Tb						0.39			0.57		
Yb						1.56			2.10		
Lu						0.24			0.35		

Continued

TABLE 1. GEOCHEMISTRY OF MAFIC ROCKS FROM THE CORDILLERA DE LA COSTA BELT, VENEZUELA *(continued)*

Sample	VO83-322	VO83-323	VO83-324	VO83-326	VO86-5	VO86-6
Region	Isla de Margarita *(continued)*					
Formation	Juan Griego	Juan Griego	Juan Griego	Juan Griego	Rinconada	Rinconada
SiO_2	43.57	50.08	49.83	47.00	48.72	48.34
Al_2O_3	14.52	15.78	16.61	14.95	15.16	16.20
TiO_2	1.80	0.20	0.99	1.67	1.15	1.26
Fe_2O_3	17.00	5.62	13.44	14.39	9.89	10.36
MnO	0.18	0.08	0.02	0.15	0.16	0.15
MgO	7.63	9.94	6.16	7.94	7.95	7.47
CaO	11.00	10.95	8.40	10.24	10.91	11.37
Na_2O	3.59	2.58	3.44	2.51	3.39	3.23
K_2O	0.07	1.02	0.12	0.12	0.16	0.12
P_2O_5	0.09	0.01	0.07	0.12	0.09	0.12
LOI	0.96	3.46	0.05	1.38	0.96	0.64
Total	100.71	99.00	99.13	100.47	98.54	99.26
Cr	144	128	171	921	234	150
Ni	48	32	56	249	69	68
Zr	33	30	21	39	30	4
Y	23	22	21	10	21	23
Nb	8.09	5.23	10.20	5.49	5.20	1
Rb	8	6	12	12	2	19
Sr	191	453	224	219	235	209
La						
Ce						
Nd						
Sm						
Eu						
Tb						
Yb						
Lu						

Note: LOI—loss on ignition; n.d.—no data.

for element mobility during subduction zone metamorphism (Sorensen and Grossman, 1989, 1993; Sorensen et al., 1997; Bebout et al., 1999; Becker et al., 2000; Sorensen et al., this volume). Zirconium is generally regarded as immobile during low-grade alteration of basaltic rocks (Humphris and Thompson, 1978; Staudigel et al., 1996). The elements TiO_2, Y, and Nb are typically well correlated with Zr in ways that appear similar to igneous rock suites, which suggests they are generally less mobile in hydrothermal and metamorphic systems. K_2O, Ba, Rb, and Sr are not. Nevertheless, we use the variation diagram K_2O–TiO_2–P_2O_5 of Pearce (1975) to distinguish ocean-floor basalts from other basalts, although these elements are mobile during post-crystallization processes. This is because Pearce et al. (1985) found that both metamorphism and weathering cause compositions to move steadily away from the ocean floor field, not into it.

In some cases, it is possible to fingerprint magmas from different tectonic settings as originally proposed by Pearce and Cann (1971). Despite the fact that this type of analysis is not perfect in all regions, we attempt to assign tectonic settings by using it in combination with regional geological relationships. Pearce (1982) proposed the Ti/Y–Nb/Y discrimination diagram for such igneous associations. Mid-oceanic-ridge basalts (MORB) are subdivided into three different types: normal or N-MORB, depleted in incompatible elements (e.g., Cs, Rb, Ba, Nb, Th, U, K, light REE, P, and Ta), enriched or E-MORB, which is enriched in incompatible elements, and transitional (T-MORB), which is between N-MORB and E-MORB. Zr, Nb, and Y are immobile during seafloor alteration and metamorphism, and show characteristic abundances in different types of MORB (e.g., Langmuir et al. 1978; Pearce and Norry, 1979). Pearce et al. (1984) proposed a similar approach for granites (loosely defined as felsic igneous with greater than 5 modal % quartz). They identified four main types of felsic rocks, including ocean ridge granites, volcanic arc granites, within-plate granites, and collisional granites. All these various discriminant diagrams for both mafic and felsic

TABLE 2. GEOCHEMISTRY OF FELSIC ROCKS FROM THE CORDILLERA DE LA COSTA BELT

Sample	VO83-1	VO83-4	VO83-7	VO83-8	VO83-12	VO83-12B	VO83-13	VO83-21	VO83-27
Region	Chichiriviche–La Victoria Transect								
Formation	Peña	Peña	Nirgua	Peña	Nirgua	Nirgua	Peña	Nirgua	Peña
SiO_2	75.83	68.99	68.08	68.71	70.91	68.65	68.38	75.03	68.98
Al_2O_3	11.29	16.15	16.45	16.57	16.09	16.09	16.57	12.01	17.35
TiO_2	0.44	0.32	0.30	0.26	0.42	0.32	0.27	0.32	0.62
Fe_2O_3	2.16	2.67	2.29	2.05	2.95	2.32	2.51	1.99	3.32
MnO	0.32	0.27	0.25	0.23	0.20	0.25	0.30	0.23	0.20
MgO	1.52	1.90	1.45	1.37	2.08	1.21	1.76	1.23	1.18
CaO	0.91	1.66	0.98	0.76	0.14	0.66	0.38	1.08	0.55
Na_2O	2.53	3.39	3.99	4.60	1.21	4.86	2.90	2.73	2.95
K_2O	5.82	2.69	2.98	2.82	3.64	2.98	4.13	6.02	2.35
P_2O_5	0.09	0.02	0.18	0.16	0.09	0.18	0.13	0.08	0.18
LOI	n.d.	n.d.	1.32	n.d.	n.d.	n.d.	n.d.	n.d.	n.d.
Total	100.91	98.06	98.27	97.53	97.73	97.52	97.33	100.72	97.68
Cr	12	10	14	35	20	37	29	19	30
Ni	32	30	22	40	30	45	48	28	50
Zr	382	393	304	334	338	336	346	324	328
Y	110	82	104	88	104	80	104	87	80
Nb	44.32	32.18	42.64	48.17	50.18	56.82	42.28	41.63	33.25
Rb	201	171	187	128	191	121	153	124	146
Sr	65	87	93	275	66	231	63	177	36
La									
Ce									
Nd									
Sm									
Eu									
Tb									
Yb									
Lu									

Continued

TABLE 2. GEOCHEMISTRY OF FELSIC ROCKS FROM THE CORDILLERA DE LA COSTA BELT *(continued)*

Sample	VO83-34	VO86-9	PM-1	PM-2	PM-3	DF-9024	DF-9062	DF-9155	DF-10042	DF-10064
Region	Chichiriviche–La Victoria Transect *(continued)*					El Avila National Park				
Formation	Peña	Peña	Peña	Peña	Peña	Peña	Peña	Nirgua	Peña	Peña
SiO_2	69.99	73.73	70.30	72.50	70.10	67.11	69.18	61.54	69.53	72.15
Al_2O_3	16.85	14.12	13.00	13.00	13.00	15.93	15.07	12.31	15.07	14.82
TiO_2	0.45	0.15	0.37	0.35	0.48	0.34	0.30	0.64	0.42	0.18
Fe_2O_3	2.89	1.10	3.74	3.86	4.63	6.02	4.09	9.68	3.98	1.99
MnO	0.24	0.02	0.05	0.02	0.05	0.06	0.04	0.08	0.03	0.07
MgO	1.24	0.35	0.34	0.43	0.59	0.47	0.61	9.31	0.33	0.10
CaO	0.24	1.85	1.45	0.62	1.62	1.58	0.63	3.04	0.83	0.51
Na_2O	3.09	5.03	3.10	3.60	2.56	3.62	3.96	3.01	4.96	4.81
K_2O	2.45	1.66	5.33	5.17	5.11	3.91	5.07	0.23	5.03	4.37
P_2O_5	0.21	0.03	0.08	0.06	0.12	0.15	0.08	0.11	0.15	0.40
LOI	n.d.	1.35	1.23	0.7	0.85	n.d.	n.d.	n.d.	n.d.	n.d.
Total	97.65	99.39	98.99	100.31	99.11	99.19	99.03	99.95	100.33	99.40
Cr	32	24	12	14	10	23	35	57	30	28
Ni	45	30	46	31	28	24	39	42	32	39
Zr	304	362	442	471	621	174	168	135	198	176
Y	75	86	137	154	92	82	95	52	75	68
Nb	30.47	48.68	45.00	41.00	33.00	54.22	60.70	53.92	53.16	47.16
Rb	120	167	269	228	162	189	132	7	198	207
Sr	209	79	111	42	186	87	234	154	83	91
La			723.8							
Ce			477.2							
Nd			219.4							
Sm			120.8							
Eu			21.7							
Tb			73.5							
Yb			66.5							
Lu			61.3							

Continued

TABLE 2. GEOCHEMISTRY OF FELSIC ROCKS FROM THE CORDILLERA DE LA COSTA BELT *(continued)*

Sample	VO83-59	VO83-60	VO83-62B	VO83-64	VO83-66	VO83-67	VO83-68	VO83-71	LV-87-1	LV-87-2
Region	La Victoria transect metadiorites and granodiorites									
	Guacamaya	Guacamaya	Guacamaya	Guacamaya	Guacamaya	Tucutunemo	Tucutunemo	Guacamaya	Guacamaya	Guacamaya
SiO_2	60.01	57.86	69.54	57.19	59.82	66.72	67.02	61.28	55.90	53.80
Al_2O_3	16.03	15.31	8.10	14.91	15.71	14.51	14.83	12.31	16.10	16.90
TiO_2	0.67	0.70	0.15	0.64	0.59	0.64	0.72	1.21	0.69	0.67
Fe_2O_3	8.12	8.22	2.13	8.46	7.04	5.15	5.02	9.89	8.57	8.90
MnO	0.12	0.10	0.03	0.10	0.08	0.03	0.07	0.12	0.16	0.17
MgO	3.96	4.41	2.92	3.78	4.20	2.38	2.09	4.20	4.19	5.02
CaO	4.32	7.00	4.40	7.10	4.04	0.99	0.78	4.53	8.15	9.61
Na_2O	3.61	2.32	1.79	2.40	3.88	2.07	2.31	2.72	2.21	2.51
K_2O	2.02	1.72	3.68	1.24	1.77	3.74	4.01	0.99	1.51	0.84
P_2O_5	0.05	0.08	0.06	0.09	0.07	0.18	0.20	0.14	0.09	0.07
LOI	n.d.	1.81	6.42	4.23	2.07	2.34	n.d.	1.83	2.08	2.23
Total	98.91	99.53	99.22	100.14	99.27	98.75	97.05	99.22	99.65	100.72
Cr	39	41	36	44	51	31	37	44	28	46
Ni	41	34	27	38	39	24	32	46	19	38
Zr	100	96	101	89	98	106	130	128	74	26
Y	26	23	24	25	27	27	21	22	19	12
Nb	22.83	19.67	17.72	21.62	23.66	30.09	29.89	23.32	17.00	11.00
Rb	45	52	31	33	34	197	202	36	51	36
Sr	260	260	239	208	203	91	88	210	223	266
La										
Ce										
Nd										
Sm										
Eu										
Tb										
Yb										
Lu										

Continued

TABLE 2. GEOCHEMISTRY OF FELSIC ROCKS FROM THE CORDILLERA DE LA COSTA BELT *(continued)*

Sample	LV-87-3	LV-87-4	MTS-85-1	MTS-85-2	MTS-85-3	Guay-85-1	VO83-300	VO83-301	VO83-303	VO83-303B
Region	La Victoria *(continued)*		Isla de Margarita							
Formation	Guacamaya	Guacamaya	Matasiete	Matasiete	Matasiete	Guayacan	El Salado	El Salado	El Salado	Matasiete
SiO_2	54.60	57.60	73.81	68.04	68.26	68.20	77.18	70.88	71.01	68.58
Al_2O_3	16.20	15.70	14.78	15.78	16.20	16.20	12.91	14.91	15.31	16.11
TiO_2	0.73	0.65	0.10	0.20	0.11	0.13	0.09	0.15	0.12	0.17
Fe_2O_3	9.01	7.91	1.77	2.60	2.40	1.90	0.90	1.95	1.15	1.83
MnO	0.16	0.14	0.02	0.03	0.02	0.02	0.02	0.02	0.01	0.02
MgO	4.27	3.57	0.92	1.60	1.02	1.55	0.44	1.17	0.55	1.27
CaO	8.07	7.68	2.13	3.40	3.20	3.47	1.30	3.20	1.00	2.64
Na_2O	2.12	2.45	5.80	5.49	5.86	5.42	5.64	5.61	6.47	6.22
K_2O	1.39	1.19	0.80	0.80	0.84	0.73	0.84	0.64	1.10	0.98
P_2O_5	0.09	0.09	0.05	0.13	0.09	0.11	0.01	0.07	0.04	0.12
LOI	2.47	2.27	0.78	0.76	0.79	1.11	1.01	1.27	2.27	1.15
Total	99.11	99.25	100.18	98.83	98.79	98.84	100.34	99.87	99.03	99.09
Cr	30	29	39	31	30	29	34	40	30	23
Ni	24	39	50	48	52	58	47	50	48	29
Zr	101	69	215	197	174	254	201	217	189	200
Y	11	25	7	6	5	5	2	4	9	7
Nb	19.00	10.00	3.00	2.00	2.00	3.00	3.00	1.00	8.57	7.55
Rb	54	48	28	23	15	15	22	23	18	23
Sr	240	245	592	524	544	650	287	616	389	403
La			39.0							
Ce			28.3							
Nd			23.5							
Sm			13.5							
Eu			9.1							
Tb			10.2							
Yb			4.4							
Lu			4.3							

Continued

TABLE 2. GEOCHEMISTRY OF FELSIC ROCKS FROM THE CORDILLERA DE LA COSTA BELT *(continued)*

Sample	VO83-304	VO83-304B	VO83-306B	VO83-313	VO83-314	VO-83-320	VO85-352	VO85-385
Region	Isla de Margarita *(continued)*							
Formation	Matasiete	Matasiete	Matasiete	Guayacan	Guayacan	Guayacan	Guayacan	El Salado
SiO_2	67.62	67.16	61.88	69.64	69.84	59.16	68.35	76.32
Al_2O_3	16.51	16.11	18.31	15.90	15.32	16.62	16.41	12.95
TiO_2	0.19	0.20	0.14	0.13	0.15	0.58	0.13	0.30
Fe_2O_3	2.09	2.70	2.84	1.45	1.82	5.62	1.96	1.36
MnO	0.02	0.03	0.03	0.02	0.03	0.06	0.02	0.02
MgO	1.56	1.87	1.88	0.95	1.39	3.91	1.42	0.76
CaO	3.54	3.47	4.33	2.85	3.40	7.20	2.94	0.18
Na_2O	5.75	5.75	8.27	6.15	5.24	6.04	5.99	5.60
K_2O	0.84	0.63	0.15	0.80	0.48	0.10	0.91	1.80
P_2O_5	0.10	0.11	0.08	0.08	0.12	0.15	0.11	0.02
LOI	1.27	0.85	0.96	0.77	1.20	1.15	n.d.	n.d.
Total	99.49	98.88	98.87	98.74	98.99	100.59	98.24	99.31
Cr	29	34	46	27	30	50	34	10
Ni	54	40	32	34	40	30	45	31
Zr	224	199	139	231	226	126	215	154
Y	7	10	13	13	10	10	29	26
Nb	8.91	8.06	13.81	7.24	9.74	8.14	15.90	14.06
Rb	20	27	41	28	30	35	78	73
Sr	354	724	239	499	547	195	350	41
La								
Ce								
Nd								
Sm								
Eu								
Tb								
Yb								
Lu								

Continued

TABLE 2. GEOCHEMISTRY OF FELSIC ROCKS FROM THE CORDILLERA DE LA COSTA BELT *(continued)*

Sample	M1	M3	N5	E9	F10
Region	Gran Roque				
Formation	Aplite	Aplite	Diorite	Andesite	Pegmatite
SiO_2	65.62	64.07	61.56	61.77	61.01
Al_2O_3	16.38	16.01	15.46	16.65	15.89
TiO_2	0.50	0.62	0.52	0.55	0.40
Fe_2O_3	5.68	5.91	8.30	8.35	7.98
MnO	0.09	0.12	0.09	0.10	0.17
MgO	1.93	2.02	3.17	2.83	4.05
CaO	5.86	6.32	6.50	5.31	6.60
Na_2O	2.62	2.97	2.87	1.59	0.90
K_2O	1.66	0.98	0.79	0.67	0.39
P_2O_5	0.06	0.10	0.11	0.09	0.13
LOI	n.d.	n.d.	0.33	n.d.	n.d.
Total	100.80	99.12	99.70	97.91	97.49
Cr	19	17	19	15	387
Ni	37	41	47	43	177
Zr	159	144	179	162	142
Y	14	16	33	11	26
Nb	16.67	17.42	22.79	17.02	17.03
Rb	53	65	17	61	11
Sr	162	148	156	135	53
La					
Ce					
Nd					
Sm					
Eu					
Tb					
Yb					
Lu					

Note: LOI—loss on ignition; n.d.—no data.

TABLE 3. GEOCHEMISTRY OF TINACO AND TINAQUILLO COMPLEX

Sample	VO83-200	VO83-203	VO83-205	VT82-135	VT82-104	VT82-105	VT82-130	VT82-132B	VT82-139	VT87-2
Transect	Tinaco	Tinaco	Tinaco	Tinaco	Tinaco	Tinaco	Tinaco	Tinaco	Tinaco	Tinaco
Rock type	La Aguadita	La Aguadita	La Aguadita	La Aguadita	La Aguadita	La Aguadita	La Aguadita	La Aguadita	La Aguadita	La Aguadita
SiO_2	49.10	49.64	53.14	49.42	49.07	48.46	48.34	48.57	48.61	48.90
Al_2O_3	11.71	14.97	14.08	14.69	18.16	9.59	14.95	15.07	16.81	17.20
TiO_2	0.35	0.33	0.90	0.37	1.34	0.71	1.26	1.19	0.25	0.89
Fe_2O_3	11.55	10.92	8.25	11.12	8.48	7.88	13.20	11.78	8.19	11.30
MnO	0.23	0.31	0.28	0.29	0.36	0.16	0.17	0.18	0.22	0.19
MgO	10.47	11.14	10.93	11.28	11.19	18.37	4.96	5.12	7.33	5.04
CaO	11.58	6.83	6.24	6.52	8.03	5.45	9.60	10.72	10.97	9.04
Na_2O	1.57	2.81	1.85	2.57	1.45	1.84	3.77	3.10	4.10	3.19
K_2O	1.77	1.45	2.61	1.23	0.33	0.34	0.92	0.32	1.60	2.03
P_2O_5	0.20	0.15	0.43	0.18	0.07	0.07	0.37	0.06	0.27	0.28
LOI	1.77	n.d.	n.d.	n.d.	n.d.	n.d.	0.78	n.d.	n.d.	2.08
Total	100.03	98.55	96.91	97.67	96.48	95.92	98.52	47.54	98.42	100.14
Cr	180	232	132	220	190	1356	130	150	168	47
Ni	82	60	41	68	72	227	67	56	53	24
Zr	9	52	39	48	40	60	44	46	39	37
Y	15	16	15	18	19	16	16	18	13	14
Nb	4.00	6.54	11.43	5.73	5.21	6.09	2.00	5.49	5.21	11.00
Rb	33	17	63	18	43	14	6	32	22	32
Sr	412	149	223	731	512	536	499	498	90	605
La	16.9				16.2		12.9			
Ce	35.7				41.1		34.7			
Nd	21.1				22.1		21.1			
Sm	3.5				5.3		5.0			
Eu	1.0				2.0		1.7			
Tb	0.5				1.0		1.0			
Yb	1.7				4.2		4.0			
Lu	0.3				0.8		0.7			

Continued

TABLE 3. GEOCHEMISTRY OF TINACO AND TINAQUILLO COMPLEX (continued)

Sample	VT82-44	VT82-51	VTO82-52	VTO82-61	VT82-100	VT82-101†	VT82-114	VT82-116	VT82-116B	VT82-118
Transect	Tinaquillo	Tinaquillo	Tinaquillo	Tinaquillo	Tinaquillo	Tinaquillo	Tinaquillo	Tinaquillo	Tinaquillo	Tinaquillo
Rock type	Gabbro	Metagabbro	Metagabbro	Metagabbro	Felsic Gneiss	Felsic Gneiss	Felsic Gneiss	Felsic Gneiss	Granulite	Granulite
SiO_2	45.34	46.08	45.10	49.34	45.97	47.68	48.80	47.18	47.06	49.88
Al_2O_3	17.03	15.78	17.98	9.55	18.97	17.93	18.69	17.03	14.52	17.45
TiO_2	0.20	0.53	1.18	1.19	1.64	1.36	1.17	0.42	0.86	0.26
Fe_2O_3	7.99	10.48	9.64	9.65	9.92	9.19	8.33	7.62	12.97	7.98
MnO	0.11	0.13	0.18	0.12	0.30	0.29	0.20	0.24	0.16	0.25
MgO	10.36	10.50	13.20	18.45	12.69	12.08	9.60	11.08	8.79	9.35
CaO	12.43	12.63	9.30	10.00	8.03	8.55	11.64	13.08	12.83	12.23
Na_2O	2.04	2.09	2.35	1.42	1.45	1.61	2.72	1.81	2.14	1.32
K_2O	0.15	0.12	0.44	0.20	0.33	0.21	0.27	0.57	0.08	0.02
P_2O_5	0.01	0.05	0.06	0.01	0.07	0.04	0.00	0.01	0.07	0.01
LOI	0.34	n.d.	n.d.	0.48	n.d.	n.d.	n.d.	n.d.	1.32	n.d.
Total	99.00	96.39	98.95	99.41	98.37	98.84	101.46	99.04	100.80	98.65
Cr	500	601	583	920	780	197	647	736	330	67
Ni	170	151	128	210	142	57	159	68	120	133
Zr	14	14	31	19	36	34	38	31	21	20
Y	9	18	20	17	14	22	15	15	19	16
Nb	1.00	5.45	5.81	1.00	5.28	6.72	5.29	6.47	2.00	10.91
Rb	20	17	11	12	10	7	9	11	12	21
Sr	93	123	109	131	173	52	834	269	124	1034
La	1.9								2.4	0.4
Ce	6.5								9.8	2.2
Nd	3.0								5.0	1.5
Sm	1.0								2.1	0.4
Eu	0.7								0.9	0.2
Tb	0.2								0.6	0.1
Yb	1.1								2.5	0.5
Lu	0.2								0.4	0.1

Continued

TABLE 3. GEOCHEMISTRY OF TINACO AND TINAQUILLO COMPLEX (continued)

Sample	VTOG-31	VTOG-82	VO83-202	VO83-205B	VO83-207	VO83-208	VO83-210B	VO83-211	VO83-212	VT82-133	VT82-134
Transect	Tinaquillo	Tinaquillo	Tinaco	Tinaco	Tinaco	Tinaco	Tinaco	Tinaco	Tinaco	Tinaco	Tinaco
Rock type	Metagabbro	Metagabbro	La Aguadita	La Aguadita	La Aguadita	La Aguadita	La Aguadita	La Aguadita	La Aguadita	La Aguadita	La Aguadita
SiO_2	45.35	49.26	56.40	69.55	70.32	59.32	66.92	56.00	57.86	71.07	67.25
Al_2O_3	11.21	16.00	12.51	14.91	14.45	14.91	15.85	9.70	14.91	14.55	13.42
TiO_2	0.58	0.20	0.25	0.18	0.18	0.64	0.34	0.19	0.64	0.17	0.20
Fe_2O_3	13.21	7.75	10.12	2.50	2.10	8.94	3.24	8.55	8.23	1.95	5.17
MnO	0.15	0.11	0.33	0.03	0.25	0.12	0.17	0.13	0.10	0.45	0.07
MgO	15.56	10.41	4.85	0.61	1.64	3.03	3.31	11.10	3.51	1.87	2.01
CaO	9.70	14.68	7.60	1.30	0.85	6.20	2.80	10.00	6.00	0.98	5.01
Na_2O	1.68	2.00	3.86	5.64	2.60	4.67	2.45	2.72	5.02	2.86	4.38
K_2O	0.25	0.12	1.95	2.07	5.59	1.60	1.45	1.30	1.03	5.89	0.87
P_2O_5	0.06	0.01	1.56	0.07	0.19	0.21	0.25	0.03	0.30	0.23	0.10
LOI	n.d.	0.64	0.39	4.22	n.d.	0.11	n.d.	1.18	1.12	n.d.	n.d.
Total	98.05	101.18	99.92	101.08	98.17	99.75	96.78	100.90	98.72	100.02	98.48
Cr	650	225	75	41	38	92	26	71	99	27	30
Ni	124	97	45	26	31	67	49	66	77	41	23
Zr	34	18	77	78	87	83	91	90	65	60	93
Y	14	18	12	2	20	18	20	19	21	28	22
Nb	5.25	5.31	1.00	23.44	24.01	22.33	24.31	16.18	23.41	25.39	27.26
Rb	24	36	29	53	59	24	33	7	23	60	45
Sr	927	394	285	372	278	389	1063	133	401	264	921
La					16.9						
Ce					36.8						
Nd					17.1						
Sm					3.1						
Eu					0.5						
Tb					0.4						
Yb					0.7						
Lu					0.1						

Continued

TABLE 3. GEOCHEMISTRY OF TINACO AND TINAQUILLO COMPLEX (continued)

Sample	VT82-136	VO82-136B	VTOG-45	RT87-4	RT87-5	VO83-61	VO83-62	VO83-63	VO83-65	VO86-17	VO86-19
Transect	Tinaco	Tinaco	Tinaco	Tinaco	Tinaco	La Victoria	La Victoria	La Victoria	La Victoria	La Victoria	La Victoria
Rock type	La Aguadita	La Aguadita	La Aguadita	La Aguadita	La Aguadita	Guacamaya	Guacamaya	Guacamaya	Guacamaya	Guacamaya	Guacamaya
SiO_2	68.34	72.09	75.50	62.10	55.70	49.26	56.93	54.94	55.51	53.80	54.31
Al_2O_3	15.15	13.67	12.94	17.20	16.30	11.71	16.79	15.71	16.06	16.61	16.61
TiO_2	0.23	0.20	0.20	0.45	0.74	1.04	0.90	0.64	0.79	0.31	0.58
Fe_2O_3	3.06	1.97	0.85	3.64	7.39	10.36	10.00	8.94	9.24	9.65	9.89
MnO	0.13	0.30	0.01	0.07	0.17	0.12	0.15	0.10	0.14	0.11	0.12
MgO	1.84	1.53	0.17	1.58	4.12	12.57	4.31	5.17	8.28	4.64	4.80
CaO	3.21	0.89	1.74	2.70	6.12	9.32	5.82	8.50	5.81	9.30	8.30
Na_2O	4.45	2.98	5.92	3.07	3.74	1.72	2.30	1.79	2.18	2.33	2.40
K_2O	0.98	6.01	0.55	8.37	4.27	0.57	1.33	2.31	2.11	1.02	1.36
P_2O_5	0.14	0.22	0.03	0.19	0.37	0.04	0.25	0.09	0.18	0.08	0.10
LOI	n.d.	n.d.	0.62	0.85	1.62	2.52	1.8	2.39	n.d.	2.44	2.48
Total	97.53	99.86	98.53	100.22	100.54	99.23	100.58	100.58	100.30	100.29	100.95
Cr	33	13	19	12	40	40	26	21	37	30	34
Ni	21	29	19	29	21	36	27	24	29	24	32
Zr	80	67	90	10	49	68	80	72	77	44	88
Y	24	24	34	23	24	20	26	23	24	18	30
Nb	22.34	16.27	19.12	10.00	10.00	8.07	9.91	9.53	10.14	10.37	10.28
Rb	49	66	68	109	54	41	31	64	52	58	60
Sr	198	418	329	381	192	246	239	222	260	215	210
La											
Ce											
Nd											
Sm											
Eu											
Tb											
Yb											
Lu											

Note: LOI—loss on ignition; n.d.—no data.

TABLE 4. GEOCHEMISTRY OF THE MAFIC ROCKS FROM THE VILLA DE CURA COMPLEX

Samples	VO86-35	VO66-35B	VO86-36	VO86-37	VO86-37B	VO86-38	VO86-40	QP-403	QP-416
Region	La Victoria Transect								
Formation	El Chino	El Chino	El Carmen	El Carmen	El Carmen	El Carmen	Santa Isabel	Hermanas	Santa Isabel
SiO_2	45.89	45.35	44.23	44.00	44.12	55.50	47.62	53.75	48.57
Al_2O_3	15.68	15.37	15.72	16.00	15.56	16.00	12.61	14.81	16.47
TiO_2	1.19	1.33	0.84	0.79	0.82	0.69	0.32	0.69	0.58
Fe_2O_3	10.62	9.65	10.08	10.60	10.34	8.55	8.91	9.01	11.07
MnO	0.11	0.13	0.22	0.20	0.20	0.16	0.19	0.09	0.12
MgO	6.04	8.47	14.06	14.15	14.00	4.15	9.55	5.93	6.74
CaO	11.27	6.70	6.17	6.36	6.01	8.10	10.91	6.72	5.10
Na_2O	1.22	1.43	1.92	2.04	1.98	2.25	1.06	3.77	1.46
K_2O	0.52	0.55	0.15	0.03	0.09	1.52	0.21	0.32	5.04
P_2O_5	0.10	0.12	0.19	0.17	0.20	0.09	0.11	0.30	0.13
LOI	n.d.	7.08	n.d.	6.56	n.d.	2.00	n.d.	n.d.	4.11
Total	91.64	96.18	93.58	100.93	94.08	99.01	91.49	95.39	99.39
Cr	746	651	803	456	490	33	679	25	6
Ni	48	57	87	280	82	119	114	43	31
Zr	68	76	64	96	84	92	124	131	95
Y	21	24	22	26	24	24	35	36	34
Nb	5.21	5.29	5.24	5.49	5.39	13.00	13.45	13.03	13.57
Rb	14	16	10	16	13	62	13	69	74
Sr	231	265	156	388	143	231	124	371	381
La	5.2					4.0			
Ce	17.3					11.9			
Nd	11.0					3.0			
Sm	3.1					1.5			
Eu	1.02					0.49			
Tb	1.05					0.39			
Yb	2.92					1.42			
Lu	0.53					0.22			

Continued

Continued

TABLE 4. GEOCHEMISTRY OF THE MAFIC ROCKS FROM THE VILLA DE CURA COMPLEX (continued)

Samples	QP-462	QP-472	QR-475	QO-530	ORR-534	QH-682	QH-689A	QO-839	QO-843
Region	La Victoria Transect (continued)								
Formation	El Carmen	El Carmen	El Carmen	El Carmen	El Carmen	Santa Isabel	Santa Isabel	El Chino	El Carmen
SiO_2	48.57	50.86	44.72	54.35	46.25	51.60	45.53	45.03	46.25
Al_2O_3	14.52	15.78	15.78	16.29	8.21	14.10	12.42	12.84	13.68
TiO_2	0.99	1.33	1.74	0.83	0.25	1.33	0.52	0.52	0.52
Fe_2O_3	9.65	8.70	11.55	10.09	8.46	10.60	11.07	11.31	11.65
MnO	0.14	0.10	0.16	0.18	0.12	0.12	0.16	0.16	0.16
MgO	8.26	7.00	7.47	6.28	13.03	5.85	11.30	11.77	10.41
CaO	10.17	9.20	11.70	4.42	16.00	8.00	11.60	12.00	11.70
Na_2O	2.72	3.95	3.01	1.57	1.14	3.91	1.43	1.35	1.60
K_2O	0.03	0.79	0.20	3.41	1.01	3.32	1.06	1.35	0.66
P_2O_5	0.11	0.14	0.20	0.20	0.05	0.17	0.17	0.59	0.15
LOI	4.76	3.78	4.03	n.d.	5.39	1.85	3.45	0.13	3.92
Total	99.93	101.63	100.56	97.62	99.91	100.85	96.71	99.47	98.47
Cr	191	136	165	37	785	123	431	420	271
Ni	104	52	65	96	124	46	158	260	140
Zr	82	80	92	102	76	110	52	36	48
Y	30	28	31	23	19	29	23	23	20
Nb	15.23	12.70	5.99	12.45	5.30	11.87	5.55	5.33	6.24
Rb	9	18	20	52	10	16	15	14	15
Sr	27	242	255	233	111	236	381	375	289
La		12.8							5.8
Ce		33.5							13.0
Nd		16.1							7.0
Sm		3.5							1.7
Eu		0.90							0.44
Tb		0.86							0.29
Yb		3.06							1.34
Lu		0.48							0.20

Continued

TABLE 4. GEOCHEMISTRY OF THE MAFIC ROCKS FROM THE VILLA DE CURA COMPLEX *(continued)*

Samples	VC-20	VC-20B	VC-22C	VC-23A	VC-30A	VC-51	VC-60
Region	Guatopo National Park						
Formation	Hermanas	Hermanas	Hermanas	Hermanas	Hermanas	Hermanas	Hermanas
SiO_2	50.67	50.67	48.57	49.01	49.16	50.86	51.50
Al_2O_3	14.19	14.19	15.35	15.97	16.29	14.76	15.97
TiO_2	0.55	0.55	0.71	0.90	1.08	1.19	1.09
Fe_2O_3	8.76	8.76	8.65	8.07	9.66	10.45	9.52
MnO	0.27	0.27	0.28	0.32	0.38	0.39	0.28
MgO	14.03	14.03	11.90	12.02	11.31	8.11	8.61
CaO	7.74	7.74	7.00	7.14	7.40	6.34	10.50
Na_2O	1.78	1.78	4.74	3.97	1.61	4.13	3.39
K_2O	0.60	0.60	1.66	1.97	0.48	0.86	0.41
P_2O_5	0.11	0.11	0.16	0.19	0.17	0.13	0.10
LOI	n.d.	n.d.	n.d.	n.d.	n.d.	n.d.	n.d.
Total	98.70	98.70	99.02	99.56	97.54	97.22	101.37
Cr	360	433	86	73	14	19	23
Ni	87	122	64	52	41	9	38
Zr	117	106	107	109	90	124	126
Y	36	35	38	34	32	30	35
Nb	8.09	8.22	7.77	7.41	7.88	7.89	7.91
Rb	7	9	16	34	23	16	12
Sr	76	83	71	77	529	214	845
La							
Ce							
Nd							
Sm							
Eu							
Tb							
Yb							
Lu							

Note: LOI—loss on ignition; n.d.—no data.

TABLE 5. GEOCHEMISTRY OF METAIGNEOUS SAMPLES FROM GRAN ROQUE

Sample	N-1	N-3	N-4	N-6	N-8	N-12	N-20	N-21	E-7	F-3	F-13
Protolith	Diabase	Diabase	Diabase	Diabase	Diabase	Diabase	Diabase	Diabase	Diabase	Diabase	Gabbro
SiO_2	47.79	49.32	50.48	49.53	50.25	49.32	48.47	48.34	49.32	49.32	51.07
Al_2O_3	13.68	14.52	15.65	14.08	14.92	14.10	16.01	15.32	14.10	14.52	15.02
TiO_2	0.72	0.80	0.81	0.96	1.02	0.86	0.95	1.04	0.86	0.99	1.12
Fe_2O_3	12.73	12.80	9.26	9.26	10.13	11.80	9.23	9.47	12.70	10.60	10.25
MnO	0.16	0.16	0.16	0.14	0.19	0.14	0.17	0.14	0.15	0.14	0.17
MgO	8.94	8.56	8.21	8.65	9.02	8.31	8.51	8.77	8.42	8.47	9.58
CaO	13.00	13.00	11.24	12.50	12.95	12.70	9.09	10.14	12.80	11.60	11.97
Na_2O	1.36	1.79	1.99	1.31	2.21	1.75	2.77	2.85	1.64	2.58	2.43
K_2O	0.05	0.12	0.27	0.30	0.18	0.07	0.39	0.41	0.11	0.07	0.34
P_2O_5	0.06	0.23	0.07	0.15	0.12	0.07	0.19	0.17	0.07	0.14	0.14
LOI	1.12	0.29	n.d.	n.d.	n.d.	1.61	n.d.	n.d.	0.91	1.73	n.d.
Total	99.13	104.29	98.14	96.88	100.99	100.73	95.78	96.65	101.08	100.16	102.09
Cr	90	914	22	170	131	182	29	22	105	162	147
Ni	74	89	28	53	67	56	79	34	61	59	70
Zr	116	133	182	180	158	156	132	123	146	162	178
Y	27	29	36	39	40	37	37	40	39	40	34
Nb	12.54	12.33	11.18	14.57	14.74	14.46	12.24	11.39	14.97	14.71	13.24
Rb	22	20	27	30	20	34	19	39	37	33	19
Sr	176	169	282	146	157	149	175	218	153	149	175

Note: LOI—loss on ignition; n.d.—no data.

rocks may not necessarily uniquely determine tectonic setting and are not applicable for all regions. In addition to the tectonic discriminant diagrams, we also have one or more REE patterns for each suite. Although these are not definitive, they can be very useful to support our conclusions.

Cordillera de la Costa Belt

The Cordillera de la Costa belt is an east-west–trending lithotectonic unit. It is a tectonic mélange that includes blocks of eclogite and blueschist in a matrix of mica schist, marble, serpentinite, and metamorphosed volcanic rocks. It also includes metamorphosed felsic igneous rocks. Some authors have subdivided this belt into two units; namely, the Margarita ophiolite belt or Franja Costera unit, and the Cordillera de la Costa belt (e.g., Stephan, 1985; Bellizzia, 1985; Bellizzia and Dengo, 1990; Giunta et al., 2002). However, we divide the Cordillera de la Costa into two subbelts on the basis of their different metamorphic histories; both of these subbelts are lithologically similar and contain metamorphosed Paleozoic felsic igneous rocks. The main difference between the two is that the northern subbelt contains knockers or lenses of eclogite and blueschist, whereas there are no mafic boudins in the southern subbelt (e.g., Avé Lallemant and Sisson, 1993; Sisson et al., 1997; Sorensen et al., this volume). Near Caracas, however, this distinction is not as well defined, because there is a blueschist layer within the southern subbelt (Talukdar and Loureiro, 1982). Mafic rocks in the Cordillera de la Costa belt include both eclogite knockers or lenses and lower grade schist. These were sampled in the following areas: (1) a transect between the cities of Chichiriviche–La Victoria–San Sebastian transect (Fig. 2), (2) between the Tacagua and Limon Rivers (Fig. 2), and (3) in El Avila National

Park, north of Caracas (Fig. 3). Table 1 gives the geochemical data for mafic samples.

Along the Chichiriviche–La Victoria–San Sebastian transect, there are diverse lithotectonic units: these include metamorphic units such as the Nirgua, Peña de Mora, Antímano, Las Mercedes, Las Brisas, Tucutunemo, and Paracotos formations and various metaigneous bodies such as the Guacamaya metadiorite and the Colonia Tovar granite (see González de Juana et al., 1980; Ostos et al., this volume, Chapter 2). Within each unit, there are a variety of lithologies; for example, the Nirgua unit contains garnet amphibolite, quartz-rich marble, serpentinite, garnetiferous schist, serpentinite, quartzite, and glaucophane schist. Most of the mafic rocks, such as garnet amphibolite, occur as discontinuous pods or knockers within marble and/or schist. On a regional scale, the Nirgua unit is correlated with the La Rinconada Formation on Margarita Island (González de Juana et al., 1980). The Antímano unit also consists of garnet amphibolite and chlorite-albite schist. In the Antímano unit, however, amphibolite occurs as a massive, concordant body tectonically overlain by schist. Despite these differences, González de Juana et al. (1980) and Urbani and Ostos (1989) group together all the mafic rock-bearing schists, such as the Antímano and Nirgua units, within the Cordillera de la Costa belt. The Peña de Mora unit is an augen gneiss and schist. This unit is correlated with the Sebastopol complex and Guaremal granite elsewhere in the Cordillera de la Costa belt (Ostos, 1990). The Las Mercedes unit is a calcareous graphitic schist and phyllite with some marble. The Las Brisas unit is a metamorphosed sequence of graywackes, conglomerates, quartz schist, and calcareous quartzites. Vignali (1976, 1979) correlated this unit with the Juan Griego Formation on Margarita Island. The Tucutunemo unit consists of muscovite-chlorite schist, volcanic clast-rich metaconglomerate, graphitic phyllite, and knockers

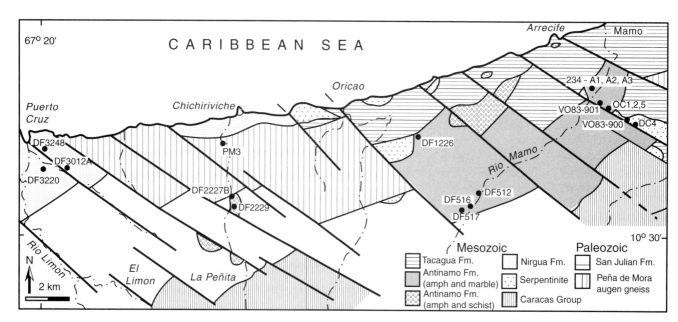

Figure 2. Geologic and sample map of Cordillera de la Costa belt between Puerto Cruz and Mamo. Thick solid lines are high angle faults; thin lines are lithologic contacts. Amph—amphibolite. Adapted from Urbani and Ostos (1989).

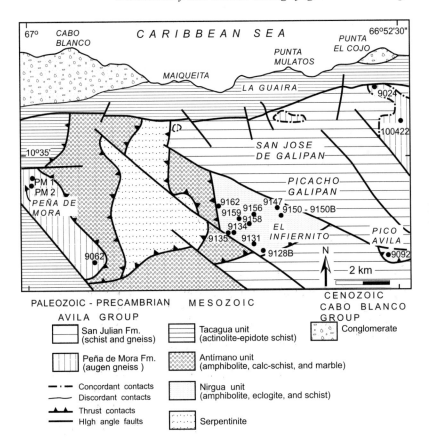

Figure 3. Geologic and sample map of the Cordillera de la Costa belt near Caracas and El Avila National Park. Adapted from Urbani and Ostos (1989).

of amphibolite. The Paracotos unit is a low-grade flysch sequence of metagraywacke and phyllite with rare marble layers and mafic blocks. The La Guacamaya metadiorite consists of deformed mafic gneiss. Although it has not been dated, MacLachlan et al. (1960) suggests it may have intruded the La Aguadita gneiss, which is basement of the Caucagua–El Tinaco belt. The Colonia Tovar granite, best seen in the headwaters of the Tuy River, is in general poorly preserved due to extreme tropical weathering. It locally displays gneissic texture and feldspar augen.

In order to characterize the diverse array of rock suites, we systematically investigated their geochemistry to ascertain possible protolith types. Six amphibolite samples from the Antímano unit along the Chichiriviche–La Victoria transect have SiO_2 content between 48–56 wt% (Table 1). The K_2O content varies from 0.05 to 1.06 wt%, but commonly is less than 0.50 wt%. Thus, these rocks are low-K tholeiites (Figs. 4 and 5). The TiO_2 content varies from 0.60 to 1.55 wt% and averages 1.25 wt%. None of these samples consistently plot within the same field; thus, they do not yield conclusive results for determining a unique protolith (Figs. 4 and 5). The REE patterns for two samples from the Chichiriviche–La Victoria transect are almost flat with a slight REE enrichment, and they have a small negative Eu anomaly (Fig. 6A). The La-Sm values are close to 1.00, which is similar to MORB. These two samples (VO-83-9 and VO-83-10) are likely both E-MORB, similar to the conclusion from Figure 5.

Twenty amphibolite samples from the Nirgua unit in the Tacagua–El Limon area range between 42–52 wt% SiO_2, with a mean of 47 wt% (Table 1). These amphibolites are the most mafic in the Cordillera de la Costa belt. Their K_2O content varies from 0.03 to 1.76 wt%, but is generally less than 0.50 wt%, while the TiO_2 varies from 0.20 to 3.70 wt%, with a mean of 1.55 wt%. Some samples, rich in Fe_2O_3, TiO_2, and CaO and poor in SiO_2 and MgO, indicate either alteration before metamorphism or they are Fe-Ti metabasalts common in the western and Italian Alps and Fe-Ti basalt seen in the Galapagos Islands. These amphibolites also have a tholeiitic basalt affinity (Fig. 4). Most samples may represent E-MORB or N-MORB (Fig. 5), and may also represent volcanic arc basalt. The REE pattern from one sample of the Tacagua–El Limon rivers (DF-2229) area is flat with La-Sm and La-Ce values of 0.97 and 0.68, respectively, typical of E-MORB (Fig. 6).

Twelve samples from the Nirgua unit in El Avila National Park, north of Caracas (Fig. 3), are amphibolites that contain relicts of high pressure-temperature (*P-T*) metamorphic minerals. The SiO_2 contents vary from 47 to 54 wt%, with a mean of 50 wt%; TiO_2 ranges from 0.18 to 1.18 wt%, with a mean of 0.77 wt%. The K_2O varies between 0.06–0.64 wt%, with a mean of 0.19 wt% (Table 1). The Ti and Nb contents are typical of tholeiites (Fig. 4). Most of these amphibolite samples appear to have MORB or island-arc tholeiite (IAT) affinities (Fig. 5). The REE patterns of the two samples from El Avila National Park are very

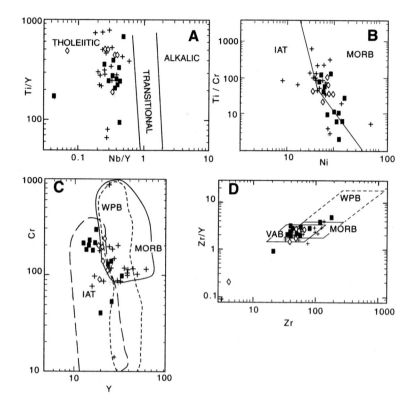

Figure 4. Trace element variation diagrams for the amphibolites from the Cordillera de la Costa belt. IAT—island-arc tholeiite; MORB—mid-oceanic-ridge basalt; WPB—within-plate basalt; VAB—volcanic arc basalt. Diamonds—Antímano unit from Chichiriviche–La Victoria transect; squares—El Avila National Park; crosses—Tacagua–El Limon rivers area. Discriminant diagrams in (A) from Pearce (1982) for Ti/Y versus Nb/Y, in (B) from Beccaluva et al. (1979) for Ti/Cr versus Ni, in (C) from Miyashiro (1975) for Cr versus Y, and in (D) from Pearce and Norry (1979) for Zr/Y versus Zr.

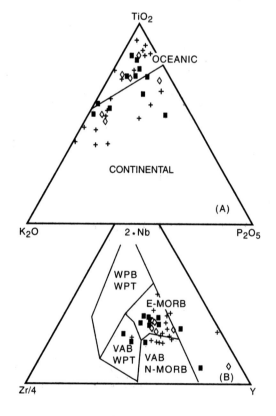

Figure 5. Triangular trace element tectonic discrimination diagrams for the Cordillera de la Costa belt. Designated fields in (A) from Pearce et al. (1975) and (B) from Meschede (1986). E-MORB—enriched mid-oceanic-ridge basalt; N-MORB—normal mid-oceanic-ridge basalt; VAB—volcanic arc basalt; WPB—within-plate alkali basalt and tholeiite; WPT—within-plate tholeiite and volcanic-arc basalt. Diamonds—Antímano unit from Chichiriviche–La Victoria transect; squares—El Avila National Park; crosses—Tacagua–El Limon rivers area.

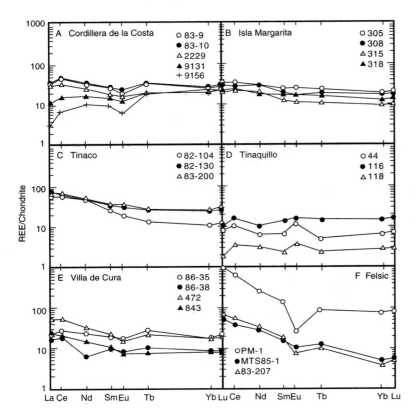

Figure 6. Chondrite-normalized (Sun and McDonough, 1989) rare earth element (REE) patterns for all igneous and metaigneous rocks analyzed for this study.

dissimilar (Fig. 6). One is light REE-enriched (9131) and the other is light REE-depleted (DF-9156), similar to E-MORB and N-MORB. Both of these patterns could represent a single mid-oceanic ridge system.

Felsic rocks are found in the Peña de Mora metaigneous body at two different localities: the Chichiriviche–La Victoria transect and El Avila National Park (Figs. 2 and 3; Table 2). Similar bodies near Puerto Cabello display a Cambrian to Ordovician protolith age (Sisson et al., this volume, Chapter 3). They may either be part of the tectonic mélange or the basement of the Cordillera de la Costa belt. Most of the granitic rocks from the Cordillera de la Costa belt have a within-plate affinity (Ostos, 1990). In two localities elsewhere in the Cordillera de la Costa belt, the felsic metaigneous bodies intrude the surrounding schists and are therefore not basement assemblages. Perhaps some of the metasedimentary rock had a Paleozoic protolith.

Whole-rock Rb-Sr data yield an initial isotopic ratio for Cordillera de la Costa basement of 0.711 ± 0.007. This standard deviation is too large to definitely assign a tectonic setting for the protolith. From geological relationships, the closest and possibly ultimate source for the granitic magmas could be the heterogeneous, older continental crust comparable to the mid-Proterozoic (1.7–1.4 or 1.2 Ga) anorogenic granites of the Rio Negro Province of northern Brazil (Dall'Agnol et al., 1987).

The REE pattern of a sample (PM-1) from the Peña de Mora Formation in El Avila National Park (Fig. 6) shows a large negative Eu anomaly, a small heavy-REE (HREE) depletion, and strong light-REE (LREE) enrichment. This pattern is similar to

that of alkali-rich, post-tectonic granite from Serra Do Iran in southwestern Goias, Brazil (Martins-Pimental and Fuck, 1987). Feldspar accumulation may have played an important role in the origin of this rock. Ostos (1990) suggested a within-plate origin based upon its trace element signature.

Caucagua–El Tinaco Belt

The Caucagua–El Tinaco region consists of three major units: the La Aguadita Gneiss of the Tinaco complex, the Tinaquillo peridotite complex and the Las Mercedes Formation (Fig. 7; Ostos et al., this volume, Chapter 8). The La Aguadita Gneiss is a hornblende-plagioclase rock that is cross-cut by trondhjemite sills and dikes. Near the Tinaquillo complex, the gneiss becomes more felsic and contains abundant quartzofeldspathic layers. The La Aguadita Gneiss has been correlated with the Sebastopol complex of the Cordillera de la Costa belt, of possible Cambro-Ordovician protolith age (Sisson et al., this volume, Chapter 3). The Tinaquillo complex consists of harzburgite, dunite, pyroxenite, and metagabbro (Seyler and Mattson, 1989, 1993; Seyler et al., 1998; Ostos et al., this volume, Chapter 8). Most units display Jurassic ages of 190–146 Ma (Seyler et al., 1998; Sisson et al., this volume, Chapter 3), and could reflect either oceanic or continental rifting (Ostos et al., this volume, Chapter 8). The Tinaquillo complex was thrust northward over low-grade metasedimentary rocks of the Las Mercedes Formation. The underlying Las Mercedes Formation is poorly exposed and consists of graphitic phyllite, calcareous quartzite, and marble. It may correlate with

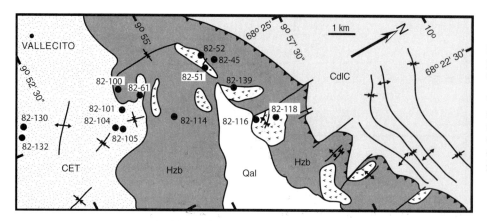

Figure 7. Geologic and sample map of a portion of the Tinaquillo and El Tinaco complexes. Adapted from Ostos (1984, 1990). Some of the samples from the Tinaco complex fall outside the region of this map (for additional locations, see Ostos, 1990). CdlC—Cordillera de la Costa belt; Hzb—Harzburgite; CET—Cacaugua–El Tinaco belt; Qal—Quaternary alluvium.

the Juan Griego Formation on Margarita Island as well as the Las Brisas Formation in the Cordillera de las Costa belt (Ostos, 1990). However, it lacks mafic rocks, in particular, amphibolite knockers, which argues against such correlation.

Mafic rocks from the Guacamaya unit of the Caucagua–El Tinaco belt along the La Victoria–San Sebastian transect (Fig. 2), the La Aguadita Gneiss of the Tinaco complex, and the Tinaquillo peridotite complex were all analyzed. The latter two units were sampled along the Tinaco River–Casupo transect (Fig. 1).

Overall, the La Guacamaya unit is a metadiorite, not mafic enough to be classified as a metabasalt (Table 3). The mean SiO_2 content of mafic samples is 54 wt%; it ranges from 49 to 57 wt%. The K_2O contents vary from 0.57 to 2.31 wt%, with a mean of 1.45 wt%, and the TiO_2 contents range from 0.31 to 1.04, with a mean of 0.71 wt%. The Cr, Ni, Zr, and Y abundances are also in the range typical of calc-alkaline rocks. Overall, then, this unit may be equivalent to a meta-andesite or meta-andesitic basalt (Baker, 1982).

Ten mafic samples of the La Aguadita Gneiss from the Tinaco complex have SiO_2 content between 48–53 wt%, but generally the values are 50 wt% (Table 3; samples VT83-200 to VT87-2). The TiO_2 contents range from 0.25 to 1.34 wt%, with a mean of 0.76 wt%, and K_2O contents are between 0.32 and 2.81 wt%, with mean of 1.45 wt%. Such Ti contents are within the range of volcanic arc basalts. Discrimination diagrams (Figs. 8 and 9) point to the tholeiitic character of the La Aguadita Gneiss, as well as to an island arc signature. The REE patterns for three samples from the Tinaco complex show light REE enrichment relative to the HREE, with 2.0–50 times chondritic values and almost flat patterns of HREE. Such REE patterns resemble island-arc tholeiites (Fig. 4). Overall, it is difficult to conclusively assign protoliths to these mafic rocks.

Twelve metagabbro samples from the Tinaquillo Peridotite Complex range from 45 to 50 wt% SiO_2, with a mean of 47 wt%, which is less than the adjacent Tinaco complex (Table 3). TiO_2 contents range from 0.20 to 1.64 wt%, with a mean of 0.80 wt%, and K_2O contents vary from 0.02 to 0.57 wt%, with a mean of 0.23 wt%. These TiO_2 contents are similar to the gabbro in the Sarmientos ophiolite, which formed in a marginal basin (Saunders et al., 1979). The Ti, Y, and Nb contents indicate the gabbros from the

Tinaquillo peridotite complex have tholeiitic affinities (Figs. 8 and 9). On the $K_2O–P_2O_5–TiO_2$ diagram, these rocks resemble MORB (Fig. 9). Other trace element abundances also suggest that these rocks may have E-MORB or N-MORB affinities. Three mafic samples from the Tinaquillo peridotite complex are characterized by flat REE patterns and positive Eu anomalies (Fig. 6). This is typical of both MORB and gabbro in the Samail Ophiolite.

Intermediate and felsic rocks of the Caucagua–El Tinaco belt were sampled along the La Victoria–San Sebastian (the La Guacamaya Metadiorite) and Tinaco River–Casupo (in the La Aguadita Gneiss) transects (Table 3; Samples VO83-61 to VO87-19). These two metaigneous bodies differ slightly in their Si, Sr, K, Ti, Zr, Nb, Fe, and Rb abundances. In some samples, the K_2O content is highly variable, but ranges less than 1 wt%; this may be the consequence of post-metamorphic weathering. The trace elements in the La Guacamaya metadiorite are very similar to those in the La Aguadita Gneiss (Figs. 8 and 9). Trace element discrimination diagrams indicate that both probably formed in an island arc setting.

The La Guacamaya metadiorite has an $^{87}Sr/^{86}Sr$ ratio between 0.70266 and 0.70674; the initial strontium ratio was not calculated, because the age of this body is poorly constrained. These Sr isotope values overlap with MORB, OIB, and island arc volcanics. In contrast, the Sr isotope ratios of the La Aguadita Gneiss (Tinaco River) range from 0.72005 to 0.71760 (samples RT-87-4 and RT-87-5) with an initial Sr ratio of 0.70475 ± 0.00197. The initial strontium ratios of the La Aguadita Gneiss suggest it was derived from island arc igneous rocks.

The REE pattern of a felsic metaigneous rock (sample VO-83-207) from the El Tinaco River is LREE enriched and shows a slight negative Eu anomaly (Fig. 6). It also has a La/Yb value of 15.0. These characteristics differ markedly from the mafic La Aguadita Gneiss. It is likely that the magma source of the felsic metaigneous rock is different from the source of the mafic rocks into which the felsic metaigneous rocks were intruded.

Villa de Cura Belt

The Villa de Cura belt consists of two major units: the Villa de Cura Group and the Las Hermanas Formation (Figs. 10 and

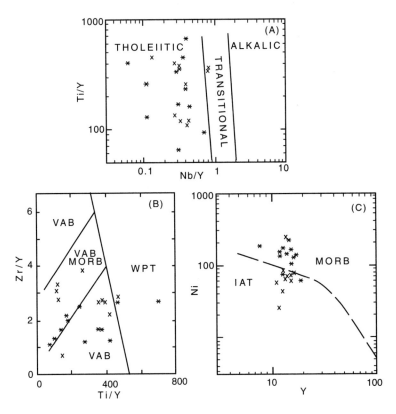

Figure 8. Trace element variation diagrams for mafic and intermediate samples from the Tinaquillo–El Tinaco belt. MORB—mid-oceanic ridge basalt; IAT—island-arc tholeiite; VAB—volcanic island basalt; WPT—within-plate tholeiite and volcanic-arc basalt. Crosses—El Tinaco complex including the La Guacamaya metadiorite and La Aguadita Gneiss; stars—metagabbros in the Tinaquillo peridotite complex.

Figure 9. Triangular trace element tectonic discrimination diagrams for the Tinaquillo–El Tinaco belt. Designated fields in (A) from Pearce et al. (1975), in (B) from Mullen (1983), and in (C) from Meschede (1986). CAB—calc-alkaline basalt; IAT—island-arc tholeiite; MORB—mid-oceanic-ridge basalt; E-MORB—enriched mid-oceanic-ridge basalt; N-MORB—normal mid-oceanic-ridge basalt; OIB—oceanic island basalt; VAB—volcanic arc basalt; WPB—within-plate alkali basalt and tholeiite; WPT—within-plate tholeiite. Crosses—El Tinaco complex including the La Guacamaya metadiorite and La Aguadita Gneiss; stars—metagabbros in the Tinaquillo peridotite complex.

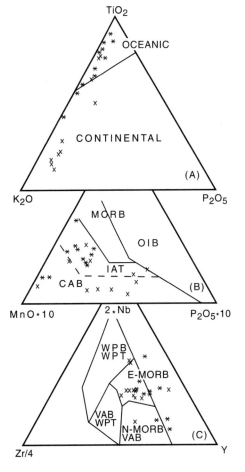

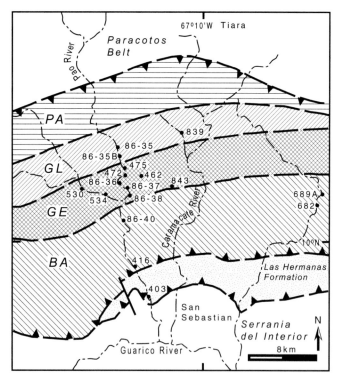

Figure 10. Geologic and sample map of the Villa de Cura belt near the town of San Sebastian de los Reyes adapted from Ostos (1990) and Smith et al. (1999). The metamorphic zones of the Villa de Cura group are, from north to south: pumpellyite-actinolite (PA), glaucophane-lawsonite (GL), glaucophane-epidote (GE), and barroisite (BA). The Las Hermanas Formation is indicated by the stippled pattern.

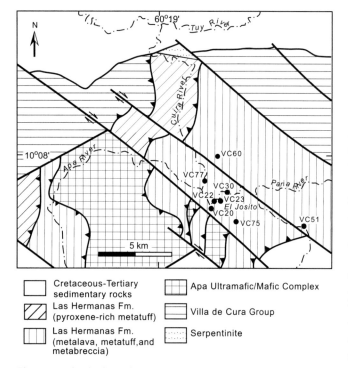

Figure 11. Geologic and sample map of the Villa de Cura belt in Guatopo National Park adapted from Urbani and Ostos (1989).

11). In the south, the Maastrichtian to lower Eocene Guárico Formation overlies this sequence (e.g., Pérez de Armas, this volume). The Villa de Cura group is subdivided into four units: El Caño, El Chino, El Carmen, and Santa Isabel (e.g., Shagam, 1960; Smith et al., 1999; Unger et al., this volume). These units comprise a sequence of blueschist facies metasediments and volcanics. From north to south, these include prehnite-actinolite, glaucophane-lawsonite, glaucophane-epidote, and barroisite facies (Fig. 10). Smith et al. (1999) identified two different metamorphic pressure-temperature-time (P-T-t) paths: one that has an almost identical clockwise progressive and retrogressive path for the northern three zones, and a counterclockwise path for the southernmost zone. They concluded that this may reflect metamorphism during the change of subduction polarity in the Late Cretaceous. The Villa de Cura group underwent at least three generations of ductile deformation and two generations of brittle deformation (Smith et al., 1999). The Las Hermanas Formation is also locally named the Tiara Formation. It includes volcanic breccia, ash tuff, lithic tuff, and lava; all metamorphosed under prehnite-pumpellyite facies (Piburn, 1968; Navarro, 1983). It is not ductily deformed.

Both the Villa de Cura Group and Las Hermanas Formation were sampled near San Sebastian de los Reyes (Fig. 10). The Las Hermanas Formation was also sampled in Guatopo National Park (Fig. 11). This sample suite is from three of the four stratigraphic units, which may create an inherent spread in the data. The samples also are from three different metamorphic grades from glaucophane-lawsonite up to the barroisite zone. The SiO_2 contents of the Villa de Cura Group range from 44 to 56 wt%, with a mean of 50 wt% (Table 4). TiO_2 contents vary from 0.25 to 1.74 wt%, with a mean of 0.85 wt%, and K_2O contents are between 0.03–3.40 wt%, with a mean of 1.08 wt%. The K_2O contents suggest that most samples are island-arc tholeiites (e.g., Unger et al., this volume) or marginal basin tholeiites (Saunders et al., 1979), although the mobility of potassium during subduction zone metamorphism (e.g., Sorensen et al., 1997) makes this conclusion suspect. Samples with Ti contents more than 1.0 wt% are likely abyssal tholeiites, whereas values between 0.25 and 0.84 wt% are characteristic of island-arc basalts (Baker, 1982) as well as some marginal basin ophiolites (Saunders et al., 1979). The compositions of some samples resemble the Washikemba Formation on Bonaire (e.g., Beets et al., 1984). Trace and minor element discrimination diagrams indicate either MORB or island arc affinities for the Villa de Cura belt and the Las Hermanas Formation (Figs. 12 and 13).

Four samples from the Villa de Cura Group near San Sebastian de los Reyes have two types of REE patterns (Fig. 6E). Samples VO-86-35 and VO-86-38 are characterized by flat patterns. The La-Sm ratio of sample VO-86-35 is 0.93, which is within the range of MORB basalts. In contrast, samples QP-472 and QO-843 show LREE enrichment. The La-Sm ratios for these are typical values for island-arc tholeiites. These patterns are slightly enriched in LREE compared to N-MORB, but might be E-MORB. The normalized Nb content is 2–7 times higher than

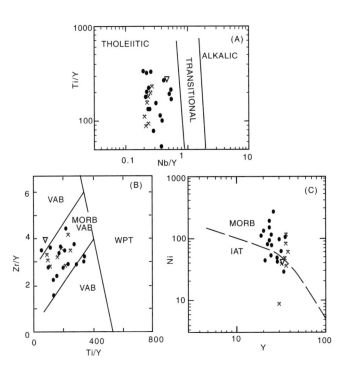

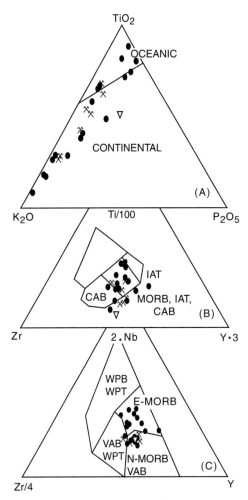

Figure 12. Trace element variation diagrams for the Villa de Cura belt. IAT—island-arc tholeiite; MORB—mid-oceanic-ridge basalt; WPT—within-plate tholeiite; VAB—volcanic island basalt. Circles—Villa de Cura Group; upside down triangle—the Las Hermanas unit near San Sebastian; crosses—the Las Hermanas unit in Guatopo National Park.

Figure 13. Triangular trace element tectonic discrimination diagrams for the Villa de Cura belt. Designated fields in (A) from Pearce et al. (1975), in (B) from Mullen (1983), and in (C) from Meschede (1986). CAB—calc-alkaline basalt; IAT—island-arc tholeiite; MORB—mid-oceanic-ridge basalt; E-MORB—enriched MORB; N-MORB—normal MORB; VAB—volcanic arc basalt; WPB—within-plate alkali basalt and tholeiite; WPT—within-plate tholeiite. Circles—Villa de Cura Group north of San Sebastian; upside down triangle—Las Hermanas Formation north of San Sebastian; crosses—Las Hermanas Formation in Guatopo National Park.

N-MORB, which suggests an Nb-enriched source. This is atypical of most arc magmas. The samples are enriched in K, Nb, La, and Ce compared to most OIB basalts. Thus, their geochemical signature is suggestive of island-arc tholeiites.

The metabasalts of the Las Hermanas Formation from Guatopo National Park show compositions similar to those from the San Sebastian de los Reyes region. SiO_2 contents are between 49–51 wt%, TiO_2 contents range from 0.55 to 1.19 wt%, and the K_2O contents vary from 0.41 to 1.97 wt%. An important difference between the metabasites from the Las Hermanas Formation in Guatopo National Park and the rocks of the Villa de Cura belt is the lower values of high field strength elements such as Zr and Y. However, the trace element signature for the Las Hermanas Formation rocks is indeterminate (Figs. 12 and 13). The basaltic rocks from this area could represent either an island arc or backarc magmatism.

Venezuelan Islands

This region consists of a string of islands that range from small coral atolls to expanses up to 33 km across. The largest is Margarita Island, which consists of three metamorphic units: the Juan Griego, La Rinconada, and Los Robles Group, as well as the Matasiete trondhjemite, Guayacan Gneiss, El Salado granite, and Agua de Vaca granite (e.g., Maresch, 1975; Guth, 1991; Stöck-

hert et al., 1995) and a large serpentinite body (Abujaber and Kimberley, 1992). Paleogene to Quaternary sedimentary rocks such as the Paleogene Pampatar Formation and Eocene Punta Carnero Group overlie all these units (see Fig. 14). The Juan Griego Group is a metasedimentary sequence of quartzo-feldspathic units, marble, and metaquartzite, and includes numerous eclogite and amphibolite knockers and lenses. The La Rinconada Group is a mafic sequence that was metamorphosed at eclogite facies conditions. The Los Robles Group is a low-grade metasedimentary sequence of quartz-chlorite phyllite, marble, dolomitic marble, calcareous phyllite, and metaconglomerate. It does not contain eclogite knockers or amphibolite.

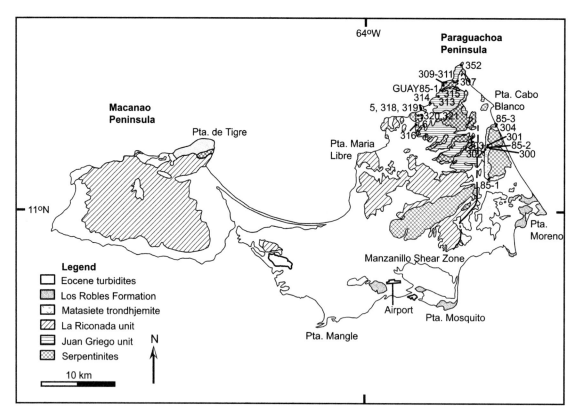

Figure 14. Geologic and sample map of Margarita Island. Adapted from Guth (1991).

The Los Roques Archipelago, part of the Dutch and Venezuelan Leeward Antilles, is underlain by metadiabase, metagabbro, and metasediment, all metamorphosed under greenschist facies conditions (Fig. 15; Table 5). Felsic plutonic rocks intrude these units. The metaigneous rocks have Neocomian K-Ar ages, whereas the felsic plutonic rocks have Maastrichtian K-Ar ages (Santamaría and Schubert, 1974).

Margarita Island

As noted, on Margarita Island, amphibolite and eclogite occur in two units, the Juan Griego Group and La Rinconada Group. The units are exposed in the Paraguachoa Peninsula of northeastern Margarita Island and the Macanao Peninsula of western Margarita Island (Fig. 14). Mafic rocks have SiO_2 content that ranges between 43 and 53 wt%, with a mean of 48 wt%; TiO_2 contents are from 0.20 to 1.88 wt%, with a mean of 0.88 wt%, and the mean K_2O content is 0.32%, with a range between 0.05–1.06 wt% (Table 1). The mafic samples from Margarita Island are similar to tholeiitic metabasalt in that they show both MORB and/or island arc affinities. It is difficult to ascertain the possible protoliths because Zr contents are low (Figs. 16 and 17). Low Zr abundances have been reported in both MORBs and ophiolites (e.g., Langmuir et al., 1977; Dupuy et al., 1984). This may indicate that mafic samples from Margarita with low Zr have a MORB protolith. These plot between N-MORB and E-MORB and are poor in Nb. Thus, they may also have had an OIB protolith.

Other trace element discriminant diagrams indicate island arc, MORB, or a backarc basin protolith for the metabasalts (Figs. 16 and 17). This suite can be divided into two suites. One suite has low TiO_2 values with high Cr and Ni, which plot in the MORB field. These include samples from Cerro Matasiete, the schist-amphibolite sequence near Manzanillo, the Juan Griego Formation near Altagracia, and two localities of eclogite boudins in Macanao. The Cerro Matasiete suite consists of the mafic boudins from the Juan Griego Group interlayered with the Matasiete Trondhjemite. These metabasites may have formed at a mid-oceanic ridge or marginal basin, or represent plateau basalt. The second suite has higher TiO_2 values, Cr < 100 ppm, Ni < 86 ppm, and variable abundances of the other trace elements, and plots mainly in the IAT field. The suite includes eclogite samples from northeastern Paraguachoa between Manzanillo and Pedro Gonzalez, a gabbro sample from Morro de Porlamar, and three mafic knockers (one from Macanao and two from Paraguachoa). The eclogites and gabbros of the second suite may originally have formed in an island arc or backarc basin, close to a volcanic arc.

REE patterns for four samples from Margarita Island are of two different types. One sample (VO-83-308B) from an undeformed post-metamorphic mafic dike, intrusive into the La Rinconada Group, has a slight negative Eu anomaly and LREE enrichment similar to island-arc volcanic rocks (Fig. 6). Three eclogite samples (VO-83-305, VO-83-315, and VO-83-318) have REE patterns similar to N-MORB and E-MORB.

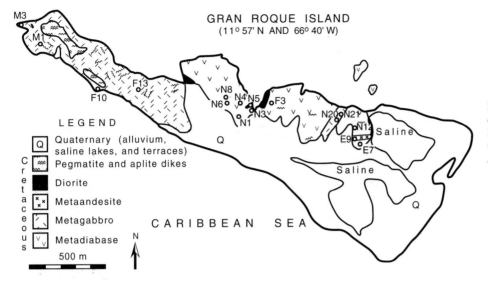

Figure 15. Geologic and sample map of Gran Roque Island (part of the Los Roques island group). Q—Quaternary, undivided. Adapted from González de Juana et al. (1980).

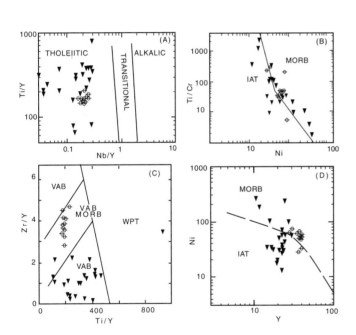

Figure 16. Trace element variation diagrams for the Venezuelan Islands including Margarita and Gran Roque. IAT—island-arc tholeiite; MORB—mid-oceanic-ridge basalt; VAB—volcanic island basalt; WPT—within-plate tholeiite. Circles with slashes—Gran Roque Island; upside down triangle—Margarita Island.

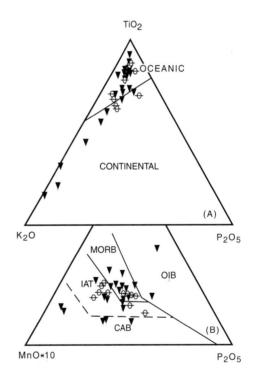

Figure 17. Triangular trace element tectonic discrimination diagrams for the Venezuelan Islands including Margarita and Gran Roque. Designated fields in (A) from Pearce et al. (1975), in (B) from Mullen (1983). CAB—calc-alkaline basalt; IAT—island-arc tholeiite; MORB—mid-oceanic-ridge basalt; OIB—ocean island basalt. Circles with slashes—Gran Roque Island; upside down triangle—Margarita Island.

Several samples of trondhjemites from Cerro Matasiete and the village of Guayacan, and granitic augen gneiss from the neighborhood of El Salado, were also analyzed (Table 2). The major- and trace-element abundances in the Matasiete and Guayacan metatrondhjemites are very similar, and these units may have a common origin. In contrast, the granitic augengneiss of El Salado is richer in Si, K, Zr, Y, Nb, and Rb. The trace element discrimination diagrams indicate that the felsic samples from Margarita Island probably have a volcanic arc affinity. The initial strontium isotopic ratios of the trondhjemites are ~0.703, which is in the range of oceanic island-arc volcanic rocks. These ratios are lower than the average of oceanic plagiogranites (0.7045–0.7059; Coleman, 1977), but are close to the average of ordinary abyssal tholeiites (0.703–0.704; Miyashiro et al., 1982). The trondhjemites may be a partial melting product of oceanic crust in a subduction zone.

Los Roques Island

Mafic samples from Los Roques Island range in SiO_2 content from 48.3 to 51.1 wt% (Figs. 16 and 17, Table 5). TiO_2 varies from 0.72 to 1.12 wt%, with a mean of 0.92 wt%, and the K_2O abundances range between 0.05 and 0.41 wt%, with a mean of 0.21 wt%. The metagabbro and metadiabase have tholeiitic affinities. The trace element discrimination diagram indicates a MORB or an island-arc protolith (Figs. 16 and 17).

The felsic samples (all aplitic dikes) from Los Roques Island fall within the volcanic island arc field. These data support the interpretation of Santamaría and Schubert (1974) that the Los Roques Islands are underlain by oceanic crust upon which a volcanic island arc was built.

DISCUSSION

The Cordillera de la Costa belt probably contains metamorphosed tholeiites formed in a MORB setting; however, a marginal basin environment cannot be excluded. This is similar to the conclusions of Sorensen et al. (this volume) that these represent both N-MORB and E-MORB. In contrast, Giunta et al. (2002) suggested these same rocks could be derived from either MORB or an oceanic plateau.

The La Guacamaya metadiorite and the La Aguadita Gneiss (Tinaco complex) are commonly considered to be the basement of the Caucagua–El Tinaco belt. The La Guacamaya metadiorite is mostly intermediate in composition and chemically similar to low-SiO_2 andesites and basaltic andesites from a calc-alkaline volcanic arc suite. In contrast, metamorphosed mafic rocks of the La Aguadita Gneiss are tholeiitic, with clear volcanic arc affinities. The REE abundances and patterns are similar to those of the calc-alkaline magmatic rocks of an island-arc–type margin. These may have formed at different intervals in an evolving island arc; for example, the "Great Arc of the Caribbean."

The Tinaquillo peridotite complex has major and trace element abundances compatible either with continental rifting, MORB, marginal basins, or island-arc tholeiites. A MORB protolith is strongly suggested by variation diagrams and by the REE patterns.

The REE patterns and isotopic signatures of some of the Tinaquillo rocks also indicate an N-MORB source (Lar, 1992; Seyler and Mattson, 1993). The tectonic affinities of the mafic rocks in the so-called "contact aureole" of the Tinaquillo peridotite complex (MacKenzie, 1960) differ from the mafic rocks within the complex. Mafic rocks within the peridotite should not be interpreted to be xenoliths of the country rock assimilated during intrusion. Both Seyler et al. (1998) and Giunta et al. (2002) interpret the Tinaquillo complex to represent subcontinental

mantle material with associated mafic intrusions indicative of a rifted continental margin.

The metabasalts from the Villa de Cura Group near San Sebastian de los Reyes clearly have tholeiitic affinities. They did not form from within-plate protoliths. They may have formed at a divergent plate boundary or in an island arc, but the REE abundances and patterns yield equivocal protolith signatures. The high P-T metamorphism that these rocks underwent supports our assignment of an oceanic protolith. Unger et al. (this volume) suggest that this suite was part of a primitive island arc, possibly the "Great Arc of the Caribbean." This sequence correlates with the La Guacamaya metadiorite or the La Aguadita Gneiss, although these units formed in similar tectonic settings. Beets et al. (1984) correlated the Villa de Cura Group with an island arc suite on Bonaire, Netherlands Antilles. The correlation is still tenable, but there is a significant difference in the metamorphic histories of these two regions.

The metabasalts of the Las Hermanas Formation in Guatopo National Park are also tholeiites and do not resemble within-plate basalts. They may be related to an island arc, marginal basin, or mid-oceanic ridge. The large volume of metatuff that is interbedded with the mafic rocks supports an island arc tectonic setting. The suggestion that there was an island-arc protolith for this sequence is similar to the interpretations of Giunta et al. (2002) and Unger et al. (this volume). Even though both the Villa de Cura Group and Las Hermanas Formation have geochemical signatures similar to island arcs, they were not necessarily part of the same arc. Differences in metamorphic grade and deformation styles imply the Villa de Cura Group underwent subduction, whereas the Las Hermanas Formation was never subducted or ductilely deformed. The Las Hermanas Formation also lacks the metachert and metagraywacke units found in the Villa de Cura group. The Las Hermanas protolith is probably close to 104 ± 10 Ma (whole rock K-Ar reported in Beck [1978] and recalculated in Smith et al. [1999]), close to the age of the unmetamorphosed El Chacao ultramafic complex (Hebeda et al., 1984). The two units may have been juxtaposed during extension-related exhumation during oblique convergence along the Caribbean margin.

The mafic rocks from Margarita are tholeiites poor in Zr and rich in Ti. The eclogites may represent marginal basin tholeiites that were erupted close to an island arc. Mafic dikes that cross-cut the eclogite-bearing units display N-MORB or E-MORB affinities. The mafic boudins and layers in the Matasiete Trondhjemite and the Juan Griego Group are compatible with MORB. Both Mottana et al. (1985) and Bocchio et al. (1990) suggest a MORB protolith. In contrast, Giunta et al. (2002) state that the mafic rocks are related to within-plate tholeiites and correlate them with the Tinaquillo complex. We prefer to correlate these with the geochemically similar Cordillera de la Costa mafic rocks (see also Sorensen et al., this volume). Both La Rinconada and Juan Griego rocks have similar high-pressure–low temperature metamorphic histories, which indicates that both, unlike the Tinaquillo Complex, were subsequently involved in subduction.

The compositions of metagabbro and metadiabase from Los Roques Island indicate that they are tholeiitic and may have formed in an either a MORB or island arc setting. This is similar to the results of Giunta et al. (2002) for the mafic rocks. The age of this unit is poorly known, because there are only K-Ar ages of 65 ± 3.6 and 66 ± 5 Ma for metadiabase and an aplite (Santamaría and Schubert, 1974).

In addition to assigning protoliths to the metabasites, tectonic constraints can also be added from trace-element discrimination diagrams, Sr isotopic ratios, and REE abundances of the felsic rocks from the Caribbean Mountain system and Venezuelan islands. These are (1) the Peña de Mora Formation, which shows a within-plate granite affinity, and it is likely that its source was an older heterogeneous continental crust; (2) the felsic basement of the Caucagua–El Tinaco belt, which may have island arc affinities; (3) the Matasiete trondhjemite of Margarita Island, which shows an island arc affinity and may reflect suprasubduction zone magmatism; and (4) the aplites on the Los Roques Islands, which have island arc affinities. Giunta et al. (2002) assert that the latter are distinct from the Villa de Cura group (Giunta et al., 2002).

CONCLUSIONS

Correlation of the allochthonous, variably metamorphosed igneous terranes of the Caribbean is an essential part of reconstructing the tectonic history of the Caribbean plate. Three major obducted portions include (1) the "Great Arc of the Caribbean" and other fragments of island-arc tholeiite, (2) the Caribbean Large Igneous Province (CLIP; depleted in REE compared to OIB), and (3) the Proto-Caribbean seaway (MORB) found throughout the Caribbean. Field and geochemical data support several possible tectono-magmatic settings for various units of northern Venezuela (Table 6). These include (1) the Cordillera de la Costa belt with MORBs included in a mélange composed primarily of passive margin sediments, (2) the Tinaco-Tinaquillo belt with Jurassic sublithospheric mantle and MORB, (3) the Villa de Cura belt with two sequences of island arc tholeiites, and (4) the Venezuelan and Dutch Leeward Antilles with ocean island basalts followed by island-arc intrusives as documented on Gran Roque Island. Two of these belts (Cordillera de la Costa, including Margarita Island and the Villa de Cura group) were metamorphosed in subduction zones before emplacement, whereas the other two (Tinaco-Tinaquillo

TABLE 6. SUMMARY OF GEOCHEMICAL DATA FOR IGNEOUS AND METAMORPHIC ROCKS, NORTHERN VENEZUELA

Location	Protolith	P-T	Possible tectonic affinity	Protolith age
Villa de Cura: barroisite zone (1, 6)*	b, s, c	400–500 °C 600–750 MPa	Great Arc of the Caribbean	Aptian-Albian (algae; Johnson, 1965)
glaucophane-epidote zone (1, 6)*	b, s, c	300–375 °C 600–750 MPa	Great Arc of the Caribbean	
glaucophane-lawsonite zone (1, 6)*	b, s, c	270–300 °C 400–600 MPa	Great Arc of the Caribbean	
prehnite-actinolite zone (1, 6)*	b, s, c	210–270 °C 200–550 MPa	Great Arc of the Caribbean	
Las Hermanas Fm. (2, 6)*	b	200–300 °C 100–200 MPa	island arc or backarc	
Margarita Island: La Rinconada Fm. (3, 5, 6)*	b, f, um, m, s	500–600 °C 1000–1400 MPa	MORB	
Juan Griego Fm.			MORB or Great Arc of the Caribbean	
post tectonic granite			Island arc	
Araya Peninsula	s	500–550 °C 500–700 MPa	Passive margin sediments	
Puerto Cabello (4, 6)	b, f, um, m, s	550–600 °C 2000–2200 MPa	N-MORB, albitized shale, passive margin sediments within plate granites	Kimmeridgian (Las Brisas Fm.; Urbani, 1969) Cambro-Ordovician (Peña de Mora granite; Sisson et al., this volume, Chapter 3)
Tinaquillo complex (5, 6)*	um, m	800 °C 500–600 MPa	backarc tholeiite sublithospheric mantle	
Gran Roque (6)*	b, f		MORB followed by island arc	f = Maastrichtian (66 Ma; Santamaría and Schubert, 1974)

Note: Abbreviations used for protoliths: m—marble; c—chert; s—felsic sediments and conglomerates; f—felsic igneous; b—basalts; g—gabbros; um—ultramafic.
*Sources for additional geochemical data: (1) Unger et al., this volume, Chapter 9; (2) Stiles, 2000; (3) Mottano et al., 1985; Bocchio et al., 1990; (4) Sorensen et al., this volume, Chapter 6; (5) Seyler and Mattson, 1993; (6) Giunta et al., 2002.

and Gran Roque in the Leeward Antilles) appear to only have been obducted onto the northern edge of Venezuela.

Because protolith ages for most of the metaigneous rocks are unknown, it is difficult to restore them to their original paleogeographic positions. The oldest igneous and metaigneous rocks studied are the Cambro-Ordovician felsic gneisses and granites. These are now part of the Cordillera de la Costa belt. Because some of these bodies appear to have intrusive contacts with the host schist, they could be related to Appalachian-Caledonian tectonic events, and possibly be correlative with the Acatlán complex in southern Mexico (e.g., Meza-Figueroa et al., 2003). The geochemical data suggests they are within-plate intrusive rocks. These were probably part of northwestern South America, although their exact location is uncertain. In the Late Jurassic, rifting appears to have created the Tinaquillo-Tinaco complex and thinned the continental margin (e.g., Ostos et al., this volume, Chapter 8). The "Great Arc of the Caribbean" began to form after rifting. Subsequently, fragments of the arc were subducted to form the Villa de Cura Group. However, continental margin was also involved in this subduction zone, as seen in the Cordillera de la Costa and Margarita Island high-pressure belts. Finally, all of these units were exhumed and emplaced on the Venezuela margin. During this same time period, the plateau basalts that form the CLIP were emplaced and subsequently accreted to form the basement of the Lesser Antilles island-arc chain.

In conclusion, our geochemical study enhances the understanding of the tectono-magmatic affiliation of the dismembered igneous and metaigneous belts of northern Venezuela. These belts have (1) MORBs included within a mélange composed primarily of passive margin sediments in the Cordillera de la Costa belt, (2) Jurassic sublithospheric mantle and MORB in the Tinaco-Tinaquillo belt, (3) island-arc tholeiites of the Villa de Cura belt, and (4) oceanic-island basalts and island-arc intrusive rocks on Gran Roque island, part of the Venezuelan and Dutch Leeward Antilles.

ACKNOWLEDGMENTS

Hans Avé Lallemant and Jay Stormer gave helpful advice during this research. Enrique Navarro and Daniel Loureiro kindly donated samples as well as contributed to our understanding of the regional geology. Universidad Central de Venezuela and Rice University supported this research. We appreciate helpful comments and discussions with Sorena Sorensen about the geochemistry of northern Venezuela. The careful and constructive reviews from Edward Lidiak and Gerard Klaver greatly improved this contribution.

TABLE A1. PETROGRAPHY OF SELECTED SAMPLES FROM THE CORDILLERA DE LA COSTA BELT

Sample	VO83-5	VO83-5C	VO83-9	VO83-9B	VO83-10	VO83-27	DF-9092	DF-9131
Location	La Victoria transect	La Victoria transect	La Victoria transect	La Victoria transect	La Victoria transect	La Victoria transect	El Avila	El Avila
Lithology	Grt amphibolite	Ms-Grt schist	Grt amphibolite	Grt amphibolite	Grt amphibolite	Ms-quartzite	Ep amphibolite	Grt amphibolite
Qtz	0	39	11	15	0	58	4	5
Pl	35	2	21	25	22	8	27	19
Kfs	0	0	0	0	0	0	0	1
Ms	3	30	4	3	0	30	4	0
Chl	1	2	14	12	6	1	0	4
Bt	0	0	0	0	0	1	0	0
Grt	14	5	9	10	5	0	47	25
Act	45	0	34	28	54	0	0	48
Bar	3	0	1	1	0	0	0	0
Cpx	0	0	0	0	0	0	0	0
Ep	1	3	4	5	12	1	13	1
Rt	0	0	0	0	0	1	0	0
Ttn	0	0	1	1	1	1	1	1
Op	1	0	1	1	0	0	0	0

Continued

TABLE A1. PETROGRAPHY OF SELECTED SAMPLES FROM THE CORDILLERA DE LA COSTA BELT *(continued)*

Sample	DF-9134	DF-9147	DF-9153	DF-9159	DF-9162	DF-91288	VO83-302	VO83-305B
Location	El Avila	El Avila	El Avila	El Avila	El Avila	El Avila	Margarita Island La Rinconada	Margarita Island La Rinconada
Lithology	Grt amphibolite	Grt amphibolite	Grt amphibolite	Grt amphibolite	Grt amphibolite	Grt amphibolite	Amphibole schist	Ep-Chl schist
Qtz	0	0	0	0	7	5	2	0
Pl	3	19	8	17	0	0	15	45
Kfs	0	0	0	0	0	0	0	0
Ms	0	4	0	0	0	0	0	0
Chl	0	0	0	0	6	0	8	25
Bt	0	0	0	0	0	0	0	0
Grt	28	13	35	11	14	16	0	0
Act	47	63	43	53	58	74	59	0
Bar	0	0	0	8	0	0	0	20
Cpx	1	0	0	0	0	0	0	2
Ep	20	0	30	10	13	3	15	7
Rt	1	0	0	0	0	0	0	0
Ttn	0	0	0	0	0	0	0	0
Op	0	1	1	1	2	1	1	1

Continued

TABLE A1. PETROGRAPHY OF SELECTED SAMPLES FROM THE CORDILLERA DE LA COSTA BELT *(continued)*

Sample	VO83-308	VO83-309	VO83-310	VO83-311	VO83-315	VO83-318	VO83-321	VO86-5
Location	Margarita Island La Rinconada	Margarita Island La Rinconada	Margarita Island La Rinconada	Margarita Island La Rinconada	Margarita Island La Rinconada	Margarita Island La Rinconada	Margarita Island La Rinconada	Margarita Island La Rinconada
Lithology	Ep-Cpx amphibolite	Bar-bearing eclogite	Bar-bearing eclogite	Ep-Cpx amphibolite	Ep-Cpx amphibolite	Bar-bearing eclogite	Bar-bearing eclogite	Ep-Cpx amphibolite
Qtz	0	0	0	0	1	0	1	0
Pl	29	0	27	45	33	44	18	8
Kfs	0	0	0	0	0	0	0	0
Ms	1	5	2	2	1	2	2	1
Chl	0	3	0	2	0	0	1	1
Bt	0	0	0	0	0	0	0	0
Grt	0	2	2	2	0	1	23	0
Act	0	0	0	2	0	0	0	0
Bar	48	44	55	17	30	13	18	57
Cpx	6	20	7	23	20	31	28	12
Ep	15	25	3	10	13	8	9	20
Rt	1	0	1	1	1	0	1	1
Ttn	0	0	0	0	0	1	0	0
Op	0	1	1	1	1	0	0	0

Note: Mineral abbreviations after Bucher and Frey (2002) with Qtz—quartz; Pl—plagioclase; Kfs—K-feldspar; Ms—muscovite; Chl—chlorite; Bt—biotite; Grt—garnet; Act—actinolite; Bar—barroisite; Cpx—clinopyroxene; Ep—epidote; Rt—rutile; Ttn—titanite; Op—opaque.

Sample	VO83-1	VO83-4	VO83-7	VO83-21	VO83-34	VO83-9	VO83-67	VO83-64	VO83-66
Unit	Cordillera de la Costa belt	Cordillera de la Costa belt	Cordillera de la Costa belt	Cordillera de la Costa belt	Cordillera de la Costa belt	Cordillera de la Costa belt	Tucutunemo Formation	Guacamaya metadiorite	Guacamaya metadiorite
Lithology	Augengneiss	Augengneiss	Schist	Marble	Quartzite	Augengneiss	Felsic schist	Mafic gneiss	Mafic gneiss
Qtz	32	21	20	10	39	32	69	15	9
Pl	39	57	49	1	32	30	3	44	55
Kfs	19	8	24	0	21	25	0	0	3
Ms	6	3	0	15	7	6	10	2	2
Chl	0	0	0	0	0	0	17	3	2
Bt	1	6	5	0	1	1	0	0	0
Cal	0	0	0	72	0	0	0	0	0
Ep	3	4	0	0	0	0	0	0	0
Hbl	0	0	0	0	0	0	0	20	19
Cpx	0	0	0	0	0	0	0	15	10
Bar	0	0	0	0	0	1	0	0	0
Grt	0	0	0	0	0	0	0	0	0
Op	0	1	0	1	0	1	1	1	0

Continued

TABLE A2. PETROGRAPHY OF SELECTED SAMPLES FROM METAIGNEOUS UNITS *(continued)*

Sample	PM-1	PM-2	VO83-300	VO83-303	VO83-303B	VO83-304	VO83-306B	VO83-320
Unit	Peña de Mora	Peña de Mora	Matasiete Margarita Island	Matasiete Margarita Island	Matasiete Margarita Island	La Rinconada Margarita Island	La Rinconada Margarita Island	La Rinconada Margarita Island
Lithology	Augengneiss	Augengneiss	Trondhjemite	Trondhjemite	Qtz-rich amphibolite	Trondhjemite	Trondhjemite	Trondhjemite
Qtz	40	55	57	59	34	35	20	20
Pl	29	25	40	25	10	54	65	59
Kfs	16	10	0	0	0	0	0	0
Ms	1	5	2	3	2	0	3	1
Chl	3	3	0	0	0	2	0	0
Bt	7	3	0	0	0	0	0	0
Cal	0	0	0	0	2	0	0	0
Ep	3	2	1	10	2	8	12	10
Hbl	0	0	0	0	0	0	0	0
Cpx	0	0	0	0	50	0	0	0
Bar	0	0	0	0	0	0	0	0
Grt	0	0	0	0	0	0	0	0
Op	1	0	0	1	1	1	0	0

Note: Mineral abbreviations after Bucher and Frey (2002): Qtz—quartz; Pl—plagioclase; Kfs—K-feldspar; Ms—muscovite; Chl—chlorite; Bt—biotite; Cal—calcite; Ep—epidote; Hbl—hornblende; Cpx—clinopyroxene; Bar—barroisite; Grt—garnet; Op—opaque.

TABLE A3. PETROGRAPHY OF SELECTED SAMPLES FROM THE TINAQUILLO COMPLEX

Sample	VT82-51	VT82-52	VT82-100	VT82-114	VT82-116	VT82-118
Lithology	Granulite	Granulite	Felsic gneiss	Granulite	Granulite	Granulite
Opx	5	4	0	9	29	8
Aug	13	13	5	23	11	12
Di	0	0	0	0	0	0
Ol	0	0	0	0	0	0
Pl	65	51	78	43	56	71
Spl	3	0	2	0	0	0
Hbl	16	27	13	23	0	0
Op	1	3	2	2	1	2
Srp	0	0	0	0	0	0
Kfs	0	0	0	0	0	6
Peri	0	0	0	0	0	1
Bt	0	2	2	0	3	0

Note: Mineral abbreviations after Bucher and Frey (2002): Opx—orthopyroxene; Aug—augite; Di—diopside; Ol—olivine; Pl—plagioclase; Spl—spinel; Hbl—hornblende; Op—opaque; Srp—serpentine; Kfs—K-feldspar; Peri—perovskite; Bt—biotite.

TABLE A4: PETROGRAPHY OF SELECTED SAMPLES FROM THE TINACO BELT

Sample	VO83-200	VO83-202	VO83-203	VO83-205	VO83-205B	VO83-207	VO83-208
Lithology	Mafic gneiss	Mafic gneiss	Mafic gneiss	Mafic gneiss	Felsic gneiss	Meta-trondhjemite	Gneiss
Qtz	1	5	16	7	49	60	30
Kfs	0	0	0	3	0	4	0
Pl	54	36	45	46	47	30	46
Mu	0	0	0	0	0	0	0
Chl	0	1	2	0	1	2	0
Bi	0	0	0	0	0	0	1
Grt	0	1	0	0	0	0	0
Hbl	40	55	30	35	0	0	20
Cpx	1	0	0	2	0	0	0
Epi	3	2	3	5	2	4	1
Tit	1	0	0	0	0	0	1
Zir	0	0	0	1	0	0	0
Ap	0	0	0	0	0	0	0
Mt	0	0	1	1	0	0	1

Continued

TABLE A4: PETROGRAPHY OF SELECTED SAMPLES FROM THE TINACO BELT *(continued)*

Sample	VO83-210	VO83-211	VO83-212	VT82-101	VT82-133	VT82-134	VT82-136	VT82-136B
Lithology	Gneiss	Gneiss	Mafic gneiss	Mafic gneiss	Felsic gneiss	Mafic gneiss	Gneiss	Gneiss
Qtz	40	28	27	0	18	5	0	4
Kfs	0	0	0	1	10	0	7	1
Pl	47	20	55	49	66	56	70	66
Mu	0	0	0	0	3	0	0	0
Chl	3	0	0	0	0	0	0	1
Bi	0	0	0	0	0	0	0	0
Grt	1	0	0	0	0	2	0	0
Hbl	6	50	15	33	0	36	18	25
Cpx	0	0	0	15	0	0	0	0
Epi	1	2	3	0	1	1	3	3
Tit	1	0	0	0	1	0	1	0
Zir	1	0	0	1	0	0	0	0
Ap	0	0	0	0	1	0	1	0
Mt	0	0	0	1	0	0	0	0

Note: Mineral abbreviations after Bucher and Frey (2002): Qtz—quartz; Kfs—K-feldspar; Pl—plagioclase; Mu—muscovite; Chl—chlorite; Bt—biotite; Grt—garnet; Hbl—hornblende; Cpx—clinopyroxene; Epi—epidote; Tit—titanite; Zir—zircon; Ap—Apatite; Mt—magnetite.

TABLE A5. PETROGRAPHY OF SELECTED SAMPLES FROM THE VILLA DE CURA GROUP

Sample	QO-843	VO86-35	VO86-36	VO86-37	VO86-38
Lithology	Metabasalt	Metalava	Metalava	Metalava	Metalava
Qtz	0	0	5	0	2
Lws	0	6	0	0	1
Pl	10	76	63	65	59
Kfs	0	0	0	0	3
Ms	6	0	7	0	0
Chl	25	3	0	3	5
Act	16	7	12	6	0
Gln	12	0	4	12	11
Cpx	14	0	6	13	13
Cal	0	0	0	0	3
Ep	0	5	0	0	0
Op	0	0	1	1	0
Prh-Pmp	0	1	2	0	3

Note: Mineral abbreviations after Bucher and Frey (2002): Qtz—quartz; Lws—lawsonite; Pl—plagioclase; Kfs—K-feldspar; Ms—muscovite; Act—actinolite; Gln—glaucophane; Cpx—clinopyroxene (relict phenocryst); Cal—calcite; Ep—epidote; Op—opaque; Prh-Pmp—prehnite-pumpellyite.

TABLE A6. PHENOCRYST ASSEMBLAGE IN THE LAS HERMANAS FORMATION IN GUATOPO NATIONAL PARK

Sample	VC-20B	VC-22C	VC-23A	VC-30A	VC-51	VC-60
Lithology	Metalava	Metalava	Metalava	Metalava	Metalava	Metalava
Qtz	2	0	0	0	2	0
Pl	2	10	25	10	66	5
Chl	0	0	0	0	5	0
Hbl	0	0	0	15	10	15
Cpx	39	15	3	0	5	0
Ttn	0	0	0	0	7	0
Ep	0	0	0	0	8	0
Op	0	0	2	0	0	0
Cal*	5	8	0	0	0	0
Qtz*	5	0	0	0	0	0
Prh-Pmp*	0	9	0	0	0	0

Note: Mineral abbreviations after Bucher and Frey (2002) with phenocrysts of Qtz—quartz; Pl—plagioclase; Chl—chlorite; Hbl—hornblende; Cpx—clinopyroxene; Ttn—titanite; Ep—epidote; Op—opaque. Matrix consists of variable proportions of Pl—Chl—Hbl—Cpx—Qtz—Cal—Ep—Ttn—Pmp as well as hematite, pyrite, magnetite, and leucoxene.
Minerals in amygdules include Cal—calcite; Qtz*—quartz; Prh-Pmp*—prehnite-pumpellyite.

REFERENCES CITED

Abujaber, N.S., and Kimberley, M.M., 1992, Origin of ultramafic-hosted magnesite on Margarita Island, Venezuela: Mineralium Deposita, v. 27, p. 234–241.

Alt, J.C., 1999, Hydrothermal alteration and mineralization of oceanic crust; mineralogy, geochemistry, and processes, *in* Volcanic-associated massive sulfide deposits; processes and examples in modern and ancient settings: Reviews in Economic Geology, v. 8, p. 133–155.

Alt, J.C., and Teagle, D.A.H., 2000, Hydrothermal alteration and fluid fluxes in ophiolites and oceanic crust, *in* Dilek, Y., Moores, E.M., Elthon, D., Nicolas, A., eds., Ophiolites and oceanic crust: New insights from field studies and the Ocean Drilling Program: Geological Society of America Special Paper 349, p. 273–282.

Avé Lallemant, H.G., 1991, The Caribbean–South American plate boundary, Araya peninsula, eastern Venezuela, *in* Larue, D.K., and Draper, G., eds., Transactions of the 12th Caribbean Geological Conference, St. Croix, U.S. Virgin Islands: Miami, Florida, Miami Geological Society, p. 461–471.

Avé Lallemant, H.G., 1997, Transpression, displacement partitioning, and exhumation in the eastern Caribbean–South American plate boundary zone: Tectonics, v. 16, no. 2, p. 272–289, doi: 10.1029/96TC03725.

Avé Lallemant, H.G., and Sisson, V.B., 1993, Caribbean–South American plate interactions: Constraints from the Cordillera de la Costa belt, Venezuela, *in* Pindell, J.L., and Perkins, B.F., eds., Mesozoic and early Cenozoic development of the Gulf of Mexico and Caribbean region—A context for hydrocarbon exploration, Proceedings, Gulf Coast Section, SEPM Foundation 13th Annual Research Conference: Houston, Texas, Society for Sedimentary Geology (SEPM) Foundation, p. 211–219.

Baker, P.E., 1982, Evolution and classification of orogenic volcanic rocks, *in* Thorpe, R.S., ed., Andesites: Orogenic andesites and related rocks: New York, John Wiley and Sons, p. 11–24.

Bebout, G.E., Ryan, J.G., Leeman, W.P., and Bebout, A.E., 1999, Fractionation of trace elements by subduction-zone metamorphism; effect of convergent-margin thermal evolution: Earth and Planetary Science Letters, v. 171, p. 63–81, doi: 10.1016/S0012-821X(99)00135-1.

Beccaluva, L., Ohnenstetter, D., and Ohnenstetter, M., 1979, Geochemical discrimination between ocean-floor and island arc tholeiites: Application to some ophiolites: Canadian Journal of Earth Sciences, v. 16, p. 1874–1882.

Beck, C.M., 1978, Polyphase Tertiary tectonics of the interior range in the central part of the western Caribbean chain, Guárico State, northern Venezuela: Geologie en Mijnbouw, v. 57, p. 99–104.

Becker, H., Jochum, K.P., and Carlson, R.W., 2000, Trace element fractionation during dehydration of eclogites from high-pressure terranes and the implications for element fluxes in subduction zones: Chemical Geology, v. 163, p. 65–99, doi: 10.1016/S0009-2541(99)00071-6.

Beets, D.J., Maresch, W.V., Klaver, G.T., Mottana, A., Bocchio, R., Beunk, F.F., and Monen, H.P., 1984, Magmatic rock series and high pressure metamorphism as constraints on the tectonic history of the southern Caribbean, *in* Bonini, W.E., Hargraves, R.B., and Shagam, R., eds., The Caribbean–South American plate boundary and regional tectonics: Geological Society of America Memoir 162, p. 95–130.

Bellizzia, A., 1985, Sistema montañoso del Caribe—una cordillera alóctona en la parte norte de América del Sur: Caracas, Memoria, VI Congreso Geológico Venezolano, v. X, p. 6657–6836.

Bellizzia, A., and Dengo, G., 1990, The Caribbean Mountain system, northern South America; A summary, *in* Dengo, G., and Case, J.E., eds., The Caribbean region: Geological Society of America, The Geology of North America, v. H, p. 167–175.

Bocchio, R., De Capitani, L., Liborio, G., Maresch, W.V., and Mottana, A., 1990, The eclogite-bearing series of Isla Margarita, Venezuela: Geochemistry of metabasic lithologies in the La Rinconada and Juan Griego Groups: Lithos, v. 25, p. 55–69, doi: 10.1016/0024-4937(90)90006-M.

Bucher, K., and Frey, M., 2002, Petrogenesis of metamorphic rocks, 7th edition: Berlin, Springer, 341 p.

Burke, K., 1988, Tectonic evolution of the Caribbean: Annual Reviews in Earth and Planetary Science, v. 16, p. 201–230, doi: 10.1146/annurev.ea.16.050188.001221.

Burke, K., Fox, P.J., and Şengör, C.A.M., 1978, Buoyant ocean floor and the evolution of the Caribbean: Journal of Geophysical Research, v. 83, p. 3949–3954.

Coleman, R.G., 1977, Ophiolites: Ancient oceanic lithosphere?: Springer-Verlag, New York, 229 p.

Dall'Agnol, R., Silva, B.J., Xafi de Silva, J.-J., De Medeiros, H., Costi, H.T., and Buenano, M.J., 1987, Granitogenesis in northern Brazil region: A review: Revista Brasileira de Geociencias, v. 17, p. 382–403.

Donnelly, T.W., and Rogers, J.J.W., 1978, The distribution of igneous rock suites throughout the Caribbean: Geologie en Mijnbouw, v. 57, p. 151–162.

Donnelly, T.W., Melson, W., Kay, R., and Rogers, J.J.W., 1973, Basalts and dolerites of late Cretaceous age from the central Caribbean: Initial Reports of the Deep Sea Drilling Project, U.S. Government Printing Office, v. 15, p. 989–1012.

Donnelly, T.W., Beets, D., Carr, M.J., Jackson, T., Klaver, G., Lewis, J., Maury, R., Schellenkens, H., Smith, A.L., and Westercamp, D., 1990, History and tectonic setting of Caribbean magmatism, *in* Case, J.E., and Dengo, G., eds., The Caribbean region: Boulder, Colorado, Geological Society of America, Geology of North America, v. H, p. 339–374.

Duncan, R.A., and Hargraves, R.B., 1984, Plate tectonic evolution of the Caribbean region in the mantle reference frame, *in* Bonini, W.E., Hargraves, R.B., and Shagam, R., eds., The Caribbean–South American plate boundary and regional tectonics: Geological Society of America Memoir 162, p. 81–93.

Dupuy, C., Dostal, J., Capedri, S., and Venturelli, G., 1984, Geochemistry and petrogenesis of ophiolites from northern Pindos (Greece): Bulletin of Volcanology, v. 47, p. 39–46.

Giunta, G., Beccaluva, L., Coltorti, M., Siena, F., and Vaccaro, C., 2002, The southern margin of the Caribbean plate in Venezuela: tectono-magmatic setting of the ophiolite units and kinematic evolution: Lithos, v. 63, p. 19–40, doi: 10.1016/S0024-4937(02)00120-2.

González de Juana, C., Iturralde, J.M., and Picard, X., 1980, Geología de Venezuela y de sus Cuencas Petrolíferas: Caracas, Ediciones Foninves, 1031 p.

Guth, L.R., 1991, Kinematic analysis of the deformational structures on eastern Isla de Margarita [Ph.D. Dissertation]: Houston, Texas, Rice University, 582 p.

Hauff, F., Hoernle, K., Schmincke, H.U., and Werner, R., 1997, A mid Cretaceous origin for the Galapagos hotspot: Volcanological, petrological and geochemical evidence from Costa Rican oceanic crustal segments: Geologische Rundschau, v. 86, p. 141–155, doi: 10.1007/s005310050126.

Hebeda, E.H., Verdurmen, E.A.Th., and Priem, H.N.A., 1984, K-Ar hornblende ages from the El Chacao complex, north-central Venezuela, *in* Bonini, W.E., Hargraves, R.B., and Shagam, R., eds., The Caribbean–South American plate boundary and regional tectonics: Geological Society of America Memoir 162, p. 413–414.

Humphris, S.E., and Thompson, G., 1978, Hydrothermal alteration of oceanic basalts: Geochimica et Cosmochimica Acta, v. 42, p. 107–125, doi: 10.1016/0016-7037(78)90221-1.

Johnson, J.H., 1965, Three Lower Cretaceous algae new to the Americas: Journal of Paleontology, v. 39, p. 719–720.

Jolly, W.T., Lidiak, E.G., Schelleckens, H.S., and Santos, S., 1998, Volcanism, tectonics, and stratigraphic correlations in Puerto Rico, *in* Lidiak, E.G., and Larue, D.K., eds., Tectonics and geochemistry of the northeast Caribbean: Geological Society of America Special Paper 322, p. 1–34.

Jolly, W.T., Lidiak, E.G., Dickin, A.P., and Wu, T.-W., 2001, Secular geochemistry of central Puerto Rican island arc lavas: Constraints on Mesozoic tectonism in the eastern Greater Antilles: Journal of Petrology, v. 42, p. 2197–2214, doi: 10.1093/petrology/42.12.2197.

Kerr, A.C., Tarney, J., Marriner, G.F., Nivia, A., Klaver, G.T., and Saunders, A.D., 1996, The geochemistry and tectonic setting of Late Cretaceous Caribbean and Colombian volcanism: Journal of South American Earth Sciences, v. 9, p. 111–120, doi: 10.1016/0895-9811(96)00031-4.

Kerr, A.C., Marriner, G.F., Tarney, J., Nivia, A., Saunders, A.D., Thirlwall, M.F., Sinton, C.W., 1997, Cretaceous basaltic in western Columbia: Elemental, chronological and Sr-Nd isotopic constraints on petrogenesis: Journal of Petrology, v. 38, p. 677–702.

Langmuir, C.H., Bender, J.F., Bence, A.E., Hanson, G.N., and Taylor, S.R., 1977, Petrogenesis of basalts from the Famous area: Mid-Atlantic Ridge: Earth and Planetary Science Letters, v. 36, p. 133–156, doi: 10.1016/0012-821X(77)90194-7.

Langmuir, C.H., Voeke, R.D., and Hanson, G.N., 1978, A general mixing equation with application to Icelandic basalts: Earth and Planetary Science Letters, v. 37, p. 380–392, doi: 10.1016/0012-821X(78)90053-5.

Lapierre, H., Dupuis, V., de Lepinay, B.M., Tardy, M., Ruiz, J., Maury, R.C., Hernandez, J., and Loubet, M., 1997, Is the lower Duarte Igneous Complex (Hispaniola) a remnant of the Caribbean plume-generated oceanic plateau?: Journal of Geology, v. 105, p. 111–120.

Lapierre, H., Bosch, D., Dupuis, V., Polve, M., Maury, R.C., Hernandez, J., Monie, P., Yeghicheyan, D., Jaillard, E., Tardy, M., de Lepinay, B.M., Mamberti, M., Desmet, A., Keller, F., and Senebier, F., 2000, Multiple plume events in the genesis of the peri-Caribbean Cretaceous oceanic plateau province: Journal of Geophysical Research, Solid Earth, v. 105, p. 8403–8421.

Lar, A.U., 1992, Etude Géochimique de Massif Basiques et Ultrabasiques (Apa, Todasana, Tinaquillo) de la Chaîne Tertaire Caraïbe du Venezuela: Genèse de magmas matelliques et interaction Manteau-Croûte [Ph.D. dissertation]: Toulouse, Universite de Paul Sabatier, 232 p.

Lebrón, M.C., and Perfit, M.R., 1994, Petrochemistry and tectonic significance of Cretaceous island-arc rocks, Cordillera Oriental, Dominican Republic: Tectonophysics, v. 229, p. 60–100.

MacKenzie, D.B., 1960, High-temperature alpine-type peridotite from Venezuela: Geological Society of America Bulletin, v. 71, p. 303–318.

MacLachlan, J.C., Shagam, R., and Hess, H.H., 1960, Geology of the La Victoria area, Aragua, Venezuela: Geological Society of America Bulletin, v. 71, p. 241–248.

Malfait, B.T., and Dinkelman, M.G., 1972, Circum-Caribbean tectonic and igneous activity and the evolution of the Caribbean plate: Geological Society of America Bulletin, v. 83, p. 251–272.

Mamberti, M., Lapierre, H., Bosch, D., Jaillard, E., Ethien, R., Hernandez, J., and Polvé, M., 2003, Accreted fragments of the Late Cretaceous Caribbean-Columbian Plateau in Ecuador: Lithos, v. 66, p. 173–199.

Maresch, W.V., 1974, Plate tectonics origin of the Caribbean Mountain system of northern South America: Discussion and proposal: Geological Society of America Bulletin, v. 85, p. 669–682, doi: 10.1130/0016-7606(1974)85<669:PTOOTC>2.0.CO;2.

Maresch, W.V., 1975, The geology of northeastern Margarita Island, Venezuela: A contribution to the study of Caribbean plate margins: Geologische Rundschau, v. 64, p. 846–883.

Martins-Pimental, M., and Fuck, R.A., 1987, Late Proterozoic granitic magmatism in southwestern Goiás, Brazil: Revista Brasileira de Geociencias, v. 17, p. 415–425.

Mattson, P.H., 1978, Subduction, buoyant braking, flipping and strike slip faulting in the northern Caribbean: Journal of Geology, v. 8, p. 293–304.

Menéndez, A., 1965, Geologia del area de El Tinaco, centro del Estado Cojedes, Venezuela: Caracas, Boletín de Geología, v. 6, p. 417–543.

Meschede, M., 1986, A method of discriminating between different types of mid-oceanic ridge basalts and continental tholeiites with the Nb-Zr-Y diagram: Chemical Geology, v. 56, p. 207–218, doi: 10.1016/0009-2541(86)90004-5.

Meza-Figueroa, D., Ruiz, J., Talavera-Mendoza, O., and Ortega-Gutierrez, F., 2003, Tectonometamorphic evolution of the Acatlán complex eclogites (southern Mexico): Canadian Journal of Earth Sciences, v. 40, p. 27–44, doi: 10.1139/e02-093.

Miyashiro, A., 1975, Volcanic rock series and tectonic setting: Annual Reviews of Earth and Planetary Science, v. 3, p. 251–269.

Miyashiro, A., Aki, K. and Şengör, C.A.M., 1982, Orogeny: John Wiley and Sons, New York, 242 p.

Mottana, A., Boccio, R., Liborio, G., Morton, L., and Maresch, W.V., 1985, The eclogite-bearing metabasaltic sequence of Isla de Margarita, Venezuela: A geochemical study: Chemical Geology, v. 50, p. 351–368, doi: 10.1016/0009-2541(85)90128-7.

Mullen, E.D., 1983, $MnO/TiO_2/P_2O_5$: A minor element discriminant for basaltic rocks of oceanic environments and its implications for petrogenesis: Earth and Planetary Science Letters, v. 62, p. 53–62.

Navarro, E., 1983, Petrología y petrogénesis de las rocas metavolcánicas del Grupo Villa de Cura: Caracas, Geos, v. 28, p. 170–317.

Ostos, M., 1984, Structural interpretation of the Tinaquillo Peridotite and its country rock, Cojedes State, Venezuela [M.S. thesis]: Houston, Rice University, 135 p.

Ostos, M., 1990, Tectonic evolution of the south-central Caribbean based on geochemical data [Ph.D. Dissertation]: Houston, Rice University, 441 p.

Oxburgh, E.R., 1966, Geology and metamorphism of Cretaceous rocks in eastern Carabobo State, Venezuela Coast Ranges, in Hess, H.H., ed., Caribbean geological investigations: Geological Society of America Memoir 98, p. 241–310.

Pearce, J.A., 1975, Basalt geochemistry used to investigate past tectonic environments on Cyprus: Tectonophysics, v. 25, p. 41–67, doi: 10.1016/0040-1951(75)90010-4.

Pearce, J.A., 1982, Trace element characteristics of lavas from destructive plate boundaries, in Thorpe, R.S., ed., Andesites: Orogenic andesites and related rocks: New York, John Wiley and Sons, p. 525–548.

Pearce, J.A., and Cann, J.R., 1971, Ophiolite origin investigated by discriminant analysis using Ti, Zr, and Y: Earth and Planetary Science Letters, v. 12, p. 339–349, doi: 10.1016/0012-821X(71)90220-2.

Pearce, J.A., and Norry, M.J., 1979, Petrogenetic implications of Ti, Zr, Y, and Nb variations in volcanic rocks: Contributions to Mineralogy and Petrology, v. 69, p. 33–47, doi: 10.1007/BF00375192.

Pearce, J.A., Gorman, B.E., and Birckett, T.C., 1975, The TiO_2-K_2O-P_2O_5 diagram: A method of discrimination between oceanic and non-oceanic basalts: Earth and Planetary Science Letters, v. 24, p. 419–426.

Pearce, J.A., Harris, N.B.W., and Tindle, A.G., 1984, Trace element discrimination diagrams for tectonic interpretation of granitic rocks: Journal of Petrology, v. 25, p. 290–300.

Pearce, J.A., Lippard, S.J., and Roberts, S., 1985, Characteristics and tectonic significance of supra-subduction zone ophiolites, in Kokelaar, B.P., and Howells, M.F., eds., Marginal basin geology; volcanic and associated sedimentary and tectonic processes in modern and ancient marginal basins: London, Geological Society Special Publication 16, p. 74–94.

Piburn, M.D., 1968, Metamorfismo y estructura del grupo Villa de Cura, Venezuela Septentrional: Boletín Geología, Ministerio de Minas e Hidrocarburos, Venezuela, v. 9, p. 183–289.

Pindell, J.L., 1993, Regional synopsis of Gulf of Mexico and Caribbean evolution, in Pindell, J.L., and Perkins, B.F., eds., Mesozoic and early Cenozoic development of the Gulf of Mexico and Caribbean region—A context for hydrocarbon exploration, Proceedings, Gulf Coast Section, SEPM Foundation 13th Annual Research Conference: Houston, Texas, Society for Sedimentary Geology (SEPM) Foundation, p. 251–274.

Pindell, J.L., 1994, Evolution of the Gulf of Mexico and Caribbean, in Donovan, S., and Jackson, T.A., eds., Caribbean geology: An introduction: Kingston, Jamaica, B.W.I. Publishers' Association, p. 13–39.

Pindell, J.L., and Barrett, S.F., 1990, Geological evolution of the Caribbean region; A plate-tectonic perspective, in Dengo, G., and Case, J.E., eds., The Caribbean region: Boulder, Colorado, Geological Society of America, Geology of North America, v. H, p. 405–432.

Pindell, J.L., Cande, S.C., Pitman, W.C., III, Rowley, D.B., Dewey, J.F., Labrecque, J., and Haxby, W., 1988, A plate-kinematic framework for models of Caribbean evolution: Tectonophysics, v. 155, p. 121–138, doi: 10.1016/0040-1951(88)90262-4.

Santamaría, F., and Schubert, C., 1974, Geochemistry and geochronology of the southern Caribbean–northern Venezuela plate boundary: Geological Society of America Bulletin, v. 85, p. 1085–1098, doi: 10.1130/0016-7606(1974)85<1085:GAGOTS>2.0.CO;2.

Saunders, J.B., Tarney, J., Stern, C.R., and Dalziel, I.W.D., 1979, Geochemistry of Mesozoic marginal basin floor igneous rocks from southern Chile: Geological Society of America Bulletin, v. 90, p. 237–258, doi: 10.1130/0016-7606(1979)90<237:GOMMBF>2.0.CO;2.

Seiders, V.M., 1962, Geology of central Miranda, Venezuela [Ph.D. dissertation]: Princeton, New Jersey, Princeton University, 255 p.

Seyler, M., and Mattson, P.H., 1989, Petrology and thermal evolution of the Tinaquillo peridotite (Venezuela): Journal of Geophysical Research, v. 94, p. 7629–7660.

Seyler, M., and Mattson, P.H., 1993, Gabbroic and pyroxenite layers in the Tinaquillo, Venezuela, peridotite: Succession of melt intrusions in a rising mantle diapir: Journal of Geology, v. 101, p. 501–511.

Seyler, M., Paquette, J.-L., Ceuleneer, G., Kienast, J.-R., and Loubet, M., 1998, Magamatic underplating, metamorphic evolution and ductile shearing in a Mesozoic lower crustal–upper mantle unit (Tinaquillo, Venezuela) of the Caribbean belt: Journal of Geology, v. 106, p. 35–58.

Shagam, R., 1960, Geology of the central Aragua State, Venezuela: Geological Society of America Bulletin, v. 71, p. 249–302.

Sinton, C.W., Duncan, R.A., and Denyer, P., 1997, Nicoya Peninsula, Costa Rica: A single suite of Caribbean oceanic plateau magmas: Journal of Geophysical Research, v. 102, p. 15,507–15,520, doi: 10.1029/97JB00681.

Sisson, V.B., Ertan, I.E., and Avé Lallemant, H.G., 1997, High pressure (~2000 MPa) kyanite- and glaucophane-bearing pelitic schist and eclogite from Cordillera de la Costa belt, Venezuela: Journal of Petrology, v. 38, p. 65–83, doi: 10.1093/petrology/38.1.65.

Smith, C.A., Sisson, V.B., Avé Lallemant, H.G., and Copeland, P., 1999, Two contrasting pressure-temperature-time paths in the Villa de Cura blueschist belt, Venezuela: Possible evidence for Late Cretaceous initiation of subduction in the Caribbean: Geological Society of America Bulletin, v. 111, no. 6, p. 831–848, doi: 10.1130/0016-7606(1999)111<0831:TCPTTP>2.3.CO;2.

Sorensen, S.S., and Grossman, J.N., 1989, Enrichment of trace elements in garnet amphibolites from a paleo-subduction zone: Catalina Schist, southern California: Geochimica et Cosmochimica Acta, v. 53, p. 3155–3177, doi: 10.1016/0016-7037(89)90096-3.

Sorensen, S.S., and Grossman, J.N., 1993, Accessory minerals and subduction zone metasomatism: A geochemical comparison of two mélanges (Washington and California, U.S.A.): Chemical Geology, v. 110, p. 269–297, doi: 10.1016/0009-2541(93)90258-K.

Sorensen, S.S., Grossman, J.N., and Perfit, M.R., 1997, Phengite-hosted LILE enrichment in eclogite and related rocks: Implications for fluid-mediated mass transfer in subduction zones and arc magma genesis: Journal of Petrology, v. 38, p. 3–34, doi: 10.1093/petrology/38.1.3.

Stöckhert, B., Maresch, W.V., Brix, M., Kaiser, C., Toetz, A., Kluge, R., and Kruckhaus-Lueder, G., 1995, Crustal history of Margarita Island (Venezuela) in detail: Constraints on the Caribbean plate-tectonic scenario: Geology, v. 23, p. 787–790, doi: 10.1130/0091-7613(1995)023<0787: CHOMIV>2.3.CO;2.

Staudigel, H., Plank, T., White, B., and Schmincke, H.-U., 1996, Geochemical fluxes during seafloor alteration of the basaltic upper oceanic crust, *in* Bebout, G.E., Scholl, D.W., Kirby, S.H., and Platt, J.P., eds., Subduction: Top to bottom: American Geophysical Union Monograph 96, p. 19–38.

Stephan, J.F., 1985, Andes et chaîne Caraibe sur la transversale de Barquisimeto (Venezuela): évolution géodynamique, *in* Mascle, A., ed., Géodynamique des Caraïbes, Symposium: Paris, Technip, p. 505–529.

Sun, S.-S., and McDonough, W.F., 1989, Chemical and isotopic systematics of oceanic basalts: Implications for mantle composition and processes, *in* Saunders, A.D., and Norry, M.J., eds., Magmatism in the ocean basins: London, Geological Society Special Publication 42, p. 313–345.

Talukdar, S., and Loureiro, D., 1982, Geología de una zona ubicada en el segmento norcentral de la Cordillera de la Costa, Venezuela: Metamorfismo y deformación. Evolución del margen septentrional de Suramérica en el marco de la tectónica de placas: Caracas, Geos, v. 27, p. 15–76.

Urbani, F., 1969, Primera localidad fosilífera del Miembro Zenda de la Formación Las Brisas: Cuevo Indio, La Guarita, Estado Miranda: Asociación Venezolana de Geología, Minería y Petróleo, Boletín Informativo, v. 12, no. 12, p. 447–453.

Urbani, F., and Ostos, M., 1989, El Complejo Ávila, Cordillera de La Costa, Venezuela: Caracas, Geos, v. 29, p. 205–217.

Vignali, M., 1976, The stratigraphy and structure of the metamorphic eastern Cordillera, Venezuela (Araya-Paria Peninsula and Margarita Island) [Ph.D. dissertation]: Zurich, Eidgenössische Technische Hochschule, 129 p.

Vignali, M., 1979, Estratigrafía y estructura de las cordilleras metamórficas de Venezuela oriental (Península de Araya–Paria e Isla Margarita): Caracas, Geos, v. 25, p. 19–66.

Ysaccis, R., 1997, Tertiary evolution of northeastern Venezuela offshore [Ph.D. thesis]: Houston, Rice University, 285 p.

MANUSCRIPT ACCEPTED BY THE SOCIETY 5 APRIL 2005

Geological Society of America
Special Paper 394
2005

Exhumation history of two high-pressure belts, northern Venezuela, based on fluid inclusions in quartz and calcite veins

Virginia B. Sisson
Rebecca Kessler Cardoso
Caren Chaika Harris
Saijin Huang
Layla M. Unger
Department of Earth Science, MS-126, Rice University, Houston, Texas 77251-1892, USA

ABSTRACT

Two metamorphic belts in northern Venezuela were metamorphosed at high-pressure–low-temperature conditions in a Cretaceous subduction zone. Both belts, the Cordillera de la Costa and Villa de Cura, contain several generations of quartz ± calcite veins that formed during two stages of orogenic development. The first stage encompasses five generations of ductile deformation structures. This was followed by at least two generations of brittle deformation. Quartz veins related to the different deformations contain several types of fluid inclusions. Most are two-phase with an aqueous NaCl-H$_2$O solution. Texturally early fluid inclusions show a wide range of homogenization temperatures with a different salinity associated with each deformation episode. In one of the early quartz veins from the Araya Peninsula, there are also fluid inclusions containing a three-phase, CO$_2$-bearing low salinity fluid. The isochores for the Villa de Cura blueschist belt do pass through the metamorphic conditions. In contrast, the isochores calculated for two suites of veins, one near Puerto Cabello and the other on the Araya Peninsula, both indicate changes in fluid density related to either leakage and/or stretching. These are interpreted to reflect relatively steep to moderate decompression paths related to plate-boundary–parallel stretching. The calculated isochores for the latest quartz veins indicate a change in cooling rate as exhumation continued during the final brittle deformation related to thrust emplacement. Two veins, one each from the Cordillera de la Costa and Villa de Cura belts, have single phase, methane-bearing fluid inclusions. These fluids may be related to methane-rich fluids expelled from underlying units related to the Serranía del Interior fold and thrust belt or to passive margin deposits such as the La Luna formation.

Keywords: fluid inclusions, exhumation, aqueous fluids, methane, pressure-temperature deformation path.

E-mails: j_sisson@netzero.com; Cardoso now at ENV America, 2247 San Diego Ave., Suite 135, San Diego, California 92110, USA, kessler_98@yahoo.com; Harris now at Occidental Oil and Gas Corp., 5 Greenway Plaza, Suite 110, Houston, Texas 77046, USA, caren_c_harris@oxy.com; Huang now at Veritas DGC Inc., 10300 Town Park, Houston, Texas 77072, USA, Saijin_Huang@veritasdgc.com; Unger now at ConocoPhillips Co., 600 N. Dairy Ashford, Houston, Texas 77079, USA, Layla.M.Unger@conocophillips.com.

Sisson, V.B., Cardoso, R.K., Harris, C.C., Huang, S., and Unger, L.M., 2005, Exhumation history of two high-pressure belts, northern Venezuela, based on fluid inclusions in quartz and calcite veins, *in* Avé Lallemant, H.G., and Sisson, V.B., eds., Caribbean–South American plate interactions, Venezuela: Geological Society of America Special Paper 394, p. 157–171, doi: 10.1130/2005.2394(05). For permission to copy, contact editing@geosociety.org. ©2005 Geological Society of America.

INTRODUCTION

One of the best ways to estimate paleofluid pressure, composition, and migration in rocks is to use fluid inclusions. These record the composition of paleofluids and, most important, fluid density, which is related to pressure and temperature. This, in turn, helps constrain the timing and evolution of tectonic events (e.g., Hollister and Crawford, 1981; Crawford and Hollister, 1986; Avé Lallemant et al., 1998; El-Shazly and Sisson, 1999, 2004; Pavlis et al., 2003). This is often the best way to constrain exhumation of various orogenic belts, such as subduction zones, since most retrograde metamorphic reactions are only temperature sensitive and not pressure sensitive. Most models for exhumation of blueschists and eclogites that formed in subduction zones call on processes that act perpendicular to the plate boundary (e.g., Cowan and Schilling, 1978; Cloos, 1982; Platt, 1986; Ernst, 1988; Platt et al., 2003). In contrast, exhumation models of Avé Lallemant and Guth (1990) and of Mann and Gordon (1996) involve plate-boundary–parallel stretching and fragmentation of the accretionary wedge. It may be possible to distinguish different exhumation pressure-temperature-time–deformation (*P-T-t*-d) paths for these two types of models. For example, fluid inclusions and mineral assemblages in high-pressure terranes often indicate a *P-T* path that displays decompression without significant cooling; this may be indicative of extensional thinning associated with plate-boundary–parallel stretching.

Since quartz veins are ubiquitous in the two high-pressure belts of northern Venezuela, we can use them to constrain the exhumation history of these subduction complexes. For this study, we examined fluid inclusions in these quartz veins in an along-strike transect of the Cordillera de la Costa belt to determine the paleofluid composition, pressure, and temperature of the fluids present at the time of vein formation. In two regions, one near Puerto Cabello and the other on the Araya Peninsula, we examined a suite of quartz veins related to a sequence of ductile to brittle deformation structures (see Avé Lallemant, 1997; Avé Lallemant and Sisson, this volume, Chapter 7). Assuming that the fluids trapped are representative of those present during exhumation, and that the inclusions have retained a constant volume and composition since entrapment, fluid inclusion data can be used to help explain observations of differences in emplacement textures and deformation between sets of veins.

We also analyzed one quartz vein that formed early in the deformation sequence in the Villa de Cura blueschist belt to help constrain the peak metamorphic pressure. In this region, late stage veins related to brittle deformation features were not analyzed because the veins we collected did not have observable fluid inclusions.

GEOLOGICAL SETTING

In northern Venezuela, two belts contain high-pressure–low-temperature metamorphic suites: the Cordillera de la Costa belt along the north coast of Venezuela from west of Puerto Cabello to east on the Araya and Paria Peninsulas and the Villa de Cura belt to the south (Fig. 1). Both belts probably formed in a Creta-

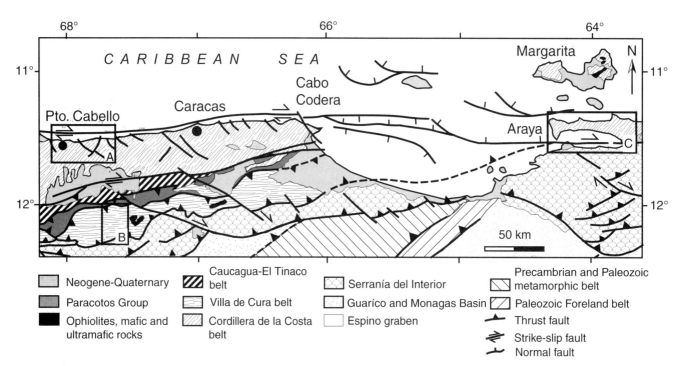

Figure 1. Tectonic map of northern Venezuela showing the two high-pressure metamorphic belts: the Cordillera de la Costa and Villa de Cura. Inset boxes show the locations of the detailed geologic maps given in Figure 2. Map is adapted from Ysaccis (1997) with contributions from A.W. Bally, J. di Croce, E. Hung, H.G. Avé Lallemant, and V.B. Sisson.

ceous subduction zone (e.g., Stöckhert et al., 1995; Sisson et al., this volume, Chapter 3).

Cordillera de la Costa Belt

The Cordillera de la Costa belt is exposed from west of Puerto Cabello to Cabo Codera in the east (Fig. 1). The belt can be correlated with similar lithologies on Margarita Island and the Araya and Paria Peninsulas (e.g., González de Juana et al., 1980; Bellizzia and Dengo, 1990). The eclogite-bearing Cordillera de la Costa belt in northern Venezuela consists of a mélange of eclogite and mica schist, metamorphosed mafic volcanic rocks, and serpentinite, along with units of marble, quartzofeldspathic gneiss, granite, and graphite schist. The eclogite bodies are boudins, blocks, and lenses confined to a narrow belt along the northern coast of Venezuela (Fig. 2). The eclogite-bearing belt is juxtaposed against lower temperature schists of the Cordillera

de la Costa belt to the south. This belt includes a suite of meta-igneous rocks including mid-oceanic-ridge basalt, gabbro, and ultramafic rocks and felsic plutonic rocks as well as some augen gneiss hosted in continentally-derived sediments (e.g., Avé Lallemant and Sisson, 1993; Ostos and Sisson, this volume; Sorensen et al., this volume).

The Cordillera de la Costa eclogite belt underwent intense deformation, which produced five synmetamorphic (D_{1a}–D_{1e}) and two postmetamorphic (D_2 and D_3) generations of deformation structures (Avé Lallemant and Sisson, this volume, Chapter 7). Petrologic and geothermobarometric results show that glaucophane + kyanite-bearing pelitic schists likely formed at P >2000 MPa and T >630 °C (Ertan et al., 1995; Sisson et al., 1997). The first phase of deformation took place under relatively high-pressure eclogite facies conditions (500–700 °C at ~2000–2200 MPa). During cooling, most of the peak metamorphic assemblages were severely overprinted by blueschist and greenschist facies retrograde

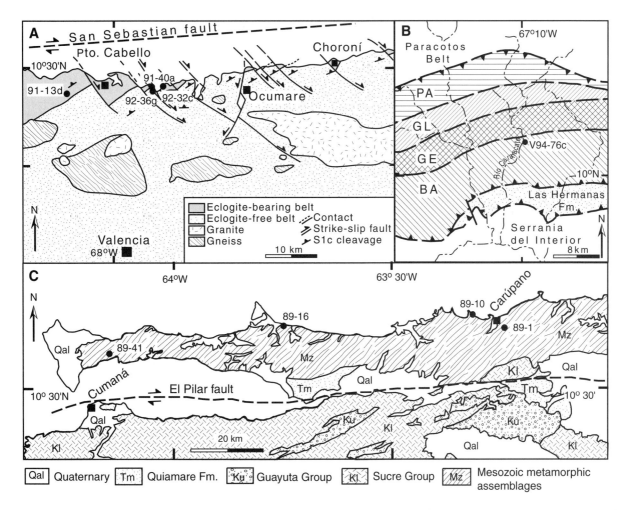

Figure 2. Tectonic maps of the three study areas. (A) Cordillera de la Costa belt. Map is adapted from Bellizzia et al. (1976) with the Cordillera de la Costa belt subdivided into a northern eclogite-bearing mélange subbelt and a southern eclogite-free schist subbelt. (B) Villa de Cura belt. BA—barroisite zone; GE—glaucophane epidote zone; GL—glaucophane lawsonite zone; PA—pumpellyte actinolite zone. Map adapted from Smith et al. (1999). (C) Araya Peninsula. Qal—Quaternary; Kl—Lower Cretaceous; Ku—Upper Cretaceous; Mz—Mesozoic; Tm—Tertiary Miocene. Map simplified from Bellizzia et al. (1976).

assemblages. The D_{1b} to D_{1e} phases of deformation occurred under decreasing temperatures and pressures, following an "Alpine-type" (Ernst, 1988) uplift and decompression path.

Araya Peninsula

About 400 km to the east are the Araya and Paria Peninsulas (Figs. 1 and 2C), also known as the Carúpano region (Avé Lallemant, 1997). This area has several metamorphic assemblages that may correlate with the schists in the southern subbelt near Puerto Cabello. These range in metamorphic grade from amphibolite facies in the Manicuare assemblage to lower greenschist grade in the Laguna Chica, Carúpano, and Tunapui assemblages. The Manicuare assemblage is part of the Coastal fringe–Margarita belt (Stephan, 1982), whereas the three other assemblages are part of the Cordillera de la Costa (sensu stricto) belt (e.g., González de Juana et al., 1980). Two of these assemblages, the Manicuare and Carúpano, were sampled for this study (Fig. 2). The timing of amphibolite facies metamorphism in the Manicuare assemblage is synchronous with the subduction zone metamorphism on Margarita Island and presumably also with the Cordillera de la Costa belt near Puerto Cabello and the Villa de Cura belt (Sisson et al., this volume, Chapter 3). The lower grade Carúpano assemblage may have been metamorphosed in the Miocene, synchronous with deformation of the Dragon augen gneiss on Paria Peninsula (Speed et al., 1997).

Only the Manicuare Formation has appropriate metamorphic mineral assemblages (staurolite + garnet + biotite in the presence of kyanite and absence of chlorite or melt) that can be used to constrain *P-T* conditions. Kyanite has been observed in some mica schists as well as in some quartz veins. Chlorite only occurs as a secondary mineral. There are no migmatites in the region; the temperatures did not reach melting conditions. The stability field for this assemblage is 550–650 °C and pressures of at least 550 MPa (e.g., Bucher and Frey, 2002). Metamorphic assemblages in the Carúpano assemblage indicate greenschist facies conditions, but no diagnostic mineral assemblages have been found to constrain their *P-T* conditions.

Avé Lallemant (1997) recognized five generations of folds, with the first three (D_{1a} to D_{1c}) being synmetamorphic and the last two (D_{2a} and D_{2b}) postmetamorphic. Note that extensional D_{1c} structures on Araya Peninsula are equivalent to extensional D_{1e} structures from the Puerto Cabello region. Avé Lallemant (1997) also recognized two generations of faults associated with the postmetamorphic folds. Both the amphibolite facies Manicuare assemblage and greenschist facies Carúpano assemblage have a similar deformation history, having formed as a result of right oblique convergence of the Caribbean plate with the South American plate.

Villa de Cura Belt

Unlike the Cordillera de la Costa belt, the Villa de Cura belt is not a mélange, but consists of four coherent imbricate slices or subbelts (Shagam, 1960; Smith et al., 1999; Ellero et al., 2001; Unger et al., this volume). Together, these four slices were meta-

morphosed at blueschist facies conditions with only little retrograde overprint; no eclogite has been encountered in this belt (Smith et al., 1999). Mineral assemblages and geothermobarometry indicate metamorphic conditions for the three northernmost subbelts ranging from 240–275 °C at ~550 MPa in the north to 300–375 °C at 700 MPa in the south. This type of metamorphic *P-T* path is indicative of "Franciscan" style exhumation (Ernst, 1988). In contrast, the southernmost barroisite (BA) subbelt underwent metamorphism at higher temperatures, 420–510 °C, at similar pressures. This subbelt also shows sodic amphibole that has partially overprinted barroisitic amphibole, indicating growth during cooling. Smith et al. (1999) proposed that this occurred during initiation of subduction related to a switch in arc polarity in the Cretaceous. The protolith of the Villa de Cura belt is a sequence of volcanic arc basalts and arc-derived volcaniclastic rocks (Unger et al., this volume). Smith et al. (1999) recognized at least four generations of ductile structures (D_{1a} to D_{1d}) as well as two generations of brittle deformation (D_{2a} and D_{2b}).

ANALYSIS OF FLUID INCLUSIONS

We used a U.S. Geological Survey heating-freezing stage made by Fluid Inc. for microthermometric measurements. Fluid inclusions ranged in size from <1 to 20 μm, with most falling between 5 and 10 μm. We avoided those inclusions that appeared to have necked down or reequilibrated to lower temperatures and pressures after entrapment. Stage calibration used synthetic CO_2 inclusions (−56.6 °C) as well as synthetic H_2O inclusions (0 °C and 374.1 °C). We typically made measurements of final ice melting temperature ($T_{M, ICE}$) and homogenization temperature (T_H). Due to the small size and low salinity of many fluid inclusions, the observation of first ice melting is difficult but was recorded where possible. $T_{M, ICE}$ measurements were recorded using cycling techniques described by Roedder (1984), Goldstein and Reynolds (1994), and Samson et al. (2003) at heating rates of 0.5 °C/min. We used faster rates of 1–5 °C/min to measure T_H. The precision of $T_{M, ICE}$ varied from 0.1 to 0.3 °C, and the precision of T_H is ~2 °C; both were determined by repeat analyses of individual fluid inclusions. All fluid inclusions examined for this study homogenized to the liquid phase. Fluid salinities (expressed as wt% NaCl equivalent) and densities were calculated using equations of state for NaCl-H_2O and CH_4 using the computer package FLUIDS (Bakker, 2003). Extrapolated isochores have an error of ~100 MPa.

Examination of doubly polished thin sections under an ultraviolet light source indicates that none of these samples had any fluorescent fluid inclusions. Thus, they did not have any higher hydrocarbon fluids.

Samples

In the Cordillera de la Costa belt near Puerto Cabello, quartz ± zoisite ± rutile ± calcite veins were emplaced during the last three ductile deformations as well as during the two brittle deformation phases. We sampled three generations of quartz veins that can be related to different deformation events (Fig. 3). Two veins are pre- to syn-D_{1c}. One of these (sample 91VSn40a) is a quartz-zoisite vein that parallels the S_{1c} foliation. In an adjacent outcrop, veins with the same mineralogy occur in boudin necks between eclogite blocks. Thus, we interpret these as having formed during D_{1c} deformation. Another quartz vein (sample 91VSn13d) also occurs both along and across S_{1c} foliation near mafic eclogite blocks as well as a kyanite-garnet-glaucophane block (Sisson et al., 1997). We interpret this texture as vein formation during D_{1c} deformation. The next generation of quartz veins crosscuts S_{1c} foliation and does not have deformed quartz (sample 92VSn32c). It probably formed during D_{1d} or D_{1e} deformation. The final vein generation (sample 92VSn36 g) occurs along N-S brittle fractures associated with D_2 deformation. In this sample, both quartz and calcite occurred in the vein.

Quartz ± calcite veins occur abundantly in all formations of the Araya Peninsula. They were emplaced during the entire deformation history. Relative ages of these veins can be established relative to the five phases of folding and faulting. Five different generations

of quartz veins were collected for a preliminary fluid inclusion study to determine pressure and temperature conditions of deformation. One syn-D_{1a} sample (VS89-41) was collected from the Manicuare Formation (Fig. 2). The other vein samples represent D_{1b}, D_{1c}, and D_{2b} and are from the Carúpano Formation (Fig. 2). No fluid inclusions were found in the syn-D_{2a} quartz vein.

In the Villa de Cura belt, we sampled a deformed quartz vein (V94CS-76c) from the barroisite zone. This represents a synmetamorphic vein that probably formed before or during D_{1b} deformation. There are other generations of quartz and quartz-calcite veins that can be related to the subsequent deformations, but these were not analyzed for this study.

Fluid Inclusion Petrography and Microthermometric Results

In most of our samples, fluid inclusions are common in relatively undeformed veins. We only made fluid inclusion observations in quartz. In a few samples that we examined, the majority of the fluid inclusions were too small for analysis. Thus, only a small number of fluid inclusion measurements could be obtained.

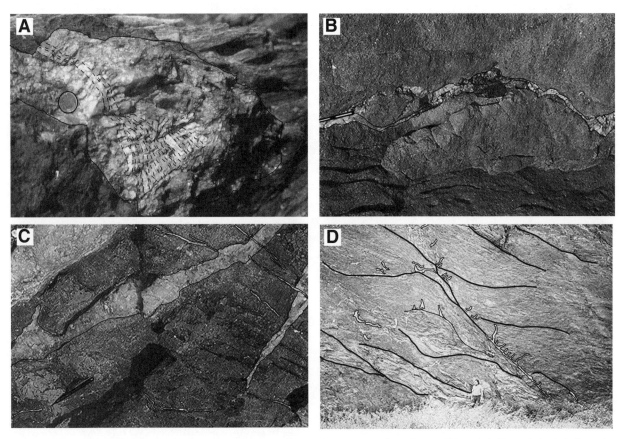

Figure 3. Photographs of representative quartz ± calcite ± zoisite veins. A–C are from the Cordillera de la Costa belt; D is from the Araya Peninsula. In all of these photographs, thin solid lines highlight quartz veins. (A) Quartz-zoisite D_{1c} vein (sample 91VSn13d) that occurs next to an eclogite block. The dashed lines outline some of the individual zoisite crystals. Coin is 1.5 cm across. (B) Quartz D_{1d} vein (sample 91VSn40a) in a quartz-mica schist. Pencil for scale on left is 14 cm long. (C) Two generations of orthogonal D_2 quartz-calcite veins (sample 92VSn36 g) cross-cutting quartz-mica schist. Pencil is 14 cm long. (D) View to south on Araya Peninsula of D_{1c} extensional quartz veins in the Carúpano assemblage. Thicker solid lines indicate fault surfaces.

We focused on obtaining microthermometric results for isolated and texturally early fluid inclusions. For most samples, there was not a systematic relationship between fluid inclusion size and either volume equivalent spherical radius (Hall and Sterner, 1993) or shape factor (Bodnar et al., 1989). If later inclusions were present, we also measured some later generations of fluid inclusions. The initial $T_{M, ICE}$ for most samples was near −20 °C, which corresponds to a NaCl-water fluid. Most of the final melting and homogenization temperatures show some scatter, as discussed in the following. None of the samples have sufficient data for rigorous statistical analysis of the histograms; however, we feel the general interpretations are probably valid.

Cordillera de la Costa Belt

Each generation of quartz (+ calcite) vein has its own typical fluid inclusion textures (Fig. 4). Most commonly, fluid inclusions occur on healed microcracks. Overall, the average fluid inclusion is ~5 μm in length. Three of the samples only have aqueous, two-phase fluid inclusions (Table 1). We did not detect any other fluid phase such as CO_2 or CH_4 in these aqueous inclusions using microthermometric techniques; this does not rule out the presence of minute amounts of these fluids, which may be detectable by other techniques.

In the two samples of early D_{1c} veins (samples 91VSn13d and 91VSn40a), fluid inclusions typically occur along linear trails that sometimes cross grain boundaries and sometimes are within a quartz grain (Fig. 4A). Some fluid inclusions occur in sparse clusters (Fig. 4B). No crosscutting relationships were seen between these different textural types of fluid inclusions. In sample 91VSn13d, sizes range from 2.5 to 25 μm. The relative percent fill of vapor bubble for sample 91VSn13d is fairly consistent at ~10% except for one cluster that had 30% vapor. Most of the fluid inclusions are subhedral or elongate with no obvious necking-down features. Sample 91VSN40a had a smaller inclusion size of only 2.5–12.5 μm; these typically have ~20%–30% vapor. These fluid inclusions are generally more elongate than other samples.

The intermediate generation of quartz vein (D_{1d}; sample 92VSn32c) also has fluid inclusions occurring along healed fractures that cross grain boundaries (Fig. 4C). These range in size from 2.0 to 20 μm with consistent vapor volume at ~10% vapor. Most of the fluid inclusions are subhedral or elongate with no obvious necking-down features.

The final stage of deformation (D_2) is represented by a quartz-calcite vein (sample 91VSn36g). The calcite was not used for fluid inclusion analysis. The most ubiquitous fluid inclusion type occurs along linear trails that cross grain boundaries (Fig. 4D). These fluid inclusions are typically 1–5 μm in length with a few up to 20 μm. The liquid to vapor ratio is fairly constant in all the linear trails observed. There are also randomly distributed euhedral to irregular one-phase fluid inclusions. These mostly occur near the center of quartz grains and ranged from 2 to 15 μm.

Each generation of quartz (+ calcite) vein has a different fluid composition as well as density (Table 1; Fig. 5). One first deformation generation (D_{1c}) quartz vein (91VSn13d) has an aqueous fluid with an average $T_{M,ICE}$ of −5 °C, which results in a calculated salinity of ~8 wt% NaCl equivalent. The other first deformation generation (D_{1c}) quartz vein (91VSn40a) has an aqueous fluid with an average $T_{M, ICE}$ of −1 °C, which results in a calculated salinity of ~1.7 wt% NaCl equivalent. The two D_{1c} samples have different ranges and distributions of $T_{M, ICE}$ for their aqueous fluid

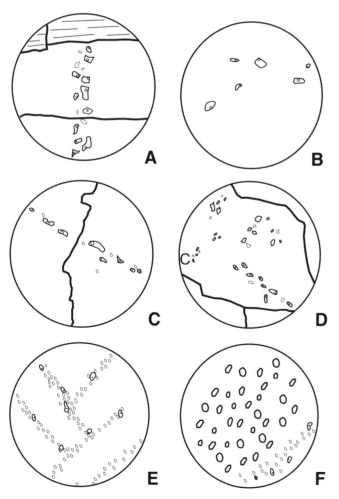

Figure 4. Sketches of fluid inclusions from the Cordillera de la Costa and Villa de Cura belts. All of the fluid inclusions are hosted in quartz. One sample (A) had some white mica included at its edge as indicated by micaceous cleavage. The diameter of each sketch is 3 mm. Fluid inclusions that occur below the plane of the sketch are schematically shown without vapor bubbles. Sketches A–D are from the Cordillera de la Costa belt. Sketches E and F are from the Villa de Cura belt. (A) Secondary fluid inclusions that cross a grain boundary in deformed D_{1c} quartz (sample 91VSn13d). (B) Relatively isolated clusters of fluid inclusions within D_{1d} quartz (sample 92VSn32d). (C) Secondary healed fracture with fluid inclusions that crosses a deformed quartz boundary in D_{1c} (sample 91VSn40a). (D) Two types of healed fractures with fluid inclusions. The single-phase inclusions are methane-rich, whereas the two-phase fluid inclusions are aqueous. These do not cross grain boundaries in D_2 quartz (sample 91VSn36g). (E) Several sets of parallel fractures with aqueous fluid inclusions in D_1 quartz (sample V94CS76a). (F) Single phase fluid inclusions that parallel a fracture of two-phase aqueous inclusions (sample V94CS76a).

TABLE 1. SUMMARY OF FLUID INCLUSION COMPOSITIONS

Region	Sample	Deformational style	Vein mineralogy	Inclusion types	Average T_M	Average T_H
Cordillera de la Costa	91VSn13d	ductile: pre to syn D_{1c}	quartz-zoisite	1	−6 to −8	150 and 220
	91VSn40a	ductile: brecciated, pre to syn D_{1c}	quartz	1	−1	240 to 250
	92VSn32c	ductile: syn D_{1d}	quartz	1	−6 to −8	190
	91VSn36g	brittle: syn D_2	quartz-calcite	1 and 2	−20	220 to 230
Araya Peninsula	VS89-41	ductile: syn D_{1a}	quartz-calcite	1 and 3	−5	
	VS89-1	ductile: syn D_{1b}	quartz	1	−1.5	100 and 310
	VS89-10	ductile: syn D_{1c} fault	quartz	1	−5 to −10	115 to 130
	VS89-16	brittle: syn D_{2b}	quartz	1	−3	125
Villa de Cura	V94CS76a	brittle: syn D_1	quartz	1 and 2	−4	200

Note: Type 1 is H_2O-rich; Type 2 is methane-rich; Type 3 is CO_2-H_2O. For Type 1 inclusions, T_M—melting temperature and T_H—homogenization temperature, both in °C.

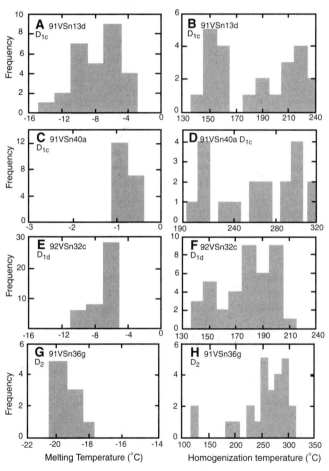

Figure 5. Histograms of $T_{M, ICE}$ (melting temperature) and T_H (homogenization temperature) for aqueous fluid inclusions from the Cordillera de la Costa belt.

The final generation D_2 also has a small range in $T_{M, ICE}$, close to the NaCl eutectic temperature, from −20.2 to −18.0 °C with a peak close to −20 °C or 22.4 wt% NaCl equivalent.

Each sample has a fairly wide range of T_H but with different types of distributions (Fig. 5). All fluid inclusions homogenize to a liquid phase. One D_{1c} vein (sample 91VSn13d) has a bimodal distribution with T_H peaks at 150 and 220 °C over the observed T_H range from 135 to 240 °C. The other D_{1c} vein (sample 91VSn40a) has a higher range of T_H from 191 to 320 °C and no distinct peak. The D_{1d} vein (sample 92VSn32c) has a skewed distribution with a peak at 190 °C over a narrow range from 135 to 210 °C. The D_2 quartz-calcite vein has the largest range of T_H from 110 to 310 °C with a peak at ~260 °C.

Two veins, 91VSn40a (D_{1c}) and 91VSn36 g (D_2) have similar trends on T_H versus salinity diagrams with a wide distribution of T_H but a relatively small range in salinity (Fig. 6). This trend contrasts with the cluster-type pattern for the D_{1d} veins (sample 92VSn32c) as well as with the distinct trend from low T_H and salinity toward higher T_H and salinity for the other D_{1c} vein (sample 91VSn13d).

Only the last generation of quartz-calcite vein (D_2) has a second fluid inclusion composition, which is methane-rich. These methane inclusions have a large range of T_H, from −122 to −105.5 °C (Fig. 7). There was no observed clathrate melting, which implies a lack of H_2O in these inclusions. It is unlikely that they represent an immiscible fluid. The distribution of T_H is not symmetric and has a peak at −114 °C.

Araya Peninsula

In the early quartz-calcite vein associated with D_{1a} (sample VS89-41 from the Manicuare Formation), there are several types of fluid inclusions with H_2O and mixed H_2O-CO_2. The dark, mixed H_2O-CO_2 fluid inclusions occur either as solitary inclusions or along healed fractures that cross grain boundaries. These have subhedral to irregular shapes and range in size from 3 to 15 μm. The volume percent of CO_2 in these inclusions is 80%–95%, which makes them appear single-phase at low magnification. Many of these fluid inclusions appear to be decrepitated, with either fractures or irregular shaped "arms" radiating from

inclusions, with sample 91VSn13d ranging from −15 to −3 °C with a slightly asymmetric peak compared to sample 81VSn40a that has a small range ~−1 °C. In contrast, the next generation D_{1d} sample 92VSn32c has a distinctly asymmetric peak for $T_{M, ICE}$ centered about −5 °C, which equates to 8 wt% NaCl equivalent.

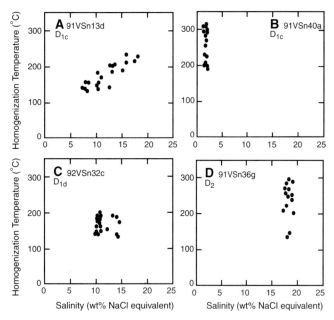

Figure 6. Plot of T_H (homogenization temperature) and salinity in wt% NaCl equivalent for the Cordillera de la Costa belt.

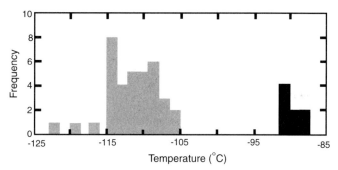

Figure 7. Histograms of T_H (homogenization temperature) for methane-rich inclusions for the Cordillera de la Costa belt (gray region) and the Villa de Cura belt (black region).

them. Some of the decrepitated inclusions do not contain any fluid. Others with the same textural features do contain measurable fluid: it is unclear if these represent original fluid compositions and densities (e.g., Johnson and Hollister, 1995; Barker, 1995). The second fluid inclusion type is rare, irregular, two-phase, clear, fluid inclusions on healed fractures that cross grain boundaries. These range in size from 5 to 30 μm. These seem to be texturally later than the mixed H_2O-CO_2 fluid inclusions.

Microthermometric observations for the syn-D_{1a} vein indicate that the mixed H_2O-CO_2 fluid inclusions have CO_2 melting temperatures (T_{M, CO_2}) between −57.1 and −56.6 °C, which indicates that the CO_2 is relatively pure, with possibly some methane or nitrogen that causes the slight decrease in melting temperature below the triple point. The clathrate melting temperatures ($T_{M, CLATH}$) are between 10.9 and 11.1 °C. The salinity of these fluid inclusions could only be calculated for a few inclusions that had T_{H, CO_2} above $T_{M, CLATH}$; this calculation yields a very low salinity of 1 wt% NaCl equivalent. Different clusters of fluid inclusions have different T_{H, CO_2} between −2.7 and 10.2 °C. The aqueous fluid inclusions have $T_{M, ICE}$ between −6.4 and −4.7 °C, indicating a salinity of 5–10 wt% NaCl equivalent.

In three samples from the Carúpano assemblage, there was only one type of fluid inclusion. These two-phase fluid inclusions typically occurred in clusters and had subhedral shapes. The majority of the fluid inclusions were 5–15 μm in length. The syn-D_{2b} vein was very milky, which made it difficult to observe fluid inclusions.

Each of these veins has a unique set of microthermometric observations (Table 1; Fig. 8). The syn-D_{1b} quartz-calcite vein (sample VS89-1) has a small range in $T_{M, ICE}$ from −3 to 0 °C, indi-

cating low salinity aqueous fluids with a peak at 1.7 wt% NaCl equivalent. This sample has a bimodal distribution of T_H with one peak near 70 °C and another at 315 °C. There is no systematic relationship between T_H and salinity. The next generation quartz vein (syn-D_{1c}: sample VS89-10) has a wide range in $T_{M, ICE}$ between −14 to −2 °C. The $T_{M, ICE}$ histogram indicates a skewed distribution corresponding to 3.4–17.7 wt% NaCl equivalent. The significant $T_{M, ICE}$ peak corresponds to 6.5 wt% NaCl equivalent. The corresponding T_H histogram has a regular distribution with a range from 95 to 135 °C and a peak at 110 °C. The last generation quartz vein (syn-D_{2b}: sample VS89-16) has a small range for $T_{M, ICE}$ from −4 to −1 °C with a peak $T_{M, ICE}$ corresponding to 6.0 wt% NaCl equivalent. The associated T_H histogram ranges from 60 to 160 °C with a peak at 125 °C. The latest generation of fluid inclusions is a one-phase low salinity aqueous fluid (with observable melting).

Villa de Cura Belt

Two types of fluid inclusions were found in the D_{1b} quartz vein (sample V94CS76a): a majority of the fluid inclusions occur along microcracks in deformed quartz grains, and a small population of secondary inclusions was found only in two isolated patches in recrystallized quartz grains (Fig. 4). The first type of fluid inclusions occurs in long, linear trails and has subhedral to anhedral shapes. These inclusions tend to be smaller than the second type of fluid inclusions. Many are too small for microthermometric observations. The second type of fluid inclusions has negative crystal to rounded shapes and occurs parallel to some of the first type of fluid inclusion microcracks. However, these do not occur as linear trails but as large, diffuse populations.

Microthermometric observations indicate two fluid compositions: the first fluid inclusion type is aqueous and the second inclusion type is methane-rich fluids. The aqueous inclusions have a range in $T_{M, ICE}$ from −1.0 to −6.0 °C with a unimodal peak at −4.2 °C (Fig. 9). This corresponds to low to moderate salinities of 1.8–10 wt% NaCl equivalent with a peak at 5 wt% NaCl equivalent. Homogenization temperatures span a large range from 88 to 258 °C with a slightly asymmetric peak at 200 °C. There is a weak relationship between the salinity versus homogenization temperature as the lower homogenization temperature inclusions

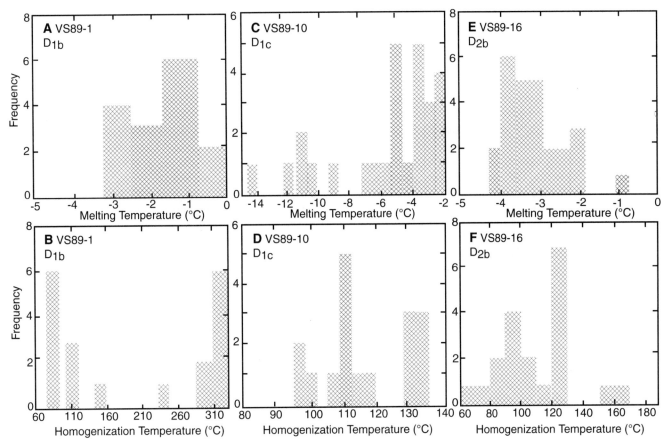

Figure 8. Histograms of $T_{M, ICE}$ (melting temperature) and T_H (homogenization temperature) for aqueous fluid inclusions from the Araya Peninsula. Note that this does not include the syn-D_{1a} vein as only 5 aqueous fluid inclusions were observed.

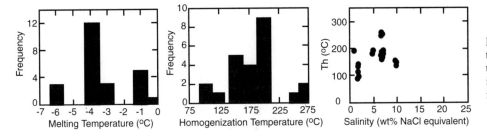

Figure 9. Histograms of $T_{M, ICE}$ (melting temperature) and T_H (homogenization temperature) and plot of T_H and salinity in wt% NaCl equivalent for aqueous fluid inclusions from the Villa de Cura belt.

tend to have lower salinity and the higher homogenization temperatures are associated with the moderate salinity. However, the highest salinity fluid inclusions do not have the highest homogenization temperatures. The methane inclusions had a small range of T_H to a liquid between −91.6 and −87.0 °C (Fig. 7).

DISCUSSION

Each quartz ± calcite vein is considered to have experienced unique *P-T* conditions depending on its formation relative to the host rock metamorphic and deformation history. A sequence of veins from one region can be used to constrain the *P-T* paths dur-

ing exhumation. Since these samples have interacted and trapped fluids at different times, their microthermometric data should be interpreted individually.

In most of these samples, it was difficult to measure the eutectic melting temperature of the aqueous fluids. We assume that most of these are filled with low to moderate salinity aqueous fluids in the NaCl-H_2O system. The observed initial melting temperature is typically lower than that for pure NaCl; thus, it is possible that there are other divalent cations such as K^+, Mg^+, or Ca^{2+} present in these fluid inclusions (e.g., Crawford, 1981; Bodnar, 2003a). In general, their presence will not greatly affect the position of the calculated isochores.

The relationships between salinity and density are complicated and must be interpreted individually for most samples. Most of the samples show a wide range in T_H values, and interpretation of this scatter for each sample is not unique. This could result from entrapment of fluids at different *P-T* conditions and stages of growth and recrystallization and/or post-entrapment modification through leakage, preferential loss of H_2O, or reequilibration of some fluid inclusions (e.g., Bakker and Jansen, 1991; Sterner et al., 1995; Johnson and Hollister, 1995; Barker, 1995; Vityk and Bodnar, 1995; Küster and Stöckhert, 1997; Audétat and Gunther, 1999; Agard et al., 2000; Bodnar, 2003b). TEM investigations coupled with experimental studies of synthetic fluid inclusions have shown that dislocations may act as conduits for migration of H_2O.

Many metamorphic terranes experience several pulses of fluid dehydration as well as hydration during later retrogression. These episodes may occur at any point along the *P-T* evolution of the region, and may be recorded as different generations of fluid inclusions within a single vein. These fluid inclusion generations usually have different compositions as well as densities. Another possible scenario is a change from lithostatic to hydrostatic pressure during vein formation, which would result in two generations of fluid inclusions with similar compositions but different densities.

Post-entrapment modification of fluid inclusions in metamorphic rocks is common during exhumation especially for high-pressure rocks (e.g., Touret, 1992; Scambelluri, 1992; Küster and Stöckhert, 1997; Scambelluri et al., 1998; El-Shazly and Sisson, 1999; Franz et al., 2001; Gao and Klemd, 2001; Fu, 2003). This is caused by an increase or decrease in the internal pressure of the inclusion, especially for larger fluid inclusions (Bodnar et al., 1989; Bodnar, 2003b). Careful observations of T_H, $T_{M, ICE}$, size, fluid inclusion shape, and liquid:vapor ratio will help distinguish between leakage, necking down, and stretching of fluid inclusions. For example, stretching of an inclusion would change its T_H but not its salinity, whereas leakage involving H_2O diffusion would change both T_H and salinity due to water loss. W. Lamb (2004, personal commun.) points out that an increase in fluid inclusion size of ~1 μm results in a 30% volume change. This corresponds to a density difference of 0.2 g/cm³ and an ~100 °C change in homogenization temperature; hence, it would be difficult to measure stretching of fluid inclusions in natural samples.

Several of the late veins from the Cordillera de la Costa belt (samples 91VSn40a and 91VSn36g) have a wide spread in T_H over a limited range of salinity (Fig. 6). This could be attributed either to stretching of the fluid inclusions without any leakage or to density changes as the quartz crystallizes. Since there is no relationship between fluid inclusion size and shape versus T_H, this may imply that spread in T_H is due to fluid changes during crystallization and not changes after entrapment. In contrast, there is a weak correlation between T_H and fluid inclusion size for the earlier D_{1c} veins (samples 91VSn13d and 92VSn32c), with the highest T_H observed in the smallest inclusions. This relationship is suggestive of changes after entrapment similar to that proposed by Küster and Stöckhert (1997), who showed that during exhumation, inclusion density may constantly reequilibrate by

dislocation creep until cooling below 300 °C. One of the samples (91VSn13d) may have undergone both stretching and leakage and/or diffusion of H_2O since there are changes in both T_H and salinity (Fig. 6). The other sample (92VSn32c) may have undergone only leakage since the range in T_H is relatively small.

The syn-D_{1a} vein from Araya Peninsula (sample VS89-41) also shows a relationship between T_H and size as each cluster of mixed CO_2-H_2O inclusions has a different density. This sample also has decrepitation textures. Thus, for the entire Cordillera de la Costa belt, care must be taken in interpreting the fluid inclusions from the early quartz veins.

It is difficult to determine whether these trends are simply due to original variations in fluid compositions and density or to post-entrapment modification. If there has been post-entrapment modification of some fluid inclusions, then our calculated isochores may not be representative of the entrapment conditions because the assumption of constant volume is no longer valid. Careful selection of microthermometric data is necessary to obtain meaningful isochores. We have calculated isochores only for inclusions that appear to be texturally early, have the lowest T_H, and are small to average size (~5–10 μm). Other studies have shown that large inclusions with variable shapes are most susceptible to stretching and leakage (e.g., Bodnar et al., 1989; Bodnar, 2003b).

Comparison between Fluid Isochores and Metamorphic *P-T* Data

The next step in the interpretation of fluid inclusion data is to compare the calculated isochores with *P-T* conditions as estimated from mineral assemblages and geothermobarometric data. Each region will be discussed separately.

Cordillera de la Costa Belt

None of the isochores for any generation of the quartz ± calcite veins are close to the peak metamorphic conditions (Fig. 10). This result is typical for subduction complexes because fluid inclusions in quartz rarely retain their original density, with a few exceptions (e.g., Sorensen and Barton, 1987; Scambelluri, 1992; Touret, 1992). In some eclogites, garnet and/or pyroxene retain primary fluid compositions and rarely their primary density (e.g., Philippot and Selverstone, 1991; Klemd et al., 1992; Gao and Klemd, 2001; Fu, 2003).

The isochores for sample 91VSn13d of the syn-D_{1c} vein pass ~500 MPa below the minimum metamorphic pressure; thus, this fluid is unrelated to subduction zone metamorphism. If this syn-D_{1c} vein formed during retrogression and growth of secondary glaucophane, then the isochores for this vein indicate pressures of ~650 MPa. An additional constraint for sample 91VSn40a is the presence of zoisite + quartz, which implies a temperature below 600 °C at 500 MPa. This temperature estimate is higher than assumed for the other D_{1c} sample. If we use the intersection of the isochore with the same temperature assumed for 91VSn13d, the second syn-D_{1c} vein would record ~550 MPa. This could indicate a regional difference for the syn-D_{1c} veins since they are found in different blocks. This tentative correlation is supported by the occurrence of the syn-D_{1c} vein (sample 91VSn13d) close to the glaucophane-kyanite pelitic whiteschist block, which indicates higher regional metamorphic pressures than for the syn-D_{1c} vein associated with mafic eclogite blocks (sample 91VSn40a). Additional observations are needed to confirm this hypothesis. The *P-T* path between the peak metamorphic conditions and D_{1c} deformation involves both a temperature and pressure decrease.

The next generation of vein is syn-D_{1d} and has a less saline fluid but an isochore similar to those for the syn-D_{1c} veins (Fig. 10B). This deformation is associated with retrograde

growth of actinolite and/or chlorite. Thus, it should reflect trapping of metamorphic fluids below ~450 °C and <500 MPa. If this assumption is correct, then pressure decreased slightly (by 50–150 MPa) between the D_{1c} and D_{1d} deformation events (Fig. 10A and 10B). The *P-T* path between these two deformational events indicates near isothermal decompression.

The first episode of brittle deformation (D_2) is assumed to have occurred at temperatures below the brittle-ductile transition for quartz, ~300 °C. Since we did not observe any crosscutting relationships between the two different fluid types, it is difficult to constrain the relative trapping sequence. If we assume that the high salinity aqueous fluid was trapped first, followed by the methane-rich fluids, then in order to have a *P-T* path cross both isochores, it must follow a relatively isobaric cooling path (Fig. 10C). However, if the methane-rich fluids were trapped first, followed by the high salinity brine, then the *P-T* path may indicate isothermal decompression at relatively high temperatures for shallow processes (~250 °C at 150 MPa). We feel this second interpretation is not valid because of the inferred high temperatures.

Overall, the *P-T* path for this suite of veins indicates initial cooling and decompression, followed by an interval of isothermal decompression, and finally relatively isobaric cooling (Fig. 10). The three different sections of the *P-T* path may correlate with the three stages of exhumation proposed by Avé Lallemant and Sisson (this volume, Chapter 7). The initial stage involves exhumation driven by buoyancy, which should follow a *P-T* path parallel to subduction conditions but at shallower levels. This is similar to the *P-T* path that involves both a temperature and pressure decrease between D_{1a-1b} and D_{1c} deformation. The next stage of exhumation involves plate-boundary–parallel stretching between D_{1c} and D_{1e} deformation. We propose that the *P-T* path for this deformation follows isothermal decompression. The final stage of exhumation involves thrusting of the Cordillera de la Costa belt onto the South American plate followed by erosion. This stage would have a relatively isobaric cooling path because

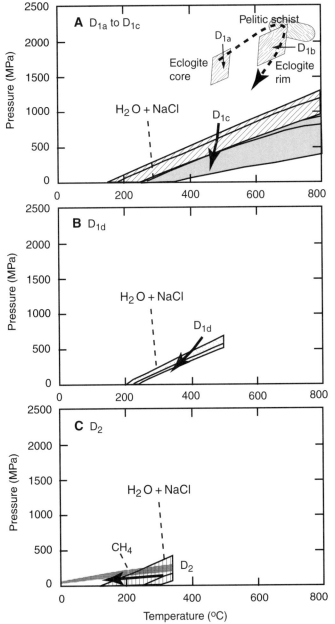

Figure 10. Plots of pressure-temperature (*P-T*) conditions of metamorphism and various calculated isochores for the Cordillera de la Costa belt near Puerto Cabello. In all figures, the heavy line with an arrow indicates a possible *P-T* path. The line within the various isochore fields corresponds to the peak T_H (homogenization temperature) value. Note: these *P-T* paths are simplified and may not represent the exact *P-T* conditions, but are the approximate slope to trap the various fluid inclusions (see text for discussion). (A) Isochores for syn-D_{1c} quartz-zoisite veins. The two wavy diagonal shaded regions indicate the *P-T* conditions for core and rim of garnet in mafic eclogite blocks and glaucophane + kyanite-bearing pelitic whiteschist. Both of these fields are from Sisson et al. (1997). The region surrounded by diagonal lines encompasses isochores for sample 91VSn13d. The shaded region covers isochores for sample 92VSn32c. The dashed heavy line indicates estimated *P-T* conditions during D_{1a} and D_{1b} deformation. The solid heavy line indicates possible *P-T* path during D_{1c} deformation. (B) Isochores for syn-D_{1d} quartz vein (sample 91VSn40a). (C) Isochores for syn-D_2 quartz-calcite vein. The area with vertical lines is for aqueous fluid inclusions, whereas the shaded area is for methane-rich fluid inclusions.

the thickness of the thrust sheets and relative amount of thrusting is small compared to the rest of the exhumation history.

Araya Peninsula

The first generation of fluid inclusions contains a mixture of CO_2-H_2O with variable amounts of CO_2. In addition, some of these have decrepitated. This implies that some the fluid isochores may not reflect trapping conditions. Figure 11 shows that some of the isochores do pass through the stability field for garnet-staurolite-kyanite. However, there are other isochores that do not. If the least dense fluid inclusions are representative of trapping conditions, this implies a minimum pressure of ~800 MPa at 550 °C. In contrast, the densest fluid inclusions could have been trapped at 1200 MPa at 510 °C. This higher pressure is close to that estimated for pelitic schists and mafic eclogites on Margarita Island (Krückhaus-Lueder and Maresch, 1992; Stöckhert et al., 1995). The evidence for decrepitated fluid inclusions could support the proposed rapid cooling and exhumation of the Margarita Island eclogite terrane (Stöckhert et al., 1995; Sisson et al., this volume, Chapter 3). Trapping of low salinity fluids followed. There are several possible *P-T* paths that can be constructed to connect these two generations of fluid (paths 1 and 2 in Fig. 11A). Path 1 shows both cooling and decompression, whereas path 2 indicates isothermal decompression. Neither the mineral assemblage data nor fluid inclusion isochores give unique solutions for determining the *P-T* path.

The data from the Carúpano assemblage can be used to estimate the maximum trapping conditions for the low-grade samples assuming they were never above greenschist facies conditions (Fig. 11B). Overall, the average density of the early fluid inclusions decreases as the vein generation gets younger. Some of the early generation veins also preserve fluids from the later brittle fluid events. These fracturing events do not seem to affect the density or composition of the early fluid inclusions. The latest generation of fluid inclusions is a one-phase low-salinity aqueous fluid, which suggests trapping below ~60 °C.

There are two possible *P-T* paths that can be constructed to explain the bimodal distribution of T_H measurements for the D_{1b} vein (sample VS89-1). The first possible *P-T* path (path 1 on Fig. 11B) would reflect nearly isothermal exhumation and initial trapping of the low T_H fluid inclusions in the D_{1b} veins. The D_{1c} veins then formed at approximately the same temperature but at a slightly lower pressure. Continued exhumation and entrapment of later, high T_H fluid inclusions in the D_{1b} vein followed. This would imply a pressure decrease of ~500 MPa during the ductile deformation. Finally, the region would have cooled at shallow crustal levels. The final fluids would have been trapped in D_{2b} veins at low temperature and low pressure.

The second possibility (path 2 on Fig. 11B) is that initial vein formation occurred at a moderate pressure of 500–600 MPa and temperatures of 350–400 °C. The fluid inclusions with high T_H would represent changes in fluid pressure and not host rock temperature while the vein system shifted from lithostatic to hydrostatic pressures, as seen in other fluid inclusion studies (e.g., Vrolijk, 1987; Weinberger and Sisson, 2003). This would imply

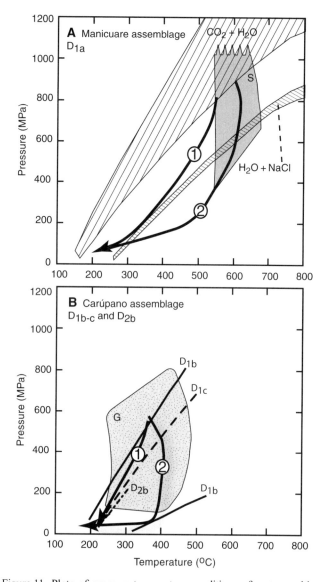

Figure 11. Plots of pressure-temperature conditions of metamorphism and various calculated isochores for the Araya Peninsula. (A) Syn-D_{1a} quartz vein from the Manicuare assemblage. The shaded area is the stability field for garnet-staurolite-kyanite-mica from Bucher and Frey (2002). The area with the wide diagonal lines indicates the range in isochores for the mixed CO_2-H_2O fluid inclusions. The area with thin diagonal lines shows the isochores for the aqueous fluid inclusions. The two heavy lines (1 and 2) indicate possible *P-T* paths during subsequent exhumation and cooling. (B) Syn-D_{1b-c} and D_{2b} quartz veins from the Carúpano assemblage. The light gray, stippled region shows possible *P-T* conditions for greenschist facies (Bucher and Frey, 2002). The two solid lines indicate isochores for syn-D_{1b} aqueous fluid inclusions (sample VS89-1). The dashed line shows the isochore for the syn-D_{1c} vein (sample VS89-10). The dot-dashed line is the isochore for the syn-D_{2b} aqueous fluid inclusions. The two heavy lines with arrowheads indicate possible *P-T* paths (1 and 2) during subsequent exhumation and cooling.

that metamorphic temperatures were above 315 °C in order to trap the inclusions as suggested by the mineral assemblages. The overall *P-T* path would not reflect these changes in fluid pressure, only the change in *P-T* conditions between the D_{1b} and D_{1c} vein formation. Once the region was below ~300 °C, the brittle D_{2b} veins would crystallize. This would indicate a minimum pressure change of ~300 MPa or ~10 km between D_{1b} and D_{2b}. Thus, the overall *P-T* would reflect both cooling and exhumation. With our data, it is not possible to determine which of these two *P-T* paths is more likely to have occurred.

Villa de Cura Belt

Figure 12 shows that the calculated isochores for the aqueous fluid inclusions passed through the peak metamorphic conditions, whereas those for the methane-rich inclusions did not. Since the stability for barroisite is poorly constrained, particularly with respect to pressure, this result confirms the pressure of ~600 MPa as estimated by Smith et al. (1999). The fluid inclusion textures are equivocal but suggestive that the methane-rich inclusions were probably trapped later and indicate low-pressure fluid influx. There is a large gap between the presumed *P-T* conditions for trapping of the aqueous inclusions versus the methane-rich inclusions; this leads to a plethora of possible *P-T* paths that would cross both sets of isochores. Without any other additional constraints, one possible path is only simple decompression (path 2 in Fig. 12), as is often documented in other subduction zones (e.g., Selverstone and Spear, 1985; El-Shazly and Sisson, 1999).

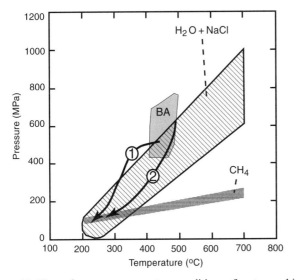

Figure 12. Plots of pressure-temperature conditions of metamorphism and various calculated isochores for the Villa de Cura belt. *P-T* conditions for the host barroisite zone (BA) shown as the gray shaded area (Smith et al., 1999). The area with the diagonal ruling indicates the range in isochores for the aqueous fluid inclusions, whereas the dark shaded area is for methane-rich fluid inclusions. The heavy lines indicate two possible *P-T* paths during subsequent exhumation and cooling: Path 1 shows isobaric cooling followed by decompression path, and 2 displays relatively isothermal decompression.

However, Smith et al. (1999) documented glaucophane overgrowths on the barroisitic amphibole and proposed an initial isobaric cooling for this zone (path 1 in Fig. 12). The fluid inclusion data neither confirms nor negates this supposition because a *P-T* path can be constructed to satisfy both this petrologic constraint and the fluid inclusion constraints (Fig. 12).

Fluid Origin

The fluid composition in the early D_{1c} veins of the Cordillera de la Costa belt near Puerto Cabello is similar to that observed in other Caribbean high-pressure terranes, such as eclogite blocks from the Samana Peninsula in the Dominican Republic (Giaramita and Sorensen, 1994) and jadeitite veins from Guatemala (Johnson and Harlow, 1999); all terranes have initial salinity below 15 wt% NaCl equivalent. In the Cordillera de la Costa belt, the composition shifts to less saline in the syn-D_{1d} ductile quartz vein. This may indicate a trend toward lower salinity during exhumation from 25 to 10 km. A decrease in salinity was also observed in the Saih Hatat eclogites of Oman (El-Shazly and Sisson, 1999) and the Shuanghe eclogites of Dabie Shan, China (Fu, 2003). A decrease in salinity may involve introduction of externally derived fluids. These could have been derived from the surrounding schists of the southern subbelt during exhumation.

This trend of decreasing salinity does not hold for the last generation of D_2 quartz-calcite veins as these are more saline. An increase in salinity is observed in other eclogitic terranes (e.g., Selverstone and Spear, 1985; Barr, 1990; Scambelluri, 1992). However, in the Cordillera de la Costa belt, this episode of brittle deformation is ~80 m.y. after the subduction zone metamorphism (Sisson et al., this volume, Chapter 3). Thus, it is probably not related to fluid flow in the subduction zone but instead to thrusting of the belt onto the Venezuelan margin. The source of the high salinity brine is unknown.

The presence of CO_2-bearing inclusions in the earliest D_{1a} vein from Araya Peninsula can be explained by the presence of graphite in the host metasediments. As is common in many metamorphic terranes, there is a later low salinity aqueous fluid. This fluid is presumably externally derived and related to the observed retrogression of biotite to chlorite.

The presence of methane-rich fluids in both high-pressure belts is unusual. In both regions, this is a late fluid and may be indicative of fluid flow from underlying basement. Both of these regions were thrust onto the Venezuelan margin between 35 and 15 Ma (Avé Lallemant and Sisson, this volume, Chapter 7). During thrusting, fluid expulsion from the underlying terranes may have been trapped as late fluids in these subduction complexes. We speculate that there are two possible sources for the methane. One scenario would involve overthrusting of the Serranía del Interior foreland sequence. To the south, near Guárico, there are gas deposits (Pérez de Armas, this volume) that could be the source of the methane. Another possibility is overthrusting of units from the west in the foreland of the Maricaibo region (Audemard, 2001). In this scenario, the La Luna Formation could be the source for the methane.

SUMMARY

The results from this fluid inclusion study are similar to previous fluid inclusion and petrographic studies for other subduction complexes. Near isothermal decompression has been documented in a wide variety of high-pressure terranes from the Alps to the Mediterranean to China as well as North America and the Caribbean (e.g., Touret, 1992; Selverstone et al., 1992; Scambelluri, 1992; Giaramita and Sorensen, 1994; Küster and Stöckhert, 1997; El-Shazly and Sisson, 1999; Gao and Klemd, 2001; Fu, 2003). Like many previous studies of metamorphic fluid inclusions, only two samples may preserve fluid inclusions that were trapped during peak metamorphic conditions; one is a barroisite-bearing sample from the Villa de Cura belt and the other is a pelitic schist from Araya Peninsula. Most of our other samples either have inclusions that underwent stretching and/or leakage or record later external influx of fluids. By integrating fluid inclusion data from two sets of veins that were related to various stages of regional deformation, we were able to further constrain the *P-T* path into various segments reflecting changes in exhumation mechanisms. In the Cordillera de la Costa belt near Puerto Cabello, there was initially isothermal decompression related to extension and plate-boundary–parallel stretching. Isobaric cooling followed this, related to the thrusting and emplacement of this belt on the northern Venezuelan margin. Further to the east on Araya Peninsula, there is a similar sequence that records an initial *P-T* path with near isothermal decompression. The final exhumation path is not as well constrained for this region as it could be either isobaric cooling or involve both cooling and decompression. The final fluid that passed through the region is methane-rich and could reflect influx of fluid from underlying units such as the Serranía del Interior fold and thrust belt or La Luna Formation.

ACKNOWLEDGMENTS

This study was partially supported by National Science Foundation grant EAR-9304377 to Avé Lallemant and Sisson. Chad Smith kindly provided the quartz vein sample from the Villa de Cura belt. We also appreciate the assistance of Marino Ostos during the fieldwork. The assistance and collaboration with Hans Avé Lallemant was essential, and he discussed many aspects of this study over many years. We appreciate the careful and insightful reviews by Will Lamb and Ken Johnson, which improved our interpretations.

REFERENCES CITED

Agard, P., Goffé, B., Touret, J.L., and Vidal, O., 2000, Retrograde mineral and fluid evolution of high-pressure metapelites (Schists lustrés unit, western Alps): Contributions to Mineralogy and Petrology, v. 140, p. 296–315, doi: 10.1007/s004100000190.

Audemard, F.E., 2001, Future petroliferous provinces of Venezuela, *in* Downey, M.W., Threet, J.C., and Morgan, W.A., eds., Petroleum provinces of the twenty-first century: American Association of Petroleum Geologists Memoir 74, p. 353–372.

Audétat, A., and Gunther, D., 1999, Mobility and H$_2$O loss from fluid inclusions in natural quartz crystals: Contributions to Mineralogy and Petrology, v. 137, p. 1–14, doi: 10.1007/s004100050578.

Avé Lallemant, H.G., 1997, Transpression, displacement partitioning, and exhumation in the eastern Caribbean–South American plate boundary zone: Tectonics, v. 16, p. 272–289, doi: 10.1029/96TC03725.

Avé Lallemant, H.G., and Guth, L.R., 1990, Role of extensional tectonics in exhumation of eclogites and blueschists in an oblique subduction setting: Northwestern Venezuela: Geology, v. 18, p. 950–953, doi: 10.1130/0091-7613(1990)018<0950:ROETIE>2.3.CO;2.

Avé Lallemant, H.G., and Sisson, V.B., 1993, Caribbean–South American plate interactions: Constraints from the Cordillera de la Costa Belt, Venezuela, *in* Pindell, J.L., and Perkins, B.F, eds., Mesozoic and early Cenozoic development of the Gulf of Mexico and Caribbean region—A context for hydrocarbon exploration, Proceedings, Gulf Coast Section, SEPM Foundation 13th Annual Research Conference: Houston, Texas, Society for Sedimentary Geology (SEPM) Foundation, p. 211–219.

Avé Lallemant, H.G., Gottschalk, R.R., Sisson, V.B., and Oldow, J.S., 1998, Structural analysis of the Kobuk Fault Zone, north-central Alaska, *in* Oldow, J.S., and Avé Lallemant, H.G., eds., Architecture of the central Brooks Range fold and thrust belt, Arctic Alaska: Geological Society of America Special Paper 324, p. 261–268.

Bakker, R.J., 2003, Package FLUIDS 1: Computer programs for analysis of fluid inclusion data and for modeling bulk fluid properties: Chemical Geology, v. 194, p. 3–23, doi: 10.1016/S0009-2541(02)00268-1.

Bakker, R.J., and Jansen, B.H., 1991, Experimental post-entrapment water loss from synthetic fluid inclusions in natural quartz: Geochimica et Cosmochimica Acta, v. 55, p. 2215–2230, doi: 10.1016/0016-7037(91)90098-P.

Barker, A.J., 1995, Post-entrapment modification of fluid inclusions due to overpressure: evidence from natural samples: Journal of Metamorphic Geology, v. 13, p. 737–750.

Barr, H., 1990, Preliminary fluid inclusion studies in a high-grade blueschist terrain, Syros, Greece: Mineralogical Magazine, v. 54, p. 159–168.

Bellizzia, A., and Dengo, G., 1990, The Caribbean Mountains system, northern South America; A summary, *in* Dengo, G., and Case, J.E., eds., The Caribbean region: Boulder, Colorado, Geological Society of America, The Geology of North America, v. H, p. 167–175.

Bellizzia, A., Pimental, N., and Bajo, R., 1976, Mapa geológico estructural de Venezuela: Caracas, Foninves, scale 1:500,000.

Bodnar, R.J., 2003a, Introduction to aqueous-electrolyte fluid inclusions, *in* Samson, I., Anderson, A., and Marshall, D., eds., Fluid inclusions: Analysis and interpretation: Mineralogical Society of Canada Short Course Series, v. 32, p. 81–100.

Bodnar, R.J., 2003b, Reequilibration of fluid inclusions, *in* Samson, I., Anderson, A., and Marshall, D., eds., Fluid inclusions: Analysis and interpretation: Mineralogical Society of Canada Short Course Series, v. 32, p. 213–231.

Bodnar, R.J., Binns, P.R., and Hall, D.L., 1989, Synthetic fluid inclusions VI: Quantitative evaluation of decrepitation behavior of fluid inclusions in quartz at one atmosphere confining pressure: Journal of Metamorphic Geology, v. 7, p. 229–242.

Bucher, K., and Frey, M., 2002, Petrogenesis of metamorphic rocks, 7th edition: Berlin, Springer, 341 p.

Cloos, M., 1982, Flow mélanges: Numerical modeling and geologic constraints on their origin in the Franciscan subduction complex: Geological Society of America Bulletin, v. 93, p. 330–345, doi: 10.1130/0016-7606(1982)93<330:FMNMAG>2.0.CO;2.

Cowan, D.S., and Schilling, R.M., 1978, A dynamic scaled model of accretion at trenches and its implications for the tectonic evolution of subduction complexes: Journal of Geophysical Research, v. 83, p. 5389–5396.

Crawford, M.L., 1981, Phase equilibria in aqueous fluid inclusions, *in* Hollister, L.S. and Crawford, M.L., eds., Short course in fluid inclusions: Applications to petrology: Mineralogical Association of Canada Short Course no. 6., p. 75–100.

Crawford, M.L., and Hollister, L.S., 1986, Metamorphic fluids: The evidence from fluid inclusions, *in* Walther, J.V. and Wood, B.J., eds., Fluid-rock interactions during metamorphism: Advances in Physical Geochemistry, v. 5, p. 1–35.

Ellero, A., Marroni, M., Padoa, E., Pandolfi, L., and Urbani, F., 2001, Deformation history of the blueschist-facies sequences from the Villa De Cura Unit (Northern Venezuela): Ofioliti, v. 26, p. 479–482.

El-Shazly, A., and Sisson, V.B., 1999, Fluid inclusion evidence for exhumation of eclogites and blueschists from Northeast Oman: Chemical Geology, v. 154, p. 193–223, doi: 10.1016/S0009-2541(98)00132-6.

El-Shazly, A.K., and Sisson, V.B., 2004, Fluid inclusions in carpholite-bearing metasediments and blueschists from NE Oman: Constraints on *P-T* evolution: European Journal of Mineralogy, v. 16, p. 221–233, doi: 10.1127/0935-1221/2004/0016-0221.

Ernst, W.G., 1988, Tectonic history of subduction zones inferred from retrograde blueschist *P-T* paths: Geology, v. 16, p. 1081–1084, doi: 10.1130/0091-7613(1988)016<1081:THOSZI>2.3.CO;2.

Ertan, I.E., Sisson, V.B., and Avé Lallemant, H.G., 1995, Metamorphic and age constraints for the Cordillera de la Costa belt, Venezuela: Geological Society of America Abstracts, v. 27, no. 6, p. 229.

Franz, L., Romer, R.L., Klemd, R., Schmid, R., Oberhänsli, R., Wagner, T., and Shuwen, D., 2001, Eclogite-facies quartz veins within metabasites of the Dabie Shan (eastern China): pressure-temperature-time–deformation path, composition of the fluid phase and fluid flow during exhumation of high-pressure rocks: Contribution to Mineralogy and Petrology, v. 141, p. 322–346.

Fu, B., 2003, Fluid regime during high- and ultrahigh-pressure metamorphism in the Dabie-Sulu terranes, Eastern China [Ph.D. Dissertation]: Vrije University, Amsterdam, 144 p.

Gao, J., and Klemd, R., 2001, Primary fluids entrapped at blueschist to eclogite transition: Evidence from the Tianshan meta-subduction complex in northwestern China: Contributions to Mineralogy and Petrology, v. 142, p. 1–14.

Giaramita, M.J., and Sorensen, S.S., 1994, Primary fluids in low-temperature eclogites: Evidence from two subduction complexes (Dominican Republic and California, USA): Contributions to Mineralogy and Petrology, v. 117, p. 279–292, doi: 10.1007/BF00310869.

Goldstein, R.H., and Reynolds, T.J., 1994, Systematics of fluid inclusions in diagenetic minerals: Society for Economic Paleontology and Mineralogy Short Course, v. 31, 199 p.

González de Juana, C., Iturralde de Arozena, J.M., and Picard, X., 1980, Geología de Venezuela y de sus cuencas petrolíferas: Caracas, Funvisis, v. 1, 407 p.

Hall, D.L., and Sterner, M.S., 1993, Preferential water loss from synthetic fluid inclusions: Contributions to Mineralogy and Petrology, v. 114, p. 489–500, doi: 10.1007/BF00321753.

Hollister, L.S., and Crawford, M.L., 1981, Short course in fluid inclusions: Applications to petrology: Mineralogical Association of Canada Short Course Series, v. 6, 304 p.

Johnson, C.A., and Harlow, G.E., 1999, Guatemala jadeitites and albitites were formed by deuterium-rich serpentinizing fluids deep within a subduction-channel: Geology, v. 27, p. 629–632, doi: 10.1130/0091-7613(1999)027<0629:GJAAWF>2.3.CO;2.

Johnson, E.L., and Hollister, L.S., 1995, Syndeformational fluid trapping in quartz: Determining the pressure-temperature conditions of deformation from fluid inclusions and the formation of pure CO_2 fluid inclusions during grain boundary migration: Journal of Metamorphic Geology, v. 13, p. 239–250.

Klemd, R., van den Kerkhof, A.M., and Horn, E.E., 1992, High-density CO_2-N_2 inclusions in eclogite facies metasediments from the Münchberg gneiss complex, SE Germany: Contributions to Mineralogy and Petrology, v. 111, p. 409–419, doi: 10.1007/BF00311200.

Krückhaus-Lueder, G., and Maresch, W.V., 1992, Hochdruckmetamorphose der pelitischen Juan-Greigo-Einheit, Insel Maragarita, Venezuela: Berichte der Deutschen Mineralogischen Gesellschaft, v. 4, p. 167.

Küster, M., and Stöckhert, B., 1997, Density changes of fluid inclusions in high-pressure low-temperature metamorphic rocks from Crete: A thermobarometric approach based on the creep strength of the host minerals: Lithos, v. 41, p. 151–167, doi: 10.1016/S0024-4937(97)82010-5.

Mann, P., and Gordon, M.B., 1996, Tectonic uplift and exhumation of blueschist belts along transpressional strike-slip fault zones, *in* Bebout, G.E., Scholl, D.W., Kirby, S.H., and Platt, J.P., eds., Subduction top to bottom: American Geophysical Union, Geophysical Monograph 96, p. 143–154.

Pavlis, T.L., Marty, K., and Sisson, V.B., 2003, Eocene dextral strike-slip within the Chugach Terrane, southern Alaska: Evidence from fabric studies along the Richardson Highway, *in* Sisson, V.B., Roeske, S.M., and Pavlis, T.P., eds., Geological consequences of ridge-trench interactions in the northern Pacific: Geological Society of America Special Publication 371, p. 171–190.

Philippot, P., and Selverstone, J., 1991, Trace-element rich brines in eclogitic veins: implications for fluid composition and transport during subduc-

tion: Contributions to Mineralogy and Petrology, v. 106, p. 417–431, doi: 10.1007/BF00321985.

Platt, J.P., 1986, Dynamics of orogenic wedges and the uplift of high-pressure metamorphic rocks: Geological Society of America Bulletin, v. 97, p. 1037–1053, doi: 10.1130/0016-7606(1986)97<1037:DOOWAT>2.0.CO;2.

Platt, J.P., Whitehouse, M.J., Kelley, S.P., Carter, A., and Hollick, L., 2003, Simultaneous extensional exhumation across the Alboran Basin: Implications for the causes of late orogenic extension: Geology, v. 31, no. 3, p. 251–254, doi: 10.1130/0091-7613(2003)031<0251:SEEATA>2.0.CO;2.

Roedder, E., 1984, Fluid inclusions: Reviews in Mineralogy, v. 12, 644 p.

Samson, I., Anderson, A., and Marshall, D., 2003, Fluid inclusions: Analysis and interpretation: Mineralogical Society of Canada Short Course Series, v. 32, 374 p.

Scambelluri, M., 1992, Retrograde fluid inclusions in eclogitic metagabbros from the Ligurian Western Alps: European Journal of Mineralogy, v. 4, p. 1097–1112.

Scambelluri, M., Pennacchioni, G., and Philippott, P., 1998, Salt-rich aqueous fluids formed during eclogitization of metabasites in the Alpine continental crust (Austroalpine Emilius unit, Italian western Alps): Lithos, v. 43, p. 151–167, doi: 10.1016/S0024-4937(98)00011-5.

Selverstone, J., and Spear, F.S., 1985, Metamorphic *P-T* paths from pelitic schists and greenstones from the south-west Tauern Window, eastern Alps: Journal of Metamorphic Geology, v. 3, p. 439–465.

Selverstone, J., Franz, G., Thomas, S., and Getty, S., 1992, Fluid variability in 2 Gpa eclogites as an indicator of fluid behavior during subduction: Contributions to Mineralogy and Petrology, v. 112, p. 341–357, doi: 10.1007/BF00310465.

Shagam, R., 1960, Geology of the central Aragua State, Venezuela: Geological Society of America Bulletin, v. 71, p. 249–302.

Sisson, V.B., Ertan, I.E., and Avé Lallemant, H.G., 1997, High pressure (~2000 MPa) kyanite- and glaucophane-bearing pelitic schist and eclogite from Cordillera de la Costa belt, Venezuela: Journal of Petrology, v. 38, p. 65–83, doi: 10.1093/petrology/38.1.65.

Smith, C.A., Sisson, V.B., Avé Lallemant, H.G., and Copeland, P., 1999, Two contrasting pressure-temperature-time paths in the Villa de Cura blueschist belt, Venezuela: Possible evidence for Late Cretaceous initiation of subduction in the Caribbean: Geological Society of America Bulletin, v. 111, p. 831–848, doi: 10.1130/0016-7606(1999)111<0831:TCPTTP>2.3.CO;2.

Sorensen, S.S., and Barton, M.D., 1987, Metasomatism and partial melting in a subduction complex: Catalina Schist, southern California: Geology, v. 15, p. 115–118, doi: 10.1130/0091-7613(1987)15<115:MAPMIA>2.0.CO;2.

Speed, R.C., Sharp, W.D., and Foland, K.A., 1997, Late Paleozoic granitoid gneisses of the Northeastern Venezuela and the North America–Gondwana collision zone: Journal of Geology, v. 105, p. 457–470.

Stephan, J.F., 1982, Andes et chaine Caraibe sur la transversale de Barquisimeto (Venezuela); Evolution Geodynamique: Symposium Geodynamique des Caraibes, p. 505–529.

Sterner, M.L., Hall, D.L., and Keppler, H., 1995, Compositional re-equilibration of fluid inclusions in quartz: Contributions to Mineralogy and Petrology, v. 119, p. 1–15.

Stöckhert, B., Maresch, W.V., Brix, M., Kaiser, C., Toetz, A., Kluge, R., and Krückhaus-Lueder, G., 1995, Crustal history of Margarita Island (Venezuela) in detail: Constraints on the Caribbean plate-tectonic scenario: Geology, v. 23, p. 787–790, doi: 10.1130/0091-7613(1995)023<0787:CHOMIV>2.3.CO;2.

Touret, J.L.R., 1992, Fluid inclusions in subducted rocks: Proceedings of the Koninklijke Nederlandse Akademie Van Wetenschappen, v. 95, p. 385–403.

Vityk, M., and Bodnar, R.J., 1995, Do fluid inclusions in high-grade metamorphic terrains preserve peak metamorphic density during retrograde decompression?: American Mineralogist, v. 80, p. 641–644.

Vrolijk, P., 1987, Tectonically driven fluid flow in the Kodiak accretionary complex, Alaska: Geology, v. 15, p. 466–469, doi: 10.1130/0091-7613(1987)15<466:TDFFIT>2.0.CO;2.

Weinberger, J., and Sisson, V.B., 2003, Fluid inclusion study of the brittle-ductile transition in the Chugach Metamorphic Complex, *in* Sisson, V.B., Roeske, S.M., Pavlis, T.P., eds., Geological consequences of ridge-trench interactions in the northern Pacific: Geological Society of America Special Paper 371, p. 217–236.

Ysaccis, R., 1997, Tertiary evolution of the northeastern Venezuela offshore [Ph.D. Dissertation]: Houston, Texas, Rice University, 285 p.

MANUSCRIPT ACCEPTED BY THE SOCIETY 5 APRIL 2005

Geological Society of America
Special Paper 394
2005

Geochemical evidence for possible trench provenance and fluid-rock histories, Cordillera de la Costa eclogite belt, Venezuela

Sorena S. Sorensen*

Department of Mineral Sciences, NHB-119, National Museum of Natural History, Smithsonian Institution, Washington, D.C. 20560-0119, USA

Virginia B. Sisson*

Hans G. Avé Lallemant*

Department of Earth Science, MS-126, Rice University, Houston, Texas 77005, USA

ABSTRACT

The Cordillera de la Costa eclogite belt, exposed along the Caribbean coastline of Venezuela near Puerto Cabello, consists of lensoid bodies and boudins of high pressure-temperature (P-T) metabasite in a heterogeneous matrix of mica schist and metacarbonate rocks. The metabasite bodies consist of eclogite and its retrogression products. Data for less mobile elements indicate that protoliths ranged from normal mid-oceanic-ridge basalt (N-MORB), to enriched (E)-MORB, to cumulate gabbro. Some eclogites and their retrogression products are enriched in large ion lithophile elements (LILE). The covariations of K and Ba are evidence that these elements were most likely incorporated into phengite, which has textures that suggest it crystallized from retrograde fluids. A similar style of LILE enrichment is also documented for eclogites of the Samana Peninsula, Dominican Republic, but not in eclogites from Isla de Margarita, Venezuela. Low-T, K-metasomatized basalts from the Bermuda Rise display different K-Ba systematics than the eclogite suites, which suggests that LILE enrichment of the latter rocks was not merely inherited from altered protoliths. In contrast to the LILE-enriched eclogites, some Cordillera de la Costa belt eclogite bodies have apparently been stripped of K, Rb, Ba, and U. Some metasedimentary rocks, in an outcrop that also contains LILE-poor metabasite, also show extreme LILE depletion relative to counterparts elsewhere in the Cordillera de la Costa. In this outcrop, LILE are most conspicuously depleted in a lens of kyanite + glaucophane schist that formed at $P > 20$ kb, $T \sim 600$ °C. Although the rock has Al/Si ratios, rare earth element, and high field strength element abundances comparable to shale, it contains <0.3 wt% K_2O.

Some rocks of the Cordillera de la Costa eclogite belt thus appear to record LILE expulsion, probably at the "peak" P-T conditions of $P > 20$ kb at $T \sim 600$ °C, whereas others chronicle LILE enrichment during retrogression at lower P-T conditions. Some outcrops show both effects. In a few outcrops, eclogitic blocks that appear to be LILE-depleted occur in metasedimentary host rocks that are not.

Keywords: Venezuela, trace elements, eclogite, garnet amphibolite, Cordillera de la Costa.

*E-mails: sorena@volcano.si.edu; j_sisson@netzero.com; ave@rice.edu

Sorensen, S.S., Sisson, V.B., and Avé Lallemant, H.G., 2005, Geochemical evidence for possible trench provenance and fluid-rock histories, Cordillera de la Costa eclogite belt, Venezuela, *in* Avé Lallemant, H.G., and Sisson, V.B., eds., Caribbean–South American plate interactions, Venezuela: Geological Society of America Special Paper 394, p. 173–192, doi: 10.1130/2005.SPE394(06). For permission to copy, contact editing@geosociety.org. ©2005 Geological Society of America.

173

INTRODUCTION

Geochemical studies of mafic rocks from subduction-zone metamorphic terranes can provide information about likely protoliths and may also document fluid-rock processes that affected the rocks during metamorphism. Subduction-related metasomatic effects identified by geochemical studies of circum-Pacific and Caribbean eclogites and related rocks include (1) the migration of rare earth elements (REE) and high field strength elements (HFSE) on the scale of decimeters to meters to produce hydrothermal rutile, titanite, zircon, and allanite in high pressure-temperature (*P-T*) garnet amphibolites (Sorensen and Grossman, 1989, 1993; Sorensen, 1991); (2) alteration of square kilometers of meta-ultramafic mélange host rock and enclosed blocks to the $\delta^{18}O$ signatures of sediment-derived fluids (Bebout and Barton, 1989, 1993); (3) hybridization via exchange between mafic blocks and meta-ultramafic mélange host rocks (Sorensen and Grossman, 1989; Bebout and Barton, 1993); (4) formation of aluminous enclaves within meta-ultramafic mélange as residues from the stripping of volatiles from metasedimentary rock protoliths (Bebout and Barton, 1993); and (5) K-metasomatism of eclogites and related rocks (Sorensen et al., 1997). Fluid inclusion studies have identified low salinity aqueous inclusions with seawater-like NaCl-equivalent compositions in K-metasomatized eclogites from the Dominican Republic and California (Giaramita and Sorensen, 1994), in metasomatized garnet amphibolites from California (Sorensen and Barton, 1987), and in metasomatic jadeitite from Guatemala, which is associated with eclogite and other high *P-T* metamorphic rocks (Harlow, 1994; Johnson and Harlow, 1999). Thus, some styles of

subduction zone metasomatism are apparently linked to the most basic hydrologic process of subduction: the recycling of seawater from the slab and subducted sediment into the mantle and ultimately into arc magmas.

Metasomatic effects can disguise the identities of protoliths and prevent accurate classification of the original tectono-magmatic settings of blueschists and eclogites. This can hamper basic interpretations of the tectonostratigraphic nature of the orogen. Subduction processes have produced blueschists and eclogites in tectonostratigraphic settings of (1) trench sediments and ocean floor sediments on a downgoing, broadly tholeiitic basalt slab, decorated with seamounts and atolls (Franciscan Complex and Pelona Schist, California; e.g., Bailey et al., 1964; Ernst, 1970; Cloos, 1984; MacPherson et al., 1990; Jacobson et al., 2000); (2) near-continent, miogeoclinal sedimentary rocks intruded by tholeiitic basalts (many Alpine and Cycladic localities; e.g., Miller et al., 1988; Okrusch and Broecker, 1990; Stosch and Lugmair, 1990; Meyre et al., 1999); or (3) a volcanic arc sequence erupted in a carbonate-rich environment (Samana Peninsula, Dominican Republic; e.g., Lewis and Draper, 1990; Joyce, 1991).

The arc-derived, K-metasomatized eclogites of the Samana Peninsula, Dominican Republic, represent only one of the high *P-T* metamorphic terranes that are distributed along both the northern and southern margins of the Caribbean plate (Bocchio et al., 1990; Lewis and Draper, 1990; Beccaluva et al., 1996; Avé Lallemant, 1997; Gonçalves et al., 2000; Fig. 1 inset). Both of these plate boundaries are now transcurrent fault zones (e.g., Avé Lallemant and Guth, 1990; Pindell, 1993; Pindell et al., this volume). Low-tem-

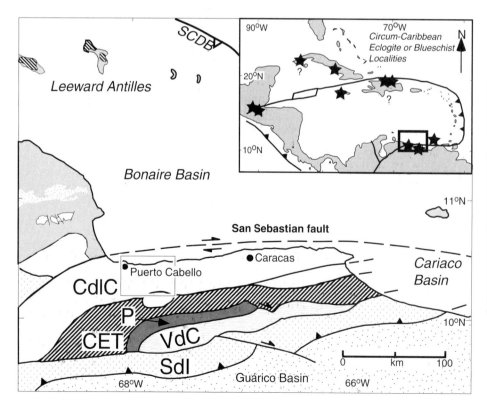

Figure 1. Regional map of the lithotectonic belts of northern Venezuela in the western Caribbean mountain system (after Smith et al., 1999; Bellizzia et al., 1976) with an inset of circum-Caribbean eclogite or blueschist localities. (For a detailed description of unlabeled units, see Figure 1 of Smith et al., 1999.) The two high *P-T* belts in the system are the eclogite-bearing Cordillera de la Costa (CdlC) and the blueschist to transitional high-*P* greenschist facies Villa de Cura (VdC). For further discussion of the latter, see Smith et al. (1999). CET—Caucagua–El Tinaco belt; IM—Isla de Margarita; P—Paracotos belt; SDI—Serranía del Interior belt; SCDB—South Caribbean deformed belt.

perature eclogite has been reported from (1) the Motagua fault zone, Guatemala (McBirney et al., 1967; Bertrand and Vuagnat, 1980; Harlow, 1994; Beccaluva et al., 1995); (2) the southern coastal mountains of Cuba (Kubovics et al., 1989); (3) Samana Peninsula and Río San Juan drainage basin, Dominican Republic (Joyce, 1991; Giaramita and Sorensen, 1994); and (4) the Cordillera de la Costa belt and Isla de Margarita, Venezuela (Morgan, 1970; Maresch and Abraham, 1981; Mottana et al., 1985; Bocchio et al., 1990, 1996). These localities, and the blueschist terranes of Jamaica and northern Venezuela (Draper, 1986; Smith et al., 1999; Unger et al., this volume), are shown in the inset to Figure 1. In general, all the high *P-T* terranes of the Caribbean plate are poorly exposed; once exposed (as, for example, in roadcuts), they readily degrade through tropical weathering. Only coastal cliffs and bluffs, recent roadcuts, and riverbeds preserve much information about outcrop-scale relationships, let alone provide samples that are adequate for petrologic and geochemical studies.

Tropical weathering notwithstanding, the eclogites of the Samana Peninsula, Dominican Republic, and Isla de Margarita, Venezuela, have been analyzed for major, minor, and trace elements (Mottana et al., 1985; Bocchio et al., 1990; Sorensen et al., 1997; Ostos and Sisson, this volume). The two localities display marked contrasts in protoliths, geochemical signatures, and probable metasomatic histories. Eclogites of the Samana Peninsula, with less mobile element signatures of arc basalt protoliths, were metamorphosed at $P = 8–10$ kb, $T = 500–600$ °C (Giaramita and Sorensen, 1994). As was noted above, omphacite grains in these rocks contain primary fluid inclusions with seawater-like salinities, which were incorporated during the crystallization of omphacite + garnet assemblages (Giaramita and Sorensen, 1994). Links among the large ion lithophile element (LILE) systematics, textures, and compositions of phengite in the rocks, along with the domainal mineral assemblages that are associated with phengite, indicate that K-metasomatism of the Samana eclogites took place under a range of conditions, from eclogite to blueschist facies (Sorensen et al., 1997).

Eclogites from Isla de Margarita, with likely mid-oceanic-ridge basalt (MORB) protoliths, are estimated to have been metamorphosed at $P = \sim12–19$ kb, $T = 450–650$ °C (Maresch and Abraham, 1981; Bocchio et al., 1996). In contrast to Samana eclogites, the LILE data for Isla de Margarita (Mottana et al., 1985; Bocchio et al., 1990) show few systematics, although these are disrupted compared to MORB. This study is an overview of the geochemistry of eclogite bodies and their metasedimentary host rocks from five localities within the Cordillera de la Costa belt, Venezuela, and also a general comparison of these data with the Isla de Margarita and Samana eclogite (± host rocks) suites. Our purposes are to elucidate information about eclogite protoliths for the Cordillera de la Costa belt, characterize alteration features, and contrast the alteration histories of the three terranes.

REGIONAL CONTEXT AND DEFORMATION HISTORY OF THE CORDILLERA DE LA COSTA ECLOGITE BELT

The eclogite- and blueschist-bearing Cordillera de la Costa belt in northern Venezuela, like the eclogite-bearing terrane of Isla de Margarita, is an east-west–trending lithotectonic unit that forms part of the boundary zone between the Caribbean and South American plates (Fig. 1; e.g., Avé Lallemant and Guth, 1990). The Cordillera de la Costa belt consists of eclogite and mica schist, metamorphosed mafic volcanic rocks, and serpentinite, along with units of marble, quartzofeldspathic gneiss, granite, and graphite schist (Fig. 2). Outcrops of the Cordillera de la Costa belt were described in detail by Bellizzia (1986) to be mixtures of "oceanic" (eclogite and blueschist) and "continental-margin" rocks (metamorphosed limestone, metamorphosed carbonaceous sedimentary rock, quartzite, and granite). The eclogite bodies are boudins, blocks, and lenses that occur on a scale of 3 cm to tens of meters. Many boudins consist of cores of eclogite that are encased in selvages of barroisite-rich eclogite or blueschist. Eclogite-bearing units in the Cordillera de la Costa are confined to a narrow belt along the northern coast of Venezuela (Fig. 2). The eclogite-bearing belt is juxtaposed against lower temperature schists of the Cordillera de la Costa belt to the south.

The Cordillera de la Costa eclogite belt underwent intense deformation, which produced five synmetamorphic generations of deformation structures (Avé Lallemant and Sisson, this volume, Chapter 7). Blueschist and eclogite boudins occur within calcareous pelitic schists (Morgan, 1970; Avé Lallemant and Sisson, 1993; Sisson et al., 1997). The boudins were retrograded at epidote-amphibolite to high-pressure (barroisite-bearing) greenschist-facies conditions. In addition to the eclogitic high *P-T* mafic rocks, glaucophane-bearing kyanite schist boudins and lenses are found within calcareous pelitic schists in a single locality of the Cordillera de la Costa belt (Sisson et al., 1997; Autopista Locality, Tables 1 and 2). Petrologic and geothermobarometric results show that glaucophane + kyanite-bearing pelitic schists likely formed at $P > 20$ kb and $T > 630$ °C (Ertan et al., 1995; Sisson et al., 1997). Results from the geothermobarometers of Ellis and Green (1979) and Massonne and Schreyer (1987) indicate that the first phase of deformation took place under relatively high-pressure eclogite facies conditions (500–700 °C at ~20–22 kb). The second to fifth phases of deformation occurred under decreasing temperatures and pressures, following an "Alpine-type" (Ernst, 1988) uplift and decompression path.

The "continental margin" matrix of the eclogite bodies, and the volumetrically most abundant unit of the Cordillera de la Costa eclogite belt, is a mixture of metasedimentary rocks: graphite schist, garnet schist, and mica schist, and marble, quartzite, and quartz-feldspar gneiss. Bellizzia (1986) suggested that because the protoliths of the metasedimentary rocks were a continental margin sequence, they had probably been deposited on the passive continental margin of northern South America and that they were less allochthonous with respect to South America than the eclogites and blueschists.

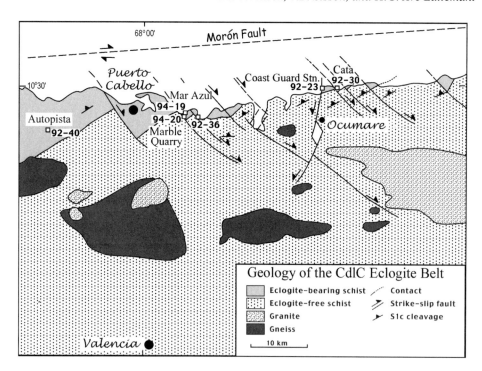

Figure 2. Simplified geologic map of the Cordillera de la Costa (CdlC) eclogite belt, which shows the localities that were sampled for this work (marked by sample numbers). The Cordillera de la Costa belt is subdivided into a northern eclogite-bearing schist unit and a southern, eclogite-free unit.

TABLE 1. LOCATIONS OF VENEZUELAN SAMPLES FOR GEOCHEMICAL ANALYSES

Sample	Latitude	Longitude	State	Town	Geographic feature	Previous sample number
92VSn23	10°29'56"	67°46'27"	Aragua	Independencia (Ocumare)	Coast Guard Point	91VSn61
92VSn30a	10°30'06"	67°44'31"	Aragua	Cata	Punta de Cata	
92VSn30d	10°30'06"	67°44'31"	Aragua	Cata	Ensenada de Cata	
92VSn36	10°28'07"	67°55'47"	Carabobo	Patanemo	Punta Patanemo	91VSn40
92VSn36a	10°28'07"	67°55'47"	Carabobo	Patanemo	Punta Patanemo	91VSn40
92VSn36e	10°28'07"	67°55'47"	Carabobo	Patanemo	Punta Patanemo	91VSn40
92VSn36f	10°28'07"	67°55'47"	Carabobo	Patanemo	Punta Patanemo	91VSn40
92VSn40	10°27'10"	68°06'54"	Carabobo	Taborda	on road to La Pastora	
94VSn17	10°26'55"	68°05'39"	Carabobo	El Cambur	marble plant	91VSn39, 92VSn14
94VSn18	10°27'10"	68°05'54"	Carabobo	La Pastora	toll booth	91VSn13, 92VSn40
94VSn19	10°28'07"	67°56'27"	Carabobo	Mar Azul-Borburata	garbage dump	91VSn3
94VSn20	10°27'31"	67°56'35"	Carabobo	Mar Azul-Borburata	marble quarry	
94VSn23	10°28'14"	67°55'44"	Carabobo	Patanemo	Punta Patanemo	near 91VSn41 & 92VSn37

GEOLOGICAL SETTING OF THE ECLOGITES

In 1967, B.A. Morgan first reported eclogites from the Puerto Cabello region in his Ph.D. thesis. He documented 18 localities, all in the northern part of the Cordillera de la Costa belt (Fig. 1). Some of these are no longer accessible; they have either been quarried or covered by urban development. At two of Morgan's localities, eclogite has been used as building material. The most impressive is a colonial-era Spanish *fortaleza* (Fortín Solano) that is presently an historic park, and the other is a modern seawall around a Venezuelan naval station. Sisson et al. (1997) reported three additional eclogite localities, all near Ocumare, east of Puerto Cabello. We sampled six localities (Table 1; Fig. 2).

Locality and Sample Descriptions

Cata (92VSn30a, b)

On the west side of the bay at Punta Cata (near Ocumare: Table 1; Fig. 2), a thick section of alternating quartz-graphite schist and quartzofeldspathic gneiss contains sparse eclogite blocks, generally <1 m in diameter. On the point itself, in rugged sea cliffs, a layer of bluish-gray marble contains more abundant, 1–1.5 m eclogite blocks. Samples from two of these were analyzed (92VSn30a, b).

The Coast Guard Station at Independencia (near Ocumare; Samples 92VSn23a, b, and c)

On a steep and rugged set of sea cliffs north of the Coast Guard station (Table 1; Fig. 2), a few decimeter-sized to several meter-sized boudins occur in a mica schist matrix that locally contains rotated garnets. A lens of serpentinite is located just land-

TABLE 2. MAJOR, MINOR, AND TRACE ELEMENT ANALYSES OF ECLOGITES AND RELATED ROCKS FROM CORDILLERA DE LA COSTA, VENEZUELA

Oxides/elements	SiO_2	TiO_2	Al_2O_3	Fe_2O_3	FeO	MnO	MgO	CaO	Na_2O	K_2O	P_2O_5	S	LOI	Total
Units	wt%	wt%	wt%	wt%	wt%	wt%	wt%	wt%	wt%	wt%	wt%	wt%	wt%	wt%
Sample name														
Cata locality														
92VSn30a-mb	52.0	1.54	13.2	2.7	11.5	0.25	7.1	9.5	3.1	0.04	0.12	<0.1	<0.07	101.0
92VSn30b-mb	50.5	1.38	13.6	3.3	10.0	0.20	6.8	11.5	3.1	0.02	0.10	0.38	<0.1	100.8
Coast Guard Station														
92VSn23a-mb	49.9	1.34	14.3	2.4	7.4	0.18	7.1	11.4	3.5	0.56	0.17	<0.1	2.44	100.7
92VSn23b-mb	50.2	1.33	14.2	2.1	7.6	0.17	7.1	11.0	3.9	0.47	0.17	<0.1	2.09	100.3
92VSn23c-mb	50.5	1.25	14.1	2.3	7.5	0.17	7.4	11.0	3.9	0.18	0.16	<0.1	2.14	100.6
Mar Azul locality														
94VSn40b-mb	49.4	1.08	16.0	2.0	8.3	0.18	8.1	12.1	1.9	0.62	0.09	<0.1	0.46	100.2
94VSn19-vein	54.6	0.12	4.9	2.5	7.2	0.14	16.9	10.0	2.1	0.09	0.01	<0.1	1.27	99.9
94VSn19b1-mat	77.4	0.58	10.7	1.3	1.4	0.02	2.3	0.3	1.7	2.02	0.07	<0.1	2.59	100.3
94VSn19b2-mat	79.6	0.52	9.8	0.9	1.3	0.01	2.1	0.2	1.8	1.67	0.06	<0.1	2.17	100.2
Punta Pantanemo (locality 92-36; Fig. 2)														
92VSn36a dk	52.8	0.67	15.4	4.4	2.5	0.08	2.3	13.1	0.1	0.62	0.11	0.36	6.77	99.2
92VSn36a lt	50.5	1.29	15.5	2.1	4.8	0.09	3.3	13.6	0.6	0.24	0.19	<0.1	8.12	100.3
92VSn36a both	49.7	0.75	15.5	3.6	3.3	0.09	3.0	14.4	0.3	0.29	0.16	0.19	8.49	99.7
92VSn36f-mb	49.4	1.23	14.3	5.5	5.5	0.13	8.2	9.6	3.9	0.02	0.11	<0.1	2.26	100.2
94VSn23a-mb	48.8	0.87	4.8	21.2	3.4	0.04	2.2	5.0	0.1	0.07	0.05	14.49	14	114.5
94VSn23c1-vein	45.1	0.67	12.8	8.7	0.0	0.10	9.0	5.6	3.5	0.08	0.08	2.84	2.04	90.5
94VSn23c2-mb	48.1	1.35	13.8	5.3	6.7	0.15	8.2	9.1	3.7	0.03	0.11	0.29	1.96	99.0
Marble Quarry locality														
94VSn20a-mat	<2	<0.03	0.1	<0.1	0.2	0.33	18.8	35.3	0.0	<0.01	0.03	<0.1	45.07	99.9
94VSn20b-mat	<2	<0.03	0.3	0.2	0.2	0.03	22.0	32.4	0.0	<0.01	0.04	<0.1	45.46	100.7
94VSn20c-mb	48.5	0.44	16.4	1.2	4.9	0.09	11.4	7.9	3.0	0.89	0.04	<0.1	4.87	99.7
94VSn20d-mb	50.1	0.46	16.7	1.3	4.4	0.08	10.8	8.4	2.3	1.82	0.04	<0.1	3.35	99.7
94VSn20e	32.7	0.70	9.4	2.3	3.0	0.08	11.9	22.0	0.3	0.23	0.05	<0.1	16.79	99.5
Autopista locality														
92VS40 all-mb	51.7	1.36	14.6	3.0	9.0	0.19	7.0	11.2	2.3	0.02	0.13	<0.1	0.33	101.0
92VS40 ox-mb	54.9	1.34	14.8	4.5	7.8	0.19	4.8	10.5	1.4	<0.01	0.21	<0.1	0.43	100.9
92VS40 gt-pyx-mb	52.1	1.36	14.6	2.8	9.2	0.19	6.7	11.1	2.4	<0.01	0.12	<0.1	0.38	101.0
92VS40 amph-mb	51.2	1.38	14.7	1.8	9.9	0.20	7.8	11.1	2.5	0.12	0.11	<0.1	0.23	101.2
94VSn18-mat	83.4	0.46	8.5	0.8	0.9	0.00	1.7	0.2	2.9	0.16	0.03	<0.1	1.22	100.3
94VSn18a1a-ms	57.3	0.90	16.0	1.4	6.1	0.04	10.6	1.0	5.1	0.28	0.06	<0.1	1.81	100.7
94VSn18a1c-ms	60.6	0.82	14.4	1.3	4.8	0.02	10.4	0.7	5.1	0.21	0.04	<0.1	2.06	100.3
94VSn18a2a-ms	62.8	0.85	14.2	1.2	5.7	0.03	8.9	0.6	4.2	0.24	0.04	<0.1	1.57	100.4
94VSn18cboth-mat	25.4	0.39	8.1	3.0	0.8	0.11	3.0	30.5	0.5	1.72	0.09	1.34	21.37	96.3
94VSn18c band	16.6	0.27	5.1	2.3	1.0	0.13	3.3	37.0	0.2	1.13	0.09	1.34	27.79	96.3
94VSn18c matrix	30.6	0.51	10.4	3.4	1.0	0.10	2.9	26.0	0.7	2.01	0.09	1.85	16.01	95.5

Continued

TABLE 2. MAJOR, MINOR, AND TRACE ELEMENT ANALYSES OF ECLOGITES AND RELATED ROCKS FROM CORDILLERA DE LA COSTA, VENEZUELA (continued)

Oxides/elements	Sc	V	Cr	Co	Ni	Cu	Zn	As	Rb	Sr	Y	Zr	Nb	Sb
Units	ppm	ppm	ppm	ppm	ppm	ppm	ppm	ppm	ppm	ppm	ppm	ppm	ppm	ppm
Sample name														
Cata locality														
92VSn30a-mb	50.4	469	18	45	48	51	165	1.18	<3	121	38	81	<2	0.12
92VSn30b-mb	47.6	417	58	53	55	163	110	<0.7	<3	155	36	72	5	<0.1
Coast Guard Station														
92VSn23a-mb	39.3	334	162	37	78	76	97	5.40	31	184	26	89	17	0.24
92VSn23b-mb	39.0	333	153	39	82	75	99	3.53	23	153	27	94	16	0.19
92VSn23c-mb	38.8	325	160	34	75	62	117	2.81	6	187	26	98	14	0.35
Mar Azul locality														
94VSn40b-mb	42.7	353	288	33	143	55	105	<0.5	15	69	28	61	7	<0.07
94VSn19-vein	20.7	222	76	20	270	20	210	<0.4	<3	<20	2	13	<2	<0.06
94VSn19b1-mat	8.5	61	37	8	14	15	47	1.01	76	52	18	329	15	0.10
94VSn19b2-mat	6.9	48	28	6	8	12	30	<0.9	64	46	18	352	15	0.12
Punta Pantanemo (locality 92-36; Fig. 2)														
92VSn36a dk	18.5	140	86	29	44	168	55	0.67	38	655	33	143	22	0.35
92VSn36a lt	33.8	310	177	24	53	126	54	1.04	17	691	20	83	11	0.15
92VSn36a both	22.7	215	113	26	55	130	64	0.48	17	729	31	123	14	0.33
92VSn36f-mb	42.9	366	284	46	134	115	100	<0.7	<3	172	31	72	7	0.16
94VSn23a-mb	0.0	77	70	239	23	1069	16	na	3	125	9	33	<2	na
94VSn23c1-vein	0.0	246	165	68	72	441	60	na	<3	104	21	73	8	na
94VSn23c2-mb	0.0	421	300	37	112	87	355	na	<3	272	38	81	6	na
Marble Quarry locality														
94VSn20a-mat	0.2	<10	1	0	7	6	8	0.40	<3	139	<2	<10	<2	0.04
94VSn20b-mat	0.3	<10	2	0	6	10	7	2.15	<3	112	3	10	8	0.07
94VSn20c-mb	35.1	219	454	19	133	18	98	17.76	35	162	13	35	<2	<0.23
94VSn20d-mb	36.4	201	452	17	113	11	84	11.58	70	182	13	29	5	0.16
94VSn20e	22.9	179	284	24	138	14	73	3.54	11	116	21	67	<2	0.18
Autopista locality														
92VS40 all-mb	44.7	400	299	49	160	105	109	<0.6	<3	146	33	84	6	<0.08
92VS40 ox-mb	43.0	389	296	70	146	186	81	1.13	3	397	36	96	8	0.09
92VS40 gt-pyx-mb	45.0	407	302	42	133	104	103	<0.6	<3	124	34	75	5	<0.2
92VS40 amph-mb	45.2	397	301	37	145	58	120	<0.6	4	84	35	76	5	0.26
94VSn18-mat	5.3	45	27	3	8	7	11	1.13	5	68	18	279	17	0.07
94VSn18a1a-ms	17.8	111	94	14	64	7	28	<0.7	8	21	23	292	19	0.20
94VSn18a1c-ms	13.0	119	81	13	48	<5	20	1.67	8	<20	19	327	17	<0.2
94VSn18a2a-ms	16.8	111	88	12	49	<5	17	<0.8	8	<20	24	322	17	<0.07
94VSn18cboth-mat	8.3	91	40	10	31	46	302	6.58	99	1727	23	145	12	0.07
94VSn18c band	4.8	64	26	7	28	27	298	5.17	65	2109	19	145	9	<0.04
94VSn18c matrix	11.7	111	52	12	33	56	321	7.51	111	1453	27	169	17	0.09

Continued

TABLE 2. MAJOR, MINOR, AND TRACE ELEMENT ANALYSES OF ECLOGITES AND RELATED ROCKS FROM CORDILLERA DE LA COSTA, VENEZUELA (continued)

Oxides/elements	Cs	Ba	La	Ce	Nd	Sm	Eu	Tb	Yb	Lu	Hf	Ta	Th	U
Units	ppm	ppm	ppm	ppm	ppm	ppm	ppm	ppm	ppm	ppm	ppm	ppm	ppm	ppm
Sample name														
Cata locality														
92VSn30a-mb	<0.13	<40	2.0	6.2	5.8	3.0	0.96	0.86	4.33	0.65	2.27	0.09	<0.11	<0.31
92VSn30b-mb	0.20	<40	1.9	5.8	6.2	2.9	1.04	0.84	3.95	0.57	1.94	0.08	0.2	<0.29
Coast Guard Station														
92VSn23a-mb	0.93	83	10.0	20.8	12.7	3.2	0.93	0.64	2.91	0.42	2.28	1.15	1.2	0.35
92VSn23b-mb	0.87	80	9.4	20.7	11.3	3.2	0.96	0.64	2.75	0.39	2.25	1.09	1.1	0.44
92VSn23c-mb	0.30	<40	9.5	19.6	11.5	3.2	1.02	0.63	2.63	0.42	2.00	1.03	1.0	0.35
Mar Azul locality														
94VSn40b-mb	0.37	90	2.8	7.5	5.9	2.23	0.79	0.59	2.98	0.44	1.61	0.26	0.2	<0.23
94VSn19-vein	<0.09	<30	0.1	<1	<1.40	0.0	<0.02	<0.04	0.14	0.02	0.14	<0.06	<0.09	<0.07
94VSn19b1-mat	2.10	282	27.1	53.8	21.7	4.66	0.79	0.57	2.04	0.30	9.26	1.20	10.9	1.61
94VSn19b2-mat	1.63	216	26.8	51.8	21.0	4.54	0.75	0.54	2.00	0.30	10.34	1.08	10.3	1.60
Punta Pantanemo (locality 92-36; Fig. 2)														
92VSn36a dk	1.16	109	35.6	70.9	29.1	6.7	1.46	0.89	3.28	0.46	3.38	1.38	12.5	4.34
92VSn36a lt	0.69	54	7.3	16.7	10.2	3.8	1.25	0.67	2.41	0.38	1.58	0.55	1.4	0.49
92VSn36a both	0.58	41	22.7	45.7	20.7	5.3	1.37	0.78	3.00	0.43	2.75	0.93	7.9	2.69
92VSn36f-mb	0.23	<40	3.4	8.8	7.0	2.9	0.98	0.75	2.98	0.45	1.93	0.33	0.4	<0.23
94VSn23a-mb	na	142	na	na	na	na	na	na	na	na	na	na	na	na
94VSn23c1-vein	na	92	na	na	na	na	na	na	na	na	na	na	na	na
94VSn23c2-mb	na	<40	na	na	na	na	na	na	na	na	na	na	na	na
Marble Quarry locality														
94VSn20a-mat	0.03	<40	0.5	0.9	<1.3	0.08	0.05	0.01	0.04	0.01	0.05	0.02	0.1	0.27
94VSn20b-mat	0.05	19	0.8	1.6	0.9	0.17	0.03	0.03	0.09	0.02	0.09	0.02	0.2	0.95
94VSn20c-mb	1.03	210	1.4	3.2	2.5	1.02	0.27	0.22	1.51	0.18	0.87	<0.06	0.4	0.32
94VSn20d-mb	2.04	395	1.6	4.5	2.7	1.13	0.29	0.28	1.42	0.20	0.75	0.10	0.3	0.27
94VSn20e	1.18	49	1.9	6.5	4.9	1.57	0.31	0.37	1.78	0.27	1.31	0.12	0.9	0.27
Autopista locality														
92VS40 all-mb	0.16	<40	3.3	8.3	7.0	3.0	1.06	0.81	3.86	0.57	2.03	0.22	0.2	0.33
92VS40 ox-mb	0.16	<40	4.6	12.5	11.3	4.7	1.65	0.89	3.75	0.58	2.08	0.26	0.4	0.73
92VS40 gt-pyx-mb	<0.12	<40	2.7	7.2	6.2	2.6	0.93	0.80	3.85	0.57	2.06	0.28	0.2	0.37
92VS40.amph-mb	0.29	79	2.7	7.9	6.8	2.5	0.91	0.84	3.93	0.59	2.13	0.25	0.3	0.14
94VSn18-mat	1.66	39	15.9	39.8	12.1	2.8	0.40	0.44	2.08	0.30	8.02	0.95	8.4	1.38
94VSn18a1a-ms	0.97	47	29.7	60.5	23.9	4.9	0.52	0.63	2.72	0.40	8.23	1.71	15.2	2.47
94VSn18a1c-ms	0.58	38	29.5	57.5	23.9	4.7	0.47	0.55	2.09	0.32	8.85	1.42	12.0	2.24
94VSn18a2a-ms	0.90	51	28.6	59.0	22.9	4.7	0.49	0.63	2.90	0.42	9.20	1.43	12.7	2.43
94VSn18cboth-mat	2.70	315	22.3	42.2	18.2	4.1	0.77	0.50	1.74	0.26	2.77	0.76	6.9	3.08
94VSn18c band	1.72	205	15.5	29.7	13.7	2.9	0.59	0.38	1.25	0.19	2.06	0.48	4.5	2.28
94VSn18c matrix	3.10	375	28.7	53.9	24.4	5.2	0.94	0.66	2.30	0.33	3.22	1.02	9.1	3.75

Note: The symbol "<" indicates that the detection limit for the element is that value; see text. LOI: loss on ignition; amph—amphibole; dk—dark-colored; gt—garnet; lt—light-colored; mat—matrix; mb—metabasite; ms—metasedimentary rock; na—not analyzed; ox—oxidized; pyx—pyroxene.

ward of the eclogite blocks. Two of these blocks were sampled. Samples 92VSn23a and b are from a single, large block (3–4 m in diameter) that forms the most landward exposure of eclogite. Sample 92VSn23c is from a 1-m-diameter block located a few meters seaward of the larger one.

Mar Azul (94VSn19; also described in Sisson et al. 1997 as 91VSn21)

These outcrops (Table 1; Fig. 2), again in ruggedly weathered sea cliffs, consist of two types of matrix. The most landward "unit" is a schist body notable for "fish," up to 3 cm long, of aggregates of graphite grains. This matrix rock contains sparse, generally <0.5-m-diameter boudins of eclogite. Seaward, a more quartzofeldspathic schist contains boudins that consist of cores of eclogite with thick margins of barroisite amphibolite. Outcrop and thin section relationships suggest that the amphibolite is retrogressed eclogite (also see Sisson et al., 1997). Spectacular assemblages of siderite + rutile (grains >1 cm long) + sulfide minerals + zoisite (grains up to 15 cm long) vein the boudins and form pressure shadows on them. Samples of a 1–2 m boudin (94VSn40b), quartzofeldspathic schist matrix (94VSn19b1), and graphitic schist matrix (94VSn19b2) were collected.

Punta Pantanemo (92VSn36a, 92VSn36f, 94VSn23a, b, c)

Steep coastal bluffs (Table 1; Fig. 2) expose a large expanse of mica schist notable for its black color (that presumably reflects large graphite content). The schist is interlayered with metacarbonate rocks. Sample 92VSn36a is typical of the dark-colored matrix rock. The mafic blocks in these exposures display conspicuous lensoid and tadpole shapes and range from 2 cm to 10 m in diameter. Some mafic blocks are aligned in groups that resemble boudinaged layers. Two types of mafic rocks were collected here: (1) sample 92VSn36f is from the boudin neck of a 10 m block of eclogite, which has been retrogressed from eclogite to an assemblage of pistacitic epidote plus barroisitic amphibole that is transitional to a high-pressure greenschist facies assemblage; and (2) samples 94VSn23a, b, and c are from a set of steep, north-facing bluffs, where a barroisitic eclogite core ~0.5 m in diameter is surrounded by a layer of sulfide-rich barroisitic amphibolite 1 m thick. Sample 94VSn23a is from the sulfide-mineral–rich zone around the block, whereas 94VSn23b and c are from the block itself. Because only extremely sulfidic or highly retrogressed samples of mafic rocks were collected at this locality, the data for these rocks are reported in Table 2, but not discussed in detail.

Marble Quarry above Mar Azul (94VSn20)

At this locality (Table 1; Fig. 2), loose riprap blocks 10 cm to 0.5 m in diameter from the fourth bench in a marble quarry were sampled. Because the quarry is active, we were not allowed to examine or sample the walls. The rock types are dolomitic marble (samples 94VSn20a and b) and metabasite blocks (samples 94VSn20c and d). A fifth sample (94VSn20e) appears to be a hybridized product of marble-metabasite interaction (Table 2).

Autopista (92VSn40)

Roadcut on highway between Valencia and Puerto Cabello, ~5 km north of the El Cambur exit. Sisson et al. (1997) described this outcrop (Table 1; Fig. 2) and sketch-mapped it from photographs (their Figure 2). The sampled rock types are a 0.2 m diameter eclogitic rock (92VSn40) in a calcareous pelitic schist matrix (94VSn18c), a pelitic schist matrix (94VSn18), and a 1.5-m-long boudin of glaucophane-kyanite-garnet-paragonite-quartz schist (94VSn18a1, 18a1a, 18a2a).

At this roadcut, two samples of matrix rock and one of the eclogitic boudin were subsampled in order to examine the relationships of element distributions to layering and retrogression. Matrix sample 94VSn18c contained a dark layer within a matrix of quartz, mica, and feldspar that displays graphitic lenses up to ~1 cm long. This sample was analyzed as a whole rock as well as on a layer-by-layer basis (Table 2). Eclogite 92VSn40 contains prominent oxidized zones and one layer in which barroisitic amphibole is much more abundant than is omphacitic clinopyroxene (in contrast to the host rock, in which omphacite is much more abundant than barroisite). This sample was cut into layers, which represent an oxidized zone, the barroisite-bearing retrograde assemblage, and the garnet + pyroxene-dominated eclogitic assemblage. The eclogitic and barroisite-rich layers were treated as different samples in order to evaluate effects of retrogression upon the eclogitic boudin (Table 2).

ANALYTICAL METHODS

Whole-rock samples were analyzed by X-ray fluorescence spectroscopy (XRF) at the Smithsonian Institution, Washington, D.C., and by instrumental neutron activation analysis (INAA) at the U.S. Geological Survey (USGS), Denver, Colorado, and Reston, Virginia, in 1995 and 1996. All of the samples were processed at the Smithsonian. There, 100–200 g of powder was ground to <100 mesh in a SPEX Al-ceramic shatterbox from rock chips that were created by a small, ceramic-lined jaw crusher. The labor-intensive sample preparation was used in order to both adequately sample these coarse-grained metamorphic rocks and to permit trace element analysis with minimum amounts of contamination. The chips fed to the jaw crusher were prepared from anvil-splitting of clean, dry, unweathered and visually metal-uncontaminated parts of sawn rock slabs. Major elements and the trace elements V, Cr, Co, Ni, Cu, Zn, Rb, Sr, Y, Nb, and Ba were analyzed by XRF. These elements are differentiated from INAA trace elements in Table 2. Major elements were analyzed on glass discs prepared by melting rock powder with the fluxing agent $Li_2B_4O_7$. Trace elements were determined on cellulose-backed discs of powdered rock. The Philips PW 1480 X-ray spectrometer in the Department of Mineral Sciences, Smithsonian Institution, uses a computer program for data reduction that employs a working curve for each element, based on a combination of powdered USGS and other rock and mineral standards. FeO was determined by titration in the Analytical Chemistry Laboratory of the Department of Mineral Sciences, Smithsonian Institution. Five samples rich in carbonate minerals (94VSn20a, b; 94VSn18c) were analyzed using a dolomite standard in addition to the silicate rock standards. Despite this procedure, an entire group of samples (94VSn18c) reported in Table 2 have low analytical totals.

Several samples are rich in graphite, and the one with the most graphite in thin section (92VSn36a dark) was analyzed for elemental C by Joseph Nelen, Chemist (now retired), Department of Mineral Sciences, National Museum of Natural History, Smithsonian Institution. The sample contained 1.91 wt% elemental carbon and 1.19 wt% CO_2. Both of these numbers are grouped within its loss on ignition value (6.77 wt%).

The trace elements Sc, Sb, Cs, La, Ce, Nd, Sm, Eu, Tb, Yb, Lu, Hf, Ta, Th, and U were analyzed by INAA. The INAA samples were irradiated in the TRIGA reactor at the USGS, Denver, at a flux of ~2×10^{12} n/cm^2/s for 8 h. Powdered obsidian spiked with a variety of elements was used as the standard for 30 elements. Samples were counted between 1 and 8 weeks after irradiation. INAA data were reduced using the SPECTRA program modified for the interactive plotting of photopeaks (Grossman and Baedecker, 1987); data were corrected for spectral and fission-product interferences (Baedecker and McKeown, 1987). This analytical method is now defunct at the USGS.

Detection Limits for K₂O, Cs, Rb, and Ba

Table 2, which combines the results of both XRF and INAA analyses, uses italics to indicate limits of detection. The XRF limits of detection are a single value for each element that depends upon instrument parameters and standardization methods. Values for INAA limits of detection for a single element vary (Table 2), because the peak-to-background ratios of any given element determined by INAA are controlled by the sample's overall composition, which can result in varying matrix effects. Important for this study is that the limits of detection of XRF and INAA for K_2O (0.01 wt%), Ba (40 ppm), Rb (3 ppm), and Cs (0.09–0.13 ppm), although much larger than those that would be obtained, for example, in analyses by laser-ablation inductively coupled plasma–mass spectrometry (LA-ICP-MS) or isotope dilution methods, are sufficient to measure the K_2O-contents of normal (N)-MORB compositions, and to obtain Ba, Rb, and perhaps Cs values for enriched (E)-MORB and at least some N-MORB compositions.

GEOCHEMICAL RESULTS

The SiO_2 contents of metabasite samples range from 48 to 52 wt%, except for one oxidized sample that contains 55 wt% of SiO_2 (Table 2). The K_2O contents of the sample suite vary from <0.01–1.82 wt%, although most are <0.50 wt%. TiO_2 contents range from 0.44 to 1.35 wt% and average 1.04 wt%. The major element data suggest these rocks were low-K tholeiitic basalts (MORB). However, the large variations of K-values render this evaluation problematic, because it seems likely that during their history, K was mobilized into (and perhaps out of) rock volumes. In order to further constrain likely protoliths, signatures of elements that are thought to be less mobile than K in aqueous fluids (e.g., Pearce, 1982) must be examined.

Covariations of Nb, TiO₂, Nd, and Y with Zr

Becker et al. (2000) compared the covariations of Nb, TiO_2, Nd, and Y with Zr to assess the protoliths of Alpine eclogites and blueschists. As these authors noted, with the possible exception of Nd, these elements are thought to be relatively immobile in aqueous fluids, and they include both HFSEs (Nb, Ti, Zr) and REEs (Nd, Y), which show systematic differences in MORB, oceanic-island basalt (OIB), and island-arc basalt (IAB). (Y is commonly plotted as a proxy for heavy REE.) The large relative error (±20%–50% 1σ for multiple measurements) for Nb concentrations <10 ppm and similar reproducibility of Ta at concentrations of <0.10 ppm indicate that plots of such data should show even less congruence with MORB fields than do Figures 3A and 4B. These are probably less reliable discriminants of their parent samples than others shown in the figures. Most Cordillera de la Costa eclogites display trace element characteristics of MORB, as do most Isla de Margarita eclogites and the suite of low-*T*, K-altered basalt samples from Ocean Drilling Program cores 417 and 418 from the Bermuda Rise (Fig. 3; Staudigel et al., 1996). The latter suite provides a comparison with the effects of low-*T* K-alteration seen in the uppermost 300 m of basaltic oceanic crust. In contrast, the TiO_2 and Y contents (at a given Zr content) of eclogites from the Samana Peninsula, Dominican Republic, are less than would be expected of MORB. This is consistent with the interpretation of Sorensen et al. (1997) that Samana eclogites are derived from arc basalts, not MORB.

Th-Ta-Yb Systematics

Most analyses of mafic blocks from the Cordillera de la Costa belt carry MORB-like signatures of the incompatible and relatively immobile elements Th, Ta, and Yb (Fig. 4). Most of the data that plot within the field for tholeiites and alkali basalts are richer in both Th and Ta (relative to Yb) than the average MORB and E-MORB values of Sun and McDonough (1989). Analyses of low-*T*, K-altered basalt (Staudigel et al., 1996) also plot near the MORB and E-MORB averages, but display smaller ratios of Th/Yb and Ta/Yb than either the Cordillera de la Costa or Samana eclogites. Pearce (1982) developed this diagram to help discriminate calc-alkaline from tholeiitic protoliths of altered basalts. (However, as Pearce noted, values for some island-arc tholeiites overlap with MORB.) Two samples (94 VSn20c, d) from the Cordillera de la Costa belt plot between the arc and MORB–within plate basalt fields. Again, in contrast to the Cordillera de la Costa belt, most Samana eclogites are arc-like in their less-mobile incompatible element systematics (Sorensen et al., 1997). The published analyses of eclogite blocks from the Juan Griego and La Rinconada Groups of Isla de Margarita (Mottana et al., 1985; Bocchio et al., 1990) lack determinations of Th, Yb, and Ta.

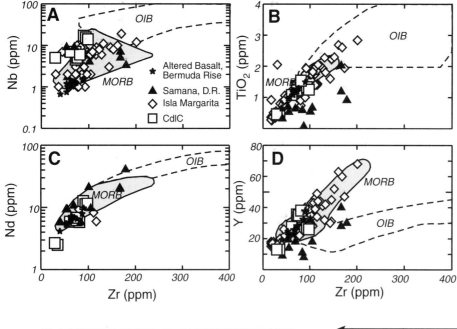

Figure 3. Trace element distributions in Cordillera de la Costa (CdlC) samples. MORB—mid-oceanic-ridge basalt; OIB—oceanic-island basalt. The fields are from Becker et al., 2000. Numbers of analyses in source database: Altered Basalt, Bermuda Rise (Staudigel et al., 1996) = 17; Samana, Dominican Republic (D.R.) (Sorensen et al., 1997) = 12; Isla de Margarita, Venezuela (Mottana et al., 1985; Bocchio et al., 1990) = 46; CdlC (this study) = 12. The number of points plotted in this figure and Figures 4 and 5 may not equal the number of analyses in the source database, because upper limits and elements not analyzed are not plotted.

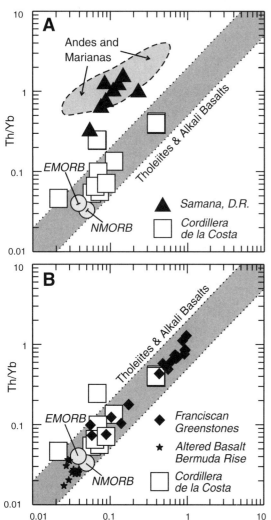

Figure 4. Th/Yb versus Ta/Yb for Cordillera de la Costa (CdlC) eclogite samples. Two shaded regions delineate fields for arc basalts from the Andes and Marianas and tholeiites and alkali basalts from the ocean floor and hotspots. Normal mid-oceanic-ridge basalt (N-MORB) and enriched (E)-MORB are from Sun and McDonough (1989). Data for 20 Franciscan greenstones from MacPherson et al. (1998).

Whole-Rock LILE Systematics

In contrast to Th, Ta, and Yb, the alkali values for a large number of samples from Isla de Margarita can be compared with both the Puerto Cabello and Samana suites. Furthermore, data from Staudigel et al.'s (1996) suite of altered basalts from the Bermuda Rise show that all three of the eclogite populations differ in alkali systematics from K-enriched (but unmetamorphosed) ocean floor basalt. Two Cordillera de la Costa belt analyses lie within a field of values for Isla de Margarita eclogites (data from Mottana et al., 1985), and one Cordillera de la Costa analysis, which is close to average E-MORB values, lies within the overlap area of the Samana and Isla de Margarita suites. Four analyses of three different Cordillera de la Costa blocks are not plotted on Figure 5A. All have K_2O values of 0.02–0.04 wt% and Ba below detection limits.

The Cordillera de la Costa and Samana suites are similar to each other, but differ from the Isla de Margarita suite in their covariations of K and Ba (Fig. 5). The Cordillera de la Costa and Samana suites both show concomitant K and Ba enrichment or depletion relative to nominal MORB values (Fig. 5A). Data for Isla de Margarita eclogites scatter around the MORB value; these rocks are best explained as MORB or E-MORB that have been enriched solely in Ba, or depleted in K_2O and enriched in Ba (Fig. 5A). In contrast, data for low-T, K-altered basalt from the Bermuda Rise

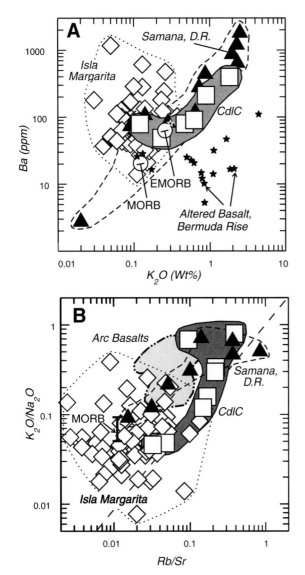

Figure 5. Alkali systematics for eclogites from Samana, Isla de Margarita, and the Cordillera de la Costa (CdlC). (A) Ba versus K₂O. (B) K₂O/Na₂O versus Rb/Sr. The data plotted as stars are from Staudigel et al. (1996). In (B), the light shaded area labeled "Arc Basalts" represents data for ~40 fresh, young basalts from the Mexican Volcanic Belt (Luhr and Carmichael, 1980; Nelson and Livieres, 1986; Luhr et al., 1989; Luhr, 1997, 2000, 2002; Mahood, 1981; Nelson and Hegre, 1990) and the Marianas Arc (Lin et al., 1989). Open squares—Cordillera de la Costa eclogites; open diamonds—Isla de la Margarita eclogites; filled triangles—Samana (Dominican Republic) eclogites.

(Staudigel et al., 1996) scatter to K₂O values greater than MORB (with one exception) at Ba values comparable to MORB.

As in the case of K₂O and Ba, the ratios of K₂O/Na₂O and Rb/Sr show considerable scatter for data from Isla de Margarita eclogites and more systematic covariations for both the Samana and the Cordillera de la Costa eclogites (Fig. 5B). Both of the latter two sets of data vary between an "average MORB" value (Sun and McDonough, 1989) and a 1:1 line for K₂O/Na₂O versus Rb/Sr.

Data arrayed along the 1:1 line suggest whole-rock scale exchange between the two variables. The Samana array ranges from MORB to the 1:1 line through a field of calc-alkaline arc basalts from the Marianas and continental arc basalts from the Mexican volcanic belt (data sources are cited in the figure caption).

Geochemical Descriptions of Metabasites by Locality

Cata (92VSn30a, b)

Two samples of different blocks from this locality (92VSn30a, b, Figs. 6A, 7A, and 7A₁; Table 2) show REE, Zr, and Hf characteristics close to those of N-MORB, but depletion of K₂O compared to N-MORB, along with Rb < 3 ppm, Ba < 40 ppm, and U < 0.3 ppm. In general, the "less mobile" elements appear to preserve a plausible N-MORB signature in the Cata samples (Fig. 6). In contrast (with the exception of Cs), the alkali and alkaline earth elements are depleted even relative to N-MORB in these rocks.

The Coast Guard Station at Independencia (Ocumare; 92VSn23a, b, and c)

All three samples show similar values for most minor and trace elements (Fig. 6B) and REE patterns (Fig. 7B, 7B₁). The samples are light rare earth element (LREE)-rich, and the relative abundances of these elements are slightly greater than those of average E-MORB (Sun and McDonough, 1989). These values are similar to those for an average of primitive, calc-alkaline, island-arc basalts from the Marianas (Lin et al., 1989). However, the eclogite samples are both richer and less fractionated in heavy rare earth elements than the island-arc basalt (Fig. 7B₁). At this locality, sample 92VSn23c, a boudin between 1 and 2 m long, contains less Cs, Rb, and K₂O than the other two samples, which are both from a much larger block. Along with REE enrichment, the abundances of alkali and alkaline earth elements increase (relative to N-MORB) from K through Cs (Fig. 6B). The Th/Yb and Ta/Yb ratios of these samples place them within the range of tholeiitic compositions (as defined by Pearce, 1982; Fig. 4), but the analyses plot at higher ratios of both than do the rest of the data for Cordillera de la Costa blocks for average MORB and E-MORB. The rocks of this locality are clearly not of typical N-MORB composition. Either E-MORB or primitive island-arc basalt are likely protoliths.

Mar Azul (94VSn19; 94VSn40b; 94VSn36f)

Most of the incompatible elements that are relatively immobile in aqueous fluids in these eclogite samples show N-MORB–like abundances and fractionations (Fig. 6C). Sample 92VSn36f is depleted in K relative to N-MORB, and also displays Rb and Ba below detection limits, which indicates that this metabasite is extremely poor in alkali elements. In contrast, sample 92VSn40b lies well within the K- and Ba-rich trend shown by Samana eclogites (Fig. 5A). Both samples contain <0.23 ppm U. In addition to eclogite, mica schist and metacarbonate layers were sampled at Mar Azul and analyzed (Table 2; Fig. 8). These data will be discussed in a following section.

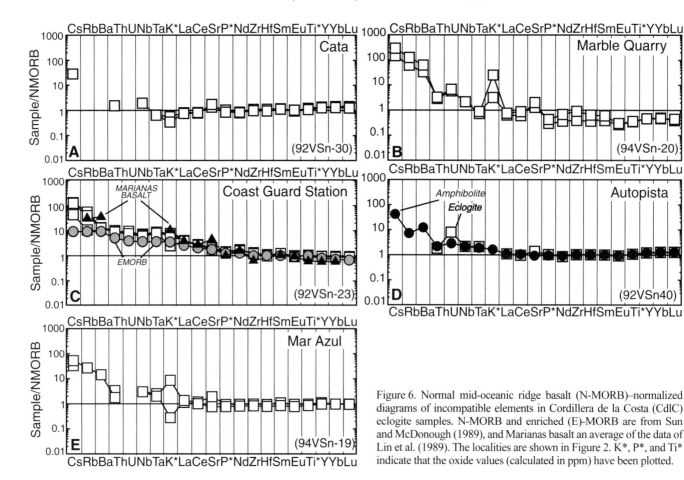

Figure 6. Normal mid-oceanic ridge basalt (N-MORB)–normalized diagrams of incompatible elements in Cordillera de la Costa (CdlC) eclogite samples. N-MORB and enriched (E)-MORB are from Sun and McDonough (1989), and Marianas basalt an average of the data of Lin et al. (1989). The localities are shown in Figure 2. K*, P*, and Ti* indicate that the oxide values (calculated in ppm) have been plotted.

Marble Quarry (94VSn20c, d)

These two eclogite samples are depleted in less mobile trace elements compared to N-MORB, yet show the greatest enrichments of LILE of the mafic suite (Figs. 6D, 7D, and 7D$_1$). They are also the only eclogite samples recovered from a large body of marble host rocks, as opposed to calc-silicate rocks or a relatively thin marble layer. Compared to average MORB, both samples are markedly depleted in REE and show slight negative Eu-anomalies (Fig. 7D$_1$). Sample 94VSn20d displays the largest K$_2$O value of any Cordillera de la Costa eclogite (1.82 wt%; Table 2; Fig. 6D) and is also rich in Rb, Cs, and Ba. Both Marble Quarry samples plot between the tholeiite-alkali basalt field and the arc basalt field in Figure 4. This, and their LILE enrichment compared with MORB, might be interpreted to reflect an arc protolith. However, the REE patterns of the rocks strongly argue against this possibility.

Autopista (92VSn40)

Roadcut on highway between Valencia and Puerto Cabello, ~5 km north of the El Cambur exit. The eclogite from this outcrop consists of interlayers of eclogite and barroisitic assemblages formed by retrogression to near-greenschist facies. These two types of layers display virtually identical contents of less mobile incompatible elements (Fig. 6E). Their Nb/Ta

ratios range from 17.8 to 20 (the retrogressed sample). However, the eclogite layer is depleted in K$_2$O, Cs, Rb, and Ba (values less than detection limits for all four elements), whereas the retrograde assemblage is greatly enriched in all of these elements compared to N-MORB. Indeed, the amphibole-rich layer contains ~2× the K$_2$O, 10× the Rb and Ba, and 45× the Cs of N-MORB (Fig. 6E). The REE values of both eclogite and the retrogressed eclogite layer are virtually identical (Fig. 7E and 7E$_1$; Table 2).

Geochemical Descriptions of Metasedimentary Rocks

Values for relatively immobile elements in most samples of the metasedimentary rock matrices of eclogitic blocks from the Cordillera de la Costa belt resemble those of the North American Shale Composite (NASC) analysis of Gromet et al. (1984; shown in Fig. 8). In Figure 8A, mica schist and quartz-feldspar gneiss samples alike show small excursions from the NASC. Except for great enrichment of Sr (no surprise in carbonate-rich rocks), one of the two analyses of calc-schists also shows evidence for a shale component that is similar in composition to that of the mica schists of the Cordillera de la Costa belt (Fig. 8B). Two samples of dolomitic marble host rocks are depleted in all elements except Sr compared to the NASC (Fig. 8B).

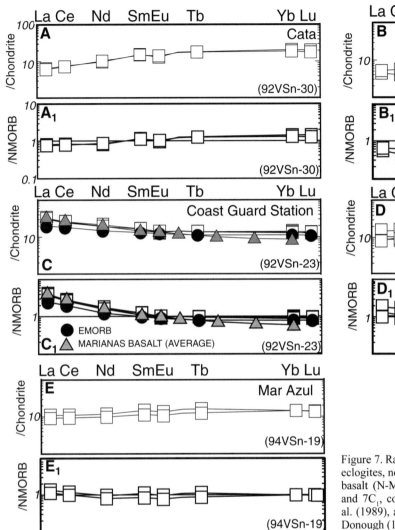

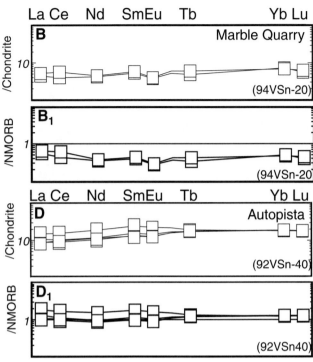

Figure 7. Rare earth element patterns for Cordillera de la Costa (CdlC) eclogites, normalized to both chondrite and normal mid-oceanic ridge basalt (N-MORB) values (Sun and McDonough, 1989). In sets 7C and 7C$_1$, comparison data for the Marianas basalts are from Lin et al. (1989), and those for enriched (E)-MORB are from Sun and McDonough (1989).

The most conspicuous feature of Figure 8 is that five samples are extremely depleted in LILE compared with the others (except for the metadolomites). Samples of mica schist and glaucophane + kyanite-bearing schist from the Autopista locality all contain very small amounts of Rb, Ba, and K compared to the NASC normalizing sample and samples of similar major element composition (Table 2) from elsewhere in the Cordillera de la Costa belt that show a similar signature of less mobile trace elements. A sample of calc-schist from Punta Pantanemo is also depleted in LILE. The Autopista outcrop is the only one in the Cordillera de la Costa belt for which Sisson et al. (1997) determined a pressure of 20 kb, and the LILE-depleted layer that displays the 20 kb assemblage is similar in its minor and trace element chemical composition to the mica schist and calc-schist matrix in which it occurs.

DISCUSSION

Protoliths of the Metamorphic Rocks

Metabasites

Four lines of evidence, all based upon elements that are relatively immobile in the presence of aqueous metamorphic fluids, show that the eclogites of the Cordillera de la Costa belt are derived from tholeiitic protoliths. Taken together, these geochemical criteria support the conclusion that three of the five eclogite localities contain blocks that had N-MORB protoliths, that one represents former pyroxene-rich cumulate rocks, and that one shows evidence for either E-MORB or primitive island-arc basalt. The first lines of evidence are the covariations of Nb, TiO$_2$, Nd, and Y with respect to Zr (Becker et al., 2000). Except for Nb, for which our

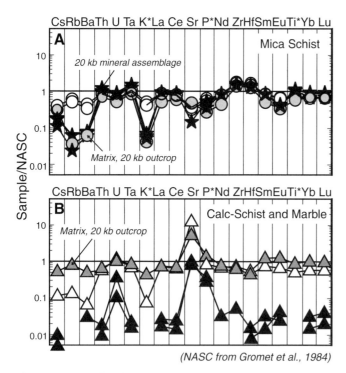

Figure 8. Incompatible elements for metasedimentary rocks from the Cordillera de la Costa (CdlC), normalized to Gromet et al.'s (1984) analysis of the North American Shale Composite (NASC). Circles—mica schist; open triangles—calc-schist and marble; filled stars—metasedimentary rock containing the 20 kb assemblage glaucophane + kyanite from the Autopista locality; shaded circles and triangles—mica schist and calc-schist, respectively, from the Autopista locality; black triangles—dolomitic marble matrix from the Marble Quarry locality. K*, P*, and Ti* indicate that the oxide values (calculated in ppm) have been plotted.

detection limit is high, all of these elements are well determined by combined XRF and INAA techniques. Niobium, TiO_2, and Nd tend to be both enriched and to increase with Zr contents in suites of OIBs compared to MORB (Fig. 3A–3C). In contrast, samples of OIB generally contain less Y at Zr-rich compositions than do MORBs of similar Zr-contents. All four diagrams of Figure 3 show that the eclogites of Isla de Margarita and the Cordillera de la Costa show the characteristics of MORB. The compositions of K-metasomatized basalts from the Bermuda Rise also plot in MORB fields in Figure 3A–3D. In contrast, Samana eclogites, previously interpreted to have arc-basalt protoliths (Sorensen et al., 1997), lie outside both the MORB and OIB fields in Figure 3B and 3D. This feature reflects the lesser amounts of TiO_2, as well as the fractionations of Y with Zr in the arc-basalt protoliths for Samana eclogites compared to MORB. The depletion of Ti in arc basalts compared to MORB is well known (e.g., Pearce, 1982; Sun and McDonough, 1989). Figure 3 shows that the Cordillera de la Costa rocks, like the Isla Margarita and Bermuda Rise comparison suites, more closely resemble MORB than OIB. Except for TiO_2 (especially at large values of Zr), the diagrams of Figure 3 are poor discriminants between arc tholeiite and MORB.

The systematics of Th, Ta, and Yb discriminate the arc-derived Samana eclogite suite from the MORB-like Cordillera de la Costa samples. At a given Ta/Yb ratio, the Th/Yb ratio is much larger for both the field for young volcanic rocks from the Andes and Marianas (Pearce, 1982) and the analyses of most Samana eclogites than for MORB, Franciscan greenstones, altered MORB from the Bermuda Rise (Staudigel et al., 1996), and the Cordillera de la Costa eclogite suite (Fig. 4A and 4B). The data for Franciscan greenstones are from MacPherson et al. (1990), who defined MORB-like and OIB-like groupings of these samples based on whole-rock geochemistry and relict pyroxene compositions. MacPherson et al.'s (1990) MORB-like Franciscan samples overlap most analyses of Cordillera de la Costa eclogites, suggesting that subduction zone greenstones might be plausible precursors for the Cordillera de la Costa rocks. The altered basalts from the Bermuda Rise show lesser ratios of both Th/Yb and Ta/Yb than average N-MORB, E-MORB, Franciscan greenstones, or the Cordillera de la Costa eclogites. Staudigel et al. (1996) concluded that seafloor alteration could disrupt the signatures of trace elements generally regarded to be immobile.

"Spider diagrams" and REE patterns for each locality establish that, even though the eclogites and related mafic rocks of the Cordillera de la Costa are tholeiitic and MORB-like, variations of relatively less mobile trace elements show that these rocks had diverse ocean-floor protoliths. Samples from Cata, Mar Azul, and the Autopista localities all show characteristics of REE and HFSE similar to those of Sun and McDonough's (1989) N-MORB (Figs. 6A, 6D, 6E, $7A_1$, $7D_1$, and $7E_1$). Samples from the Coast Guard station and the Marble Quarry deviate from N-MORB values. The Coast Guard Station rocks show patterns of REE, HFSE, Sr, and P_2O_5 that resemble either E-MORB or primitive island-arc basalt compositions (Figs. 6C and 7C). La, Ce, Sr, P, and Nd are enriched relative to N-MORB in a systematic way: the LREE pattern increases in relative abundances toward lighter REE. A possible guide for protolith interpretation is the concentration of Ti, Nb, and Ta relative to N-MORB in these samples. Compared to N-MORB, arc basalt is generally depleted in these elements. The rocks from the Marble Quarry are depleted in REE compared with N-MORB (Figs. 6B and 7B) and show a slight negative Eu anomaly (Fig. 7B). The Marble Quarry rocks also have a relatively large Mg/Fe ratio for their Si contents. These features are all consistent with a protolith that had accumulated pyroxene in an igneous fractionation process. Such characteristics are seen in cumulate gabbros from the ocean floor, but are atypical of N-MORB.

Metasedimentary Rocks

The trace element values for calc-schists and mica schist from the Cordillera de la Costa belt show that the two had a similar detrital component, which within a factor of two resembles the NASC (Fig. 8). However, this "pelitic" component shows larger fractionations of HFSE and REE than do passive margin shales used as USGS analytical standards (http://minerals. cr.usgs.gov/geo_chem_stand) or metagraywacke and meta-argillite of the Pelona Schist (Fig. 9). The Pelona Schist is a continent-

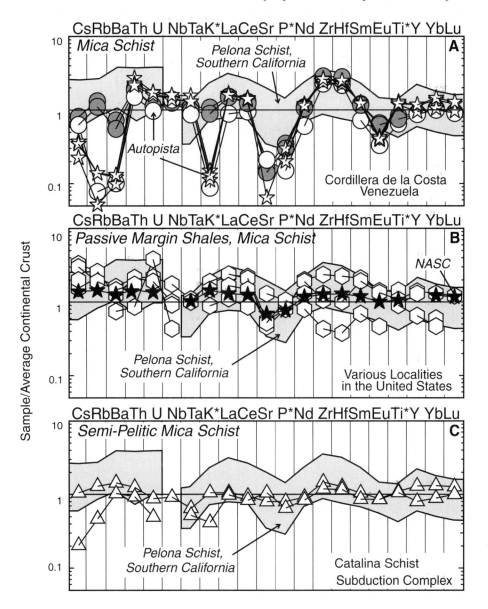

Figure 9. Incompatible element variations for mica schists from the Cordillera de la Costa compared to subduction-related and passive margin sedimentary and metasedimentary rock units. All data are normalized to values for average continental crust (Taylor and McLennan, 1986, 1995; Rudnick and Fountain, 1995). The shaded region in all three diagrams is a field for 17 analyses of metasedimentary rock from the Pelona Schist (Moran, 1993). (A) CdlC data: open circles and stars are samples from the Autopista locality; the stars designate samples with the 20 kb assemblage glaucophane + kyanite. (B) Data for the North American Shale Composite (NASC; filled stars) and 4 specimens of shale from the U.S. Geological Survey analytical standards archive (open hexagons; http://minerals. cr.usgs.gov/geo_chem_stand). (C) Open triangles represent analyses of migmatitic metasedimentary rock from the amphibolite unit of the Catalina Schist, southern California. K*, P*, and Ti* indicate that the oxide values (calculated in ppm) have been plotted.

detritus–rich, Cretaceous paleosubduction complex in southern California (Fig. 9; Jacobson et al., 2000) from which 17 samples of metasedimentary rock were analyzed for major and trace elements by Moran (1993). The trace element signatures of NASC and passive margin shales cannot be easily distinguished from the subduction-complex–related Pelona Schist samples (Fig. 9B). This lack of trace element geochemical distinction between feldspar-dominated versus mica-dominated detrital sediment is perhaps not surprising; much of the "immobile element" signature of detrital sedimentary rocks resides in accessory minerals such as allanite, apatite, Fe-Ti oxide minerals, rutile, and zircon, and white mica, like alkali feldspar, can accommodate LILE.

The wide range of compositions represented by the comparison suites of Figure 9 also provide a context for evaluating the mica schist matrix and the glaucophane + kyanite–bearing layer of

the "20 kb outcrop." The most significant geochemical feature of the latter rocks is their extreme depletions in Rb, Ba, and K$_2$O compared to other pelitic or semi-pelitic rock types (Fig. 9). Another subduction zone pelitic rock that shows some LILE depletion is a sample of migmatitic semi-pelitic schist from Santa Catalina Island, California (Sorensen and Barton, 1987; Sorensen, 1988). However, it is less depleted in Ba and more depleted in U than the metasedimentary rocks from the Autopista locality and therefore has a distinct signature compared to the latter rocks. In addition, the Catalina migmatites show evidence that a component dominated by feldspar constituents was lost during subduction zone anatexis (Sorensen and Barton, 1987; Sorensen, 1988). There is no field or petrographic evidence that the Autopista locality partially melted and lost a melt component; instead, interaction with a subduction zone fluid seems to have removed LILE.

LILE Depletion in the Cordillera de la Costa

LILE depletion relative to the NASC and other metasedimentary rocks in the Cordillera de la Costa is common to 2 of 3 metasedimentary rock types of the Autopista outcrop (Fig. 10A). One sample of a ~0.2-m-long eclogite boudin from this locality (sample 92VSn40, gar + cpx) is depleted in LILE relative to N-MORB; all LILEs are below detection limits in this rock (Fig. 10B). Values for LILE in published averages of N-MORB suggest that any random population of unaltered N-MORB should contain some rocks that yield values for Ba, Rb, and Cs of less than the detection limits of a combination of XRF and INAA. This means that even if Ba, Rb, and Cs were not depleted relative to the protolith, combined XRF and INAA might not detect these elements in some isochemically metamorphosed eclogite samples. However, most samples of N-MORB contain enough K_2O to be measured by XRF (detection limit of 100 ppm). Indeed, the XRF K_2O values shown in Figures 5A and C are both less than Sun and McDonough's (1989) N-MORB average. Because its K_2O value is <100 ppm, Figure 10 implies that eclogite from the Autopista locality has been stripped of K_2O (and likely of other LILEs) relative to N-MORB, its most plausible protolith.

Perhaps the 0.2 m size of the eclogite body from the Autopista locality made it more susceptible to LILE depletion than larger ones. However, three other blocks show K_2O < average N-MORB; namely, both of the samples from the Cata locality (92VSn30a, b) and eclogite 92VSn36f from the Mar Azul locality. Thus, the evidence for LILE depletion found in all but one rock type at the Autopista locality (including a small eclogite

block) is also found in meter-sized blocks elsewhere in the Cordillera de la Costa eclogite belt (Fig. 2).

Is the evidence for LILE depletion in the Cordillera de la Costa significant to subduction zone processes? Becker et al. (2000) used XRF and isotope dilution, followed by thermal ionization mass spectrometry to determine 22 trace elements in 35 samples of blueschist and eclogite, most from Alpine localities. By comparing P-T estimates with LILE contents and indexing protoliths by means of trace element and Nd-isotopic compositions of the rocks, they determined that although most of the samples they analyzed had originally been MORB, most had been affected by sub-seafloor alteration, which affected contents of such "immobile" elements such as Nb, TiO_2, Nd, Y, and Zr. This result contrasts with both the Isla de Margarita and Cordillera de la Costa eclogites, which appear to preserve plausible N-MORB, ocean-floor gabbro, and E-MORB signatures of these trace elements. Becker et al. (2000) focused on LILE depletion, for which they found widespread evidence. These authors concluded that LILE had been stripped from eclogite via a subduction zone process that took place at temperatures of <600–700 °C by transport in fluids that were evolved from metamorphic dehydration reactions.

An experimental study suggests that high pressures can promote reactions that produce K-rich fluids from biotite + K-feldspar or quartz-bearing assemblages. Massonne (1992) studied the system K_2O-MgO-Al_2O_3-SiO_2-H_2O (KMASH), and found that ultrapotassic siliceous fluids could be extracted from K-rich metasediments via two reactions: K-feldspar + phlogopite + H_2O = phengite + quartz + K, Mg-rich siliceous fluid, or phlogopite + quartz/coesite + H_2O = phengite + talc + K, Mg-rich siliceous fluid, in the temperature range of 300° to 600 °C and pressures between 15 and 30 kb. The fluid-bearing product assemblage is the higher P, not the higher T, side of the reaction. Massonne (1992) suggested that deep subduction of K-rich quartzofeldspathic sedimentary rocks could yield K-rich fluids plus residual assemblages rich in phengite + quartz or phengite + quartz + talc. Sisson et al. (1997) reported that most of the feldspathic schists in the Cordillera de la Costa belt lack biotite and instead display phengite and that their feldspar is albite with <1% An. Samples 94VSn18a1a, 94VSn18a1c, and 94VSn182a, from the metasedimentary rock lens that displays the 20 kb assemblage of kyanite and Mg-glaucophane, also contain talc + phengite + paragonite (mineral assemblages reported in Sisson et al., 1997) and are extremely depleted in LILE. The mineralogy and geochemistry of this lens are consistent with it being the solid portion of a product assemblage of a reaction that yielded K-rich fluid.

A comparison of Cordillera de la Costa data with Becker et al.'s (2000) and Massonne's (1992) results and conclusions suggests the following: because both metasedimentary and metaigneous rocks of the Autopista locality record LILE depletion, and this is the only place we have found that preserves evidence for a 20 kb, 600 °C metamorphic event in the Cordillera de la Costa (Sisson et al., 1997), the high P-T event was likely the one that depleted LILE. If this was the case, because other eclogites from the Cordillera de la Costa show LILE depletion, even

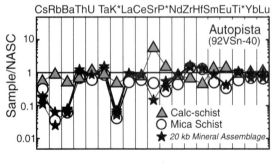

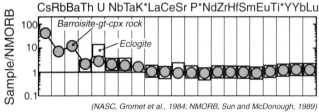

(NASC, Gromet et al., 1984; NMORB, Sun and McDonough, 1989)

Figure 10. Incompatible element diagrams for samples from the Autopista locality. (A) Data normalized to the North American Shale Composite (NASC; Gromet et al., 1984). (B) Data normalized to normal mid-oceanic-ridge basalt (N-MORB) (Sun and McDonough, 1989). K*, P*, and Ti* indicate that the oxide values (calculated in ppm) have been plotted.

though these rocks display evidence only for lower *P-T* conditions (Sisson et al., 1997), they may also record LILE depletion at 20 kb, 600 °C. The Cordillera de la Costa belt would then be the first metamorphic complex to preserve geochemical evidence of a regional metasomatic event that was related to peak metamorphic conditions and that had subsequently been mostly eradicated by retrograde metamorphic and metasomatic events.

Retrograde Reintroduction of LILE to the Cordillera de la Costa Belt

The only rock type in the Autopista outcrop that shows LILE *enrichment* with respect to a N-MORB protolith is a retrogressed, barroisite-bearing layer in the eclogite. The barroisite-bearing layer contains ~50% more K_2O than does N-MORB and even larger amounts of Ba, Rb, and Cs. This suggests that LILE were reintroduced to the eclogite boudin as it was retrogressed to the barroisite-bearing mineral assemblage.

Alkalis and alkaline elements can be mobilized in aqueous fluids at low to high temperatures—this is why so many protolith discriminant diagrams for metabasites avoid them. As is the case for subduction zone eclogites in California and Dominican Republic, the Ba and K values of some Cordillera de la Costa blocks show systematically disrupted alkali and alkaline earth element signatures (assuming the protolith was MORB). Sorensen et al. (1997) suggested that mixing between metasomatically introduced phengite and MORB could not only explain the K/Ba systematics of the eclogite suites of the Samana Peninsula, it was also similar to variations of these values for arc rocks. Even though the Samana eclogites show many incompatible element characteristics of arc basalt, they are greatly enriched in LILE and alkalis relative to these plausible protoliths. In Figure 5A, data for most blocks from the Cordillera de la Costa lie within a field defined by analyses of Samana eclogites, which ranges between MORB and K/Ba values of Samana and Franciscan phengite (Sorensen et al., 1997).

The K-enriched basalts of the Bermuda Rise (Staudigel et al., 1996) and the Ba-rich Isla Margarita eclogites were evidently enriched in LILE by different mechanisms, which are not controlled by the crystallization of phengite. The different K/Ba signature of altered basalts from either Franciscan greenstones or the Cordillera de la Costa eclogites (Fig. 5) may reflect the minerals into which K is incorporated in each rock type. In the basalts, these are clay minerals (developed from glass; Staudigel et al., 1996). Less K is incorporated into illite and smectite than into white mica. A phengite-controlled K/Ba signature (also seen in retrograde metasomatism of Franciscan Complex eclogites; Sorensen et al., 1997) strongly suggests that the LILE components in the Cordillera de la Costa eclogites reside in phases that crystallized during lower-*T*, subduction-zone metasomatism events, such as that which produced barroisite-rich assemblages in these rocks.

Correlation between the ratios K_2O/Na_2O and Rb/Sr can be evidence for alkali-exchange on a whole-rock scale (e.g., Sorensen et al., 1998). A 1:1 exchange (solid line, Fig. 5B) could reflect feldspar replacement of the form:

$$K, Rb_{orthoclase} = Na, Sr_{sanidine, plagioclase}$$

(e.g., Rougvie and Sorensen, 2002). In eclogite, similar effects could result from modal metasomatism, in which secondary phengite is added to eclogite. In eclogite, omphacite contains most of the rock's Na and Sr, but has negligible amounts of K and Rb. The bulk composition of omphacite-rich eclogite, which contained little K and Rb prior to metasomatism, could be "diluted" along a 1:1 line by the addition of phengite, a mineral rich in K and Rb, but lacking in Na and Sr. Unlike the analyses of eclogites from the Isla de Margarita suite, which scatter in Figure 5B, values for the Samana and Cordillera de la Costa eclogites range from MORB-like to compositions slightly richer in Rb (relative to Sr) than those from calc-alkaline basalts of continental arcs (comparison data cited by Sorensen et al., 1998). Six of 8 samples from the Cordillera de la Costa belt plot close to the 1:1 line, suggesting that the mechanism for metasomatism is the net addition of phengite to the rock. Sorensen et al. (1997) proposed that Samana eclogites preserved evidence for addition of LILE under retrograde conditions. These authors speculated that phengite-depositing fluids were derived at depth in a subduction complex, and migrated to higher structural levels within the effect mass transfer. It at least seems possible that the Cordillera de la Costa belt contains evidence for mechanisms that operated at both sources and sinks for LILE within a subduction zone.

Regional Contrasts in Retrograde Alteration Style

As noted, data for eclogites of the Cordillera de la Costa belt show systematic variations of K_2O versus Ba (Fig. 5A) that resemble those of counterparts from Samana, Dominican Republic, even though the latter rocks had arc, rather than MORB, protoliths. Rocks from both of these suites display samples with values of K_2O and Ba that both are greatly increased with regard to MORB values. In sharp contrast, samples of the Isla de Margarita eclogites display Ba values up to two orders of magnitude greater than MORB, but K_2O tends to be within a factor of two of MORB values, or depleted with regard to MORB (Fig. 5). Either the eclogites of Isla de Margarita did not undergo the same style of LILE alteration during metamorphism as their Cordillera de la Costa counterparts, our sampling was biased toward samples altered by phengite crystallization, or only samples not altered by this mechanism were collected for the geochemical investigations of Isla de Margarita. At present, it seems that the styles of LILE enrichment of eclogites from the two localities differ. Therefore, they did not share the same fluid regime during retrogression, the phase of metamorphism linked to LILE enrichment. This in turn suggests that despite the general overall similarities of Isla de Margarita eclogite-bearing units to that of the Cordillera de la Costa eclogite, the two terranes are not the same structural slices of a single subduction complex.

CONCLUSIONS

1. Analyses of eight eclogite blocks (and their regression products) from five localities of the Cordillera de la Costa belt indicate that five had N-MORB, two E-MORB (or perhaps primitive island-arc basalt), and one a cumulate gabbro protolith. The results are less suggestive of a continental margin setting than of slab provenance for these metabasites.

2. Two subduction-related metasomatic events that mobilized LILE appear to be recorded by an eclogite block at the Autopista locality of Cordillera de la Costa: first, depletion of LILE at 20 kb, 600 °C (*P-T* conditions estimated by Sisson et al., 1997), then enrichment of LILE on the retrograde path, linked to the formation of barroisite-bearing mineral assemblages. Three other eclogite samples from two other Cordillera de la Costa belt localities also show evidence for LILE depletion.

3. Metasedimentary rock matrices of the Cordillera de la Costa eclogites contain a shale-like component of trace elements in both calc-schists and mica schists, but these trace element compositions are not discriminants of a protolith sediment source. Mica schist and a layer that records $P = 20$ kb, $T = 600$ °C from the Autopista locality are strongly depleted in Rb, Ba, and K, but two samples of mica schist from elsewhere in the Cordillera de la Costa belt are not. However, mineral assemblages (Sisson et al., 1997) suggest that the latter rocks may have been depleted in LILE prior to retrogression. If this holds with a larger sampling, secondary LILE enrichment may have accompanied retrograde metamorphism that attended uplift.

4. Based on trace element geochemistry, the matrices of the Cordillera de la Costa eclogite blocks could represent a trench complex that was fed by a proximal continent (like the well-studied Pelona Schist of southern California, USA) or a rifted continental margin sequence.

5. The eclogite-bearing units of Isla de Margarita and that of the Cordillera de la Costa belt evidently did not share the same fluid-rock history during retrogression. If this is correct, despite their overall similarities, the two terranes either represent more than one eclogite-bearing subduction complex, or they are not from the same structural slice of a single subduction complex.

ACKNOWLEDGMENTS

First, we are extremely grateful to Mark Cloos and William P. Leeman for their detailed and constructive reviews, which proved to be essential guides in revising this manuscript. We are grateful for the assistance of Marino Ostos Rosales for his help in arranging logistical support. We also thank Chad Smith and Inci Ertan for assistance and discussions of Venezuelan geology. The X-ray reflectance spectrometry rock analyses were performed by Victoria Avery, and the instrumental neutron activation analysis data were reduced by Dr. Jeffrey N. Grossman. This study was partially supported by National Science Foundation grant EAR-9304377 to Avé Lallemant and Sisson and by awards from the Sprague and Becker Funds of the Smithsonian Institution to Sorensen.

REFERENCES CITED

Avé Lallemant, H.G., 1997, Transpression, displacement partitioning, and exhumation in the eastern Caribbean–South American plate boundary: Tectonics, v. 16, no. 2, p. 272–289, doi: 10.1029/96TC03725.

Avé Lallemant, H.G., and Guth, L.R., 1990, Role of extensional tectonics in exhumation of eclogites and blueschists in an oblique subduction setting: Northeastern Venezuela: Geology, v. 18, p. 950–953, doi: 10.1130/0091-7613(1990)018<0950:ROETIE>2.3.CO;2.

Avé Lallemant, H.G., and Sisson, V.B., 1993, Caribbean-South American plate interactions: Constraints from the Cordillera de la Costa Belt, Venezuela, in Pindell, J.L., and Perkins, B.F, eds., Mesozoic and early Cenozoic development of the Gulf of Mexico and Caribbean region—A context for hydrocarbon exploration, Proceedings, Gulf Coast Section, SEPM Foundation 13th Annual Research Conference: Houston, Texas, Society for Sedimentary Geology (SEPM) Foundation, p. 211–219.

Baedecker, P.A., and McKeown, D.M., 1987, Instrumental neutron activation analysis of geological samples, in Baedecker, P.A., ed., Methods for Geochemical Analysis: U.S. Geological Survey Bulletin 1770, p. H1–H14.

Bebout, G.E., and Barton, M.D., 1989, Fluid flow and metasomatism in a subduction zone hydrothermal system, Catalina Schist terrane, California: Geology, v. 17, p. 976–980, doi: 10.1130/0091-7613(1989)017<0976:FFAMIA>2.3.CO;2.

Bebout, G.E., and Barton, M.D., 1993, Metasomatism during subduction: Products and possible paths in the Catalina Schist, California: Chemical Geology, v. 108, p. 61–92, doi: 10.1016/0009-2541(93)90318-D.

Beccaluva, L., Bellia, S., Coltorti, M., Dengo, G., Mendez, J., Romero, J., Rotolo, S., and Siena, F., 1995, The northwestern border of the Caribbean plate in Guatemala: New geological and petrological data on the Motagua ophiolite belt: Ofioliti, v. 20, p. 1–15.

Beccaluva, L., Coltorti, M., Giunta, G., Vinet, M.I., Navarro, E., Sienna, F., and Urbani, F., 1996, Cross sections through the ophiolitic units of the southern and northern margins of the Caribbean plate in Venezuela (northern Cordilleras) and central Cuba: Ofioliti, v. 21, p. 85–103.

Bailey, E.H., Irwin, W.P., and Jones, D.L., 1964, Franciscan and related rocks and their significance in the geology of western California: California Division of Mines and Geology Bulletin 183, 177 p.

Becker, H., Jochum, K.P., and Carlson, R.W., 2000, Trace element fractionation during dehydration of eclogites from high-pressure terranes and the implications for element fluxes in subduction zones: Chemical Geology, v. 163, p. 65–99, doi: 10.1016/S0009-2541(99)00071-6.

Bellizzia, A., 1986, Sistema montañoso del Caribe—una cordillera alóctona en la parte norte de América del Sur, in Bellizzia, N.P., and Iturralde, J.M., eds., Memoria, VI Congreso Geológico Venezolano: Caracas, Sociedad Venezolana de Geólogos, v. X, p. 6657–6836.

Bellizzia, A., Pimental, N., and Bajo, R., 1976, Mapa geológico estructural de Venezuela: Caracas, Foninves, scale 1:500,000.

Bertrand, J., and Vuagnat, M., 1980, Inclusions in the serpentine mélanges of the Motagua fault zone, Guatemala: Archives des Sciences (Sociètè de Physique et D'Histoire Naturelle de Geneve), v. 33, p. 321–336.

Bocchio, R., DeCapitani, L., Liborio, G., Maresch, W.V., and Mottana, A., 1990, The eclogite-bearing series of Isla de Margarita, Venezuela: Geochemistry of metabasic lithologies in the La Rinconada and Juan Griego Groups: Lithos, v. 25, p. 55–69, doi: 10.1016/0024-4937(90)90006-M.

Bocchio, R., DeCapitani, L., Liborio, G., Maresch, W.V., and Mottana, A., 1996, Equilibration conditions of eclogite lenses from Isla de Margarita, Venezuela: Implications for the tectonic evolution of the metasedimentary Juan Griego Group: Lithos, v. 37, p. 39–59, doi: 10.1016/0024-4937(95)00014-3.

Cloos, M., 1984, Flow melanges and the structural evolution of accretionary wedges, in Raymond, L.A., ed., Melanges: Their nature, origin, and significance: Geological Society of America Special Paper 198, p. 71–80.

Draper, G., 1986, Blueschists and associated rocks in eastern Jamaica and their significance for Cretaceous plate-margin development in the northern Caribbean: Geological Society of America Bulletin, v. 97, p. 48–60, doi: 10.1130/0016-7606(1986)97<48:BAARIE>2.0.CO;2.

Ellis, D.H., and Green, D.H., 1979, An experimental study of the effect of Ca upon garnet-clinopyroxene Fe-Mg exchange equilibria: Contributions to Mineralogy and Petrology, v. 71, p. 13–22, doi: 10.1007/BF00371878.

Ernst, W.G., 1970, Tectonic contact between the Franciscan mélange and the Great Valley sequence, crustal expression of a Late Mesozoic Benioff zone: Journal of Geophysical Research, v. 75, p. 886–902.

Ernst, W.G., 1988, Tectonic history of subduction zones inferred from retrograde blueschist *P-T* paths: Geology, v. 16, p. 1081–1084, doi: 10.1130/0091-7613(1988)016<1081:THOSZI>2.3.CO;2.

Ertan, I.E., Sisson, V.B., and Avé Lallemant, H.G., 1995, Metamorphic and age constraints for the Cordillera de la Costa belt, Venezuela: Geological Society of America Abstracts with Programs, v. 27, no. 6, p. 229.

Giaramita, M.J., and Sorensen, S.S., 1994, Primary fluids in low-temperature eclogites: evidence from two subduction complexes (Dominican Republic, and California, USA): Contributions to Mineralogy and Petrology, v. 117, p. 279–292, doi: 10.1007/BF00310869.

Gonçalves, P., Guillot, S., Lardeaux, J.-M., Nicollet, C., and Mercier de Lepinay, B., 2000, Thrusting and sinistral wrenching in a pre-Eocene HP-LT Caribbean accretionary wedge (Samana Peninsula, Dominican Republic): Geodynamica Acta, v. 13, p. 119–132, doi: 10.1016/S0985-3111(00)00116-9.

Grossman, J.N., and Baedecker, P.A., 1987, Interactive methods for data reduction and quality control in INAA: Journal of Radioanalytical and Nuclear Chemistry, v. 113, p. 43–59.

Gromet, L.P., Dymek, R.F., Haskin, L.A., and Korotev, R.L., 1984, The "North American shale composite": Its compilation, major and trace element characteristics: Geochimica et Cosmochimica Acta, v. 48, p. 2469–2482, doi: 10.1016/0016-7037(84)90298-9.

Harlow, G.E., 1994, Jadeitites, albitites, and related rocks from the Motagua fault zone, Guatemala: Journal of Metamorphic Geology, v. 12, p. 49–68.

Jacobson, C.E., Barth, A.P., and Grove, M., 2000, Late Cretaceous protolith age and provenance of the Pelona and Orocopia schists, southern California; implications for evolution of the Cordilleran margin: Geology, v. 29, p. 15–18.

Johnson, C.A., and Harlow, G.E., 1999, Guatemala jadeitites and albitites were formed by deuterium-rich serpentinizing fluids deep within a subduction zone: Geology, v. 27, p. 629–632, doi: 10.1130/0091-7613(1999)027<0629:GJAAWF>2.3.CO;2.

Joyce, J., 1991, Blueschist metamorphism and deformation on the Samana Peninsula; a record of subduction and collision in the Greater Antilles, *in* Mann, P., Draper, G., and Lewis, J.F., eds., Geologic and tectonic development of the North America–Caribbean plate boundary in Hispaniola: Geological Society of America Special Paper 262, p. 47–76.

Kubovics, I., Andó, J., and Szakmány, G., 1989, Comparative petrology and geochemistry of high-pressure metamorphic rocks from eastern Cuba and western Alps: Szeged, Acta Mineralogica-Petrographica, v. 30, p. 35–54.

Lewis, J.F., and Draper, G., 1990, Geology and tectonic evolution of the northern Caribbean margin, *in* Dengo, G., and Case, G.E., eds., The Caribbean region: Boulder, Colorado, Geological Society of America, The Geology of North America, v. H, p. 77–140.

Lin, P.-N., Stern, R.J., and Bloomer, S.H., 1989, Shoshonitic volcanism in the northern Mariana arc 2. Large-ion lithophile and rare earth element abundances: Evidence for the source of incompatible element enrichments in interoceanic arcs: Journal of Geophysical Research, v. 94, p. 4497–4514.

Luhr, J.F., 1997, Extensional tectonics and diverse primitive volcanic rocks in the western Mexican Volcanic Belt: Canadian Mineralogist, v. 35, p. 473–500.

Luhr, J.F., 2000, The geology and petrology of Volcán San Juan (Nayarit, México) and the compositionally zoned Tepic Pumice: Journal of Volcanology and Geothermal Research, v. 95, p. 109–156, doi: 10.1016/S0377-0273(99)00133-X.

Luhr, J.F., 2002, Petrology and geochemistry of the 1991 and 1998–1999 lava flows from Volcán Colima, México: Journal of Volcanology and Geothermal Research, v. 117, p. 169–194.

Luhr, J.F., and Carmichael, I.S.E., 1980, The Colima Volcanic Complex, Mexico: 1. Post-caldera andesites from Volcán Colima: Contributions to Mineralogy and Petrology, v. 71, p. 343–372, doi: 10.1007/BF00374707.

Luhr, J.F., Allan, J.F., Carmichael, I.S.E., Nelson, S.A., and Hasenaka, T., 1989, Primitive calc-alkaline and alkaline rock types from the Mexican Volcanic Belt: Journal of Geophysical Research, v. 94, p. 4515–4530.

MacPherson, G.J., Phipps, S.P., and Grossman, J.N., 1990, Diverse sources for igneous blocks in Franciscan mélanges, California Coast Ranges: Journal of Geology, v. 98, p. 845–862.

Mahood, G.A., 1981, Chemical evolution of a Pleistocene rhyolitic center: Sierra La Primavera, Jalisco, Mexico: Contributions to Mineralogy and Petrology, v. 77, p. 129–149, doi: 10.1007/BF00636517.

Maresch, W.V., and Abraham, K., 1981, Petrography, mineralogy, and metamorphic evolution of an eclogite from the Island of Margarita, Venezuela: Journal of Petrology, v. 22, p. 337–362.

Massonne, H.-J., 1992, Evidence for low-temperature ultrapotassic siliceous fluids in subduction zone environments from experiments in the system $K_2O\text{-}MgO\text{-}Al_2O_3\text{-}SiO_2\text{-}H_2O$ (KMASH): Lithos, v. 28, p. 421–434.

Massonne, H.-J., and Schreyer, W., 1987, Phengite barometry based on the limiting assemblage with K-feldspar, phlogopite and quartz: Contributions to Mineralogy and Petrology, v. 96, p. 212–224, doi: 10.1007/BF00375235.

MacPherson, G.J., Phipps, S.J., and Grossman, J.N., 1990, Diverse sources for igneous blocks in Franciscan mélanges: Journal of Geology, v. 98, p. 845–862.

McBirney, A.R., Aoki, K.-I., and Bass, M., 1967, Eclogites and jadeite from the Motagua fault zone, Guatemala: American Mineralogist, v. 52, p. 908–918.

Meyre, C., de Capitane, C., Zack, T., and Frey, M., 1999, Petrology of high-pressure metapelites from the Adula Nappe (Central Alps, Switzerland): Journal of Petrology, v. 40, p. 199–213, doi: 10.1093/petrology/40.1.199.

Miller, C., Stosch, H.-G., and Hoernes, S., 1988, Geochemistry and origin of eclogites from the type locality Koralpe and Saualpe: Chemical Geology, v. 67, p. 103–118, doi: 10.1016/0009-2541(88)90009-5.

Moran, A., 1993, The effect of metamorphism on the trace element composition of subducted oceanic crust and sediment [Ph.D. thesis]: Houston, Rice University, 366 p.

Morgan, B.A., 1967, Geology of the Valencia area, Carabobo, Venezuela [Ph.D. thesis]: Princeton, New Jersey, Princeton University, 220 p.

Morgan, B.A., 1970, Petrology and mineralogy of eclogite and garnet amphibolite from Puerto Cabello, Venezuela: Journal of Petrology, v. 11, p. 101–145.

Mottana, A., Bocchio, R., Liborio, G., Morton, L., and Maresch, W.V., 1985, The eclogite-bearing metabasaltic sequence of Isla de Margarita, Venezuela: A geochemical study: Chemical Geology, v. 50, p. 351–368, doi: 10.1016/0009-2541(85)90128-7.

Nelson, S.A., and Hegre, J., 1990, Volcán La Navajas, a Pliocene-Pleistocene trachyte/peralkaline rhyolite volcano in the northwestern Mexican volcanic belt: Bulletin Volcanologique, v. 52, p. 186–204, doi: 10.1007/BF00334804.

Nelson, S.A., and Livieres, R.L., 1986, Contemporaneous calc-alkaline and alkaline volcanism at Sanguanguey Volcano, Nayarit, Mexico: Geological Society of America Bulletin, v. 97, p. 798–808, doi: 10.1130/0016-7606(1986)97<798:CCAAVA>2.0.CO;2.

Okrusch, M., and Broecker, M., 1990, Eclogites associated with high-grade blueschists in the Cyclades archipelago, Greece: A review: European Journal of Mineralogy, v. 2, p. 451–478.

Pearce, J.A., 1982, Trace element characteristics of lavas from destructive plate boundaries, *in* Thorpe, R.S., ed., Andesites: Chichester, John Wiley & Sons, p. 525–548.

Pindell, J.L., 1993, Regional synopsis of Gulf of Mexico and Caribbean evolution, *in* Pindell, J.L., and Perkins, B.F., eds., Mesozoic and early Cenozoic development of the Gulf of Mexico and Caribbean region—A context for hydrocarbon exploration, Proceedings, Gulf Coast Section, SEPM Foundation 13th Annual Research Conference: Houston, Texas, Society for Sedimentary Geology (SEPM) Foundation, p. 251–274.

Rudnick, R.L., and Fountain, D.M., 1995, Nature and composition of the continental crust; a lower crustal perspective: Reviews of Geophysics, v. 33, p. 267–309, doi: 10.1029/95RG01302.

Sisson, V.B., Ertan, I.E., and Avé Lallemant, H.G., 1997, High-pressure (~2000 MPa) kyanite- and glaucophane-bearing pelitic schist and eclogite from Cordillera de la Costa belt, Venezuela: Journal of Petrology, v. 38, p. 65–83, doi: 10.1093/petrology/38.1.65.

Smith, C.A., Sisson, V.B., Avé Lallemant, H.G., and Copeland, P., 1999, Two contrasting pressure-temperature-time paths in the Villa de Cura blueschist belt, Venezuela: Possible evidence for Late Cretaceous initiation of subduction in the Caribbean: Geological Society of America Bulletin, v. 111, p. 831–848, doi: 10.1130/0016-7606(1999)111<0831:TCPTTP>2.3.CO;2.

Sorensen, S.S., 1991, Petrogenetic significance of zoned allanite in garnet amphibolites from a paleo-subduction zone: Catalina Schist, southern California: American Mineralogist, v. 76, p. 589–601.

Sorensen, S.S., 1988, Petrology of amphibolite-facies mafic and ultramafic rocks from the Catalina Schist, southern California: Metasomatism and migmatization in a subduction zone metamorphic setting: Journal of Metamorphic Geology, v. 6, p. 405–435.

Sorensen, S.S., and Barton, M.D., 1987, Metasomatism and partial melting in a subduction complex: Catalina Schist, southern California: Geology, v. 15, p. 115–118, doi: 10.1130/0091-7613(1987)15<115:MAPMIA>2.0.CO;2.

Sorensen, S.S., and Grossman, J.N., 1989, Enrichment of trace elements in garnet amphibolites from a paleo-subduction zone: Catalina Schist, southern California: Geochimica et Cosmochimica Acta, v. 53, p. 3155–3177, doi: 10.1016/0016-7037(89)90096-3.

Sorensen, S.S., and Grossman, J.N., 1993, Accessory minerals and subduction zone metasomatism: A geochemical comparison of two mélanges (Washington and California, U.S.A.): Chemical Geology, v. 110, p. 269–297, doi: 10.1016/0009-2541(93)90258-K.

Sorensen, S.S., Grossman, J.N., and Perfit, M.R., 1997, Phengite-hosted LILE enrichment in eclogite and related rocks: Implications for fluid-mediated mass transfer in subduction zones and arc magma genesis: Journal of Petrology, v. 38, p. 3–34, doi: 10.1093/petrology/38.1.3.

Sorensen, S.S., Dunne, G.C., Hanson, R.B., Barton, M.D., Becker, J., Tobisch, O.T., and Fiske, R.S., 1998, From Jurassic shores to Cretaceous plutons: Geochemical evidence for paleoalteration environments of metavolcanic rocks, eastern California: Geological Society of America Bulletin, v. 110, p. 326–343, doi: 10.1130/0016-7606(1998)110<0326: FJSTCP>2.3.CO;2.

Staudigel, H., Plank, T., White, B., and Schmincke, H.-U., 1996, Geochemical fluxes during seafloor alteration of the basaltic upper oceanic crust, *in* Bebout, G.E., Scholl, D.W., Kirby, S.H., and Platt, J.P., eds., Subduction: Top to bottom: American Geophysical Union Monograph 96, p. 19–38.

Stosch, H.-G., and Lugmair, G.W., 1990, Geochemistry and evolution of MORB-type eclogites from the Munchberg Massif, southern Germany: Earth and Planetary Science Letters, v. 99, p. 230–249, doi: 10.1016/0012-821X(90)90113-C.

Sun, S.S., and McDonough, W.F., 1989, Chemical and isotopic systematics of oceanic basalts; implications for mantle composition and processes, *in* Saunders, A.D. and Norry, M.J., eds., Magmatism in the ocean basins: London, Geological Society Special Publication 42, p. 313–345.

Taylor, S.R., and McLennan, S.M., 1986, The chemical composition of the Archaean crust, *in* Dawson, J.B., Carswell, D.A., Hall, J., and Wedepohl, K.H., eds., The nature of the lower continental crust: London, Geological Society Special Publication 24, p. 173–178.

Taylor, S.R., and McLennan, S.M., 1995, The geochemical evolution of the continental crust: Journal of Geology, v. 104, p. 369–377.

MANUSCRIPT ACCEPTED BY THE SOCIETY 5 APRIL 2005

Geological Society of America
Special Paper 394
2005

Exhumation of eclogites and blueschists in northern Venezuela: Constraints from kinematic analysis of deformation structures

Hans G. Avé Lallemant*
Virginia B. Sisson
Department of Earth Science, MS-126, Rice University, Houston, Texas 77005, USA

ABSTRACT

The Cordillera de la Costa belt, exposed for at least 600 km along the EW-trending coast of Venezuela, is a subduction mélange that contains fragments (knockers) of many rock types, notably eclogite and blueschist included in a matrix of mostly mica and graphite schist. The exhumation of the eclogite occurred in three stages. During the first stage (mid-Cretaceous), buoyancy forces drove the eclogite and its enclosing low-density matrix upward along the subduction zone from ~75 to ~25 km depth. During the second stage (Late Cretaceous), the mélange was severely fragmented by plate boundary–parallel stretching that caused the eclogite to ascend to ~10 km depth. During the third stage (Oligocene-Miocene), the Cordillera de la Costa belt was thrust onto the South American plate and erosion was responsible for the ultimate exhumation of the eclogite.

Keywords: Caribbean, tectonics, structural geology, high-pressure metamorphism, subduction.

INTRODUCTION

The EW-trending Caribbean–South American plate boundary zone in northern Venezuela and offshore consists, from north to south, of the South Caribbean Deformed belt, the Leeward Antilles volcanic arc, a zone of Tertiary extension, the Caribbean Mountains system, and the Llanos foreland basins (see Prologue Fig. 1, this volume). The Leeward volcanic arc seems to be underlain by older plateau-type basalts and younger primitive island arc basalts (e.g., Beets et al., 1984; White et al., 1999). The Caribbean Mountains system is subdivided into, from north to south, the Cordillera de la Costa, Caucagua–El Tinaco, Paracotos, Villa de Cura, and Serranía del Interior fold and thrust belts (Bellizzia and Dengo, 1990; Ostos et al., this volume, Chapter 2).

Two of these belts contain high-pressure–low-temperature (HP-LT) metamorphic rocks. Generally, such rocks are assumed to have formed in a subduction zone (e.g., Ernst, 1988). These

two belts are the Cordillera de la Costa belt along the north coast of Venezuela and the Villa de Cura belt in the south (Unger et al., this volume).

Cordillera de la Costa Belt

The Cordillera de la Costa belt is exposed from west of Puerto Cabello in the west to Cabo Codera in the east (Fig. 1). The belt can be correlated with similar lithologies on Margarita Island and the Araya and Paria Peninsulas (e.g., González de Juana et al., 1980; Bellizzia and Dengo, 1990). The Cordillera de la Costa belt in the study area (Fig. 1) consists of three rock associations. One has oceanic affinities, the second consists of continental margin deposits, and the third consists of continental crust (granites and granitic gneisses [Avé Lallemant and Sisson, 1993]).

The oceanic rocks are mainly mica schists and serpentinites with rounded, elongate, or lozenge-shaped eclogite, blueschist,

*E-mail: ave@rice.edu

Avé Lallemant, H.G., and Sisson, V.B., 2005, Exhumation of eclogites and blueschists in northern Venezuela: Constraints from kinematic analysis of deformation structures, *in* Avé Lallemant, H.G., and Sisson, V.B., eds., Caribbean–South American plate interactions, Venezuela: Geological Society of America Special Paper 394, p. 193–206, doi: 10.1130/2005.2394(07). For permission to copy, contact editing@geosociety.org. ©2005 Geological Society of America.

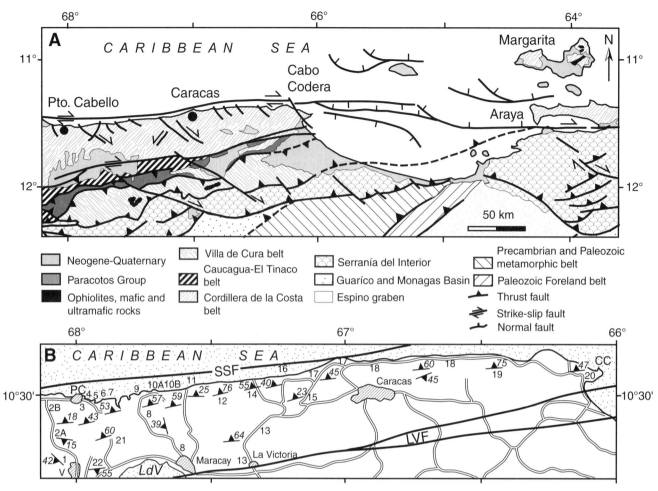

Figure 1. (A) Map of the study area in northern Venezuela (for location, see Prologue Fig. 1, this volume). (B) Double lines are roads; thick lines are the La Victoria (LVF) and the San Sebastian (SSF) right-lateral strike-slip faults. Regular numbers refer to structural domains. Strike and dip (in italics) symbols are average strike and dip of S$_{1c}$ foliation. Geographic names: CC—Cabo Codera; LdV—Lago de Valencia; PC—Puerto Cabello; V—Valencia.

and amphibolite fragments (as small as a few cm to hundreds of meters in length). The second assemblage consists of graphite and mica schists, marble, quartzite, and quartzofeldspathic gneisses. They have been correlated with passive-continental margin deposits of Jurassic-Cretaceous age (e.g., Bellizzia and Dengo, 1990). The third association consists of granites and gneisses that are of Cambrian-Ordovician age (U-Pb zircon ages; see Sisson et al., this volume, Chapter 3). Thus, the Cordillera de la Costa belt is a true mélange that formed by subduction of both oceanic and continental rocks. The three associations are intermixed to such extent that they cannot be mapped separately.

Most exposed rocks in the Cordillera de la Costa belt must have undergone prograde metamorphism; however, no trace of it could be identified because of severe overprinting by retrograde metamorphism (Sisson et al., 1997). The eclogite knockers display the highest grade of metamorphism. They often have rinds of blueschist. Individual blueschist knockers may have a retrograde origin as well. All rock assemblages were subsequently overprinted by

epidote amphibolite and greenschist facies metamorphism. The age of eclogite metamorphism is probably mid-Cretaceous.

Villa de Cura Belt

The protolith of the Villa de Cura belt is a sequence of volcanic arc basalts and arc-derived volcaniclastic rocks (see Prologue Fig. 1, this volume; Unger et al., this volume). It was metamorphosed also in mid-Cretaceous time (Smith et al., 1999) but at blueschist facies conditions; no eclogite has been encountered in this belt. The belt is not a mélange, but consists of four coherent imbricate slices each recrystallized at slightly different conditions (Smith et al., 1999). Together, these four assemblages display a prograde metamorphic history with only little retrograde overprint. Snoke et al. (2001) correlated Cretaceous rocks on Tobago with the Villa de Cura belt.

Notwithstanding the different natures of the Cordillera de la Costa and Villa de Cura HP-LT belts, they both are thought to have formed in the same subduction zone at the same time (e.g., Smith et al., 1999). However, the Villa de Cura belt formed in an oceanic environment far away from continental sediment supply sources, whereas the Cordillera de la Costa belt involved subduction of a slice or slices of the South American continent.

Exhumation of HP-LT Rocks

It is easy to understand how HP-LT metamorphic rocks continue to descend along a subduction zone because of their relative high density. However, it is problematic how they, in particular eclogite, return to the surface of Earth. Many models have been proposed to explain the exhumation of these rocks (e.g., Cowan and Schilling, 1978; Cloos, 1982; Platt, 1986; Ernst, 1988; Avé Lallemant and Guth, 1990; Mann and Gordon, 1996; Platt et al., 2003). The problem of exhuming ultra-high pressure (UHP) metamorphic rocks is even greater (e.g., Ernst and Peacock, 1996). In most models, flow lines related to the exhumation process have to be perpendicular to the plate boundary. However, the exhumation models of Avé Lallemant and Guth (1990) and of Mann and Gordon (1996) involve plate boundary–parallel stretching and fragmentation of the accretionary wedge; flow lines are parallel to the plate margin rather than perpendicular to them. The model by Avé Lallemant and Guth (1990) was based on a relatively small area in northeastern Venezuela. The goal of the present study was to test this hypothesis across the entire Cordillera de la Costa belt over a distance of ~600 km.

STRUCTURAL GEOLOGY

The rocks of the Cordillera de la Costa belt were heavily deformed during at least two orogenic phases. The first (D_1) was synmetamorphic, was apparently caused by subduction zone processes, and probably occurred in mid-Cretaceous time. The second deformation (D_2) was non-metamorphic, occurred in Tertiary time, and was caused by the obduction of these rocks onto the South American craton.

Structural analysis was performed with the purpose of constraining kinematic models for the ascent of the eclogite back to the surface of Earth and for the emplacement of these rocks onto the South American margin. The common techniques of kinematic analysis of ductile structures (e.g., Passchier and Trouw, 1996) and of brittle structures (e.g., Petit, 1987) were applied.

D_1 Structures

Deformation structures related to the descent of these rocks into a subduction zone were not encountered; the overprint by the D_1 deformation was apparently too strong. The D_1 deformation structures formed during peak and retrograde metamorphism, the oldest structures (D_{1a}) at eclogite facies conditions (~700 °C and 20 kbar; Sisson et al., 1997) and the youngest (D_{1e}) at the lowest greenschist facies conditions. Locally, D_{1e} structures are brittle.

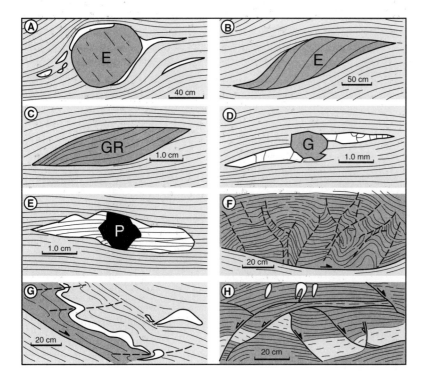

Figure 2. Sketches after photographs of deformation structures; all figures are oriented EW with east to the right and west to the left. (A) Clock-wise rotation (D_{1c}) of eclogite (E) knocker with pressure shadows filled with quartz veins, in mica schist. (B) Asymmetric eclogite (E) lens in mica schist having undergone NS flattening and right-lateral simple shearing parallel to S_{1c} foliation and L_{1c} stretching lineation. (C) Asymmetric graphite-rich particle (GR) having undergone NS flattening and right-lateral simple shearing parallel to S_{1c} foliation and L_{1c} stretching lineation; matrix is mica schist. (D) Garnet crystal (G) with asymmetric pressure shadows filled with quartz grains parallel to L_{1c} lineation, in a matrix of mica, chlorite, and quartz; EW extensile strain ~400%. (E) Pyrite crystal (P) with symmetric pressure shadows parallel to L_{1c} lineation, filled with quartz and calcite fibers in phyllitic matrix; EW extensile strain ~250%. (F) D_{1d} kink-style folds in graphite-rich mica schist. (G) D_{1d} folds with large radius of curvature in mica schist. (H) Semi-brittle left- and right-lateral (D_{1e}) shear zones in mica schists and quartz-feldspar rock; EW extensile strain ~60%.

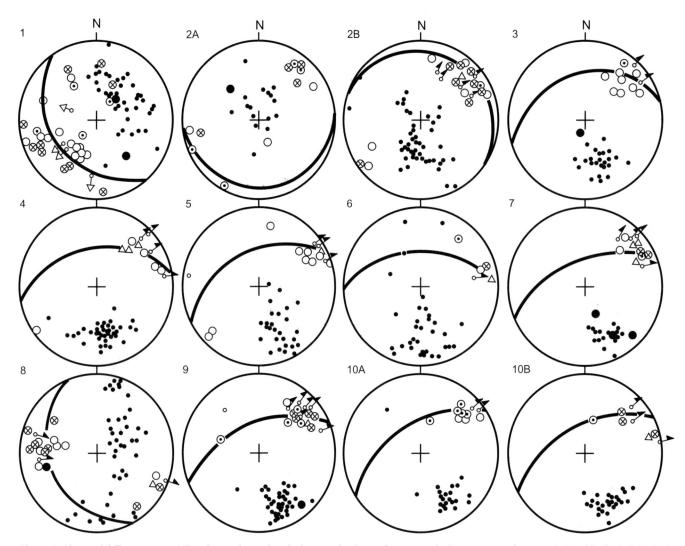

Figure 3 *(this and following page.)* Equal-area, lower-hemisphere projections of mesoscopic D_{1c} structures in areas 1, 2A, 2B, 3, 4, 5, 6, 7, 8, 9, 10A, 10B, 11, 12, 13, 14, 15, 16, 17, 18, 19, 20, 21, and 22 (locations in Fig. 1). Filled circles and dots are poles to fold axial planes and cleavages, respectively; dotted, open, and crossed circles are fold axes, mineral lineations, and intersection lineations, respectively; triangles are stretching lineations; filled half arrows are right-lateral shear directions. Great circles are average cleavages.

D_{1a} and D_{1b} Structures

The D_{1a} structures are foliations in the eclogites. They are formed by parallel orientation of tabular or elongate clinopyroxene crystals. The eclogite knockers clearly rotated in their matrix during later deformation (Fig. 2A). Thus, the foliation cannot be used to construct kinematic models, and the orientations of the D_{1a} structures are not shown here. D_{1b} structures formed during retrograde blueschist facies metamorphism. The blueschist knockers have rotated as well and, thus, the orientations of their deformation structures are also not interpretable.

D_{1c} Structures

The D_{1c} deformation structures formed during retrograde epidote amphibolite to greenschist facies metamorphism. They are the most penetrative structures in the Cordillera de la Costa

belt. They consist of foliations (S_{1c}), folds (B_{1c}), and very pronounced lineations (L_{1c}) (Figs. 3 and 4).

Cleavages and foliations are the result of concentration and parallel orientation of mica, graphite, and amphibole crystals. Locally, these foliations are refolded by apparently late D_{1c} structures.

Folds (B_{1c}) are generally isoclinal and have similar (class 2; Ramsay, 1967) geometry. Sheath folds have been observed. Fold axes tend to be subhorizontal and ~ENE-trending.

At least three types of lineations were observed: intersection, mineral, and stretching. Generally, all lineations have the same orientation and are subparallel to the fold axes. The stretching lineations are the result of parallelism of elongate particles or pressure shadows. In many cases the elongate and stretched particles have asymmetric tails indicating shortening

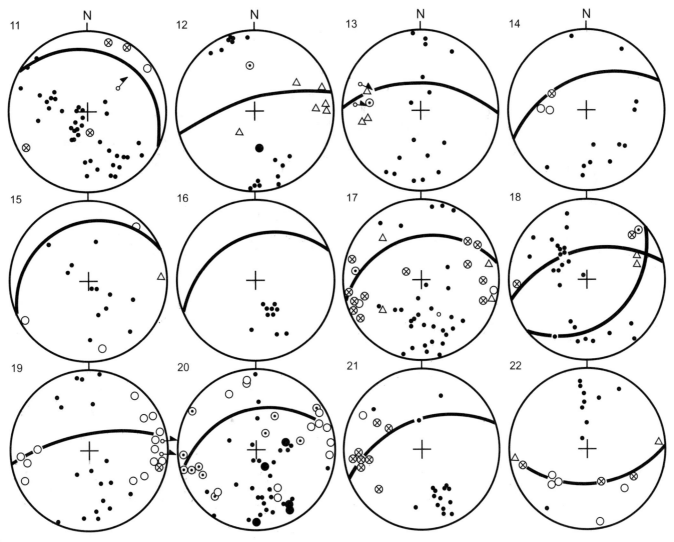

Figure 3 (*continued*).

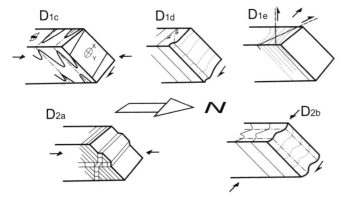

Figure 4. Block diagram showing average orientations of D_{1c} to D_{2b} structures. X and Y are the major and intermediate principal strain axes, respectively.

normal to the foliation and right-lateral simple shear parallel to the foliation and lineation (Fig. 2A–D). Whereas in some cases it is clear that coaxial shortening and non-coaxial (simple) shear occurred simultaneously (Fig. 2D), in other cases the straight, non-curved nature of the calcite or quartz fibers in the pressure shadows indicates that the fibers formed during coaxial stretching (Fig. 2E). The strains involved with the stretching can be quite high (locally up to 700%, but elsewhere lacking).

The D_{1c} structures are similar in style as well as orientation throughout the Cordillera de la Costa from Puerto Cabello in the west to Cabo Codera in the east (Figs. 1, 3, and 4). They are also similar to the ones described in the Araya and Paria Peninsulas in eastern Venezuela (Avé Lallemant, 1997). The S_{1c} foliations trend EW to ENE-WSW. The dip of the foliation is variable; along the coast, it generally dips to the north to northwest, whereas it dips to the south or southwest in the south (Figs. 1 and 3). Thus, the Cordillera de la Costa belt may be a major anticlinorium (as proposed by Morgan, 1970).

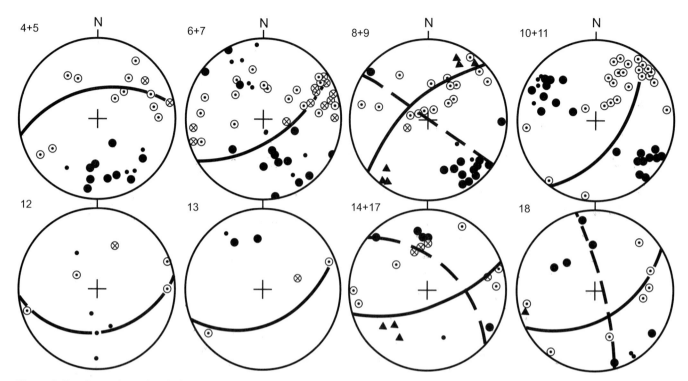

Figure 5. Equal-area, lower-hemisphere projections of mesoscopic D$_{1d}$ structures in areas 4 + 5, 6 + 7, 8 + 9, 10 + 11, 12, 13, 14 + 17, and 18 (locations in Fig. 1). Filled circles and dots are poles to NE-trending fold axial planes and cleavages, respectively; triangles are poles to NW-trending fold axial planes; dotted and crossed circles are fold axes and intersection lineations, respectively. Solid and dashed great circles are average NE- and NW-trending axial planes, respectively.

D$_{1d}$ Structures

The D$_{1d}$ folds (Figs. 2F, 2G, 4, and 5) have a kink-like style (small radius of curvature) in strongly foliated rocks (Fig. 2F), but in more massive rocks, they have a large radius of curvature (Fig. 2G) and have a class 1c geometry (Ramsay, 1967). The folds are almost always asymmetric. The axial planes of Z-folds (clockwise rotation) trend northeastward, whereas the axial planes of S-folds (counter-clockwise rotation) trend southeastward.

Although the D$_{1d}$ structures are cut by the D$_{1e}$ shears, the two seem to be related as the intensity of D$_{1d}$ deformation increases toward the D$_{1e}$ shears (Figs. 2F and 2G). The D$_{1d}$ folds occur generally in restraining bends in D$_{1e}$ shears: where the shears are right-lateral, Z-folds form, and S-folds occur where the shears are left-lateral (see Figure 4 *in* Berthé and Brun, 1980; Figure 5c *in* Grond et al., 1995). As these structures are relatively rare and folds are open (Fig. 2F and 2G), the strains involved in the D$_{1d}$ structures are quite small.

D$_{1e}$ Structures

Ductile D$_{1e}$ shear zones that crosscut all previous structures occur generally in pairs: ~WNW-trending right lateral and NE-trending left lateral shears (Figs. 2H, 4, and 6); the WNW-trending shear zones are dominant. Another set of shears are E- and W-

dipping and have normal sense of displacement. Generally, these structures were formed at elevated temperatures at which quartz recrystallized (above 300 °C); however, some of these structures are semi-brittle and have formed at lower temperatures.

D$_2$ Structures

The D$_2$ structures are not penetrative. Folds are generally of the kink-band and chevron style, although in more massive rocks, folds with large radii of curvature are present. These structures seem to have formed at low temperatures and they are post-metamorphic.

D$_{2a}$ Structures

Poles to D$_{2a}$ kink bands lie in a NS-trending girdle (Figs. 4 and 7), but two main orientations exist somewhat symmetrically disposed about the S$_{1c}$ cleavage plane. They generally trend EW.

D$_{2b}$ Structures

The D$_{2b}$ kink bands are steep and trend ~NS to NW-SE (Figs. 4 and 8). They also are low-temperature post-metamorphic structures. It is not always clear whether they are older or younger than the D$_{2a}$ deformation structures because cross-cutting relationships were not always found.

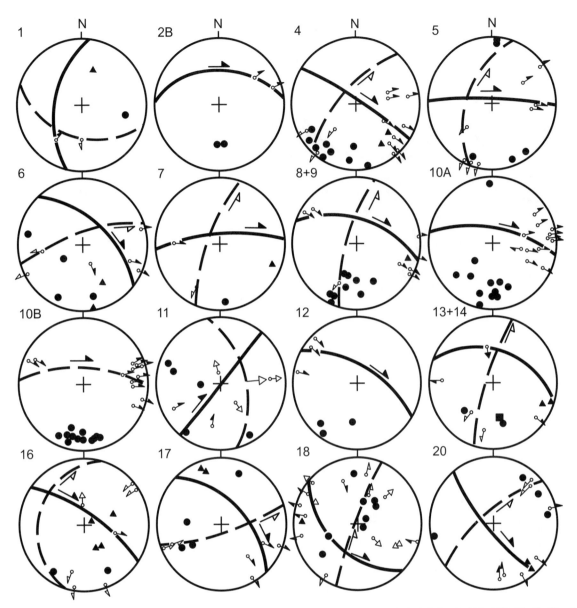

Figure 6. Equal-area, lower-hemisphere projections of mesoscopic D_{le} structures in areas 1, 2B, 4, 5, 6, 7, 8 + 9, 10A, 10B, 11, 12, 13 + 14, 16, 17, 18, and 20 (locations in Fig. 1). Filled circles and triangles are poles to right- and left-lateral strike-slip shear zones, respectively; filled and open half arrows are right- and left-lateral shear directions, respectively. Solid and dashed great circles are average right- and left-lateral shears, respectively.

Faulting

Brittle faults are common in the area. Most lack good shear sense indicators probably because of tropical weathering. Crosscutting relationships to determine relative ages of faults were not observed.

Mesoscopic thrust faults (F_1) are rare (Fig. 9). One set trends EW and dips to the south. Another set trends NE-SW and dips to the SE. The two sets may be conjugate.

The most common faults are strike-slip faults. These faults are divided into two groups, each of which consists of two appar-

ently conjugate sets. One group (F_2; Fig. 10) consists of NNE-trending left-lateral and NW-SE–trending right-lateral faults. The angle between the two fault sets is ~45°; the acute bisector is the NS-trending shortening axis.

The second group of strike-slip faults (F_3; Fig. 11) consists of NE-trending right-lateral and NW-trending left-lateral strike-slip faults. The angle between the two sets is between 60° and 90°; the shortening axis bisects the obtuse angle.

Most of the normal faults (F_4; Fig. 12) encountered show a large component of EW extension. North-dipping normal faults are rare.

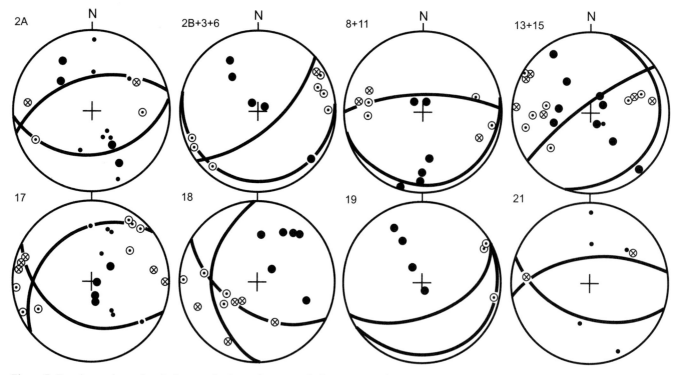

Figure 7. Equal-area, lower-hemisphere projections of mesoscopic D_{2a} structures in areas 2A, 2B + 3 + 6, 8 + 11, 13 + 15, 17, 18, 19, and 21 (location in Fig. 1). Filled circles and dots are poles to kink bands and cleavages, respectively; dotted circles and crossed circles are fold axes and intersection lineations, respectively. Great circles are average kink bands and cleavages.

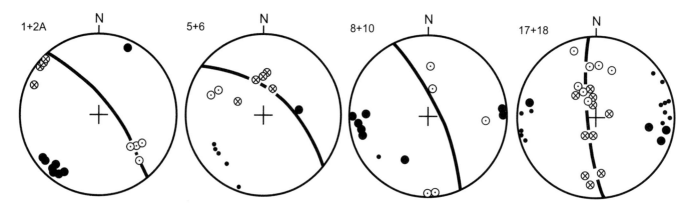

Figure 8. Equal-area, lower-hemisphere projections of mesoscopic D_{2b} structures in areas 1 + 2A, 5 + 6, 8 + 10, and 17 + 18 (location in Fig. 1). Filled circles and dots are poles to kink band boundaries and cleavages, respectively; dotted circles and circles with a cross are fold axes and intersection lineations, respectively. Solid great circles are average kink band and cleavage orientations.

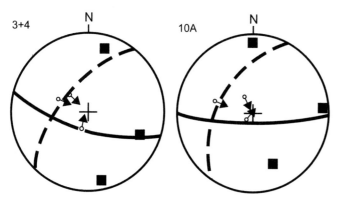

Figure 9. Equal-area, lower-hemisphere projections of mesoscopic thrust faults (F_1) in areas 3 + 4, and 10A (location in Fig. 1). Filled squares are poles to fault planes; filled arrows are shear directions. Solid and dashed great-circles are average conjugate thrust faults.

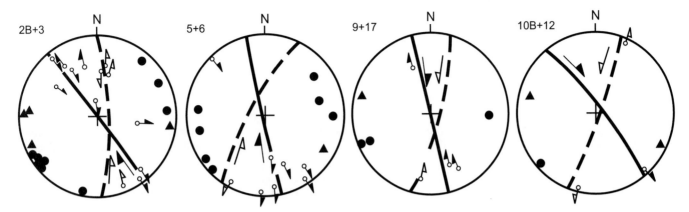

Figure 10. Equal-area, lower-hemisphere projections of mesoscopic strike-slip faults (set 1; F₂) in areas 2B + 3, 5 + 6, 9 + 17, and 10B + 12 (locations in Fig. 1). Filled circles and triangles are poles to right- and left-lateral faults, respectively; filled and open half arrows are right- and left-lateral slip directions, respectively. Solid and dashed great-circles are average right- and left-lateral strike-slip faults, respectively.

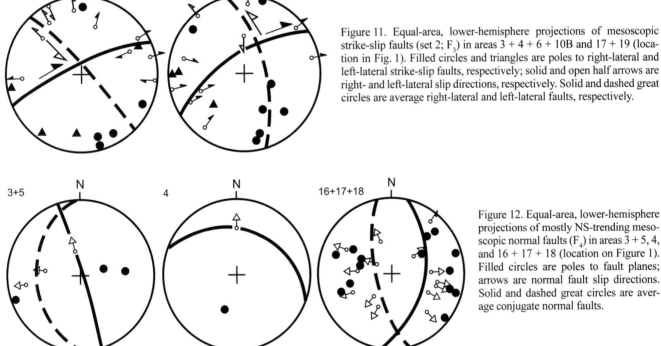

Figure 11. Equal-area, lower-hemisphere projections of mesoscopic strike-slip faults (set 2; F₃) in areas 3 + 4 + 6 + 10B and 17 + 19 (location in Fig. 1). Filled circles and triangles are poles to right-lateral and left-lateral strike-slip faults, respectively; solid and open half arrows are right- and left-lateral slip directions, respectively. Solid and dashed great circles are average right-lateral and left-lateral faults, respectively.

Figure 12. Equal-area, lower-hemisphere projections of mostly NS-trending mesoscopic normal faults (F₄) in areas 3 + 5, 4, and 16 + 17 + 18 (location on Figure 1). Filled circles are poles to fault planes; arrows are normal fault slip directions. Solid and dashed great circles are average conjugate normal faults.

Age of the Deformations

D_1 Deformation

The D_{1a} and D_{1b} structures formed during eclogite and blueschist metamorphism, respectively. The age of metamorphism in the Cordillera de la Costa belt is not very well known. U-Pb zircon age-dating of rocks from Margarita Island that are very similar to rocks in the Cordillera de la Costa belt suggests that the peak metamorphism occurred at ca. 110 Ma (Stöckhert et al., 1995).

$^{40}Ar/^{39}Ar$ white mica and amphibole ages for Margarita Island and the Araya Peninsula (Avé Lallemant, 1997; Guth, 1991; Stöckhert et al., 1995) indicate that an epidote amphibolite overprint occurred between 85 and 95 Ma, which may be the time that the D_{1c} structures formed. Biotite K-Ar ages of granites from the Cordillera de la Costa belt near north of Maracai and Puerto Cabello are 31–33 Ma, while $^{40}Ar/^{39}Ar$ white mica ages for samples from Puerto Cabello are ca. 35–40 Ma (Sisson et al., this volume, Chapter 3). However, diorites from near Cabo Codera have biotite K-Ar ages of 77 and 76 Ma (Santamaría and Schubert, 1974). Thus, it is likely that the younger (Eocene to Oligocene) ages do not represent true ages of the D_{1c} deformation but are related to the Paleogene collision event (e.g., Pindell, 1993).

$^{40}Ar/^{39}Ar$ white mica and amphibole ages for the blueschist metamorphism in the Villa de Cura belt are mid-Cretaceous as well (78–95 Ma; Smith et al., 1999). It is generally assumed that the Villa de Cura blueschists formed in the same subduction complex as the Cordillera de la Costa HP-LT metamorphic rocks (Sisson et al., 1997; Smith et al., 1999).

D_2 Deformation

Little hard data exists to constrain the age of D_2 structures in the Cordillera de la Costa belt. However, they may be correlated with unconformities in the foreland basins (e.g., Beck, 1978). The foreland basins were deformed diachronously from west to east: in the Eocene in western Venezuela, in the Oligocene in north-central Venezuela, and in the Miocene in eastern Venezuela (e.g., Pindell et al., 1998). However, zircon and apatite fission-track analysis (Pérez de Armas, this volume) indicates that major uplift and erosion occurred in the Miocene along the entire northern coast of Venezuela. This is corroborated by zircon and apatite fission-track ages in the Cordillera de la Costa belt (Sisson et al., this volume, Chapter 3).

KINEMATIC MODEL FOR ASCENT AND EXHUMATION OF HP-LT ROCKS

Any kinematic model for the ascent and exhumation of the HP-LT metamorphic rocks should be constrained by the deformation structures, protolith ages, and metamorphic ages of the rocks. Furthermore, such models ought to be consistent with the plate tectonic evolution of the region (Fig. 13).

Ascent and Exhumation of the HP-LT Metamorphic Rocks

Little is known about the descent of the HP-LT metamorphic rocks of the Cordillera de la Costa belt. Deformation structures and prograde metamorphic assemblages were destroyed during the ascent and return of these rocks along the subduction zone. Paleothermobarometry indicates that the rocks reached at least a depth of ~75 km (Sisson et al., 1997), whence they started to turn back and moved upward. The return of the eclogite to the surface of the Earth seems to have occurred in three stages. During the first stage, the eclogite ascended from 75 to ~25 km depth, undergoing blueschist retrograde metamorphism. Unfortunately, no coherent, systematic deformation structures were observed related to this stage. The oldest coherent deformation structures (D_{1c}) formed at continuously decreasing pressures and temperatures from epidote-amphibolite to greenschist facies conditions; during this second stage, the eclogite may have ascended from ~25 to ~10 km depth. During the third and last stage, the eclogite belt was obducted onto the South American craton. This deformation resulted in D_2 structures. Ultimately, the rocks were exhumed by erosion.

Stage #1 (Ascent from ~75 to ~25 km Depth)

The kinematic model for the first stage of ascent of the HP-LT rocks from ~75–25 km depth is speculative. The eclogite and blueschist have well-developed cleavages (S_{1a} and S_{1b}, respectively), but as the knockers probably rotated during later deformation (Fig. 2A), their internal structure cannot be used to constrain kinematic models. The density of eclogite is higher than that of the adjacent mantle peridotites, and, thus, eclogites generally would continue to descend along the subduction zone, even if the rate of subduction would decrease. However, the eclogites in the Cordillera de la Costa belt are only a minor constituent of the entire assemblage that consists mostly of low-density rocks (schists, marble, granites, etc.). Thus, as the rate of subduction decreases, the entire Cordillera de la Costa belt may have traveled upward along the subduction zone driven by buoyancy forces (e.g., Ernst, 1988; Ernst and Peacock, 1996) until it became part of the accretionary wedge.

Stage #2 (Ascent from ~25 to ~10 km Depth)

Whereas the kinematic model for the first stage of ascent of the HP-LT metamorphic rocks is not constrained by structural data, the model for the second stage is well constrained by the D_{1c} and D_{1e} structures. Typically, these structures have approximately the same orientation throughout the Cordillera de la Costa belt over a distance of at least 600 km from Puerto Cabello in the west to the Paria Peninsula in the east (Prologue Fig. 1, this volume).

As mentioned before, most models for the emplacement of HP-LT metamorphic rocks require flow lines to be perpendicular to the plate margin. If one assumes that the (L_{1c}) stretching lineations in the Cordillera de la Costa belt are approximately parallel to the flow direction (see Tikoff and Greene, 1997), then only two kinematic models fit the deformation structures: (1) extension related to the formation of pull-apart basins (Mann and Gordon, 1996), and (2) extension related to increasing obliquity of convergence (Avé Lallemant and Guth, 1990; Avé Lallemant and Oldow, 2000). Both mechanisms can operate only if plate convergence is oblique to the plate boundary and if displacement partitioning occurs. Today, more than 60% of convergent plate boundaries (Woodcock, 1986) have a considerable obliquity (the angle between the convergence rate vector and the normal to the plate boundary), and arc-parallel strike-slip faults ought to be common.

Displacement partitioning. It has been recognized for some time that displacement partitioning often occurs when the convergence rate vector of two plates is oblique to their mutual boundary (e.g., Fitch, 1972; Jarrard, 1986). The vector component normal to the plate boundary causes the formation of arc-parallel thrust faults and folds in the toe of the accretionary wedge. The margin-parallel vector component causes displacements along arc-parallel strike-slip faults in the back (hinterland) of the accretionary wedge. At depth, the arc-parallel shear causes non-coaxial (simple shear) deformation in the rocks.

Pull-apart structures. No matter whether the plate boundary is straight or arcuate, between en echelon, margin-parallel

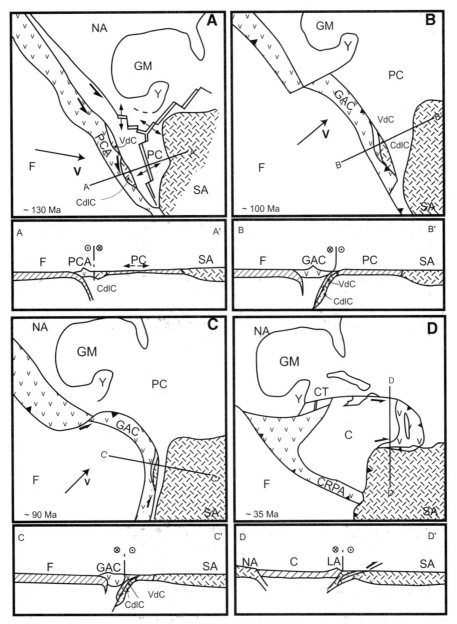

Figure 13. Speculative tectonic model for ascent and exhumation of Cordillera de la Costa and Villa de Cura HP-LT metamorphic rocks in Venezuela. Maps and cross sections of Caribbean region at ca. 130 Ma (A), 100 Ma (B), 90 Ma (C), and 35 Ma (D), modified from Pindell (1993). Legend: C—Caribbean plate; CdlC—Cordillera de la Costa belt; CT—Cayman Trough; F—Farallon plate; GAC—the "Great Arc of the Caribbean" (see Burke, 1988); GM—Gulf of Mexico; LA—Leeward Antilles arc; NA—North American plate; PC—Proto-Caribbean seafloor; PCA—Proto-Caribbean Arc; SA—South American plate; V—convergence rate vector; VdC—Villa de Cura complex; Y—Yucatán; v-pattern—volcanic island arc; diagonally striped pattern on cross sections is mid-oceanic-ridge basalt and Farallon intra-plate basalts; criss-cross pattern is continental crust. (A) Between ca. 160 and 120 Ma, Proto-Caribbean lithosphere formed by NW-SE spreading, separating the North American and South American plates. A fragment of the South American crust (CdlC) is torn off and resides east of the Proto-Caribbean arc. Left-lateral shear along the arc caused a piece of the arc (VdC) to be juxtaposed to the CdlC fragment. (B) At ca. 120 Ma, subduction beneath PCA ceased, possibly the result of collision of oceanic plateau. The PCA became a northeast-facing arc (renamed GAC). The arc and continental fragments were subducted and are protoliths of the Villa de Cura (VdC) and Cordillera de la Costa (CdlC) belts, respectively. (C) Until ca. 90 Ma, the VdC and CdlC belts migrated northward parallel to the GAC due to obliquity of the convergence rate vector, V. The arc-normal component of V decreased considerably, whereas the arc-parallel component increased: the CdlC belt started to ascend due to buoyancy forces. When both CdlC and VdC belts were incorporated in an accretionary wedge, they were deformed in D_{1c} structures; arc-parallel extension (D_{1e} structures) resulted in crustal thinning (see Avé Lallemant and Guth, 1990; Avé Lallemant and Oldow, 2000), and, thus, decompression and further ascent. (D) Before Eocene time, the Caribbean plate moved northeastward; in the Eocene, the GAC collided with the Bahamas plateau and henceforward migrated east-southeastward with respect to the South American plate. Collision of the arc with South America started in the west at ca. 35 Ma and in the east in Recent time; the plate boundary–normal component of convergence resulted in south-vergent D_{2a} folds and F_1 thrust faults by which CdlC and VdC belts were emplaced on the South American plate; the plate boundary–parallel component of convergence resulted in major (F_2) east-west–trending, right-lateral strike-slip faults. Ultimate exhumation of the HP-LT metamorphic rocks occurred by erosion.

strike-slip faults, pull-apart basins may form with an extension axis (sub) parallel to the plate margin (Mann and Gordon, 1996). Such basins are well developed in the zone of Tertiary extension between the South Caribbean Deformed Belt and the Cordillera de la Costa belt (see Ysaccis, 1997). The normal faults bounding the pull-apart structures are not perpendicular to the plate margin, but at an angle of 45° to 60°.

Extension resulting from changing obliquity. When a convergent plate boundary is arcuate (as most modern oceanic margins are), the obliquity of convergence increases along the arc, causing the subduction component to decrease and the strike-slip component to increase. This causes the forearc region from the trench to the arc-parallel strike-slip fault to undergo margin-parallel extension. The trend of any normal fault or dike is about perpendicular to the margin (Avé Lallemant and Oldow, 2000).

Generally, there is more than one arc-parallel fault or shear zone along which the forearc and part of the arc complex are displaced parallel to the arc. The accretionary complex between these faults and the subduction zone has been named "forearc sliver" by Jarrard (1986). As some of these strike-slip faults occur in the backarc, Avé Lallemant and Oldow (1988) suggested that the name "transpressional terrane" is more appropriate. Beck (1983) suggested that displacement partitioning should not take place if the dip of the subduction zone was much steeper than 20°. Thus, the depth of the transpressional terranes is expected to be less than 50 km.

The D_{1c} structures in the Cordillera de la Costa belt may have formed in a right-oblique subduction zone: the S_{1c} foliations may be the result of margin-perpendicular shortening, and the asymmetric L_{1c} stretching lineations are related to the arc-parallel shear. The D_{1e} structures have formed by EW extension as well.

Both mechanisms (pull-apart basin formation and obliquity-controlled extensional shearing) result in tectonic thinning of the transpressional terrane and, thus, decompression. It is not easy, however, to determine by which of the two mechanisms the actual deformation structures formed. The obliquity-controlled extension is favored here, because most normal faults are perpendicular to the plate boundary (Fig. 11).

The parallelism of the X strain axis with the plate boundary in the Venezuelan mélanges is not exceptional. Toriumi (1985) found stretching lineations in blueschists in Japan perpendicular to the plate boundary in mildly strained rocks and parallel to the boundary in highly strained areas. Brown (1987) reported thrust-direction–parallel stretching lineations in blueschists in Washington that were overprinted by boundary parallel stretching lineations. Ellero et al. (2001) described similar structures in the Villa de Cura belt. Thus, it appears that the flow lines in the shallower part of the accretionary wedge are perpendicular to the trench and that arc-parallel strike-slip shear occurs in the deeper parts.

Stage #3 (Ascent from ~10 km to the Surface)

Stage #3 of the exhumation history may be related to the highly right-oblique Tertiary convergence and collision of the Caribbean plate with South America (Fig. 13). Again, displace-

ment partitioning occurred. The subnormal component of convergence caused the S- to SSE-directed obduction or thrusting of the accretionary wedge. Deformation structures related to the obduction are the D_{2a} folds as well as the F_1 thrust and F_2 strike-slip faults. They may have been contemporaneous with the formation of the Cordillera de la Costa belt anticlinorium. Uplift and erosion related to these structures may have caused the ultimate exhumation of the eclogite. The boundary-parallel component resulted in displacements along EW-trending right-lateral strike-slip faults such as the San Sebastian and La Victoria faults (Fig. 1).

The D_{2b} folds and F_3 strike-slip faults may have formed in restraining bends. The F_4 normal faults are consistent with plate boundary–parallel stretching.

Is the Exhumation History Compatible with the Plate Tectonic Models?

Several models exist for the origin and evolution of the Caribbean plate and surrounding regions. One family of models has the Caribbean plate formed far to the west of the Central American (Costa Rica–Panama) arc (e.g., Pindell et al., 1988, 1998; Pindell, 1993; Pindell et al., this volume) and others have the plate form approximately near the Central American arc (e.g., Meschede and Frisch, 1998). In the present paper, we follow Pindell et al.'s model based on the strong arguments they presented.

The Late Triassic breakup of Pangea may have resulted in a ridge-ridge-ridge triple junction between the North and South American plates and the Farallon plate (Fig. 13A; see Pindell, 1993). The new seafloor was separated from the Farallon plate by a Proto-Caribbean volcanic arc (the future "Great Arc of the Caribbean"; Burke, 1988). A fragment of the South American crust (the protolith of the Cordillera de la Costa belt) may have been incorporated in the arc. Fragments of the volcanic arc (the future Villa de Cura belt; Smith et al., 1999; Unger et al., this volume) may have been juxtaposed to the continental fragment by strike-slip faulting. The arc faced southwestward and the Farallon plate, moving northeastward, was subducted beneath it.

At ca. 120 Ma, subduction polarity reversed along the Proto-Caribbean arc, possibly because of the unsuccessful subduction of an oceanic plateau, often assumed to be related to the Galapagos hotspot. However, the basalts of the Caribbean plate (B″) are much younger (Campanian; e.g., ODP Leg 165 Scientific Party, 1996) and must have formed at another hotspot (see Pindell et al., 1988, 1998). As a result of the subduction reversal, the Farallon plate between North and South America started to migrate to the NE, consuming Proto-Caribbean lithosphere (Fig. 13B).

From 120 to 90 Ma, the straight Great Arc of the Caribbean became curved (Fig. 13C), and the normal component of convergence decreased. The relatively low-density Cordillera de la Costa belt began its ascent as buoyancy forces became larger than tectonic forces. Displacement partitioning and arc-parallel stretching resulted in arc-parallel S_{1c} cleavage and L_{1c} lineation and D_{1e} shear zones.

At ca. 80 Ma, the west-facing Costa Rica–Panama arc formed far to the west of Central America, making the NE-moving prong of the Farallon plate a separate plate: the Caribbean plate.

At ca. 55 Ma, the Caribbean arc collided with the Bahama Bank upon which the arc started to migrate to the east. As North and South America started to converge again (e.g., Pindell, 1993), the relative motion of the Caribbean with respect to South America was to the SE. The southern portion of the Caribbean arc (Leeward Antilles) collided with South America and the arc and accretionary wedge were obducted onto South America. The collision was strongly diachronous: it occurred in western Venezuela in the Eocene and in eastern Venezuela in the Miocene (Fig. 13D). The normal component of convergence resulted in east-west–trending kink folds (D_{2a}), south-vergent thrust faults (F_1), and a set of strike-slip faults (F_2). The plate boundary parallel component is expressed by megascopic right-lateral strike-slip faults. One set of mesoscopic strike-slip faults (F_3) may have formed in restraining bends of the megascopic, EW-trending strike-slip faults. Normal faults (F_4) are consistent with plate boundary–parallel stretching.

CONCLUSIONS

The Cordillera de la Costa belt, northern Venezuela, is a subduction mélange containing fragments of eclogite, blueschist, amphibolite, quartzite, granite, gneiss, and marble in a matrix of mica and graphite schist and serpentinite. It formed in mid-Cretaceous time during SW-directed subduction of the Proto-Caribbean (Atlantic) lithosphere underneath the Caribbean (Farallon) plate, upon which the arcuate Greater-Lesser-Leeward Antilles volcanic arc was built (e.g., Pindell, 1993). The ascent and ultimate exhumation of the eclogite knockers occurred in three stages.

In the first stage (ca. 120 to ca. 90 Ma), the mélange traveled upward from ~75 to ~25 km depth (at a rate of ~2.0 mm/year). Buoyancy forces probably drove the ascent, because the bulk density of the mélange was much lower than the density of the surrounding mantle. Furthermore, the arc-normal component of the convergence rate or subduction rate was diminishing as the angle of obliquity increased.

During the second stage (ca. 90 Ma to ca. 60 Ma), the mélange moved from ~25–10 km depth (the rate of stretching might have been 0.5 mm/year for homogeneous deformation; the rate might have been much higher if deformation was heterogeneous). The mesoscopic deformation structures suggest that displacement partitioning and arc-parallel stretching occurred in the Cordillera de la Costa subduction complex. The arc-normal component of the plate convergence rate vector causes arc-normal shortening (arc-parallel folds, cleavage, and thrust faults), whereas the arc-parallel component causes dextral simple-shear along the cleavage plane, and arc-parallel migration of the forearc–transpressional terrane along one or more arc-subparallel dextral strike-slip faults. The arcuate shape of the arc causes the convergence obliquity to increase, the arc-normal component to

decrease (decrease of subduction rate), and the arc-parallel component to increase, which causes arc-parallel stretching.

During the third stage (ca. 60 Ma to ca. 10 Ma), the convergence between the Caribbean and South American plates was considerably right-oblique. The Cordillera de la Costa belt, the other belts of the Caribbean Mountains system, and the Leeward Antilles belt collided with and were emplaced on the South American plate. In the west, this happened in the Eocene; in the east, it happened in Miocene time.

ACKNOWLEDGMENTS

This study was made possible by National Science Foundation grants EAR-9019243, EAR-9304377, and EAR-9706521, and American Chemical Society Petroleum Research Fund grant 27788-AC2. Financial and logistical support came also from Amoco (in particular Bob Erlich and Jon Blickwede), Conoco (in particular Bill Schmidt, Larry Standlee, and Keith James), and Mobil. Marino Ostos gave enthusiastic support in the field. James Joyce and Basil Tikoff reviewed this paper and made invaluable suggestions to improve it.

REFERENCES CITED

Avé Lallemant, H.G., 1997, Transpression, displacement partitioning, and exhumation in the eastern Caribbean–South American plate boundary zone: Tectonics, v. 16, no. 2, p. 272–289, doi: 10.1029/96TC03725.

Avé Lallemant, H.G., and Guth, L.R., 1990, Role of extensional tectonics in exhumation of eclogites and blueschists in an oblique subduction setting: Northwestern Venezuela: Geology, v. 18, p. 950–953, doi: 10.1130/0091-7613(1990)018<0950:ROETIE>2.3.CO;2.

Avé Lallemant, H.G., and Oldow, J.S., 1988, Early Mesozoic southward migration of Cordilleran transpressional terranes: Tectonics, v. 7, p. 1057–1075.

Avé Lallemant, H.G., and Oldow, J.S., 2000, Active displacement partitioning and arc-parallel extension of the Aleutian volcanic arc based on Global Positioning System geodesy and kinematic analysis: Geology, v. 28, no. 8, p. 739–742, doi: 10.1130/0091-7613(2000)028<0739:ADPAAP>2.3.CO;2.

Avé Lallemant, H.G., and Sisson, V.B., 1993, Caribbean–South American plate interactions: Constraints from the Cordillera de la Costa Belt, Venezuela, in Pindell, J.L., and Perkins, B.F., eds., Mesozoic and Early Cenozoic development of the Gulf of Mexico and Caribbean region—A context for hydrocarbon exploration, Proceedings, Gulf Coast Section, SEPM Foundation 13th Annual Research Conference: Houston, Texas, SEPM (Society for Sedimentary Geology) Foundation, p. 211–219.

Beets, D.J., Maresch, W.V., Klaver, G.T., Mottana, A., Bocchio, R., Beunk, F.F., and Monen, H.P., 1984, Magmatic rock series and high pressure metamorphism as constraints on the tectonic history of the southern Caribbean, in Bonini, W.E., Hargraves, R.B., and Shagam, R., eds., The Caribbean–South American plate boundary and regional tectonics: Geological Society of America Memoir 162, p. 95–130.

Beck, C.M., 1978, Polyphase Tertiary tectonics of the interior range in the central part of the western Caribbean chain, Guárico State, northern Venezuela: Geologie en Mijnbouw, v. 57, p. 99–104.

Beck, M.E., Jr., 1983, On the mechanism of tectonic transport in zones of oblique subduction: Tectonophysics, v. 93, p. 1–11, doi: 10.1016/0040-1951(83)90230-5.

Bellizzia, A., and Dengo, G., 1990, The Caribbean Mountains system, northern South America; A summary, in Dengo, G., and Case, J.E., eds., The Caribbean region: Boulder, Colorado, Geological Society of America, Geology of North America, v. H, p. 167–175.

Berthé, D., and Brun, J.P., 1980, Evolution of folds during progressive shear in the South Armorican shear zone, France: Journal of Structural Geology, v. 2, p. 127–133, doi: 10.1016/0191-8141(80)90042-5.

Brown, E.H., 1987, Structural geology and accretionary history of the North-west Cascade system, Washington and British Columbia: Geological Society of America Bulletin, v. 99, p. 201–214, doi: 10.1130/0016-7606(1987)99<201:SGAAHO>2.0.CO;2.

Burke, K., 1988, Tectonic evolution of the Caribbean: Annual Review of Earth and Planetary Sciences, v. 16, p. 201–230, doi: 10.1146/annurev.ea.16.050188.001221.

Cloos, M., 1982, Flow mélanges: Numerical modeling and geologic constraints on their origin in the Franciscan subduction complex: Geological Society of America Bulletin, v. 93, p. 330–345, doi: 10.1130/0016-7606(1982)93<330:FMNMAG>2.0.CO;2.

Cowan, D.S., and Schilling, R.M., 1978, A dynamic scaled model of accretion at trenches and its implications for the tectonic evolution of subduction complexes: Journal of Geophysical Research, v. 83, p. 5389–5396.

Ellero, A., Marroni, M., Padoa, E., Pandolfi, L., and Urbani, F., 2001, Deformation history of the blueschist-facies sequences from the Villa De Cura Unit (northern Venezuela): Ofioliti, v. 26, p. 479–482.

Ernst, W.G., 1988, Tectonic history of subduction zones inferred from retrograde blueschist *P-T* paths: Geology, v. 16, p. 1081–1084, doi: 10.1130/0091-7613(1988)016<1081:THOSZI>2.3.CO;2.

Ernst, W.G., and Peacock, S.M., 1996, A thermotectonic model for preservation of ultrahigh-pressure phases in metamorphosed continental crust, *in* Bebout, G.E., Scholl, D.W., Kirby, S.H., and Platt, J.P., eds., Subduction top to bottom: American Geophysical Union, Geophysical Monograph 96, p. 113–118.

Fitch, T.J., 1972, Plate convergence, transcurrent faults, and internal deformation adjacent to southeast Asia and the western Pacific: Journal of Geophysical Research, v. 77, p. 4432–4469.

González de Juana, C., Iturralde de Arozena, J.M., and Picard, X., 1980, Geología de Venezuela y de sus cuencas petrolíferas: Caracas, Ediciones Foninves, v. 1, 407 p.

Grond, R., Wahl, F., and Pfiffer, M., 1995, Polyphase Alpine deformation and metamorphism in the northern Cima Lunga unit, Central Alps (Switzerland): Schweizerische Mineralogische Mittteilungen, v. 75, p. 371–386.

Guth, L.R., 1991, Kinematic analysis of the deformational structures on eastern Isla de Margarita [Ph.D. Dissertation]: Houston, Texas, Rice University, 582 p.

Jarrard, R.D., 1986, Terrane motion by strike-slip faulting of forearc slivers: Geology, v. 14, p. 780–783, doi: 10.1130/0091-7613(1986)14<780:TMBSFO>2.0.CO;2.

Mann, P., and Gordon, M.B., 1996, Tectonic uplift and exhumation of blueschist belts along transpressional strike-slip fault zones, *in* Bebout, G.E., Scholl, D.W., Kirby, S.H., and Platt, J.P., eds., Subduction top to bottom: American Geophysical Union, Geophysical Monograph 96, p. 143–154.

Meschede, M., and Frisch, W., 1998, A plate-tectonic model for the Mesozoic and early Cenozoic history of the Caribbean plate: Tectonophysics, v. 296, p. 269–291, doi: 10.1016/S0040-1951(98)00157-7.

Morgan, B.A., 1970, Petrology and mineralogy of eclogite and garnet amphibolite from Puerto Cabello, Venezuela: Journal of Petrology, v. 11, p. 101–145.

ODP (Ocean Drilling Program) Leg 165 Scientific Party, 1996, Deep-sea cores from the Caribbean reveal history of volcanism, tectonics, and oceanic change: Eos (Transactions, American Geophysical Union), v. 77, p. 291.

Passchier, C.W., and Trouw, R.A.J., 1996, Microtectonics: New York, Springer-Verlag, 289 p.

Petit, J.P., 1987, Criteria for the sense of movement on fault surfaces in brittle rocks: Journal of Structural Geology, v. 9, p. 597–608, doi: 10.1016/0191-8141(87)90145-3.

Pindell, J.L., 1993, Regional synopsis of Gulf of Mexico and Caribbean evolution, *in* Pindell, J.L., and Perkins, B.F., eds., Mesozoic and Early Cenozoic development of the Gulf of Mexico and Caribbean region—A context for hydrocarbon exploration, Proceedings, Gulf Coast Section, SEPM Foundation 13th Annual Research Conference: Houston, Texas, SEPM (Society for Sedimentary Geology) Foundation, p. 251–274.

Pindell, J.L., Cande, S.C., Pitman, W.C., III, Rowley, D.B., Dewey, J.F., Labrecque, J., and Haxby, W., 1988, A plate-kinematic framework for models of Caribbean evolution: Tectonophysics, v. 155, p. 121–138, doi: 10.1016/0040-1951(88)90262-4.

Pindell, J.L., Higgs, R., and Dewey, J.F., 1998, Cenozoic palinspastic reconstruction, paleogeographic evolution and hydrocarbon setting of the northern margin of South America, *in* Pindell, J.L., and Drake, C., eds., Paleogeographic evolution and non-glacial eustasy, North America: Society for Sedimentary Geology (SEPM) Special Publication 58, p. 45–86.

Platt, J.P., 1986, Dynamics of orogenic wedges and the uplift of high-pressure metamorphic rocks: Geological Society of America Bulletin, v. 97, p. 1037–1053, doi: 10.1130/0016-7606(1986)97<1037:DOOWAT>2.0.CO;2.

Platt, J.P., Whitehouse, M.J., Kelley, S.P., Carter, A., and Hollick, L., 2003, Simultaneous extensional exhumation across the Alboran Basin: Implications for the causes of late orogenic extension: Geology, v. 31, no. 3, p. 251–254, doi: 10.1130/0091-7613(2003)031<0251:SEEATA>2.0.CO;2.

Ramsay, J.G., 1967, Folding and fracturing of rocks: New York, McGraw-Hill, 568 p.

Santamaría, F., and Schubert, C., 1974, Geochemistry and geochronology of the southern Caribbean–northern Venezuela plate boundary: Geological Society of America Bulletin, v. 85, p. 1085–1098, doi: 10.1130/0016-7606(1974)85<1085:GAGOTS>2.0.CO;2.

Sisson, V.B., Ertan, I.E., and Avé Lallemant, H.G., 1997, High pressure (~2000 MPa) kyanite- and glaucophane-bearing pelitic schist and eclogite from Cordillera de la Costa belt, Venezuela: Journal of Petrology, v. 38, p. 65–83, doi: 10.1093/petrology/38.1.65.

Smith, C.A., Sisson, V.B., Avé Lallemant, H.G., and Copeland, P., 1999, Two contrasting pressure-temperature-time paths in the Villa de Cura blueschist belt, Venezuela: Possible evidence for Late Cretaceous initiation of subduction in the Caribbean: Geological Society of America Bulletin, v. 111, no. 6, p. 831–848, doi: 10.1130/0016-7606(1999)111<0831:TCPTTP>2.3.CO;2.

Snoke, A.W., Rowe, D.W., Yule, J.D., and Wadge, G., 2001, Petrologic and structural history of Tobago, West Indies: A fragment of the accreted Mesozoic oceanic-arc of the southern Caribbean: Geological Society of America Special Paper 354, 54 p.

Stöckhert, B., Maresch, W.V., Brix, M., Kaiser, C., Toetz, A., Kluge, R., and Kruckhaus-Lueder, G., 1995, Crustal history of Margarita Island (Venezuela) in detail: Constraints on the Caribbean plate-tectonic scenario: Geology, v. 23, no. 9, p. 787–790, doi: 10.1130/0091-7613(1995)023<0787:CHOMIV>2.3.CO;2.

Tikoff, B., and Greene, D., 1997, Stretching lineations in transpressional shear zones: an example from the Sierra Nevada batholith, California: Journal of Structural Geology, v. 19, p. 29–39, doi: 10.1016/S0191-8141(96)00056-9.

Toriumi, M., 1985, Two types of ductile deformation–regional metamorphic belt: Tectonophysics, v. 113, p. 307–326, doi: 10.1016/0040-1951(85)90203-3.

White, R.V., Tarney, J., Kerr, A.C., Saunders, A.D., Kempton, P.D., Pringle, M.S., and Klaver, G.T., 1999, Modification of an oceanic plateau, Aruba, Dutch Caribbean: Implications for the generation of continental crust: Lithos, v. 46, p. 43–68, doi: 10.1016/S0024-4937(98)00061-9.

Woodcock, N.H., 1986, The role of strike-slip fault systems at plate boundaries: Philosophical Transactions of the Royal Society, London, series A, v. 317, p. 13–29.

Ysaccis, R., 1997, Tertiary evolution of the northeastern Venezuela offshore [Ph.D. Dissertation]: Houston, Texas, Rice University, 285 p.

MANUSCRIPT ACCEPTED BY THE SOCIETY 5 APRIL 2005

Geological Society of America
Special Paper 394
2005

The alpine-type Tinaquillo peridotite complex, Venezuela: Fragment of a Jurassic rift zone?

Marino Ostos
Escuela de Geología, Minas, y Geofísica, Universidad Central de Venezuela, Caracas, Venezuela,
and *Estudios de Ingeniería Geológica Litos, C.A., Caracas, Venezuela*
H.G. Avé Lallemant*
V.B. Sisson
Department of Earth Science, MS-126, Rice University, Houston, Texas 77251-1892, USA

ABSTRACT

The Tinaquillo complex in north central Venezuela is a subhorizontal, 3-km-thick sheet consisting mostly of mylonitized harzburgitic peridotite. Along a thrust contact it overlies low-grade meta-sedimentary rocks of the Cordillera de la Costa belt. The Tinaquillo complex underlies high-grade metamorphic rocks of the Caucagua–El Tinaco belt. Based on olivine and orthopyroxene microstructures and paleothermometry, two distinct phases of deformation have been identified that occurred at different depths: coarse-grained porphyroclasts may have formed at ~80 km depth in the asthenosphere, while fine-grained crystals (neoblasts) formed during mylonitization at ~25–30 km depth. Gabbro sills in the complex have trace-element abundances indicating a subcontinental source; they may have formed by partial melting of the peridotite in a rising mantle diapir. Whereas, initially, rifting resulted in symmetric north-northwest–south-southeast extension ("pure shear") above the rising diapir, kinematic analysis indicates that the mylonite formed as the result of northwest-directed "simple shear." The timing of extension is Jurassic as indicated by several new $^{40}Ar/^{39}Ar$ age determinations. This extension may be related to the breakup of Pangea and the oblique divergence between the North and South American plates. In Tertiary time, the complex was emplaced by NS contraction as a result of oblique convergence between North and South America.

Keywords: peridotite mylonite, granulite, Jurassic continental rifting, Caribbean tectonics, olivine fabrics.

INTRODUCTION

Ultramafic, ultrabasic peridotites occur in several settings: (1) ultramafic-mafic stratiform complexes, such as the Stillwater complex, Montana (e.g., Jackson, 1961); (2) ophiolite complexes that are thought to have formed at mid-oceanic ridges, or at back-arc spreading centers (e.g., Coleman, 1977), or in volcanic island arcs (Xenophontos and Bond, 1977); (3) in concentric intrusions, also known as Alaska-type intrusions (e.g., Taylor, 1967); (4) as fragments occurring along plate boundary zones, called Alpine-type peridotites that generally are considered to be fragments of Earth's upper mantle exhumed as the result of lithospheric plate

*ave@rice.edu

Ostos, M., Avé Lallemant, H.G., and Sisson, V.B., 2005, The alpine-type Tinaquillo peridotite complex, Venezuela: Fragment of a Jurassic rift zone?, *in* Avé Lallemant, H.G., and Sisson, V.B., eds., Caribbean–South American plate interactions, Venezuela: Geological Society of America Special Paper 394, p. 207–222, doi: 10.1130/2005.2394(08). For permission to copy, contact editing@geosociety.org. ©2005 Geological Society of America.

interactions (e.g., De Roever, 1957; Den Tex, 1969); and (5) as xenoliths in basaltic lavas (e.g., Jackson and Wright, 1970). Mafic-ultramafic complexes of the first four terranes are relatively easy to distinguish (e.g., Jackson and Thayer, 1972) on the basis of their megascopic structure, their mineralogy, and texture. However, if these complexes have undergone penetrative deformation and have been dismembered, it may be difficult to place them in one of these classes. In many cases geochemical analyses, in particular of rare earth element (REE) and other trace elements, can distinguish between these terranes (e.g., Lambert and Simmons, 1987; Harper, 2003).

MacKenzie (1960) considered the Tinaquillo ultramafic-mafic complex in northern Venezuela to have been emplaced as a crystal-mush intrusion. During a reconnaissance trip to the complex, we got the impression that the complex was a tectonically emplaced fragment possibly from the upper mantle. To resolve this controversy, we decided to carry out a structural study (Ostos, 1984) of the complex using principles of kinematic analysis (Zwart, 1962; Simpson and Schmid, 1983; Passchier and Trouw, 1996). We collected some samples for geochemical analysis (see Ostos and Sisson, this volume) and age dating (see Sisson et al., this volume, Chapter 3). The main approach of the study was to analyze the deformation structures in the complex and in the adjacent belts with the intent to understand the origin and emplacement of the complex and to place the results in a plate-kinematic model.

TECTONIC SETTING

The Tinaquillo complex occurs in the boundary zone of the Caribbean and South American plates. This boundary zone (Fig. 1) consists of several tectonic slices (e.g., Bellizzia, 1967; Case et al., 1984; Ostos et al., this volume, Chapter 2). These belts are, from north to south: (1) the South Caribbean deformed belt, (2) the Leeward Antilles volcanic arc, (3) a zone of Neogene extension, and (4) the Caribbean Mountain system. The Caribbean Mountain system is divided into the following belts, from north to south: (4a) the Cordillera de la Costa belt, (4b) the Caucagua–El Tinaco belt, (4c) the Paracotos or Loma de Hierro belt, (4d) the Villa de Cura belt, and (4e) the Serranía del Interior foreland fold and thrust belt (Bellizzia and Dengo, 1990).

The South Caribbean deformed belt is thought to be a Neogene structure along which the Caribbean oceanic crust is being subducted southward. The plate convergence rate is very small and very right oblique; the north-south component is zero near Trinidad and ~10 mm in the west near the Panama–Costa Rica arc; the east-west component is ~20 mm/yr (Weber et al., 2001).

The Leeward Antilles terrane is a volcanic island arc, built on a basaltic plateau (White et al., 1999). As the arc collided diachronously because of the oblique convergence, arc magmatism ceased in the west at ca. 80 Ma and in eastern Venezuela in Miocene time (Santamaría and Schubert, 1974).

In the Neogene, the major component of slip was along major east-west–striking right-lateral strike-slip faults. They tend to be stepping to the right, causing large pull-apart basins to form

(Bonaire, Cariaco, and Carúpano basins; see Ostos et al., this volume, Chapter 2).

The Cordillera de la Costa belt is a subduction mélange of mid- to Late Cretaceous age. It consists of three lithological assemblages (Avé Lallemant and Sisson, 1993): oceanic rocks, continental slope deposits, and granitic rocks. The first consists of serpentinites, amphibolites, and mica schists containing blocks of eclogite and blueschist. The second assemblage consists of graphite and mica schists, marbles, and quartzofeldspathic schists and gneisses; the protoliths of these rocks are often assumed to be continental slope deposits of Late Jurassic and Cretaceous age (e.g., Menendez, 1966; Urbani, 1969); blocks of eclogite and blueschist occur in this assemblage as well. The third assemblage consists of granites and granitic gneisses; some were dated as Ordovician (U-Pb; Avé Lallemant and Sisson, 1993; Sisson et al., this volume, Chapter 3).

The Caucagua–El Tinaco belt consists of Paleozoic high-grade metamorphic rocks overlain by Permian and Cretaceous low-grade metasedimentary and metavolcanic rocks (e.g., Menendez, 1966). The volcanic rocks are somewhat alkalic. The Tinaquillo ultramafic complex is considered part of the Caucagua–El Tinaco belt.

The Paracotos belt consists of Campanian to Maastrichtian sedimentary rocks and several slices of serpentinite, gabbro, pillow basalts, and radiolarian chert. They may be fragments of ophiolites (e.g., Menendez, 1966). The Paracotos Formation has sedimentary structures akin to flysch, suggesting that the region was deformed in latest Cretaceous time (González de Juana et al., 1980); however, it is possible that the blocks in which Cretaceous fossils were found are olistostromes.

The Villa de Cura belt (e.g., Navarro, 1983) consists of four coherent tectonic slices of blueschist, each with a slightly different pressure-temperature (*P-T*) path (Smith et al., 1999). The protolith of the blueschists is primitive island arc basalt (Unger et al., this volume). They were metamorphosed at 96–80 Ma (Smith et al., 1999). The Villa de Cura blueschists may have formed at the same time and in the same subduction zone as the eclogites and blueschists (e.g., Smith et al., 1999).

The Serranía del Interior foreland fold and thrust belt is underlain by Upper Cretaceous to Cenozoic sedimentary rocks. Upper Cretaceous rocks may have been deposited on an Atlantic-type margin (González de Juana et al., 1980; Ostos et al., this volume, Chapter 2). In northwestern Venezuela, deposition of Paleogene flysch indicates initial collision of the Leeward Antilles arc with South America (Beck, 1985; Ostos et al., this volume, Chapter 2). In north central Venezuela, these orogenic deposits are of Oligocene and Neogene age, and in northeastern Venezuela, they are Neogene (Ostos et al., this volume, Chapter 2).

Contacts between the belts are major faults; some are mostly strike-slip faults, others are thrust faults, and yet others may have been strike-slip faults reactivated as thrust faults and vice-versa (e.g., Ostos et al., this volume, Chapter 2). Fragments of mafic and ultramafic rocks, in particular serpentinites, occur along most of the fault zones (Bellizzia, 1967). Dismembered ophiolites

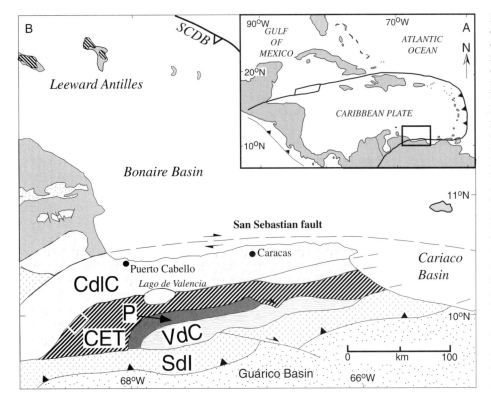

Figure 1. (A) Simplified tectonic map of Caribbean region; box is location of Figure 1B. (B) Simplified terrane map of north central Venezuela and offshore region; box is location of Figure 1C. CdlC—Cordillera de la Costa belt; CET—Caucagua–El Tinaco belt; P—Paracotos belt; SCDB—South Caribbean deformed belt; SdI—Serranía del Interior foreland fold and thrust belt; VdC—Villa de Cura belt. (C) Map and (D) cross section of the central portion of the Tinaquillo complex; dark gray (Hzb)—harzburgite mylonite; v-pattern (Gb)—gneissic gabbro; light gray (CdlC)—Cordillera de la Costa belt; stippled (CET)—Caucagua–El Tinaco belt; white (Qal)—Quaternary; line with teeth—Manrique thrust fault (teeth on hanging wall); strike and dip symbols—S_1 cleavage (numbers—dip angles); arrows—stretching lineations with arrowhead pointing downward; long lines crossed by short arrows—D_2 antiforms and synforms; north-trending lines—tear faults; large dots with numbers—sample locations (#55 is short for VT-82-55; #83 is short for VT-82-83, etc.).

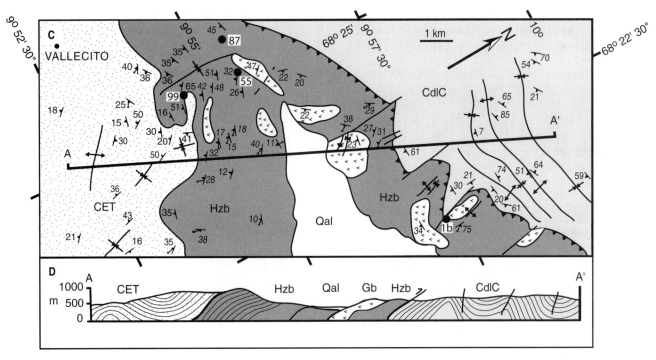

were recognized along the Paracotos belt (Bellizzia, 1967) and in the Cordillera de la Costa belt (Siquisique ophiolite; e.g., Bartok et al., 1985). Alaska-type complexes were recognized in the Villa de Cura belt (Murray, 1972).

GEOLOGY OF THE STUDY AREA

Rock Associations

The alpine-type Tinaquillo complex occurs along the contact of the Caucagua–El Tinaco and Cordillera de la Costa belts (Fig. 1). It is reasonably well exposed, and not too strongly serpentinized.

Previous studies of the Tinaquillo complex include MacKenzie (1960), Bellizzia (1967), Ostos (1984), Seyler and Mattson (1989, 1993), and Seyler et al. (1998). The map and north-south transect through the complex (Fig. 1C) are from Ostos (1984). The northeast-southwest dimension (parallel to the structural grain) of the complex is ~14 km; it is ~11 km wide. The complex is a shallowly southeast-dipping sheet of ~3 km thickness. It consists mainly of peridotite with sills of gabbro. Both are strongly mylonitized. MacKenzie (1960) interpreted the complex as a magmatic or crystal-mush intrusion. Ostos (1984) and Seyler et al. (1998) interpreted it as a fragment of the upper mantle possibly having ascended in a mantle diapir, but having been mylonitized during relatively shallow emplacement of the complex onto the South American continent.

To the northwest, the Tinaquillo complex overlies low-grade phyllites of the Cordillera de la Costa belt along the shallowly southeast dipping Manrique thrust fault. To the southeast, it is overlain along a southeast-dipping contact that subparallels the peridotite sheet by the high-grade metamorphic gneisses of the Tinaco complex of the Caucagua–El Tinaco belt. The interpretation of this contact is controversial. MacKenzie (1960) considered it intrusive, but Ostos (1984) and Seyler et al. (1998) proposed that it is tectonic.

Tinaquillo Complex

The Tinaquillo complex consists of ~90% tectonite ultramafic rocks and 10% gneissic gabbro. The ultramafic rocks consist of ~75% harzburgite (= olivine-orthopyroxene rock; clinopyroxene content <5%), 20% dunite (>90% olivine), and 5% serpentinite. Pyroxenite and amphibolite sills and dikes are volumetrically insignificant as are hornblende plagioclase pegmatites.

The harzburgites have a mylonitic texture. They contain large porphyroclasts of orthopyroxene (up to 6 cm in length) and smaller ones of olivine (up to 6 mm); rare clinopyroxene occurs as small equidimensional grains (<2 mm) and elongate spinel (<4 mm). The matrix of the mylonite is fine-grained (~0.1 mm). The porphyroclasts show a strong shape preferred orientation (SPO) resulting in a penetrative cleavage (S_1) and a strong lineation (L_1).

Dunite occurs in bands (a few cm to m thick) parallel to S_1 in the harzburgite. It has a mylonitic cleavage that parallels S_1.

The rare orthopyroxenite and amphibolite sills and dikes are generally parallel to S_1 in the harzburgite. They are open (Fig. 2A) to tight (Fig. 2B) to isoclinal (Fig. 2C). Some hornblende veins are at an angle to the cleavage and are post-tectonic.

Serpentinization has occurred in the entire complex. Most harzburgites and dunites are serpentinized to some degree. Toward the Manrique thrust fault in the northwest, the harzburgite changes gradually first to a massive unfoliated serpentinite, subsequently to a foliated serpentinite, and ultimately to a serpentinite breccia, which includes fragments of the northern phyllite belt. Serpentinites also occur near the northwest-trending tear faults, along the contact with the Tinaco complex, and adjacent

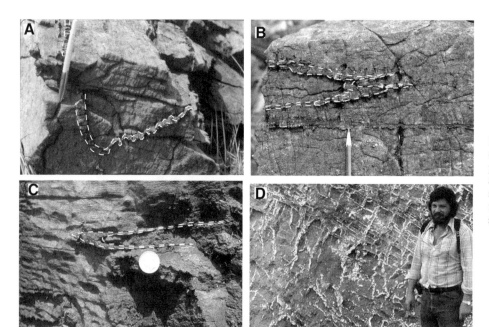

Figure 2. Open (A), tight (B), and isoclinal (C) D_1 (first deformation) folds of pyroxenite layers in harzburgite; cleavage S_1 is parallel to the fold axial plane; stretching lineation (L_1) is parallel to fold axes. (D) Serpentinite with magnesite veins.

to some of the gabbros. Most of the serpentinites consist of antigorite, but near the Manrique fault, chrysotile is dominant. Locally, near the northern contact along the Manrique thrust fault, the serpentinites are penetratively fractured, and the fractures are filled with magnesite (Fig. 2D).

The gabbro occurs in lenses or sills parallel to the S_1 cleavage in the harzburgite. The gabbro often shows a compositional banding (Fig. 3A) and a mylonitic cleavage parallel to S_1 in the harzburgite. Similar to the harzburgite, the gabbro has also a bimodal grain size distribution. Porphyroclastic grains (~1 mm in length) of plagioclase, diopside, orthopyroxene, and minor garnet occur in a finer-grained matrix of the same minerals. The gneissic hornblende pegmatites occur as sills of a few cm to more than a meter in thickness. It consists of a plagioclase matrix (grain size ~1 mm) with porphyroclasts of hornblende up to 5 cm long (Fig. 3B). Some undeformed or little-deformed hornblende veins crosscut the harzburgite cleavage (Fig. 3C).

MacKenzie (1960) suggested that the gabbros in the Tinaquillo complex were xenoliths, related to amphibole gneisses in the Tinaco complex. Although they indeed look alike, they are geochemically very different. Trace-element compositions (in particular REE) indicate that these gabbros may have had a mid-oceanic-ridge basalt (MORB)-like source (Ostos, 1990; Ostos and Sisson, this volume). Other geochemical data including REE patterns and isotopic signatures also indicate a normal (N-) MORB source (Lar, 1992; Seyler and Mattson, 1993) for some of the complex. Other portions of the complex are similar to back-arc basin basalts or possibly to oceanic-island basalts. Giunta et al. (2002) investigated two samples from the Tinaquillo complex as well as two correlative complexes and concluded they were representative of subcontinental mantle with a rifted continental margin signature. Thus, several sources may have been present.

Tinaco Complex

The Tinaco complex (Caucagua–El Tinaco belt) in the study area consists of two lithologic belts. Note that this belt is called the Tinaquillo crustal formation by Seyler et al. (1998). The northern belt is ~0.5 km thick and consists of amphibole and granulitic gneisses. The southern belt consists of quartzofeldspathic gneisses interlayered with amphibolites. Although the northern amphibole gneisses are tectonites, and in fact are locally mylonitic, MacKenzie (1960) described them as contact metamorphic rocks related to the magmatic or crystal-mush intrusion of the peridotite. Mineralogically and structurally, they strongly resemble the gneissic gabbro of the Tinaquillo complex. They consist of plagioclase (andesine), diopside, hornblende, and, rarely, orthopyroxene and garnet. However, geochemically, they are different. On the basis of trace element abundances (in particular REE) Ostos (1990) and Ostos and Sisson (this volume) concluded that they formed in a volcanic or magmatic arc. Seyler et al. (1998) also note a different trace-element trend for some of the felsic samples from the Tinaco complex.

The quartzofeldspathic gneisses and the amphibolites of the southern belt conformably overlie the amphibole gneisses. Generally, the quartzofeldspathic gneisses are interlayered with amphibolite layers. They are folded very tightly (Fig. 3D). The quartzofeldspathic bands are 1–5 cm thick and the amphibolites are generally 4–30 cm thick. The amphibolites consist of plagioclase (oligoclase), green hornblende, and epidote with minor amounts of quartz, microcline, biotite, chlorite, titanite, garnet, zircon, and allanite. The quartzofeldspathic gneisses consist of plagioclase (oligoclase), quartz, and muscovite, with minor epidote, microcline, green hornblende, titanite, apatite, and allanite.

Figure 3. (A) Gabbroic gneiss in the Tinaquillo peridotite; mafic layer is boudinaged and stretched parallel to lineation (L_1); sense of shear is shown with arrows. (B) Hornblende pegmatite gneiss in Tinaquillo complex; δ structure at the tips of the hornblende porphyroclast (18 mm in diameter) shows counterclockwise rotation. (C) Two subvertical hornblende veins crosscutting cleavage in harzburgite, dipping ~30° to the right. (D) Tight D_1 fold in gneiss in the Tinaco complex.

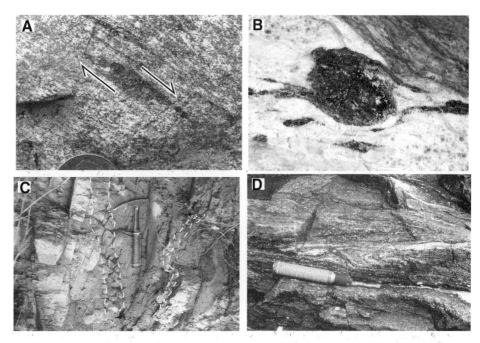

Cordillera de la Costa Belt

The metasedimentary rocks underlying the Tinaquillo complex in the north are deformed calcareous quartz-muscovite and quartz-graphite phyllites grading into marble. Based on lithological similarities, these rocks were assigned to the Mercedes Formation of the Caracas Group, a major rock group in the Cordillera de la Costa belt, (Wehrmann, 1972; see also Ostos et al., this volume, Chapter 2). The depositional age of these rocks is unknown, but they are generally assumed to be of Jurassic to Late Cretaceous age (Menendez, 1966).

Metamorphism and Paleothermometry

Tinaquillo Complex

The chemical composition of coexisting clinopyroxenes and orthopyroxenes in peridotites can be used to estimate temperatures at which these rocks were metamorphosed and recrystallized (Wood and Banno, 1973; Wells, 1977; Lindsley, 1983; Taylor, 1998; Nimis and Taylor, 2000). Each equation of state results in different temperatures. The Lindsley (1983) pyroxene geothermometer has the advantage over the other thermometers in that the plotted pyroxene compositions also indicate whether the pyroxenes are in Fe-Mg equilibrium. According to Taylor (1998), the Wells (1977) geothermometer yields the best results for mantle assemblages.

Taylor (1998) and Nimis and Taylor (2000) calibrated experimental results for four phase lherzolites and derived enstatite-in-clinopyroxene geothermometers. These may not yield appropriate temperatures for the Tinaquillo complex since these samples are not in equilibrium with garnet (Nimis and Taylor, 2000).

The harzburgites of the Tinaquillo complex contain both orthopyroxene and clinopyroxene porphyroclasts as well as small recrystallized matrix grains (neoblasts) of the same minerals. Pyroxene compositions were measured in two samples (Table 1) using an ETEC electron microprobe at Rice University. Operation conditions were 15kV and 15 nA using a 5 micron beam. Natural and synthetic oxides were used as standards. The data was processed using the Bence-Albee reduction scheme. The orthopyroxene is not zoned in either sample, whereas the clinopyroxene is zoned in one sample. The recrystallized clinopyroxene has a lower ferrosilite component than the original grains.

Depending on the method used (Table 2), the temperatures vary considerably. As discussed above, the method proposed by Wells (1977) is the most reliable. Even then, the temperatures, in particular of the porphyroclasts, vary greatly. Temperatures for the cores of the porphyroclasts are between 900 °C

TABLE 1. REPRESENTATIVE PYROXENE COMPOSITIONS

	VTO-82-99						VTO-82-87					
	Opx core	Opx rim	Cpx core	Cpx rim	Opx mylonite	Cpx mylonite	Opx core	Opx rim	Cpx core	Cpx rim	Opx mylonite	Cpx mylonite
SiO_2	55.10	56.10	51.18	51.17	56.62	51.20	54.47	55.93	51.10	53.89	56.23	51.73
TiO_2	0.07	0.05	0.37	0.38	0.03	0.12	0.11	0.06	0.28	0.24	0.04	0.20
Al_2O_3	3.36	2.86	5.28	4.93	2.80	2.49	4.91	4.06	5.76	4.49	2.47	2.89
FeO	6.40	6.55	2.23	2.24	6.41	3.14	5.83	6.22	2.16	2.11	6.49	2.27
MgO	34.57	34.86	15.93	16.39	35.24	17.67	33.21	32.57	22.31	15.38	33.21	16.71
MnO	0.18	0.17	0.07	0.14	0.14	0.10	0.17	0.18	0.10	0.12	0.22	0.10
CaO	0.39	0.37	22.01	22.63	0.34	22.82	0.87	0.35	18.04	25.12	0.31	24.82
Na_2O	0.02	0.02	1.19	1.06	0.00	1.09	0.11	0.03	1.26	0.19	0.02	0.59
Cr_2O_3	0.23	0.15	0.66	0.65	0.20	0.09	0.33	0.46	0.57	0.34	0.16	0.35
Total	100.32	101.10	98.92	99.57	101.77	98.70	99.99	99.85	101.56	101.88	99.15	99.63
cations per 6<O>												
Si	1.900	1.918	1.879	1.871	1.921	1.901	1.881	1.929	1.813	1.920	1.955	1.901
Ti	0.002	0.001	0.010	0.010	0.001	0.003	0.003	0.002	0.007	0.006	0.001	0.005
Al	0.137	0.115	0.228	0.212	0.112	0.109	0.200	0.165	0.241	0.189	0.101	0.125
Fe	0.185	0.187	0.068	0.069	0.182	0.097	0.168	0.179	0.064	0.063	0.189	0.070
Mg	1.777	1.777	0.872	0.893	1.783	0.978	1.710	1.675	1.180	0.817	1.722	0.915
Mn	0.005	0.005	0.002	0.004	0.004	0.003	0.005	0.005	0.003	0.004	0.006	0.003
Ca	0.014	0.013	0.866	0.887	0.012	0.908	0.032	0.013	0.685	0.959	0.012	0.977
Na	0.001	0.001	0.085	0.075	0	0.078	0.007	0.002	0.086	0.013	0.001	0.042
Cr	0.006	0.004	0.019	0.019	0.005	0.003	0.009	0.012	0.016	0.010	0.004	0.010
Wo	1.3	1.2	45	45	1.1	45.2	2.7	1.2	36.5	47.9	1.1	47
En	88.6	88.7	50.9	51	89	49.7	87.5	88.6	60	48.3	88.7	49.2
Fs	10.2	10.2	4.1	4	9.9	5.0	9.7	10.2	3.5	3.7	10.2	3.8

Note: Pyroxene components calculated according to Lindsley (1983).

and 1395 °C. The variability is related to the fact that it is not known whether the analyzed cores of the orthopyroxenes and clinopyroxenes formed at the same time. Furthermore, the core of a pyroxene grain may not have been cut by the thin sectioning. The rims of the porphyroclasts and the neoblasts may have formed at temperatures between 570 °C and 900 °C according to the Well's method.

These temperatures are similar to those of Seyler and Mattson (1989) for the Tinaquillo peridotite. They estimated initial temperatures of 1350 °C at >1500–2100 MPa using olivine-orthopyroxene-spinel geothermometry and Al-in-enstatite for a pressure estimate. They also found neoblasts that record 860–790 °C at 700 MPa, estimated using the Wells (1977) geothermometer. Also, Seyler et al. (1998) analyzed three gabbro gneisses in the complex. They concluded that the gabbro gneisses equilibrated at temperatures of 700–800 °C at 680 MPa using garnet-orthopyroxene geothermometry and garnet-clinopyroxene-plagioclase-quartz geobarometry.

Serpentinization (formation of antigorite) of the harzburgite may have started at temperatures of 550 °C to 600 °C, depending on the ambient pressure. Antigorite is stable to temperatures as low as 250 °C. Below 250 °C, chrysotile is stable (Bucher and Frey, 1994).

The gabbroic gneisses show two generations of metamorphic minerals. The metamorphic assemblage of the porphyroclastic grains in the gabbro is plagioclase (andesine) + diopside ± orthopyroxene ± garnet. This assemblage is characteristic of granulite facies metamorphism. Depending on fluid composition, it may have formed at temperatures of 650 °C to 850 °C (Bucher and Frey, 1994). The second assemblage consists of plagioclase (andesine) + brown hornblende; some of the other minerals may also be stable. This assemblage is typical of the middle amphibolite facies corresponding to temperatures of 550 °C to 650 °C (Bucher and Frey, 1994).

Tinaco Complex

South of the Tinaquillo complex, amphibole gneisses of the Tinaco complex have the same metamorphic assemblages as the gabbros in the Tinaquillo complex and, thus, may have formed at comparable temperatures (650 °C to 850 °C). Seyler et al. (1998) reported paleotemperatures of 750 °C to 800 °C. *P-T* paths indicate initial conditions of 500–600 MPa with an increase of 150 MPa during deformation followed by near isobaric cooling (Sey-

ler et al., 1998). This type of anticlockwise *P-T* path may be associated with crustal extension such as intracontinental rifts.

The quartzofeldspathic gneisses of the southern belt consist of plagioclase (oligoclase) + quartz + muscovite ± epidote ± quartz ± microcline ± green hornblende ± titanite. The mafic rocks contain plagioclase (oligoclase) + green hornblende + epidote ± quartz ± microcline ± chlorite ± titanite ± garnet. The occurrence of microcline rather than sanidine in these rocks limits the maximum temperature of reequilibration to 450 °C (Bambauer and Bernotat, 1982). Quartz grains show recrystallization textures requiring temperatures above 300 °C (Voll, 1976). Thus, these rocks were metamorphosed between 300 °C and 450 °C, equivalent to low greenschist facies conditions (Bucher and Frey, 1994).

Cordillera de la Costa Belt

The characteristic metamorphic assemblage is calcite + dolomite + quartz + graphite ± muscovite with pyrite and hematite as accessory minerals. The association calcite + dolomite + quartz + white mica is characteristic of marls subjected to the low-grade greenschist facies (<420 °C), although the presence of graphite may indicate higher temperatures (Bucher and Frey, 1994).

Geochronology

Tinaquillo Complex

Previous radiometric age for the Tinaquillo complex include one U-Pb and one Nd-Sm age (Lar, 1992; Seyler et al., 1998). The best estimate for initial emplacement is at ca. 150 Ma, as indicated by a U-Pb age of for a felsic dike that crosscuts pyroxenite-hornblende dikes (Seyler et al., 1998). The Nd-Sm geochronologic result is from a garnet gabbro that records an age of 94.7 ± 3.3 Ma (Lar, 1992).

We acquired $^{40}Ar/^{39}Ar$ hornblende ages for six samples of the complex: three gabbro pegmatites and three amphibole dikes. None of the rocks yielded very good plateau ages because of Ar loss or enrichment. The best ages for the pegmatites are 190 Ma, 165 Ma, and 154 Ma. The best results for the amphibolite are 190 Ma, 174 Ma, and 156 Ma (for details, see Sisson et al., this volume, Chapter 3).

Tinaco Complex

Published ages for the Tinaco complex are biotite and hornblende K-Ar ages of 112 Ma and 117 Ma, respectively, for gneiss

TABLE 2. TWO PYROXENE GEOTHERMOMETRY

| | VTO-82-99 | | | VTO-82-87 | | |
	core	rim	mylonite	core	rim	mylonite
Wood and Banno (1973)	1035	850	1025	1425	935	710
Wells (1977)	900	710	900	1395	895	575
Lindsley (1983) 15 kbar	na	680	595	1110	na	610
Lindsley (1983) 5 kbar	na	605	510	1050	na	500
Taylor (1998) 15 kbar	685	620	400	1152	562	na
Nimis and Taylor (2000) 15 kbar	630	570	350	1100	510	na

and hornblende and plagioclase K-Ar ages of 236 Ma and 191 Ma, respectively, for a gneiss sample just south of the Tinaquillo complex (Urbani, 1982). More recent results include a peraluminous granulite with a lower intercept U-Pb age of 125 ± 1 Ma; the upper intercept is poorly defined at 1.1 Ga (Seyler et al., 1998). Thus, this may constrain either Pb loss or growth of metamorphic zircon. In addition, a Nd-Sm age for a garnet granulite records as 87.1 ± 3.1 Ma (Seyler et al., 1998). We acquired a hornblende $^{40}Ar/^{39}Ar$ plateau age of 146 Ma for a granulite sample just south of the ultramafics.

Cordillera de la Costa Belt

The age of the deformation and metamorphism is not very well known. We acquired several $^{40}Ar/^{39}Ar$ dates for samples collected east of Puerto Caballo of between 35 and 40 Ma. Similar rocks in eastern Venezuela (Margarita Island and Araya Peninsula) yielded ages of between 89 and 65 Ma (see Sisson et al., this volume, Chapter 3). Presumably, the Eocene ages may be related to the collision of the Caribbean plate with South America.

Mesoscopic and Megascopic Deformation Structures

Deformation structures in the Tinaquillo alpine-type peridotite complex, the mafic-silicic Tinaco complex, and in the Cordillera de la Costa belt were analyzed to constrain kinematic models of emplacement of the Tinaquillo complex. The Tinaquillo complex is separated from the Cordillera de la Costa belt in the north by the Manrique thrust fault. To the south, the Tinaco complex overlies the Tinaquillo complex concordantly.

Tinaquillo Complex

The oldest deformation structures (D_1) in the harzburgites observed in the field (Fig. 2A) are a penetrative mylonitic cleavage (S_1) and mineral lineation (L_1). The cleavage is characterized by large, strongly flattened orthopyroxene crystals (generally 1–2 cm long, but occasionally up to 6 cm with an aspect ratio of 2.5:12) and small spinel grains (generally <2 mm, but locally up to 4 mm with an aspect ratio of 2.0:5.0). Generally, the cleavage strikes east-west and dips moderately to the south (Fig. 4A). The large aspect ratios indicate that the spinel and in particular the orthopyroxene crystals were sheared and extended parallel to the mineral lineation. Thus, this lineation is also a stretching lineation. It plunges to the southeast (Fig. 4A). Pyroxenite and amphibolite layers or veins are gently to isoclinally folded, with fold axial planes parallel to the S_1 cleavage and fold axes parallel to the L_1 lineation (Fig. 2A, 2B, and 2C). Parallelism of stretching lineations and fold axes indicate that large strains and strain rotations have occurred (e.g., Cobbold and Quinquis, 1980). Field investigation of the stretched orthopyroxene crystals revealed that most grains have asymmetric shapes indicating non-coaxial deformation. Generally, the sense of shear can be determined from these asymmetries (e.g., Simpson and Schmid, 1983; Passchier and Trouw, 1996). In the Tinaquillo complex, however, the sense of shear is not systematic: in nineteen (19) outcrops, the sense of shear is to the northwest, and in nine (9), the shear sense is to the southeast (Fig. 4A).

The gabbro gneisses have a cleavage S_1 and lineation L_1 that parallel S_1 and L_1 in the peridotites. These structures are the result of the parallel orientation of porphyroclastic grains (0.5–1.5 mm) of plagioclase, clinopyroxene, and orthopyroxene. Boudinage and asymmetric deformation in these rocks can be used as kinematic indicators (Fig. 3A). The gneissic pegmatites have the same SPO as the peridotites. They consist of large (up to 5 cm) amphibole porphyroclasts in a matrix of finer-grained (~1.0 mm) plagioclase (Fig. 3B).

The second deformation (D_2) that deformed all D_1 structures is best seen on the map and cross section (Fig. 1C and

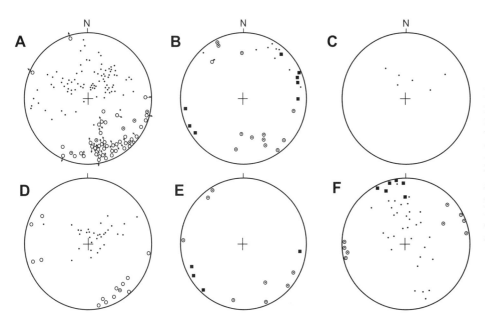

Figure 4. Equal-area, lower-hemisphere projections of mesoscopic fabric elements of the Tinaquillo complex (A to C), the Tinaco complex (D and E), and the Cordillera de la Costa belt (F). Dots—poles to cleavage; filled squares—poles to fold axial planes; circles—lineations, and arrows show sense of shear; dotted circles—fold axes. (F) Dots—poles to D_3 cleavages; filled squares and dotted circles—poles to D_4 fold axial planes and fold axes, respectively.

1D). The penetrative S_1 cleavage is folded into large wavelength (~2 km), open to gentle folds that plunge shallowly to the southeast (Fig. 4B). Mesoscopic folds were not found. The fold axial planes trend generally northwest and are subvertical parallel to a semi-penetrative spaced cleavage (Fig. 4B).

The third (D_3) generation of deformation structures is the Manrique thrust fault separating the Tinaquillo peridotite complex from the Cordillera de la Costa belt (Fig. 1C). The fault is rarely exposed, but where exposed, it dips 30° to 40° to the south. The sense of shear could not been ascertained. Several north-south–striking faults in the northern part of the Tinaquillo complex resulted in segmentation of the Manrique fault (Fig. 1C). This suggests that they are tear faults related to the Manrique thrust. Serpentinization of the peridotites is most penetrative near the thrust fault. A weak southeast-southwest–trending cleavage developed parallel to the S_1 cleavage in a broad zone south of and parallel to the Manrique thrust fault (Fig. 4C); near the Manrique, this serpentinite cleavage is disrupted by brecciation.

Tinaco Complex

The rocks in the Tinaco complex are penetratively deformed. The most obvious structure is a well-developed S_1 cleavage (parallelism of plagioclase and clinopyroxene 0.5–1.5 mm in length) that is axial planar to extremely rare mesoscopic folds (Fig. 3D). The cleavage is subhorizontal or dips shallowly to the south (Fig. 4D). Near the contact with the Tinaquillo complex, a subhorizontal southeast-plunging stretching lineation (L_1) is developed that parallels the single measured fold axis (B_1). These structures are all parallel to S_1 and L_1 in the Tinaquillo gabbros.

The S_1 structures have been refolded into megascopic, open to gentle, approximately upright folds (Fig. 1C) plunging shallowly to the southeast (Fig. 4E).

Cordillera de la Costa Belt

The phyllites north of the Tinaquillo complex are very poorly exposed. Locally, fossils have been found (e.g., González de Juana et al., 1980), indicating that the deformation must be post-Coniacian. They have undergone only one penetrative deformation that on the basis of the metamorphic grade may be contemporaneous with the D_3 deformation of the Tinaquillo complex; hence, the cleavage in these rocks will be named S_3. The layering-parallel cleavage S_3 is parallel to the axial planes of mesoscopic isoclinal folds (B_3) that trend to the east-northeast (Fig. 4F). The S_3 cleavage is megascopically folded about a horizontal east-northeast–trending axis (Fig. 4F).

Microstructural Analysis

More than 160 oriented hand specimens were collected from all three belts to study the microstructures: both microfabrics and microtextures. This was done not only to verify field observations, but also to get more information on the kinematics and mechanisms of deformation. Furthermore, microstructural data combined with

published experimental deformation data can be used to estimate strain rates and viscosities of the upper mantle of which the Tinaquillo complex was part. Microfabric analysis of crystals in rocks deformed at intermediate to high temperatures ($T/T_m > 0.5$; T = temperature and T_m = melting temperature in K) show that these crystals often develop a lattice preferred orientation (LPO) from which the principal finite strain axes can be deduced.

The two main competing mechanisms of deformation occurring in rocks at intermediate and high temperatures are dislocation and diffusion creep (e.g., Karato et al., 1986; Mei and Kohlstedt, 2000a, 2000b). Diffusion creep is dominant in very fine-grained materials at high temperatures and low stresses (Twiss and Moores, 1992). Ultramylonites are fine-grained (grain size <0.01 mm) and may have formed by diffusion processes. Diffusion creep may not be dominant in coarse-grained rocks. The mylonites of the Tinaquillo complex are much too coarse (Fig. 5) and show strong SPOs as well as LPOs. Both features are typical of dislocation creep and atypical for diffusion creep (Twiss and Moores, 1992).

Tinaquillo Complex

The olivine LPOs of six harzburgite samples from the Tinaquillo complex were determined. These LPOs are quite unusual (only two are shown in Fig. 6; all microfabrics are presented in Ostos, 1984). The best-developed element of the LPO shows a well-developed concentration of $Y = [001]$ axes, which lie in the cleavage plane S_1 at a large angle to the stretching lineation L_1. Both the $X = [010]$ and $Z = [100]$ axes form great-circle girdles about $Y = [001]$. In two samples, the Z axes girdle has no obvious maximum, but in four samples a maximum occurs at ~45° to the cleavage. Kunze and Avé Lallemant (1981), Wenk and Tomé (1999), and Jung and Karato (2001) described such LPO in experimentally deformed dunite samples. Tommasi et al. (2000) described such orientations in naturally deformed peridotite xenoliths in kimberlite. This microfabric may have formed dominantly by slip on the system (010) [100] but also on (100) [010], although the latter is unusual. The asymmetry of the Z fabric allows for determination of the sense of shear (e.g., Etchecopar and Vasseur, 1987). Of the six samples, two have orthorhombic symmetry, three samples show northwest-directed sense of shear, and one is consistent with southeast-directed transport.

Tinaco Complex

The rocks of the Tinaco complex, south of the Tinaquillo complex, have microtextures similar to the ones of the Tinaquillo gabbros. The preferred orientations of quartz c-axes were determined in two oriented samples of quartzofeldspathic gneiss of the Tinaco complex (Fig. 7). The quartz c-axes in both samples are concentrated in two maxima, approximately at 45° to the cleavage S_1. One of the maxima is much stronger, suggesting that the rocks were deformed non-coaxially (e.g., Etchecopar and Vasseur, 1987). In both cases, the shear sense is to the northwest.

Figure 5. Photomicrographs of Tinaquillo rocks. (A) Two large porphyroclasts of orthopyroxene (Opx) in a fine-grained matrix of olivine neoblasts (Ol). (B) Enlarged picture of A: olivine (Ol) neoblasts, generally with an aspect ratio of 2:1 with one porphyroclast of orthopyroxene (Opx). (C) Heavily deformed orthopyroxene porphyroclast (Opx) in a matrix of fine-grained olivine neoblasts. (D) Gneissic gabbro from the Tinaquillo complex consisting of plagioclase (Pl), quartz (Qtz), and brown hornblende (Hbl).

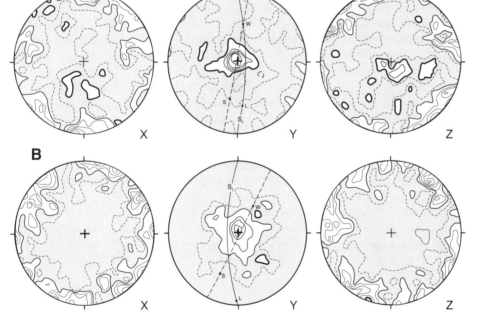

Figure 6. Equal-area, lower-hemisphere projections of olivine crystallographic axes in two samples from the Tinaquillo complex: (top) VT-82-1b and (bottom) VT-82-40. Diagrams from left to right are for the $X = [010]$, $Y = [001]$, and $Z = [100]$ crystallographic axes. Contours are at 1% interval per 1% area; 1% contour is dashed; 2% contour is bold. Dashed great circles represent the horizontal plane with S and W indicating geographic south and west, respectively. Fully drawn great circles represent the orientation of the S_1 cleavage, and L is the L_1 lineation.

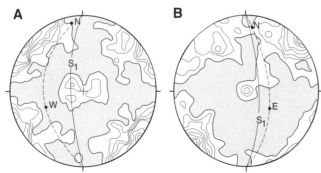

Figure 7. Equal-area, lower-hemisphere projections of 200 quartz c-axes in samples (A) VT-82-11a and (B) VT-82-83 from the Tinaco complex. Contours are at 1% interval per 1% area; 1% contour is bold. Dashed great circles represent the horizontal plane with N, W, and E indicating geographic north, west, and east, respectively. Fully drawn great circles represent the orientation of the S_1 cleavage.

Cordillera de la Costa Belt

Two samples of the phyllites in the Cordillera de la Costa belt were investigated microscopically. The orientation of quartz c-axes was measured in both. The results are not shown here, because the fabrics are not interpretable. The data are shown, however, in Ostos (1984).

Upper Mantle Flow in the Tinaquillo Peridotite

The Tinaquillo peridotite mylonites have features indicating that they formed and were deformed in the upper mantle. These rocks have a bimodal grain size distribution with large porphyroclasts of orthopyroxene, olivine, and clinopyroxene in a fine-grained matrix of recrystallized grains (neoblasts) of the same minerals, indicating that at least two thermal and deformation events occurred. Flow models for the Tinaquillo upper mantle, proposed here, are based on results of high-temperature–high-pressure deformation experiments of peridotite (Hirth and Kohlstedt, 1996) and on temperatures and stresses acquired from field samples presented here. It should be noted though that the values of almost every "constant" in the flow equations are poorly known. Therefore, the models are very speculative.

As described above, study of the small olivine neoblast grains in the peridotite mylonites indicates that they not only have a strong LPO (Fig. 6), but also a strong SPO (Fig. 5B). Both features indicate that the dominant mechanism of deformation was dislocation creep (e.g., Twiss and Moores, 1992). Several olivine dislocation creep laws have been proposed (e.g., Carter and Avé Lallemant, 1970; Ross et al., 1980; Hirth and Kohlstedt, 1996; Mei and Kohlstedt; 2000b). These flow laws are expressed by the following dislocation creep equation:

$$d\varepsilon/dt = A \, \sigma^n \exp - (Q/RT),$$ (1)

where $d\varepsilon/dt$ = strain rate; A, n, and Q (activation energy for creep) are constants; σ = differential stress = $(\sigma_1 - \sigma_3)$ [compression = positive]; R = gas constant; and T = temperature. Temperatures and stresses are determined from the study of field samples and inserted into Equation (1). Strain rates ($d\varepsilon/dt$) and viscosities ($\eta = 2\sigma/[d\varepsilon/dt]$) can be calculated. More difficult to determine are the confining pressure (depth) and the water content. However, the flow law is not strongly influenced by confining pressure, but it is sensitive to water content. Hirth and Kohlstedt (1996) suggested that the upper mantle is "wet" at depths >~65 km, but that at shallower depths, because of partial melting and removal of the melt, the upper mantle is "dry." The occurrence of deformed hornblende pegmatite and undeformed amphibole veins in the Tinaquillo complex suggests that fluids have been active at shallow levels of the mantle as well. At very shallow levels (<20 km), water must be able to penetrate the uppermost mantle to explain the generally strong serpentinization. The development of magnesite (Pennock et al., 2003) is also late and may require reaction of olivine with the ubiquitous marble and limestone in the Cordillera de la Costa belt.

At intermediate and high temperatures, crystals deformed by dislocation creep are consumed by new grains that formed by grain boundary migration recrystallization. The grain size of these neoblasts is mostly a function of the differential stress at which the rock was deformed (e.g., Ross et al., 1980; Karato, 1984; Van der Wal et al., 1993). The relationship can be expressed as (e.g., Twiss and Moores, 1992):

$$D = B(\sigma)^{-m},$$ (2)

where D = grain size; B = a constant; σ = differential stress [strength]; and m = a constant. It should be noted that this relationship can only be applied to monomineralic rocks or monomineralic areas in polymineralic rocks.

Stresses

Olivine and orthopyroxene grain sizes were measured in two samples of harzburgite mylonite (Table 3). Inserting the olivine and orthopyroxene grain sizes into Equation (2) using the values for olivine from Van der Wal et al. (1993) and for orthopyroxene from Ross and Nielsen (1978) results in stresses of ~5 MPa and 1 MPa for olivine and orthopyroxene porphyroclasts, respectively. Neoblasts were formed under stresses of ~70 MPa and 90 MPa in olivine and orthopyroxene, respectively.

Temperatures

As described above, temperatures were determined by the two-pyroxene geothermometer of Wells (1977). The temperatures acquired are quite variable (Table 2). The highest temperature found in cores of porphyroclastic pyroxenes (~1400 °C) was used for the flow law. The temperatures during mylonitization determined from the chemistry of the rim of porphyroclasts and in neoblasts are also very variable. For our calculations, we used a temperature of 900 °C, because two of the four values cluster around 900 °C; the lower temperatures (575 °C and 710 °C) are probably the result of later and shallower deformation in the field of brittle-ductile transition (Carter and Tsenn, 1987).

Flow Laws

Inserting the stresses and temperatures into the "wet" flow equation of Hirth and Kohlstedt (1996) results in strain rates of

TABLE 3. GRAIN SIZE AND CALCULATED STRESS

Grain size (mm) Sample number	VTO-82-55	VT-82-1b
Olivine (P)	2.07 ± 0.66	1.26 ± 0.45
Olivine (N)	0.053 ± 0.032	0.051 ± 0.24
Opx (P)	2.61 ± 1.85	2.93 ± 2.33
Opx (N)	0.054 ± 0.023	0.049 ± 0.025
Differential stress (MPa)		
Olivine (P)	4	6
Olivine (N)	70	71
Opx (P)	1	1
Opx (N)	85	95

P—porphyroclast; N—neoblast; Opx—Orthopyroxene.

$d\varepsilon/dt = 10^{-12.0}$ s^{-1} and $10^{-13.0}$ s^{-1} for olivine and orthopyroxene porphyroclasts, respectively. The strain rates during the mylonitization are estimated to be $10^{-12.8}$ s^{-1} and $10^{-11.1}$ s^{-1} for the olivine and orthopyroxene neoblasts, respectively. Twiss and Moores (1992) report that "normal" strain rates in the upper mantle are $\sim 10^{-14}$ to 10^{-15} s^{-1}, but in upper mantle shear zones they can be as high as 10^{-12} s^{-1}.

Viscosity can be derived from the following equation (e.g., Twiss and Moores, 1992):

$$\sigma = 2\eta \, d\varepsilon/dt, \tag{3}$$

where σ = differential stress = $\sigma_1 - \sigma_3$ (in Pa); η = dynamic viscosity (in Pa s); $d\varepsilon/dt$ = strain rate (s^{-1}). The viscosity of the Tinaquillo upper mantle based on the olivine porphyroclasts is $\sim 2.5 \times 10^{18}$ Pa s, and based on the olivine neoblasts, $\sim 3.5 \times 10^{19}$ Pa s. These values are low in comparison to published mantle viscosity of 7×10^{20} Pa s (Peltier and Andrews, 1976). However, the latter was based on glacial isostasy, whereas the Tinaquillo viscosities are related to a hot diapir.

TECTONIC MODEL

Introduction

The model proposed here for the origin and evolution of the Tinaquillo complex is based on field observations, geochemical analysis, paleothermometry, geochronology, and microstructural analysis. The model consists of two parts. In the first part, we describe the structural evolution of the complex, and in the second we try to describe the complex in term of Caribbean plate tectonics.

Mantle Diapir

Geothermometric estimates suggest that the maximum temperature at which the coarse-grained porphyroclasts in the Tinaquillo harzburgite formed was ~ 1400 °C. Such temperatures could have existed at ~ 80 km depth if the Tinaquillo complex was part of a continental upper mantle lithosphere with a heat flow of ~ 90 mW/m^2 or a thermal gradient of ~ 17.5 °C/km (e.g., Lenardic and Moresi, 2000). The complex may have ascended diapirically (Ostos, 1984; Seyler et al., 1998) from ~ 80 km depth and 1400 °C to ~ 30 km depth and ~ 900 °C (T_1 to T_2 in Fig. 5) based on the geothermometer of Wells (1977). If the upward flow started at 190 Ma, the age of the initial breakup of Pangea (e.g., Pindell et al., 1988), and ended at ca. 145 Ma, the ascent rate was 1.1 mm/yr. The rate of cooling would have been ~ 10 °C/m.y. Due to decompression, partial melting may have occurred to form the gabbro lenses and the gabbro pegmatites in the complex (e.g., Seyler and Mattson, 1989).

Simple Shear Continental Extension

At the end of the diapiric ascent, the Tinaquillo complex was juxtaposed to the lower continental crustal rocks of the Tinaco complex (T_2 in Fig. 8) along a subhorizontal extensional shear zone. Together, these rocks were sheared and mylonitized at a rate of $10^{-12.8}$ s^{-1} and at granulite facies conditions (900 °C [Wells, 1977]). Initially, the rifting process may have occurred by pure shear and the rift zone was symmetrical (Hamilton, 1987). However, at a later stage during mylonitization, flow must have occurred by northwest-directed simple shear (Wernicke, 1985), as the majority of kinematic indicators suggest northwest-directed flow. The simple shear strain rate is $d\gamma/dt = 2d\varepsilon/dt = 2 \times 10^{-12.8}$ or ~ 10 °/m.y. As most of the displacement may have occurred in the 3-km-thick mylonite, displacement rates may have been 30 mm/yr.

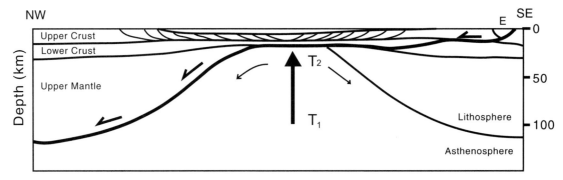

Figure 8. Model for the deformation history of the Tinaquillo peridotite after Vissers et al. (1997). The Tinaquillo peridotites have a bimodal grain size distribution. Coarse grains may have formed at ~ 1400 °C and 80 km depth (T_1). Upward flow from 80 to 30 km (T_2) occurred in a mantle diapir between 190 and 150 Ma. Initial rifting above the diapir may have been symmetrical, but the mylonitization of the Tinaquillo peridotite and the lowermost part of the continental crustal Tinaco complex must have been asymmetrical, because kinematic indicators favor a northwest tectonic transport. Some graben such as the Espino graben (E) may be related to Late Jurassic rifting.

Late Stage Thrust Emplacement

The spreading in the Caribbean ceased in the Late Cretaceous and convergence between North and South America may have started in early Eocene time (e.g., Pindell and Barrett, 1990). This convergence may have caused contraction along the Venezuelan margin, which caused the emplacement of the Tinaquillo complex by northward thrusting along the Manrique thrust fault. Radiometric ages in the Cordillera de la Costa belt north of the Tinaquillo complex (Sisson et al., this volume, Chapter 3) suggest rapid exhumation from ca. 40 Ma (muscovite $^{40}Ar/^{39}Ar$) to 15 Ma (apatite fission track). However, Kohn et al. (1984) presented three zircon fission-track ages of 49–42 Ma for samples from the Caucagua–El Tinaco belt to the east and an apatite fission-track age of 6 Ma from a sample just south of the Tinaquillo complex, indicating lower exhumation rates. Thus, the emplacement of the complex may have occurred from late Eocene to middle Miocene time.

Plate Tectonic Setting

The Tinaquillo mylonites were formed by northwest-southeast extension and northwest-directed shear during Early to Late Jurassic time. Although the Tinaquillo complex could have rotated with respect to the boundaries between the various allochthonous belts of northern Venezuela, it is attractive to assume that the south-

east-trending stretching lineations (L_1) are parallel to a northwest-southeast extension direction related to the divergence of the North and South American plates after the breakup of Pangea.

It has been proposed (e.g., Pindell et al., 1998) that the segmented nature of the Caribbean Mountain system is a reflection of the continental margin of northern South America, which may be segmented as well (Fig. 9). The segmentation may be the result of oblique divergent plate motion during the Mesozoic breakup of Pangea. The northwest-trending segments are interpreted as transform faults and the northeast-trending segments may be parallel to segments of the mid-oceanic spreading center along which the North and South American plates were separated (e.g., Pindell et al., 1998).

In the area of the Maracaibo basin in northwestern Venezuela, several northeast to north-northeast–trending graben have been identified (e.g., Maze, 1984; Lugo and Mann, 1995). These graben formed in the Jurassic and contain thick sequences of volcanic and volcaniclastic rocks (La Quinta Formation; see Ostos et al., this volume, Chapter 2). U-Pb and whole-rock K-Ar ages of the volcanics are between 168–146 Ma (Dasch and Banks, 1981; Maze, 1984; Ostos et al., this volume, Chapter 2).

Basaltic lavas in the Espino graben (Fig. 9) were collected from drill cores. They yielded whole-rock K-Ar ages of 162 Ma, suggesting a Jurassic age of northwest-southeast rifting (Feo-Codecido et al., 1984; see Ostos et al., this volume, Chapter 2). The Espino graben may extend to the southwest into the Apure-Mantical graben (Bartok, 1993).

The Bolivar dike system (MacDonald and Opdyke, 1974) trends northeast. Whole-rock K-Ar dating yielded an age of 199 Ma (calculated with old decay constant).

The Takutu graben in Guyana and Brazil has been described extensively (e.g., Berrangé, 1975; Crawford et al., 1985). It trends approximately northeast-southwest and is filled with a thick package of Cretaceous sedimentary rocks overlying Middle to Late Jurassic mafic volcanics (180–150 Ma; Berrangé, 1975; old decay constant). Rifting started in the late Triassic to Early Jurassic.

The origin of the rift systems has generally been attributed to opening of the Atlantic Ocean (e.g., McConnell, 1969; Burke, 1976; Pindell, 1985; Bartok, 1993; Seyler et al., 1998). Some of these graben may have been failed arms formed at triple junctions (Burke, 1976); others may seem to be abandoned rifts parallel to the oceanic spreading center.

While the amount of extension in these graben is probably quite small, the extension recorded in the Tinaquillo complex must have been appreciable (Fig. 8). Based on the paleopiezometric and geothermometric estimates described above, displacement rates during mylonitization may have been 30 mm/yr, which is about half of the seafloor spreading rate of 67 mm/yr of Pindell and Barrett (1990), suggesting that the remaining 37 mm/yr occurred elsewhere in the Caribbean realm.

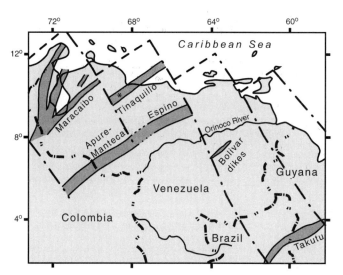

Figure 9. Proposed tectonic setting of the Tinaquillo complex (Tinaquillo is marked by the asterisk *). Dark gray areas indicate possible locations of Jurassic graben in the Maracaibo Lake area (after Lugo and Mann, 1995; Espino graben after Pindell et al. [1998]; Apure-Mantecal graben after Bartok [1993]; Bolivar dikes after MacDonald and Opdyke [1974]; Takutu graben after Teitz [1991]). Dashed northeast-trending lines are continental margin segments; northwest trending dot-dash lines are transform faults. Note that this map shows present-day geography; the terranes north of the San Sebastian fault (Fig. 1) and its extension to the west and the east and the entire Caribbean Mountain system are allochthonous and probably were not in place in Jurassic times.

SUMMARY AND CONCLUSIONS

We propose that the Tinaquillo alpine-type peridotite in north-central Venezuela is a fragment of the upper mantle that during the Jurassic breakup of Pangea moved upward in a upper mantle diapir until it reached the continental crust whereupon the vertical flow became horizontal and moved to the northwest, parallel to the direction of seafloor spreading between the North and South America plates. At present, the Tinaquillo complex is an ~3-km-thick subhorizontal sheet of mostly harzburgite with small bodies of gabbroic gneiss, and thin layers and dikes of pyroxenite, hornblende plagioclase pegmatite, and hornblendite. Trace-element abundances in the gabbro indicate a MORB-like source. All rocks with the exception of the hornblendites are mylonitized and have bimodal grain size distribution. The coarse-grained crystals (olivine, orthopyroxene, and rare clinopyroxene) are porphyroclastic and are surrounded by recrystallized neoblasts of the same minerals; spinels are generally small.

Based on geothermometry and estimated pressures, the large porphyroclasts may have formed syntectonically at depths of ~80 km and at temperatures of ~1400 °C. All deformation structures were destroyed by the later mylonitization. The fine-grained neoblasts may have formed at ~30 km depth and temperatures of 900 °C during the oldest recognizable deformation (D_1). The strain rate at which rocks were deformed is estimated at ~10^{-13}/s. The estimate of the ascent rate is 1.35 mm/yr.

The D_1 deformation structures are shallowly south-dipping mylonite cleavages and southeast-plunging stretching lineations. D_1 fold axes are also southeast plunging having rotated into parallelism with the stretching lineation. Microstructural analysis shows that the neoblasts have strong SPO as well as LPO, indicating that they were deformed by the dislocation creep mechanism {dominantly (010) [100]}. If the Tinaquillo complex did not rotate after D_1, these mylonite structures indicate southeast-northwest extension and northwest-directed simple shear. We hypothesize that these structures formed after the upper mantle flow turned from vertical to horizontal. We estimate that the displacement rate in the D_1 Tinaquillo mylonites was ~30 mm/yr, which is substantially less than the 67 mm/yr displacement rate between the North and South American plates (Pindell and Barrett, 1990), leaving 37 mm/yr for the opening of the Caribbean.

After the D_1 deformation, the mylonite sheet was deformed during D_2 into megascopic folds with upright axial planes. The B_2 fold axes are parallel to B_1 and may have formed parallel to the flow direction during convergent flow.

Generally brittle D_3 structures (north-vergent thrust faults, tear faults, cleavage) formed during collision of the Caribbean plate with South America in Paleogene time. Most thrust faults in the Caribbean Mountain system are south vergent, but north-vergent thrust faults do occur (Avé Lallemant, 1997).

ACKNOWLEDGMENTS

This study was partly supported by grants EAR-8517383 and EAR-9019243 from the National Science Foundation. Larry Snee and Peter Copeland did the ^{40}Ar/^{39}Ar age determinations. We thank Dick George and Aaron Yoshinobu for their extensive comments.

REFERENCES CITED

Avé Lallemant, H.G., 1997, Transpression, displacement partitioning, and exhumation in the eastern Caribbean–South American plate boundary zone: Tectonics, v. 16, no. 2, p. 272–289, doi: 10.1029/96TC03725.
Avé Lallemant, H.G., and Sisson, V.B., 1993, Caribbean–South American plate interactions: Constraints from the Cordillera de la Costa belt, Venezuela, in Pindell, J.L., and Perkins, B.F., eds., Mesozoic and early Cenozoic development of the Gulf of Mexico and Caribbean region—A context for hydrocarbon exploration, Proceedings, Gulf Coast Section, SEPM Foundation 13th Annual Research Conference: Houston, Texas, Society for Sedimentary Geology (SEPM) Foundation, p. 211–219.
Bambauer, H.U., and Bernotat, W.H., 1982, The microcline/sanidine transformation isograd in metamorphic regions. I. Composition and structural state of alkali feldspars from granitoid rocks of two N-S traverses across the Aar massif and Gotthard "massif," Swiss Alps: Schweizerische Mineralogische und Petrographische Mittteilungen, v. 62, p. 185–230.
Bartok, P., 1993, Pre-breakup geology of the Gulf of Mexico–Caribbean: its relation to Triassic and Jurassic rift systems of the region: Tectonics, v. 12, p. 441–459.
Bartok, P.E., Renz, O., and Westermann, G.E.G., 1985, The Siquisique ophiolites, northern Lara State, Venezuela: A discussion on their Middle Jurassic ammonites and tectonic implications: Geological Society of America Bulletin, v. 96, p. 1050–1055, doi: 10.1130/0016-7606(1985)96<1050:TSONLS>2.0.CO;2.
Beck, C.M., 1985, La chaîne caraïbe au meridien de Caracas: géologie, tectonogénèse, place dans l'évolution géodinamique Mésozoique-Cénozoique des Caraïbes Meridionales [Ph.D. dissertation]: Lille, France, Université de Sciences et Techniques de Lille, 462 p.
Bellizzia, A., 1967, Rocas ultrabásicas en el Sistema montañoso del Caribe y yacimientos minerales asociados: Caracas, Boletín de Geología, v. 8, no. 16, p. 160–193.
Bellizzia, A., and Dengo, G., 1990, The Caribbean mountain system, northern South America; A summary, in Dengo, G., and Case, J.E., eds., The Caribbean region: Geological Society of America, The Geology of North America, v. H, p. 167–175.
Berrangé, J.P., 1975, The Apoteri volcanic formation-tholeiitic flows in the North Savannas graben of Guyana and Brazil: Geologische Rundschau, v. 64, no. 3, p. 883–899.
Bucher, K., and Frey, M., 1994, Petrogenesis of metamorphic rocks (6th complete revision of Winkler's Textbook): New York, Springer-Verlag, 318 p.
Burke, K., 1976, Development of graben associated with the initial ruptures of the Atlantic Ocean: Tectonophysics, v. 36, p. 93–112, doi: 10.1016/0040-1951(76)90009-3.
Carter, N.L., and Avé Lallemant, H.G., 1970, High temperature flow of dunite and peridotite: Geological Society of America Bulletin, v. 81, no. 8, p. 2181–2202.
Carter, N.L., and Tsenn, M.C., 1987, Flow properties of continental lithosphere: Tectonophysics, v. 136, p. 27–63, doi: 10.1016/0040-1951(87)90333-7.
Case, J.E., Holcombe, T.L., and Martin, R.G., 1984, Map of geologic provinces in the Caribbean region, in Bonini, W.E., Hargraves, R.B., and Shagam, R., eds., The Caribbean–South American plate boundary and regional tectonics: Geological Society of America Memoir 162, p. 1–30.
Cobbold, P.R., and Quinquis, H., 1980, Development of sheath folds in shear regimes: Journal of Structural Geology, v. 2, p. 119–126, doi: 10.1016/0191-8141(80)90041-3.
Coleman, R.G., 1977, Ophiolites: Ancient oceanic lithosphere? New York, Springer-Verlag, 229 p.
Crawford, F.D., Szelewski, C.E., and Alvey, G.D., 1985, Geology and exploration in the Takutu graben of Guyana and Brazil: Journal of Petroleum Geology, v. 8, no. 1, p. 5–36.

Dasch, L.E., and Banks, P., 1981, Zircon U-Pb ages from the Sierra de Perijá, Venezuela: Geological Society of America Abstracts with Programs, v. 13, no. 7, p. 436.

Den Tex, E., 1969, Origin of ultramafic rocks, their tectonite setting and history: A contribution to the discussion of the paper "The origin of ultramafic and ultrabasic rocks" by P.J. Wyllie: Tectonophysics, v. 7, p. 457–488.

De Roever, W.P., 1957, Sind die Alpinotypen Peridotitmassen vieleicht tektonisch verfrachtete Bruckstücke der Peridotitschale?: Geologische Rundschau, v. 46, p. 137–146.

Etchecopar, A., and Vasseur, G., 1987, A 3-D kinematic model of fabric development in polycrystalline aggregates: comparisons with experimental and natural examples: Journal of Structural Geology, v. 9, p. 705–717, doi: 10.1016/0191-8141(87)90154-4.

Feo-Codecido, G., Smith, F.D., Jr., Aboud, N., and de Di Giacomo, E., 1984, Basement and Paleozoic rocks of the Venezuelan Llanos basins, in Bonini, W.E., Hargraves, R.B., and Shagam, R., eds., The Caribbean–South American plate boundary and regional tectonics: Geological Society of America Memoir 162, p. 213–216.

Giunta, G., Beccaluva, L., Coltorti, M., Siena, F., and Vaccaro, C., 2002, The southern margin of the Caribbean plate in Venezuela: Tectono-magmatic setting of the ophiolite units and kinematic evolution: Lithos, v. 63, p. 19–40, doi: 10.1016/S0024-4937(02)00120-2.

González de Juana, C., Iturralde de Arozena, J.M., and Picard, X., 1980, Geología de Venezuela y de sus cuencas petrolíferas: Caracas, Foninves, v. 1, 407 p.

Harper, G.D., 2003, Fe-Ti basalts and propagating-rift tectonics in the Josephine ophiolite: Geological Society of America Bulletin, v. 115, no. 7, p. 771–787, doi: 10.1130/0016-7606(2003)115<0771:FBAPTI>2.0.CO;2.

Hamilton, W., 1987, Crustal extension in the Basin and Range Province, southwestern United States, in Coward, M.P., Dewey, J.F., and Hancock, P.L., eds., Continental extensional tectonics: London, Geological Society Special Publication 28, p. 155–176.

Hirth, G., and Kohlstedt, D.L., 1996, Water in the oceanic upper mantle: Implications for rheology, melt extraction and the evolution of the lithosphere: Earth and Planetary Science Letters, v. 144, p. 93–108, doi: 10.1016/0012-821X(96)00154-9.

Jackson, E.D., 1961, Primary textures and mineral associations in the ultramafic zone of the Stillwater Complex, Montana: U.S. Geological Survey Professional Paper 358, 106 p.

Jackson, E.D., and Thayer, T.P., 1972, Some criteria for distinguishing between stratiform, concentric and Alpine–peridotite-gabbro complexes: Transactions of the 24th International Geological Congress, Section 2, p. 289–296.

Jackson, E.D., and Wright, T.L., 1970, Xenoliths in the Honolulu volcanic series, Hawaii: Journal of Petrology, v. 11, no. 2, p. 405–430.

Jung, H., and Karato, S., 2001, Water-induced fabric transitions in olivine: Science, v. 293, p. 1460–1463, doi: 10.1126/science.1062235.

Karato, S.-I., 1984, Grain-size distribution and rheology of the upper mantle: Tectonophysics, v. 104, p. 155–176, doi: 10.1016/0040-1951(84)90108-2.

Karato, S.-I., Paterson, M.S., and FitzGerald, J.D., 1986, Rheology of synthetic olivine aggregates: Influence of grain size and water: Journal of Geophysical Research, v. 91, no. B8, p. 8151–8176.

Kohn, B.P., Shagam, R., and Subieta, T., 1984, Results and preliminary implications of sixteen fission-track ages from rocks of the western Caribbean Mountains, Venezuela, in Bonini, W.E., Hargraves, R.B., and Shagam, R., eds., The Caribbean–South American plate boundary and regional tectonics: Geological Society of America Memoir 162, p. 415–421.

Kunze, F.R., and Avé Lallemant, H.G., 1981, Non-coaxial experimental deformation of olivine: Tectonophysics, v. 74, p. T1–T13, doi: 10.1016/0040-1951(81)90187-6.

Lambert, D.D., and Simmons, E.C., 1987, Magma evolution in the Stillwater Complex, Montana; I, Rare-earth element evidence for the formation of the Ultramafic Series: American Journal of Science, v. 287, p. 1–32.

Lar, A.U., 1992, Étude gochimique de massifs basiques et ultrabasiques (Apa, Todasana, Tinaquillo) de la Chaîne Tertiaire Caraïbe du Venezuela: Genèse de magmas mantelliques et interaction manteau-croûte [Thesis]: Toulouse, France, Université Paul Sabatier, 232 p.

Lenardic, A., and Moresi, L., 2000, A new class of equilibrium geotherms in the deep thermal lithosphere of continents: Earth and Planetary Science Letters, v. 176, p. 331–338, doi: 10.1016/S0012-821X(00)00025-X.

Lindsley, D.H., 1983, Pyroxene thermometry: American Mineralogist, v. 68, p. 477–493.

Lugo, J., and Mann, P., 1995, Jurassic-Eocene tectonic evolution of Maracaibo Basin, Venezuela, in Tankard, A., Suárez, R., and Welsink, H.J., eds., Petroleum basins of South America: American Association of Petroleum Geologists Memoir 62, p. 699–725.

MacDonald, W.D., and Opdyke, N.D., 1974, Triassic paleomagnetism of northern South America: AAPG Bulletin, v. 58, p. 208–215.

MacKenzie, D.B., 1960, High-temperature alpine-type peridotite from Venezuela: Geological Society of America Bulletin, v. 71, p. 303–318.

Maze, W.B., 1984, Jurassic La Quinta Formation in the Sierra de Perijá, western Venezuela, in Bonini, W.E., Hargraves, R.B., and Shagam, R., eds., The Caribbean–South American plate boundary and regional tectonics: Geological Society of America Memoir 162, p. 263–282.

McConnell, R.B., 1969, Fundamental fault zones in the Guyana and West African shields in relation to presumed axes of Atlantic spreading: Geological Society of America Bulletin, v. 80, p. 1775–1782.

Mei, S., and Kohlstedt, D.L., 2000a, Influence of water on plastic deformation of olivine aggregates: 1. Diffusion creep regime: Journal of Geophysical Research, v. 105, no. B9, p. 21,457–21,469, doi: 10.1029/2000JB900179.

Mei, S., and Kohlstedt, D.L., 2000b, Influence of water on plastic deformation of olivine aggregates: 2. Dislocation creep regime: Journal of Geophysical Research, v. 105, no. B9, p. 21,471–21,481, doi: 10.1029/2000JB900180.

Menendez, A., 1966, Tectónica de la parte central de las Montañas Occidentales del Caribe: Caracas, Boletín de Geología, v. 8, p. 116–139.

Murray, C.G., 1972, Zoned ultramafic complexes of the Alaska type: Feeder pipes of andesitic volcanoes, in Shagam, R., Hargraves, R.B., Morgan, W.J., Van Houten, F.B., Burk, C.A., Holland, H.D., and Hollister, L.C., eds., Studies in earth and space sciences: A memoir in honor of H.H. Hess: Geological Society of America Memoir 132, p. 313–335.

Navarro, E., 1983, Petrología y petrogénesis de las rocas metavolcánicas del Grupo Villa de Cura: Caracas, Geos, v. 28, p. 170–317.

Nimis, P., and Taylor, W.R., 2000, Single clinopyroxene thermobarometry for garnet peridotites: Part 1: Calibration and testing of a Cr-in-Cpx barometer and an enstatite-in-Cpx thermometer: Contributions to Mineralogy and Petrology, v. 139, p. 541–554, doi: 10.1007/s004100000156.

Ostos, M., 1984, Structural interpretation of the Tinaquillo Peridotite and its country rock, Cojedes State, Venezuela [M.A. thesis]: Houston, Rice University, 135 p.

Ostos, M., 1990, Tectonic evolution of the south-central Caribbean based on geochemical data [Ph.D. Dissertation]: Houston, Rice University, 441 p.

Passchier, C.W., and Trouw, R.A.J., 1996, Microtectonics: New York, Springer-Verlag, 289 p.

Peltier, W.R., and Andrews, J.T., 1976, Glacial isostatic adjustment, I. The forward problem: Geophysical Journal of the Royal Astronomical Society, v. 46, p. 605–646.

Pennock, G.M., Drury, M.R., and Avé Lallemant, H.G., 2003, Grain size reduction and deformation mechanisms in ultra-fine grained shear zones from the Lherz peridotite: Eos (Transactions, American Geophysical Union), v. 84, no. 46, p. F1422.

Pindell, J.L., 1985, Alleghenian reconstruction and subsequent evolution of the Gulf of Mexico, Bahamas, and Proto-Caribbean: Tectonics, v. 4, p. 1–39.

Pindell, J.L., and Barrett, S.F., 1990, Geological evolution of the Caribbean region: A plate tectonic perspective, in Dengo, G., and Case, J.E., eds., The Caribbean region: Geological Society of America, The Geology of North America, v. H., p. 405–432.

Pindell, J.L., Cande, S.C., Pitman, W.C., III, Rowley, D.B., Dewey, J.F., Labrecque, J., and Haxby, W., 1988, A plate-kinematic framework for models of Caribbean evolution: Tectonophysics, v. 155, p. 121–138, doi: 10.1016/0040-1951(88)90262-4.

Pindell, J.L., Higgs, R., and Dewey, J.F., 1998, Cenozoic palinspastic reconstruction, paleogeographic evolution and hydrocarbon setting of the northern margin of South America: Society for Sedimentary Geology (SEPM) Special Publication 58, p. 46–85.

Ross, J.V., and Nielsen, K.C., 1978, High-temperature flow of wet polycrystalline enstatite: Tectonophysics, v. 44, p. 233–261, doi: 10.1016/0040-1951(78)90072-0.

Ross, J.V., Avé Lallemant, H.G., and Carter, N.L., 1980, Stress dependence of recrystallized grain and subgrain size in olivine: Tectonophysics, v. 70, p. 39–61, doi: 10.1016/0040-1951(80)90020-7.

Santamaría, F., and Schubert, C., 1974, Geochemistry and geochronology of the southern Caribbean–northern Venezuela plate boundary: Geological

Society of America Bulletin, v. 85, p. 1085–1098, doi: 10.1130/0016-7606(1974)85<1085:GAGOTS>2.0.CO;2.

Seyler, M., and Mattson, P.H., 1989, Petrology and thermal evolution of the Tinaquillo peridotite (Venezuela): Journal of Geophysical Research, v. 94, p. 7629–7660.

Seyler, M., and Mattson, P.H., 1993, Gabbroic and pyroxenite layers in the Tinaquillo, Venezuela, peridotite: Succession of melt intrusions in a rising mantle diapir: Journal of Geology, v. 101, p. 501–511.

Seyler, M., Paquette, J.-L., Ceuleneer, G., Kienast, J.-R., and Loubet, M., 1998, Magamatic underplating, metamorphic evolution and ductile shearing in a Mesozoic lower crustal–upper mantle unit (Tenaquillo, Venezuela) of the Caribbean belt: Journal of Geology, v. 106, p. 35–58.

Simpson, C., and Schmid, S.M., 1983, An evaluation of criteria to deduce the sense of movement in sheared rocks: Geological Society of America Bulletin, v. 94, p. 1281–1288, doi: 10.1130/0016-7606(1983)94<1281:AEOCTD>2.0.CO;2.

Smith, C.A., Sisson, V.B., Avé Lallemant, H.G., and Copeland, P., 1999, Two contrasting pressure-temperature-time paths in the Villa de Cura blueschist belt, Venezuela: Possible evidence for Late Cretaceous initiation of subduction in the Caribbean: Geological Society of America Bulletin, v. 111, no. 6, p. 831–848, doi: 10.1130/0016-7606(1999)111<0831:TCPTTP>2.3.CO;2.

Taylor, H.P., Jr., 1967, The zoned ultramafic complexes of southeastern Alaska, *in* Wyllie, P.J., ed., Ultramafic and related rocks: New York, John Wiley and Sons, p. 97–121.

Taylor, W.R., 1998, An experimental test of some geothermometer and geobarometer formulations for upper mantle peridotites with application to the thermobarometry of fertile lherzolite and garnet websterite: Neues Jahrbuch für Mineralogy, Abhandlungen, v. 172, p. 381–408.

Teitz, H.H., 1991, Takutu basin, Republic of Guyana: A Mesozoic rift basin: Journal of Petroleum Geology, v. 14, no. 4, Supplement II, p. IX–X.

Tommasi, A., Mainprice, D., Canova, G., and Chastel, Y., 2000, Visco-plastic self-consistent and equilibrium-based modeling of olivine lattice preferred orientations: Implications for the upper mantle seismic anisotropy: Journal of Geophysical Research, v. 105, no. B4, p. 7893–7908, doi: 10.1029/1999JB900411.

Twiss, R.J., and Moores, E.M., 1992, Structural geology: New York, W.H. Freeman and Company, 532 p.

Urbani, P.F., 1969, Primera localidad fosilífera del Miembro Zenda de la Formación Las Brisas: Cueva El Indio, La Guarita, Estado Miranda: Caracas, Asociación Venezolana de Geología, Minas, y Petroleo, Boletín Informativo, v. 12, no. 12, p. 447–453.

Urbani, P.F., 1982, Comentarios sobre algunas edades de las rocas de la parte central de la Cordillera de la Costa: Caracas, Geos, v. 27, p. 77–84.

Van der Wal, D., Chopra, P., Drury, M., and FitzGerald, J., 1993, Relationships between dynamically recrystallized grain size and deformation conditions in experimentally deformed olivine rocks: Geophysical Research Letters, v. 20, no. 14, p. 1479–1482.

Vissers, R.L.M., Drury, M.R., Newman, J., and Fliervoet, T.F., 1997, Mylonitic deformation in upper mantle peridotites of the North Pyrenean Zone (France): Implications for strength and strain localization in the lithosphere: Tectonophysics, v. 279, p. 303–325, doi: 10.1016/S0040-1951(97)00128-5.

Voll, G., 1976, Recrystallisation of quartz, biotite and feldspar from Erstfeld to the Leventina nappe, Swiss Alps, and its geological significance: Schweitzerische Mineralogische und Petrographische Mittteilungen, v. 56, p. 641–647.

Weber, J.C., Dixon, T.H., DeMets, C., Jansma, P., Mattioli, G., Saleh, J., Sella, G., Biham, R., and Pérez, O., 2001, GPS estimate of relative motion between the Caribbean and South American plates, and geologic implications for Trinidad and Venezuela: Geology, v. 29, p. 75–78, doi: 10.1130/0091-7613(2001)029<0075:GEORMB>2.0.CO;2.

Wehrmann, M., 1972, Geología de la región de Guatire-Colonia Tovar: Caracas, Boletín de Geología, Publicacíon Especial, v. 5, no. IV, p. 2093–2119.

Wenk, H.-R., and Tomé, C.N., 1999, Modeling dynamic recrystallization of olivine aggregates deformed in simple shear: Journal of Geophysical Research, v. 104, no. B11, p. 25,513–25,527, doi: 10.1029/1999JB900261.

Wells, P.R.A., 1977, Pyroxene thermometry in simple and complex systems: Contributions to Mineralogy and Petrology, v. 62, p. 129–139, doi: 10.1007/BF00372872.

White, R.V., Tarney, J., Kerr, A.C., Saunders, A.D., Kempton, P.D., Pringle, M.S., and Klaver, G.T., 1999, Modification of an oceanic plateau, Aruba, Dutch Caribbean: Implications for the generation of continental crust: Lithos, v. 46, p. 43–68, doi: 10.1016/S0024-4937(98)00061-9.

Wood, B.J., and Banno, S., 1973, Garnet-orthopyroxene-clinopyroxene relationships in simple and complex systems: Contributions to Mineralogy and Petrology, v. 42, p. 109–124, doi: 10.1007/BF00371501.

Wernicke, B., 1985, Uniform-sense normal shear of the continental lithosphere: Canadian Journal of Earth Sciences, v. 22, p. 108–125.

Xenophontos, C., and Bond, G.C., 1977, Petrology, sedimentation and paleogeography of the Smartsville terrane (Jurassic)—Bearing on the genesis of the Smartsville ophiolite, *in* Howell, D.G., and McDougall, K.A., eds., Mesozoic paleogeography of the western United States, Pacific Coast paleogeography symposium 2: Los Angeles, California, Pacific Section, Society for Sedimentary Geology (SEPM), p. 291–302.

Zwart, H.J., 1962, On the determination of polymetamorphic mineral associations, and its application to the Bosost area (Central Pyrenees): Geologische Rundschau, v. 52, p. 38–65.

MANUSCRIPT ACCEPTED BY THE SOCIETY 5 APRIL 2005

Geological Society of America
Special Paper 394
2005

Geochemical evidence for island-arc origin of the Villa de Cura blueschist belt, Venezuela

Layla M. Unger*
ConocoPhillips Inc., 600 N. Dairy Ashford, Houston, Texas 77079, USA
Virginia B. Sisson*
Hans G. Avé Lallemant*
Department of Earth Science, MS-126, Rice University, Houston, Texas 77251-1892, USA

ABSTRACT

New geochemical data from the Villa de Cura blueschist belt indicate that it is a subducted (and exhumed) oceanic island-arc terrane. The majority of the metabasalts were oceanic island-arc tholeiites (7–23 wt% MgO), though more evolved tholeiites are also found. Rare earth element (REE) and immobile trace element data from the Villa de Cura belt exhibit island-arc signatures, including (1) flat to light enriched REE patterns, and (2) enrichment of large ion lithophile elements relative to high field strength elements with a strongly negative Nb anomaly. Thus, the Villa de Cura belt is similar to other Albian-Aptian age oceanic island-arc tholeiites documented throughout the Caribbean in Cuba, Hispaniola, Puerto Rico, Tobago, and Bonaire. It is not related to the Cretaceous Caribbean-Colombian oceanic plateau. From our new geochemical data and previously published metamorphic data, we propose that the Villa de Cura blueschist sequence represents two forearc slivers of the "Great Arc of the Caribbean" that were subsequently subducted and amalgamated during exhumation.

Keywords: geochemistry, Villa de Cura Group, island-arc tholeiite, metabasalt, forearc sliver.

INTRODUCTION

Subduction related magmatic arcs and other oceanic terranes are key elements in deciphering Caribbean plate tectonic history (e.g., Pindell and Barrett, 1990). To correlate these terranes and thus develop better constrained and more accurate models of Caribbean plate tectonic evolution, we must understand the protolith, age, metamorphic history, and emplacement history of fragments of metaigneous and igneous crust around the Caribbean margin. The Villa de Cura blueschist belt in northern Venezuela is one of the many pieces of the volcanic "puzzle" strewn around the Caribbean plate margin. In this study, we present new detailed major and trace element geochemical data for the Villa de Cura belt. Results of geochemical analysis show that the Villa de Cura blueschist belt is derived from an oceanic, tholeiitic island-arc. This data is compared with similar Aptian-Albian island-arc terranes throughout the Caribbean. Geochemical and metamorphic data are used to

*E-mails: Layla.M.Unger@conocophillips.com; j_sisson@netzero.com; ave@rice.edu

Unger, L.M., Sisson, V.B., and Avé Lallemant, H.G., 2005, Geochemical evidence for island-arc origin of the Villa de Cura blueschist belt, Venezuela, *in* Avé Lallemant, H.G., and Sisson, V.B., eds., Caribbean–South American plate interactions, Venezuela: Geological Society of America Special Paper 394, p. 223–249, doi: 10.1130/2005.2394(09). For permission to copy, contact editing@geosociety.org. ©2005 Geological Society of America.

develop a model for the origin and later subduction of the Villa de Cura blueschist belt.

Tectonic Setting of the Villa de Cura Belt

The Villa de Cura belt is one of five belts in the Caribbean Mountain system in northern Venezuela (Fig. 1). They are, from north to south: (1) the Cordillera de la Costa eclogite-blueschist belt, (2) the Caucagua–El Tinaco belt, (3) the Paracotos belt, (4) the Villa de Cura belt, and (5) the Serranía del Interior fold and thrust belt (e.g., Bellizzia and Dengo, 1990). All of these belts are thought to be allochthonous except the Serranía del Interior. These belts, excluding the Serranía del Interior, were emplaced onto the northern South American margin as a series of nappes from Late Cretaceous to Recent time (e.g., Pérez de Armas, this volume).

Caribbean Plate Tectonic History

The Caribbean Plate

Most authors agree that the Caribbean plate originally formed in a hotspot environment in the Pacific and thus is an oceanic plateau allochthonous to the Caribbean realm called either the Caribbean large igneous province or Cretaceous Caribbean-Colombian oceanic plateau (e.g., Duncan and Hargraves, 1984; Burke, 1988; Pindell et al., 1988; Pindell, 1993; Kerr et al., 2003). One reason for this interpretation is that much of the Caribbean plate crust is thicker (15–20 km) than typical crust formed at an oceanic spreading center (~6 km). High-volume, short lived eruption cycles typical of an oceanic plateau could be responsible

for the thick basaltic crust (seismic horizon B″) of the Caribbean plate (Burke et al., 1978). In addition, Jurassic cherts found interbedded with mid-oceanic-ridge basalts (MORBs) documented in La Desirade, Puerto Rico, and the Dominican Republic are older than the opening of the Proto-Caribbean seaway; thus, they must have formed outside of the Caribbean realm, most likely in the Pacific (e.g., Montgomery et al., 1994).

Allochthonous basalts in Colombia, Costa Rica, Curaçao, and other places along the Caribbean margin are now considered portions of the Cretaceous Caribbean-Colombian oceanic plateau (Kerr et al., 1997a, 2003, 2004; Sinton et al., 1998; White et al., 1999; Hoernle et al., 2004). The oldest $^{40}Ar/^{39}Ar$ dated plateau eruption took place at 139 Ma, another major pulse at 92–88 Ma, while a younger phase occurred at 76–72 Ma (e.g., Kerr et al., 1997a; Sinton et al., 1998; Hoernle et al., 2004). In addition, Mauffret and Leroy (1997) postulate an earlier Aptian eruptive phase based on seismic and sedimentary evidence. The initial plume head of the Galápagos hot spot has been most frequently called upon as the source of the Cretaceous Caribbean-Colombian oceanic plateau (e.g., Duncan and Hargraves, 1984; Kerr et al., 1996, 2003; Sinton et al., 1998; Hauff et al., 2000; Hoernle et al., 2004); however, this has been disputed (e.g., Pindell et al., this volume).

Tectonic History

The Caribbean realm formed in the Triassic, with seafloor spreading between North and South America, which resulted in formation of the Proto-Caribbean seaway (e.g., Pindell et al., 1988; Pindell and Barrett, 1990; Pindell, 1993). As rifting progressed, a Late Jurassic to Early Cretaceous intra-oceanic island-

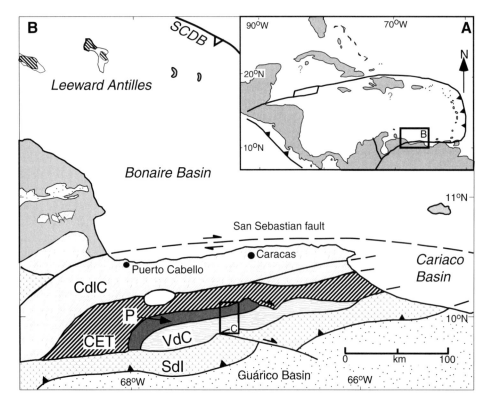

Figure 1. (A) Map of the Caribbean; inset box is location of B. (B) Map of the Caribbean Mountain system. SCDB—Southern Caribbean deformed belt; CdlC—Cordillera de la Costa belt; CET—Caucagua–El Tinaco belt; P—Paracotos belt; VdC—Villa de Cura belt; SdI—Serranía del Interior belt. Box on map B indicates location of Río Caramacate study area (C). Lightly stippled pattern indicates unmetamorphosed sedimentary cover. Adapted from Bellizzia et al. (1976) and Smith et al. (1999).

arc (Burke [1988] terms this the Great Arc of the Caribbean) began to form (e.g., Duncan and Hargraves, 1984; Pindell, 1993). This island-arc initiated above an east-dipping subduction zone (Duncan and Hargraves, 1984; Burke, 1988).

In the Albian, subduction polarity along the arc switched from east-directed to west-directed, and Proto-Caribbean lithosphere was consumed beneath the overriding Caribbean plate (e.g., Pindell, 1993). The cause and timing of polarity reversal is under debate, but was most likely a result of either: (1) increase in spreading rates in the Atlantic at ca. 100 Ma (e.g., Pindell, 1993), or (2) choking of the west facing subduction zone by the Cretaceous Caribbean-Colombian oceanic plateau (e.g., Burke, 1988; White et al., 1999).

After the polarity reversal, the Great Arc of the Caribbean formed the leading edge of the northeastward drifting Caribbean plate. As the Caribbean plate rafted between North and South America, contraction segmented the arc into three smaller arcs: (1) The Leeward Antilles, (2) the Lesser Antilles, and (3) the Greater Antilles. The Villa de Cura blueschist belt was part of the Leeward Antilles arc.

Initial collision of the Leeward Antilles arc occurred in the latest Cretaceous, along the northwestern coast of South America (Burke, 1988; Pindell, 1993). Subsequent clockwise rotation of the Leeward Antilles arc began in the Late Cretaceous–early Cenozoic (Beets et al., 1984; Burke, 1988). Migration of the arc resulted in diachronous emplacement of nappes, including the Villa de Cura belt, onto the Venezuelan margin since the Paleocene (Pindell, 1993).

Allochthonous Cretaceous Basaltic Provinces in the Caribbean

Correlation of allochthonous basaltic terranes distributed throughout the Caribbean is an essential part of reconstructing Caribbean plate tectonic history. It has been proposed that portions of the Great Arc of the Caribbean, the Cretaceous Caribbean-Colombian oceanic plateau, and the Proto-Caribbean seaway can be found throughout the margins of the Caribbean plate (Donnelly and Rogers, 1978; Beets et al., 1984; Donnelly et al., 1990; Kerr et al., 1997b, 2003; Ostos and Sisson, this volume). Figure 2 shows the distribution and association of igneous rock types throughout the Caribbean, and Table 1 gives a sample of published age dates for these terranes. In this study, we will focus on the tectono-magmatic protolith of the Villa de Cura blueschist belt and how this association fits into Caribbean plate tectonic reconstructions.

GEOLOGY OF THE VILLA DE CURA BELT

The E-W–trending Villa de Cura Belt is exposed in the southern Caribbean Mountain system in northern Venezuela. It averages 250 km in length, 20 km in width, and is ~3–6 km thick (Shagam, 1960; Smith et al., 1999). This southward dipping (Shagam, 1960; Oxburgh, 1966) Cretaceous blueschist belt was emplaced over the mildly deformed Paracotos Formation and the autochthonous Serranía del Interior in Paleocene to early Miocene time (e.g., Beets et al., 1984; Pindell, 1993). It is debated whether it forms a klippe (Shagam, 1960; Smith et al., 1999) or a thrust sheet (e.g., J. Lugo, 1998, personal commun.).

Figure 2. Distribution of allochthonous basaltic provinces throughout the Caribbean plate margin. Fields shown in gray are derived from the Caribbean oceanic plateau; those in black have island-arc affinities. CCOP—Cretaceous Caribbean-Colombian oceanic plateau; DSDP—Deep Sea Drilling Program; ODP—Ocean Drilling Program. For simplicity, the distribution of Jurassic oceanic crust is not shown. Figure after Donnelly et al. (1990) and Kerr et al. (2003).

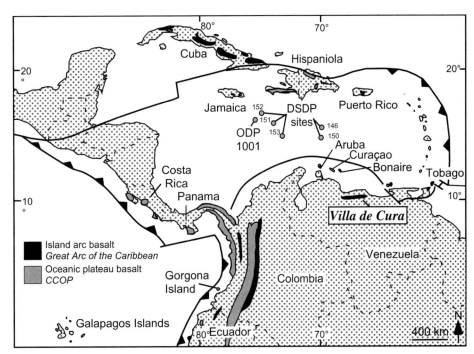

TABLE 1. GEOCHRONOLOGICAL DATA FOR SELECTED IGNEOUS SUITES IN THE CARIBBEAN

Location	Formation	Protolith	Age (Ma)	Method	Material	Reference
Aruba	Aruba batholith	Great Arc of the Caribbean	84.9 ± 0.2	Ar/Ar	biotite	White et al. (1999)
		Great Arc of the Caribbean	81.8 ± 0.3	Ar/Ar	hornblende	
Bonaire	Washikemba Formation	Great Arc of the Caribbean	93.5–85.8	fossil	inoceramids	Beets et al. (1984)
		Great Arc of the Caribbean	112–99	fossil	ammonite imprints	
		Great Arc of the Caribbean	93.5–95.8	fossil	planktonic forams	Priem et al. (1986)
		Great Arc of the Caribbean	88 ± 2	fossil	planktonic forams	Thompson et al. (2004b)
		Great Arc of the Caribbean	96 ± 4	Ar/Ar	feldspar	
Cuba	Cretaceous volcanic arc	Great Arc of the Caribbean	100.1 ± 3.8	K/Ar	whole rock	Iturralde-Vinent et al. (1996)
		Great Arc of the Caribbean	90.9 ± 4.3	K/Ar	feldspar	
	Cretaceous plutonic rocks	Great Arc of the Caribbean	99 ± 6	K/Ar	whole rock	
		Great Arc of the Caribbean	92.3 ± 1.9	K/Ar	biotite	
	Northern ophiolites	MORB and CCOP	126.3 ± 8.3	K/Ar	whole rock	Wiedmann (1978)
		MORB and CCOP	108 ± 3	K/Ar	mica	
Curaçao	Curaçao Lava Formation	CCOP	113–97.5	fossil	ammonites	Sinton et al. (1998)
		CCOP	75.8 ± 2.0	Ar/Ar	whole rock	
		CCOP	88.0 ± 1.2	Ar/Ar	whole rock	Walker et al. (1999)
		CCOP	85.6 ± 8	Re/Os	isochron	
		CCOP	89.5 ± 1.0	Ar/Ar	whole rock	
Hispaniola	Duarte Complex*	MORB and/or CCOP	123	K/Ar	whole rock	Kesler et al. (1991)
		MORB and/or CCOP	121.4 ± 6	Ar/Ar	hornblende	Hernaiz Huerta et al. (2000)
		MORB and/or CCOP	85.4 ± 1.7	Ar/Ar	amphibole	Lapierre et al. (1999)
		MORB and/or CCOP	88.6 ± 2.4	Ar/Ar	amphibole	
	Dumisseau Formation	CCOP	92.0–88.7	Ar/Ar	feldspar	Sinton et al. (1998)
	Loma la Vega volcanics	Great Arc of the Caribbean	84.3 ± 17.9	Rb/Sr	feldspar	Lebrón and Perfit (1994)
Puerto Rico	Bermeja Complex	Great Arc of the Caribbean	152–144	fossil	radiolarian chert	Mattson and Pessagno (1979)
		Great Arc of the Caribbean	131–97.5	fossil	radiolarian chert	
		Great Arc of the Caribbean	113–97.5	fossil	radiolarian chert	
Tobago	Tobago Volcanic Group	Great Arc of the Caribbean	112–99	fossil	radiolaria	Snoke and Noble (2001)
		Great Arc of the Caribbean	112–99	fossil	ammonites	Snoke and Noble (2001)
	North Coast Schist	Great Arc of the Caribbean	>120 Ma	Ar/Ar	hornblende	Snoke et al. (1990)
	Plutonic-volcanic dyke complex	Great Arc of the Caribbean	103 ± 1	Ar/Ar	hornblende	Sharp and Snoke (1988)
		Great Arc of the Caribbean	91 ± 2	Ar/Ar	hornblende	
Venezuela	Villa de Cura Group	Great Arc of the Caribbean	79.8 ± 0.4	Ar/Ar	white mica	Smith et al. (1999)
		Great Arc of the Caribbean	89–91	Ar/Ar	white mica	
		Great Arc of the Caribbean	96.3 ± 0.4	Ar/Ar	amphibole	
DSDP Site 146		CCOP	92.1–90.6	Ar/Ar	whole rock	Sinton et al. (1998)
DSDP Site 150		CCOP	94.3	Ar/Ar	whole rock	Sinton et al. (1998)
ODP Site 1001		CCOP	81.3–80.8	Ar/Ar	whole rock	Sinton et al. (2000)

Note: Fossil ages represent period ranges. MORB—mid-oceanic-ridge basalt; CCOP—Cretaceous Caribbean oceanic plateau.
*Montgomery et al. (1994) describe intercalated Jurassic cherts in the Duarte Complex.

We follow the terminology adapted by Smith et al. (1999) with the Villa de Cura Belt including two units: one is the Villa de Cura Group, which includes only the high-pressure metamorphosed section; the second is the relatively low-grade Las Hermanas Formation. Beck (1985) and Giunta et al. (2002) use the term Dos Hermanas for this latter unit. The nomenclature of Shagam (1960) is utilized by the Venezuelan Stratigraphic Code (http://www.pdv.com/lexico/) and therefore will be used in this study. We do not include the Tiara Formation as this is commonly correlated with the Loma de Hierro Complex in the Paracotos belt (e.g., Beck, 1985; http://www.pdv.com/lexico/).

Protolith for the Villa de Cura Group

The Villa de Cura Group is composed of variable amounts of interbedded and metamorphosed lava, tuff, chert, volcaniclastic rocks, and graphitic schists, as well as minor breccia and possible conglomerates. Shagam (1960) divided the Villa de Cura Group into four formations of metavolcanic and metasedimentary rocks, excluding the previous inclusion of Paleocene limestone (the Morro Limestone of San Juan de Los Morros). These formations are, from north to south: the El Caño Formation, the El Chino Formation, the El Carmen Formation, and the Santa Isabel Formation (Fig. 3). Navarro (1983) defined four units, which, from north to south, are the Unit of Metabasalts, the Unit of Metalavas, the Unit of Granofels, and finally the Unit of Lavas, Breccias, and Tuffs. Navarro (1983) combines the El Caño and El Chino Formations of Shagam (1960) into one Unit of Metabasalts. The final unit of Navarro corresponds with the Las Hermanas Formation of Shagam (1960), which includes weakly metamorphosed lavas with intercalated breccias and tuffs.

The Chacao complex crosscuts the Villa de Cura Group and has been interpreted by Murray (1973) as a zoned Alaska-type ultramafic intrusion. This interpretation is problematic as Loubet et al. (1985) report four K-Ar ages on hornblende from this complex ranging from 91.0 ± 3.5 Ma to 104 ± 4 Ma, which is older than some of the metamorphic ages reported by Smith et al. (1999). In our study area, tropical weathering obscures any contact relationships to help resolve whether these unmetamorphosed ultramafic rocks are intrusive or an olistolith.

El Caño Formation

The El Caño Formation (Unit of Metabasalts of Navarro, 1983), is marked by the south dipping Agua Fría thrust fault (Shagam, 1960). The El Caño Formation is dominated volumetrically by pale green, finely laminated metatuffs that occasionally exhibit primary depositional structure indicating that they formed by pyroclastic eruption. The matrix of these tuffs is generally composed of fine-grained chlorite with augite, epidote, and albite common in varying proportions (Shagam, 1960). Also important in the El Caño Formation are blue-green pyroxene metalavas that contain diopside phenocrysts in a matrix of chlorite, epidote, amphibole, and albite (Shagam, 1960). The only primary structure observed in the metalavas is cut-and-fill deposition of under-

lying metatuff units. Rare serpentinite is found near the village of Aqua Fría, but the nature of the contact is indeterminable. Other units in the El Caño Formation include thin layers of white and pale green metachert, metasandstone, and graphitic phyllite.

El Chino Formation

The El Chino Formation (Unit of Metabasalts of Navarro, 1983) is poorly exposed in the study area. However, the El Chino Formation is described by Shagam (1960) as consisting of large volumes of aphanitic metasedimentary rocks and "bluish-green porphyritic metabasalt." Minor constituents are chlorite-quartz-albite schist, epidote-lawsonite-chlorite schist, black carbonaceous metachert, and graphitic phyllite (Shagam, 1960). The relative abundance of metalava increases toward the El Chino–El Carmen boundary.

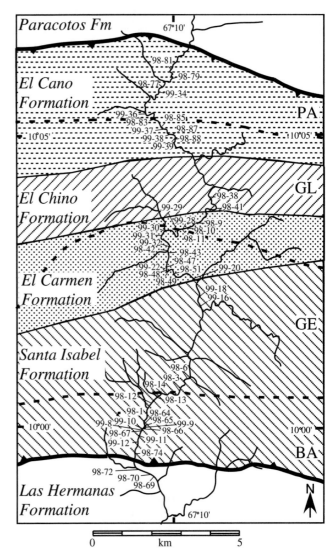

Figure 3. Map of the Río Caramacate including sample locations. Formations are represented by patterned fields; metamorphic zones are indicated by dashed lines. Adapted from Smith et al. (1999).

El Carmen Formation

The El Carmen Formation (Unit of Metalavas of Navarro, 1983) consists of metalava flows and intercalated metatuff. The metalavas range from massive to slightly foliated, are much thicker than metatuff, and contain large diopside phenocrysts, which vary in abundance from <1% up to 15% of the rock volume. These diopside phenocrysts are generally euhedral and are rarely altered. Some metalava units show evidence of mechanical brecciation. Metatuffs are dominantly chlorite schist with random small diopside phenocrysts and are generally only a few centimeters thick. These massive lava flows and metatuffs form a canyon of continuous exposure for over 2 km. The El Carmen Formation contains most of the metalava in the Villa de Cura Group.

Santa Isabel Formation

The Santa Isabel Formation (Unit of Granofels of Navarro, 1983) is more siliceous than the other three formations. Lithologies vary from SiO_2-rich quartz-albite schists to the more ferromagnesian glaucophane-chlorite-epidote-quartz-albite schists. Other rock types include intercalated metachert, metatuffs, and some metalavas.

The El Caño, El Chino, and El Carmen Formations are easily derived from the same temporal and spatial source (Shagam, 1960; Navarro, 1983). The characteristics of the metalavas, metatuffs, metacherts, and graphitic phyllites are such that formation boundaries only indicate a change in relative proportion of rock type, rather than the introduction of different lithologies (Shagam, 1960; Navarro, 1983). However, the more siliceous Santa Isabel Formation is markedly different from the three underlying formations, though it is still considered consanguineous as it is intercalated with metalavas at its base and in thin flows throughout the sequence (Shagam, 1960). Thus, Shagam (1960) considers the boundary between the El Carmen and Santa Isabel Formations as marking only a short discontinuity rather than a major unconformity.

Previous geochemical studies for the Villa de Cura sequence (e.g., Donnelly and Rogers, 1978; Beets et al., 1984; Beccaluva et al., 1996; Giunta et al., 2002; Ostos and Sisson, this volume) indicate either island-arc and/or MORB affinities for the protolith of these various formations. None of the previous studies systematically studied all the different formations and lithologies throughout the entire metamorphic sequence.

Metamorphism

Metamorphic Zones

The Villa de Cura blueschist belt is a coherent assemblage of blueschist facies metavolcanic and metasedimentary rocks. This belt has been divided into four metamorphic subbelts by Smith et al. (1999), which are, from north to south and lowest to highest grade: pumpellyite-actinolite (PA), glaucophane-lawsonite (GL), glaucophane-epidote (GE), and barroisite (BA) (Fig. 3). Characteristic assemblages of the metamorphic zones within the Villa de Cura belt are as follows (Smith et al., 1999):

PA: pumpellyite + chlorite + quartz + albite ± actinolite ± white mica ± titanite ± calcite;

GL: glaucophane + lawsonite + chlorite + quartz + albite ± white mica ± titanite;

GE: glaucophane + epidote + quartz + albite ± chlorite ± titanite ± white mica;

BA: epidote + chlorite + quartz + albite ± barroisite ± white mica ± titanite.

Pressure-Temperature-Time Conditions

The metamorphic history of the Villa de Cura blueschist belt is complex. Geothermobarometry results from Smith et al. (1999) indicate peak temperatures of ~375 °C for the pumpellyite-actinolite, glaucophane-lawsonite, and glaucophane-epidote zones. Peak pressure estimates increase from ~550 MPa in the pumpellyite-actinolite zone, to ~650 MPa in the glaucophane-lawsonite zone, to ~750 MPa in the glaucophane-epidote zone (Smith et al., 1999). The barroisite belt formed under peak conditions of 500 °C and ~500–700 MPa (Smith et al., 1999). A $^{40}Ar/^{39}Ar$ analysis of a barroisitic amphibole from the barroisite belt yielded a peak metamorphic age of 96.3 ± 0.4 Ma. In contrast, a $^{40}Ar/^{39}Ar$ analysis of white mica yielded an age of 79.8 ± 0.4 Ma. This age is interpreted to represent the time of peak metamorphism in the lower grade belts (Smith et al., 1999).

The pumpellyite-actinolite, glaucophane-lawsonite, and glaucophane-epidote belts share a similar metamorphic history, whereas the history of the barroisite belt is quite different. The parallel pressure-temperature (*P-T*) path of the first three zones indicates a similar prograde and retrograde history in a refrigerated subduction zone at ca. 79 Ma (Smith et al., 1999). The counterclockwise *P-T* path of the barroisite belt suggests that it was subducted in an environment of elevated geothermal gradients, perhaps during initiation of subduction at 96 Ma (Smith et al., 1999).

CLASSIFICATION OF ROCKS IN THE VILLA DE CURA BELT

Samples of metavolcanic and metasedimentary lithologies were collected from a 20 km transect along the Río Caramacate (Fig. 3). Metavolcanic samples were categorized into three basic groups of volcanic protoliths: (1) pyroxene metabasalt, (2) picritic metatuff, and (3) andesitic metabasalt. Epidosite veins crosscut all lithologies in the Villa De Cura belt. Younger quartz and calcite veins cross cut all lithologies and also epidosite veins.

Pyroxene Metabasalt

Pyroxene metabasalt is the most distinctive rock type in the Villa de Cura Group. It is synonymous with the "El Carmen basalts" of Shagam (1960) and is found within the Unit of Metalavas of Navarro (1983). In the field, pyroxene metabasalt crops out as individual lava flows several meters thick and can be found as a series of individual flows up to 100 m thick. It is blue-green, with large clinopyroxene phenocrysts up to 15 mm in diameter. In thin section, pyroxene metabasalt exhibits abundant relict diopside phenocrysts showing little to no reaction texture in a matrix of chlorite ± amphibole ± epidote ± albite ± white mica (Fig. 4A). This rock type is found throughout the three formations of the Villa de Cura belt but is rare in the Santa Isabel Formation. Therefore, all samples of pyroxene metabasalt in this study are from the El Caño, El Chino, and El Carmen Formations.

Picritic Metatuff

Picritic metatuff occurs as light green, finely laminated chlorite schists in thin beds centimeters to a meter thick. It is characterized in thin section as an aphanitic rock with a crenulated matrix of chlorite + white mica + lawsonite ± amphibole ± clinopyroxene ± quartz and rare clinopyroxene phenocrysts (Fig. 4B). Picritic metatuff is found distributed throughout the Villa de Cura

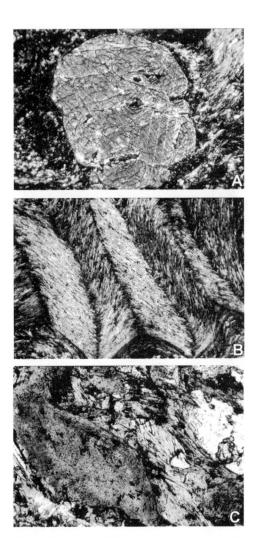

Figure 4. Photomicrographs of the three types of metabasalt. (A) Photomicrograph of a pyroxene metabasalt. (B) Photomicrograph of a picritic metatuff. (C) Photomicrograph of an andesitic metabasalt. See text for a detailed description of rock types.

Group, but it is most common in the El Caño Formation and least common in the Santa Isabel Formation. All samples of picritic metatuff in this study are from the El Caño Formation.

Andesitic Metabasalt

Andesitic metabasalt is most common in the Santa Isabel Formation. In the field it has a light blue-green color and generally occurs in centimeter to meter thick bands. It is interbedded with pyroxene metabasalt, picritic metatuff, and metasedimentary rocks. It is well foliated and lacks phenocrysts. Andesitic metabasalt is composed of chlorite + amphibole + albite + quartz + epidote ± white mica ± lawsonite ± calcite (Fig. 4C).

Metasedimentary Rocks

Seven samples of metasedimentary rocks were analyzed in this study. Table 2 lists rock names (Pettijohn, 1963) for each sample, as well as minerals found in thin section. Samples found in the lower grade (pumpellyite-actinolite zone) El Caño Formation have the most obvious metasedimentary features, including rip-up clasts and conglomerates with angular clasts (no conglomerates were collected for this study). Thin layers of graphitic schist are only found in the El Caño Formation. Two metasedimentary samples from the El Carmen Formation (glaucophane-epidote zone) are classified as metasandstone and metagraywacke. These samples are found thinly interbedded with pyroxene metabasalts (synonymous with the "El Carmen basalts" of Shagam [1960]) and define periods of quiescence in lava flows. Metasedimentary rocks are more abundant in the Santa Isabel Formation (barroisite zone). Sample 98-64 is a chert found thinly interbedded with layers of picritic metatuff. Samples 98-66 and 98-67 are classified as metagraywackes based on thin section analysis. These samples are found in thick, well-foliated beds near the boundary of the Santa Isabel Formation and the Las Hermanas Formation. This rock type is unique in the Villa de Cura belt because it is found only in this outcrop and has a distinct red, white, and green color due to the combination of quartz + albite + epidote + stilpnomelane in well-foliated layers.

GEOCHEMISTRY

Analytical Methods

Samples for geochemical analysis were chosen based upon probable protolith and lack of weathering. Fifty samples from all four formations in the Villa de Cura belt were analyzed for major and trace elements at Washington State University (Table 3). Most samples are metabasaltic (≤55 wt% SiO_2). Representative samples of metasedimentary rocks were also analyzed. Major elements and select trace elements (Sc, V, Ni, Cr, Ba, Sr, Zr, Y, Rb, Nb, Ga, Cu, Zn, Pb, La, Ce, and Th) were analyzed using X-ray fluorescence spectrometry (XRF) methods (Johnson et al., 1999). Twenty-six trace elements including the rare earth elements (REEs) Ba, Th,

TABLE 2. MINERALOGY OF METASEDIMENTARY ROCKS IN THE VILLA DE CURA GROUP

Sample	Rock type	Formation	Zone	qtz	chl	epid	laws	alb	wm	cc	opq	ser	stilp
98-81	metasandstone	El Caño	PA	x	x			x		x	x	x	
98-79	graphitic sandstone	El Caño	PA	n.d.									
98-47	metasandstone	El Carmen	GE	x		x			x		x		
98-49	metagraywacke	El Carmen	GE	x		x	x		x		x		
98-64	metachert	Santa Isabel	BA	x		x		x			x		
98-66	metagraywacke	Santa Isabel	BA	x		x		x					x
98-67	metagraywacke	Santa Isabel	BA	n.d.									

Note: qtz—quartz; chl—chlorite; epid—epidote; laws—lawsonite; alb—albite; wm—white mica; cc—calcite; opq—opaque; ser—sericite; stilp—stilpnomlane; n.d.—not determined; BA—barroisite; GE—glaucophane-epidote; PA—pumpellyite-actinolite. "x" indicates presence in thin section.

Nb, Y, Hf, Ta, U, Pb, Rb, Cs, Sr, and Sc were analyzed using inductively coupled plasma–mass spectrometry (ICP-MS) techniques. The accuracy and precision for various elements is given in Johnson et al. (1999) for XRF techniques and Knaack et al. (1994, http://www.wsu.edu/~geology/Pages/Services/ICP.html) for ICP-MS techniques. Due to the high-grade metamorphism of these rocks, loss on ignition (LOI) values were measured for all samples. Use of Ta is omitted in geochemical interpretation because 1998 samples were probably contaminated as a result of processing in a tungsten carbide mill.

Element Mobility

The metabasalts of the Villa de Cura Group have most likely seen some degree of element mobility during their history of high-pressure–low-temperature metamorphism (e.g., Sorensen and Grossman, 1989; Sorensen and Grossman, 1993; Sorensen et al., 1997; Bebout et al., 1999; Becker et al., 1999). Thus, it is necessary to understand these effects on the rocks of the Villa de Cura Group. There is a remarkable consistency in geochemical trends of most elements, as will be shown later in this section. Figure 5 shows variation diagrams of selected major elements versus silica. Scatter is evident in K_2O and P_2O_5, while the other major oxides exhibit reliable geochemical trends. Zirconium has been plotted against all other elements because it is generally regarded as immobile during low-grade alteration of basaltic rocks (Humphris and Thompson, 1978; Staudigel et al., 1996; Kerr et al., 1997b). Figure 6 indicates that compatible elements such as TiO_2, Y, and Nb (not shown) are well correlated with Zr, while the incompatible elements K_2O, Ba, and Rb (not shown) are widely scattered.

Field and geochemical evidence shows that despite the high grade of metamorphism, element mobility was similar to that seen during seafloor alteration (e.g., Staudigel et al., 1996). This is most likely due to the fact that the Villa de Cura blueschist belt formed in a relatively closed system; i.e., there was little water loss. Evidence of a closed system resides in the unaltered nature of the pyroxene phenocrysts, as well as the minor volume of metasomatic veins. Most veins are filled with quartz and epidote and occur throughout the Villa de Cura Group. However, the proportion of these veins

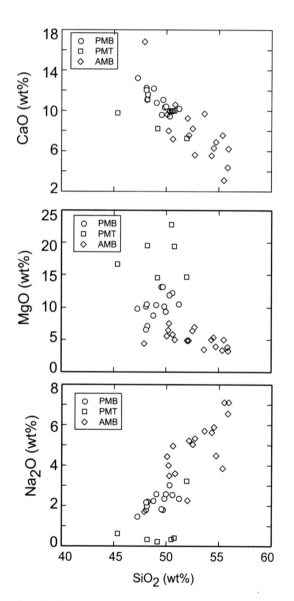

Figure 5. Variation diagram of select major elements plotted versus silica. AMB—andesitic metabasalt; PMB—pyroxene metabasalt; PMT—picritic metatuff.

TABLE 3. MAJOR, MINOR AND TRACE ELEMENT GEOCHEMICAL DATA FOR THE VILLA DE CURA BELT

	Las Hermanas Formation			Santa Isabel Formation				
Sample	98-69	98-70	98-72	98-74	99-12	99-11	98-67	99-8
Unit				amb	amb	amb	mgw	amb
Grade				BA	BA	BA	BA	BA
SiO_2	53.69	54.52	50.25	49.12	51.64	54.27	73.04	53.82
TiO_2	1.12	0.95	0.97	1.16	1.11	0.87	0.38	0.84
Al_2O_3	16.91	15.01	14.89	16.01	16.08	16.09	14.02	16.88
FeO	9.79	9.11	9.92	11.95	11.74	10.59	2.13	11.23
MnO	0.14	0.16	0.23	0.20	0.21	0.17	0.07	0.15
MgO	5.81	5.09	5.29	6.39	4.81	5.33	0.61	4.94
CaO	6.13	7.69	9.71	7.86	7.51	6.24	0.59	5.54
Na_2O	1.96	2.13	2.21	3.90	5.16	5.86	7.33	5.57
K_2O	0.74	0.65	1.25	1.17	0.61	0.06	0.84	0.04
P_2O_5	0.21	0.17	0.16	0.12	0.14	0.10	0.09	0.06
Total	96.49	95.49	94.87	97.88	99.01	99.58	99.10	99.07
LOI%	4.83	5.40	6.67	3.35	1.62	1.94	1.53	2.47
Ni	3	3	7	3	13	6	9	47
Cr	21	19	28	40	37	19	0	22
V	303	231	297	394	394	283	31	236
Zr	100	91	71	67	59	57	145	52
Ga	22	20	19	20	22	17	12	18
Cu	71	72	106	73	58	58	23	19
Zn	89	89	84	69	78	77	23	84
Pb	3	1	0	4	0	0	0	4
La	8.70	7.86	7.06	4.25	5.52	3.49	11.68	2.75
Ce	19.62	17.65	15.45	10.47	12.57	8.98	23.13	7.40
Pr	2.77	2.54	2.24	1.63	1.87	1.41	2.91	1.10
Nd	13.79	13.16	11.14	8.43	9.44	7.55	12.61	5.78
Sm	4.18	4.12	3.43	2.87	3.15	2.66	2.91	2.11
Eu	1.55	1.43	1.21	1.11	1.21	0.96	0.86	0.86
Gd	4.86	4.87	4.05	3.78	3.78	3.37	3.51	2.57
Tb	0.85	0.80	0.71	0.66	0.63	0.61	0.59	0.49
Dy	5.38	5.14	4.47	4.12	3.99	3.97	3.69	3.23
Ho	1.14	1.07	0.95	0.88	0.88	0.83	0.80	0.68
Er	3.22	2.94	2.70	2.46	2.43	2.35	2.42	1.94
Tm	0.47	0.44	0.38	0.34	0.36	0.35	0.38	0.30
Yb	2.95	2.76	2.47	2.11	2.24	2.16	2.49	1.92
Lu	0.48	0.44	0.39	0.33	0.35	0.34	0.44	0.30
Ba	270	285	274	290	226	17	938	9
Th	1.06	0.97	0.75	0.36	0.63	0.36	1.95	0.34
Nb	2.45	2.26	1.57	2.42	1.19	0.82	3.84	0.70
Y	30.32	28.33	26.03	22.42	22.72	21.46	23.95	16.69
Hf	2.80	2.62	1.89	1.74	1.77	1.67	4.16	1.40
Ta	0.52	0.48	0.26	0.71	0.08	0.06	2.29	0.05
U	0.39	0.35	0.30	0.13	0.21	0.13	0.65	0.10
Pb	2.32	2.42	1.51	3.72	1.12	1.16	1.54	3.87
Rb	14.1	11.0	20.5	12.4	6.3	0.5	9.8	0.7
Cs	0.24	0.26	0.70	0.04	0.02	0.00	0.08	0.00
Sr	392	350	249	169	108	52	51	333
Sc	40.6	36.1	37.5	46.8	40.8	41.1	8.2	40.2

Continued

TABLE 3. MAJOR, MINOR, AND TRACE ELEMENT GEOCHEMICAL DATA FOR THE VILLA DE CURA BELT *(continued)*

	Santa Isabel Formation *(continued)*						
Sample	98-66	99-10	99-9	98-65	98-64	98-12	98-13
Unit	mgw	amb	amb	amb	mc	amb	amb
Grade	BA	BA	BA	BA	BA	BA	BA
SiO_2	73.14	52.44	50.45	54.89	79.47	51.56	54.45
TiO_2	0.40	1.02	1.44	1.25	0.37	0.90	0.88
Al_2O_3	14.00	16.13	17.24	15.75	6.26	13.86	15.49
FeO	2.28	10.31	12.21	9.34	3.20	10.94	9.89
MnO	0.07	0.16	0.22	0.21	0.07	0.21	0.17
MgO	0.71	6.36	5.79	3.78	2.24	3.38	3.21
CaO	0.62	8.24	7.14	4.32	4.64	9.31	6.08
Na_2O	7.34	5.04	4.95	6.45	1.23	5.49	6.94
K_2O	0.88	0.05	0.03	1.57	0.06	0.32	0.05
P_2O_5	0.09	0.12	0.18	0.73	0.05	0.18	0.26
Total	99.53	99.87	99.65	98.29	97.60	96.15	97.42
LOI%	1.29	2.10	2.50	2.12	1.48	3.23	1.56
Ni	8	22	1	1	36	2	2
Cr	2	42	25	14	63	24	18
V	37	315	393	182	108	371	295
Zr	145	60	81	78	29	72	63
Ga	10	14	18	19	7	21	19
Cu	20	94	53	12	49	110	109
Zn	19	67	101	83	30	77	82
Pb	0	0	7	3	1	4	3
La	12.56	4.94	4.89	8.07	1.61	13.01	5.97
Ce	25.40	11.94	12.24	18.14	3.91	25.28	13.70
Pr	3.08	1.81	1.90	2.57	0.62	3.13	2.04
Nd	13.09	9.29	9.98	12.80	3.09	14.08	10.37
Sm	3.30	3.06	3.54	3.86	0.99	3.83	3.40
Eu	0.90	1.10	1.46	1.37	0.41	1.29	1.18
Gd	3.54	3.70	4.38	4.75	1.24	4.11	4.05
Tb	0.60	0.65	0.80	0.78	0.22	0.66	0.73
Dy	4.03	4.05	5.17	4.93	1.36	4.12	4.63
Ho	0.87	0.86	1.08	1.02	0.29	0.88	1.01
Er	2.58	2.40	2.95	2.79	0.79	2.40	2.84
Tm	0.40	0.34	0.42	0.40	0.11	0.34	0.42
Yb	2.73	2.11	2.60	2.53	0.67	2.16	2.73
Lu	0.45	0.34	0.40	0.40	0.11	0.35	0.43
Ba	971	22	13	474	15	431	31
Th	2.20	0.41	0.40	0.89	0.13	1.75	0.58
Nb	4.47	1.66	1.64	2.24	2.21	2.34	1.39
Y	23.88	22.41	28.34	27.11	7.60	22.80	27.18
Hf	4.26	1.65	1.96	2.26	0.73	1.98	1.89
Ta	3.29	0.12	0.11	0.37	3.18	0.87	0.97
U	0.69	0.14	0.13	0.28	0.05	0.51	1.60
Pb	0.97	1.30	6.63	1.47	0.99	3.46	2.27
Rb	10.2	0.7	0.5	19.2	0.8	4.8	1.4
Cs	0.09	0.00	0.00	0.07	0.01	0.08	0.02
Sr	51	115	429	84	53	196	70
Sc	8.1	41.4	45.2	32.0	13.6	36.4	30.2

Continued

TABLE 3. MAJOR, MINOR, AND TRACE ELEMENT GEOCHEMICAL DATA FOR THE VILLA DE CURA BELT *(continued)*

	Santa Isabel Formation *(continued)*					El Carmen Formation	
Sample	98-14	98-3	98-6	99-16	99-18	99-20	98-51
Unit	amb	amb		amb	amb	pmb	amb
Grade	BA	GE	GE	GE	GE	GE	GE
SiO_2	50.49	53.93	58.89	49.67	50.10	50.13	53.85
TiO_2	0.98	0.90	0.85	1.02	0.94	0.54	1.13
Al_2O_3	17.23	17.00	14.18	16.40	17.70	13.50	13.86
FeO	9.52	9.91	9.54	12.18	8.78	10.91	13.59
MnO	0.18	0.16	0.11	0.22	0.17	0.19	0.21
MgO	6.69	4.80	4.93	5.56	7.45	11.91	3.29
CaO	5.43	3.06	4.67	9.53	9.88	9.42	7.35
Na_2O	5.10	6.92	0.52	4.42	3.47	3.02	3.74
K_2O	0.04	0.39	3.18	0.06	1.03	0.03	0.05
P_2O_5	0.12	0.16	0.32	0.12	0.08	0.07	0.21
Total	95.79	97.23	97.20	99.17	99.59	99.70	97.28
LOI%	5.49	3.42	3.71	3.80	2.26	3.46	2.40
Ni	25	28	1	8	42	117	0
Cr	57	17	9	35	97	488	18
V	294	257	183	*545	215	238	351
Zr	69	70	79	42	65	33	83
Ga	20	18	22	18	15	12	22
Cu	68	127	119	*274	51	*327	142
Zn	103	69	123	75	54	66	103
Pb	5	1	12	2	2	0	1
La	4.81	5.64	19.41	4.11	3.05	2.73	7.73
Ce	11.67	13.43	33.35	9.24	8.03	5.94	16.97
Pr	1.72	2.04	4.58	1.46	1.27	0.96	2.50
Nd	8.54	10.47	23.19	7.81	6.74	4.95	12.75
Sm	2.87	3.51	6.94	2.66	2.42	1.74	4.12
Eu	1.13	1.20	2.26	1.02	1.03	0.74	1.33
Gd	3.39	4.21	9.28	3.03	3.17	2.02	5.12
Tb	0.61	0.73	1.55	0.53	0.58	0.36	0.89
Dy	3.95	4.81	10.40	3.35	3.74	2.28	5.79
Ho	0.84	1.00	2.31	0.71	0.79	0.48	1.20
Er	2.30	2.76	6.57	1.93	2.22	1.38	3.40
Tm	0.32	0.40	0.95	0.28	0.32	0.20	0.49
Yb	2.06	2.63	5.72	1.75	1.93	1.27	3.12
Lu	0.32	0.40	0.87	0.28	0.30	0.20	0.49
Ba	21	124	550	14	565	15	76
Th	0.41	0.62	0.64	0.40	0.23	0.29	0.86
Nb	1.95	1.23	2.01	0.52	1.15	0.50	2.11
Y	22.44	26.03	67.04	18.39	20.78	13.01	32.76
Hf	1.75	2.02	2.27	1.18	1.55	0.92	2.35
Ta	0.60	0.37	1.22	0.04	0.09	0.03	0.96
U	0.16	0.26	0.35	0.19	0.07	0.14	0.34
Pb	6.14	2.21	11.76	1.95	1.49	0.53	3.44
Rb	1.2	3.7	64.5	0.7	10.4	0.5	1.5
Cs	0.00	0.03	0.90	0.00	0.05	0.01	0.06
Sr	207	124	368	239	216	21	291
Sc	41.5	32.3	29.6	49.8	43.8	49.4	41.7

Continued

TABLE 3. MAJOR, MINOR, AND TRACE ELEMENT GEOCHEMICAL DATA FOR THE VILLA DE CURA BELT *(continued)*

	El Carmen Formation *(continued)*						
Sample	98-49	98-48	99-22	98-47	98-43	98-42	99-32
Unit	mgw	pmb	pmb	ms	amb	amb	pmb
Grade	GE	GE	GE	GE	GE	GE	GE
SiO_2	72.79	50.17	50.87	70.95	53.62	50.38	47.15
TiO_2	0.35	0.74	0.74	0.33	1.17	1.06	0.71
Al_2O_3	12.08	13.09	12.18	13.96	16.74	16.59	15.21
FeO	2.42	9.87	10.58	3.02	9.96	11.99	11.08
MnO	0.04	0.18	0.19	0.07	0.23	0.24	0.21
MgO	1.97	10.31	12.33	1.75	3.81	4.74	9.85
CaO	2.42	9.99	10.09	3.40	6.75	8.98	13.21
Na_2O	7.04	2.32	2.57	1.31	4.38	2.18	1.47
K_2O	0.09	1.15	0.92	3.35	1.09	0.53	0.76
P_2O_5	0.08	0.20	0.19	0.06	0.26	0.16	0.18
Total	99.28	98.02	100.66	98.19	98.01	96.85	99.82
LOI%	0.54	3.07	2.26	2.58	3.53	3.99	3.91
Ni	29	216	269	10	0	0	149
Cr	59	460	589	2	11	22	304
V	109	249	256	33	231	303	292
Zr	100	56	43	185	92	72	29
Ga	11	16	17	13	20	19	16
Cu	8	104	104	16	19	9	136
Zn	10	79	82	57	85	88	73
Pb	5	2	0	4	0	0	0
La	9.26	4.78	4.10	10.42	8.47	5.56	2.83
Ce	13.25	10.01	8.84	25.99	19.01	11.72	6.15
Pr	2.38	1.51	1.35	3.71	2.70	1.80	0.96
Nd	10.88	7.49	6.62	17.39	13.18	9.10	4.92
Sm	3.16	2.43	2.30	5.34	3.97	2.94	1.69
Eu	0.59	0.88	0.82	1.00	1.42	1.09	0.69
Gd	3.71	3.04	2.61	6.33	4.41	3.70	2.13
Tb	0.67	0.51	0.47	1.09	0.80	0.64	0.36
Dy	4.44	3.25	2.95	7.64	4.82	4.08	2.34
Ho	0.96	0.66	0.64	1.68	1.04	0.87	0.48
Er	2.84	1.79	1.77	4.79	2.95	2.40	1.33
Tm	0.43	0.28	0.25	0.75	0.40	0.34	0.18
Yb	2.86	1.69	1.55	4.92	2.53	2.12	1.15
Lu	0.47	0.27	0.25	0.81	0.41	0.34	0.18
Ba	100	460	399	2110	371	371	394
Th	1.37	0.49	0.42	2.09	0.86	0.55	0.21
Nb	3.46	1.80	1.44	3.90	5.43	2.23	0.79
Y	27.28	17.68	16.29	45.99	28.59	22.70	12.45
Hf	3.10	1.52	1.24	5.05	1.98	1.49	0.73
Ta	3.09	0.43	0.10	0.99	0.95	0.37	0.05
U	1.04	0.23	0.21	0.69	0.30	0.18	0.08
Pb	0.33	1.64	1.49	5.06	1.91	1.55	1.20
Rb	1.9	23.1	15.0	75.0	12.2	5.9	16.7
Cs	0.04	0.29	0.23	0.93	0.46	0.33	0.36
Sr	48	253	238	606	397	484	418
Sc	17.3	38.4	43.0	12.6	35.1	41.1	46.7

Continued

TABLE 3. MAJOR, MINOR, AND TRACE ELEMENT GEOCHEMICAL DATA FOR THE VILLA DE CURA BELT *(continued)*

	El Carmen Formation *(continued)*						
Sample	99-31	99-30	99-29	98-11	99-28	98-10	98-9
Unit	pmb	pmb	pmb	pmb	pmb	pmb	pmb
Grade	GE	GE	GE	GL	GL	GL	GL
SiO_2	49.13	47.88	47.97	46.73	48.57	47.00	48.11
TiO_2	0.68	0.79	0.75	0.66	0.66	0.83	0.72
Al_2O_3	15.23	17.26	14.96	14.26	15.59	16.04	14.24
FeO	10.32	10.77	10.88	10.79	10.48	11.12	9.75
MnO	0.18	0.19	0.19	0.18	0.18	0.18	0.18
MgO	10.40	6.64	10.48	9.91	8.81	6.96	9.87
CaO	10.81	12.02	11.04	11.96	12.15	11.38	10.05
Na_2O	2.61	2.17	2.01	1.76	2.24	2.16	2.29
K_2O	0.62	1.72	1.16	0.75	0.76	1.67	1.25
P_2O_5	0.17	0.25	0.20	0.16	0.17	0.24	0.20
Total	100.15	99.68	99.63	97.17	99.61	97.58	96.65
LOI%	3.80	3.68	3.86	4.30	3.63	3.97	4.19
Ni	150	68	180	155	97	69	183
Cr	311	145	396	346	266	180	365
V	305	310	303	282	296	331	276
Zr	28	36	31	28	26	40	52
Ga	13	18	16	13	18	16	14
Cu	130	60	125	132	119	88	119
Zn	67	71	78	69	68	72	68
Pb	0	0	0	2	0	0	2
La	2.59	3.06	3.35	2.62	2.42	3.30	3.62
Ce	5.51	7.13	7.10	5.53	5.40	7.22	7.78
Pr	0.90	1.08	1.12	0.90	0.87	1.17	1.20
Nd	4.63	5.63	5.71	4.52	4.53	6.13	6.23
Sm	1.59	2.06	1.87	1.55	1.70	2.03	1.90
Eu	0.69	0.78	0.76	0.62	0.68	0.77	0.65
Gd	1.99	2.58	2.42	1.99	2.13	2.74	2.53
Tb	0.35	0.46	0.41	0.34	0.38	0.46	0.43
Dy	2.27	2.90	2.53	2.27	2.39	2.98	2.76
Ho	0.48	0.59	0.55	0.46	0.50	0.60	0.58
Er	1.28	1.69	1.48	1.22	1.43	1.71	1.54
Tm	0.19	0.23	0.22	0.17	0.19	0.25	0.22
Yb	1.14	1.48	1.30	1.11	1.23	1.48	1.37
Lu	0.17	0.23	0.20	0.17	0.18	0.24	0.22
Ba	370	528	618	376	445	721	919
Th	0.21	0.36	0.24	0.18	0.23	0.25	0.26
Nb	0.85	0.83	0.88	0.88	0.66	1.11	0.99
Y	12.33	15.38	14.23	12.02	12.13	16.79	14.57
Hf	0.71	1.00	0.81	0.67	0.72	1.05	0.94
Ta	0.06	0.06	0.06	0.33	0.04	0.40	0.29
U	0.08	0.09	0.09	0.07	0.09	0.09	0.12
Pb	0.81	0.37	0.94	2.05	0.73	0.39	2.13
Rb	12.6	35.4	24.8	14.2	17.7	39.4	23.5
Cs	0.35	0.57	0.45	0.37	0.35	0.57	0.53
Sr	130	95	236	121	117	174	581
Sc	44.1	29.8	45.1	45.9	43.4	38.0	41.4

Continued

L.M. Unger, V.B. Sisson and H.G. Avé Lallemant

TABLE 3. MAJOR, MINOR, AND TRACE ELEMENT GEOCHEMICAL DATA FOR THE VILLA DE CURA BELT *(continued)*

	El Chino Formation		El Cano Formation				
Sample	98-41	98-38	99-39	98-88	99-38	98-87	99-37
Unit		amb	pmb	pmb	pmt	pmt	pmt
Grade	GL	GL	PA	PA	PA	PA	PA
SiO_2	53.40	44.80	49.64	47.54	49.03	48.80	48.10
TiO_2	1.16	0.83	0.83	0.85	0.72	0.50	0.50
Al_2O_3	16.50	17.65	13.65	10.97	11.93	6.45	8.83
FeO	10.38	8.07	11.57	11.85	11.93	10.80	11.02
MnO	0.22	0.17	0.19	0.20	0.19	0.21	0.20
MgO	3.78	4.11	9.35	12.73	14.58	18.72	19.50
CaO	6.60	15.72	10.36	9.24	8.17	9.65	11.09
Na_2O	4.35	1.60	2.56	1.77	0.24	0.40	0.34
K_2O	1.02	0.40	0.90	0.68	2.68	0.45	0.03
P_2O_5	0.26	0.18	0.29	0.21	0.18	0.16	0.14
Total	97.66	93.53	99.34	96.03	99.65	96.14	99.76
LOI%	3.35	11.04	3.55	4.50	4.01	4.05	4.09
Ni	0	2	65	215	280	589	447
Cr	12	28	260	659	799	1138	1125
V	237	290	292	312	291	185	218
Zr	91	57	54	44	35	30	26
Ga	20	19	21	16	16	10	14
Cu	14	103	114	137	164	62	89
Zn	87	54	87	82	87	83	71
Pb	0	0	0	2	0	0	0
La	9.10	7.34	4.61	4.28	3.38	3.48	1.73
Ce	19.49	14.30	10.17	9.53	7.74	6.93	3.83
Pr	2.72	2.13	1.52	1.45	1.17	1.05	0.65
Nd	13.31	9.92	8.02	7.52	5.84	5.02	3.36
Sm	4.21	3.03	2.69	2.34	1.84	1.54	1.32
Eu	1.46	0.99	0.95	0.79	0.64	0.54	0.51
Gd	4.68	3.18	3.21	2.84	2.32	1.83	1.75
Tb	0.78	0.52	0.57	0.46	0.39	0.31	0.32
Dy	4.92	3.27	3.47	2.90	2.48	1.97	2.04
Ho	1.03	0.69	0.73	0.57	0.51	0.38	0.41
Er	2.93	1.81	2.03	1.55	1.34	0.99	1.17
Tm	0.41	0.25	0.28	0.22	0.20	0.14	0.16
Yb	2.63	1.58	1.78	1.27	1.17	0.82	1.00
Lu	0.41	0.25	0.28	0.20	0.19	0.13	0.16
Ba	383	158	401	309	951	163	7
Th	0.85	0.51	0.43	0.26	0.26	0.34	0.22
Nb	5.31	2.68	1.71	1.67	0.75	1.14	0.52
Y	27.08	18.61	18.69	15.57	12.86	10.00	10.89
Hf	2.11	1.05	1.54	1.27	1.01	0.76	0.74
Ta	0.84	0.41	0.12	0.46	0.05	0.18	0.03
U	0.29	0.19	0.26	0.12	0.12	0.17	0.12
Pb	1.45	1.54	1.37	1.29	0.33	0.36	0.16
Rb	11.8	6.8	18.2	15.0	54.3	8.0	0.4
Cs	0.45	0.13	1.58	0.33	1.08	0.23	0.02
Sr	362	350	74	97	21	27	23
Sc	34.8	29.5	48.9	43.4	40.3	31.6	35.5

Continued

TABLE 3. MAJOR, MINOR, AND TRACE ELEMENT GEOCHEMICAL DATA FOR THE VILLA DE CURA BELT *(continued)*

	El Cano Formation *(continued)*						
Sample	98-85	98-83	99-36	99-34	98-77	98-79	98-81
Unit	pmb	pmt	pmt	pmt		ms	ms
Grade	PA	PA	PA	PA	PA	PA	PA
SiO_2	47.94	43.51	51.45	50.10	58.71	67.16	70.61
TiO_2	0.62	0.75	0.68	0.40	0.90	0.62	0.73
Al_2O_3	11.74	12.63	11.19	5.71	16.25	12.16	11.07
FeO	10.22	12.34	10.09	9.76	8.31	4.33	4.68
MnO	0.20	0.22	0.17	0.19	0.12	0.06	0.04
MgO	12.80	15.96	14.59	22.59	4.78	2.09	1.87
CaO	10.73	9.38	7.17	9.89	3.08	5.78	3.94
Na_2O	1.74	0.61	3.19	0.35	1.07	0.84	1.59
K_2O	0.44	0.33	0.33	0.10	2.14	2.46	1.51
P_2O_5	0.17	0.18	0.22	0.13	0.11	0.15	0.15
Total	96.59	95.91	99.08	99.22	95.46	95.64	96.18
LOI%	4.33	6.21	3.94	3.49	6.58	7.55	5.87
Ni	238	318	140	720	12	48	50
Cr	706	1074	482	1235	32	98	122
V	259	283	252	149	174	149	136
Zr	35	37	34	22	102	169	150
Ga	14	15	10	9	23	16	14
Cu	109	140	108	57	98	50	34
Zn	77	93	78	68	109	139	134
Pb	0	0	1	0	7	10	6
La	2.06	1.77	2.90	2.13	13.47	19.63	20.43
Ce	4.64	4.31	6.32	4.41	25.58	35.95	37.53
Pr	0.81	0.78	0.95	0.73	3.75	4.57	4.58
Nd	4.29	4.22	5.05	3.70	18.41	18.45	18.32
Sm	1.58	1.95	1.83	1.29	5.43	4.18	4.13
Eu	0.60	0.74	0.64	0.46	1.50	0.81	0.92
Gd	2.13	2.62	2.16	1.48	6.30	4.29	4.06
Tb	0.39	0.46	0.38	0.24	1.11	0.69	0.72
Dy	2.56	3.00	2.32	1.50	7.20	4.55	4.86
Ho	0.52	0.63	0.47	0.30	1.57	0.95	1.03
Er	1.42	1.69	1.25	0.82	4.51	2.73	2.94
Tm	0.21	0.23	0.18	0.12	0.67	0.42	0.43
Yb	1.30	1.44	1.07	0.73	4.31	2.68	2.62
Lu	0.20	0.23	0.17	0.11	0.71	0.44	0.41
Ba	241	154	88	22	1160	1142	675
Th	0.20	0.20	0.29	0.28	1.85	7.69	5.44
Nb	0.78	0.69	1.44	0.87	2.93	10.99	9.63
Y	14.56	16.59	11.60	7.92	42.21	28.38	29.66
Hf	0.91	1.03	1.04	0.68	3.30	4.71	4.22
Ta	0.21	0.09	0.09	0.06	1.41	1.69	1.41
U	0.15	0.10	0.16	0.16	1.11	2.07	1.60
Pb	1.59	3.71	1.92	1.45	6.74	10.72	7.35
Rb	7.8	6.2	7.3	1.6	42.4	92.1	62.1
Cs	0.21	0.16	0.11	0.05	0.99	4.92	2.93
Sr	126	29	258	25	136	221	162
Sc	40.0	49.7	48.0	28.3	33.9	14.4	15.0

Note: amb—andesitic metabasalt; mar—meta-arkose; mc—metachert; mgw—metagraywacke; ms—metasandstone; pmb—pyroxene metabasalt; pmt—picritic metatuff; BA—barroisite; GL—glaucophane-lawsonite; GE—glaucophane-epidote; PA—pumpellyite-actinolite. Ta values from 1998 analyses are possibly contaminated.

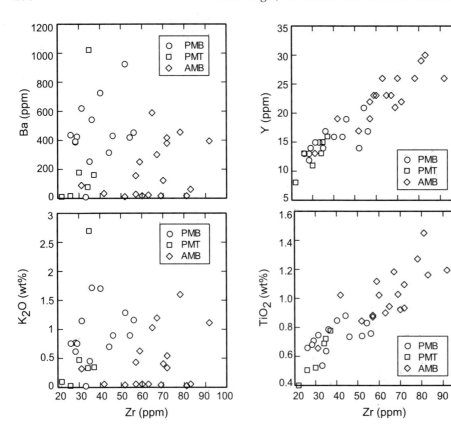

Figure 6. Variation diagrams of select major and trace elements plotted against the compatible element Zr. Diagrams of K_2O and Ba illustrate mobility of incompatible elements during metamorphism. Diagrams of TiO_2 and Y illustrate immobility of compatible elements. AMB—andesitic metabasalt; PMB—pyroxene metabasalt; PMT—picritic metatuff.

varies on an outcrop scale and is not pervasive anywhere along the section. Care was used to avoid taking samples near these veins. In addition, the occurrence of epidosites in metavolcanics is indicative of seafloor alteration. Thus, this study excluded Sr, K, Rb, Ba, Pb, and P, which are well documented in the literature as mobile during seafloor alteration and high-pressure metamorphism (Staudigel et al., 1996). All other elements are discussed with the confidence that inversion of geochemical data is a useful tool in deciphering the protolith of the Villa de Cura blueschist belt.

Major and Trace Element Analysis

Metabasalts

Major and trace element analyses of 37 metabasalts are given in Table 3. Metabasalts are primarily tholeiitic, with only minor overlap into the calc-alkaline field. This trend toward alkalinity is a result of mobility in alkali elements during seafloor alteration and subsequent metamorphism rather than calc-alkaline evolution of an arc magma source.

The three types of metabasalts in the Villa de Cura belt can be distinguished on the basis of their geochemistry (Fig. 5 and 6). Picritic metatuff is MgO-rich and TiO_2-poor with values of 14.6–22.8 wt% MgO and 0.4–0.8 wt% TiO_2. These MgO-rich basalts have high SiO_2 concentrations; three of the six analyses contain >50 wt% SiO_2. In contrast, SiO_2 values in pyroxene metabasalts are lower at 47.3–51.2 wt% SiO_2, where only 20% of

the analyzed rocks have values >50 wt% SiO_2. MgO values for pyroxene metabasalts are intermediate at 6.7–13.3 wt% MgO, and TiO_2 is depleted similar to picritic metatuff. Andesitic metabasalt samples are mafic to intermediate with 47.9–55.9 wt% SiO_2. They are high in Al_2O_3 (14.2–18.9 wt%), low in MgO (3.3–7.5 wt%), and higher in TiO_2 (0.8–1.4 wt%) than picritic metatuff and pyroxene metabasalt.

Variation diagrams of Mg# {Mg# = [MgO/(FeO_{total} + MgO) × 100]} versus selected trace elements (Fig. 7) exhibit a consistent trend of evolution of the basaltic protolith from the most mafic picritic metatuff, to pyroxene metabasalt, to the more evolved andesitic metabasalt. These diagrams also further support the categorization of metabasalts from thin section analysis and field observation.

Trace element discrimination diagrams (Fig. 8) show the same evolution of magmas within the Villa de Cura from picritic metatuff to pyroxene metabasalt to andesitic metabasalt. Samples of pyroxene metabasalt and picritic metatuff plot entirely within the island-arc tholeiite (IAT)–volcanic arc basalt (VAB) field, and show little overlap with MORB and backarc basin basalt (BAB). Samples of andesitic metabasalt also dominantly plot within the arc tholeiite field; however, there is an overlap with the fields of MORB and BAB.

Three basalt samples of the Las Hermanas Formation have geochemical signatures compatible with IAT (Table 3) and overlap with Villa de Cura samples. This interpretation is similar to that of Giunta et al. (2002) and Ostos and Sisson (this volume).

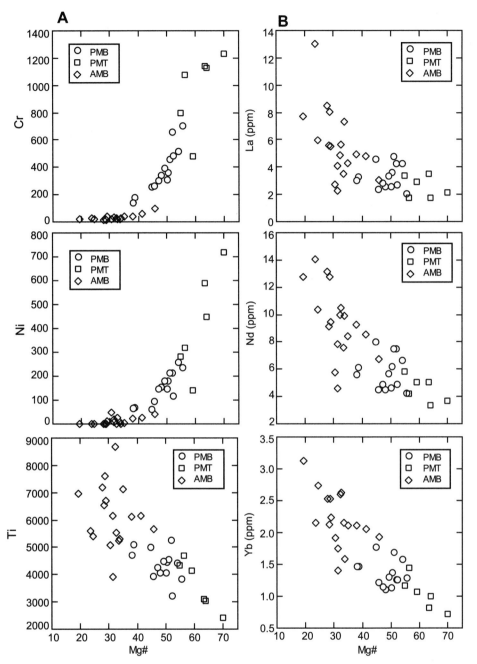

Figure 7. Variation diagrams plotted against Mg# {Mg# = [MgO/(FeO$_{total}$ + MgO)] × 100} for the Villa de Cura metabasalts. (A) Variation diagrams of high-field strength trace elements. (B) Variation diagrams of trace metals. AMB—andesitic metabasalt; PMB—pyroxene metabasalt; PMT—picritic metatuff.

Multi-element diagrams. MORB-normalized multi-element diagrams modeled after Pearce (1983) (Fig. 9) are shown with Sr, K, Rb, Ba, and P omitted because of element mobility during seafloor alteration and metamorphism. It is also important to note that Ta is marked by an "x" (Fig. 9) to indicate a major discrepancy between the 1998 and 1999 analytical year (1998 samples are possibly contaminated). All three groups of metabasalt in the Villa de Cura belt are high field strength element (HFSE) depleted relative to normal (N)-MORB and have a strongly negative Nb anomaly. Ratios of La/Nb range from 2.0 to 4.5 in picritic

metatuff, 2.6–5.5 in pyroxene metabasalt, and 1.6–7.9 in andesitic metabasalt. An overall trace element enrichment trend is seen from picritic metatuff to pyroxene metabasalt to andesitic metabasalt. There is an apparent gradation between the pyroxene metabasalt and andesitic metabasalt.

REE diagrams. All samples in the Villa de Cura belt are moderately to strongly light-REE (LREE) enriched, indicating derivation from a depleted mantle wedge source typical of that found above a subduction zone (Fig. 10). La/Yb ratios are positive in all samples and range from 1.2 to 4.2 in picritic metatuff, 1.6–3.4 in

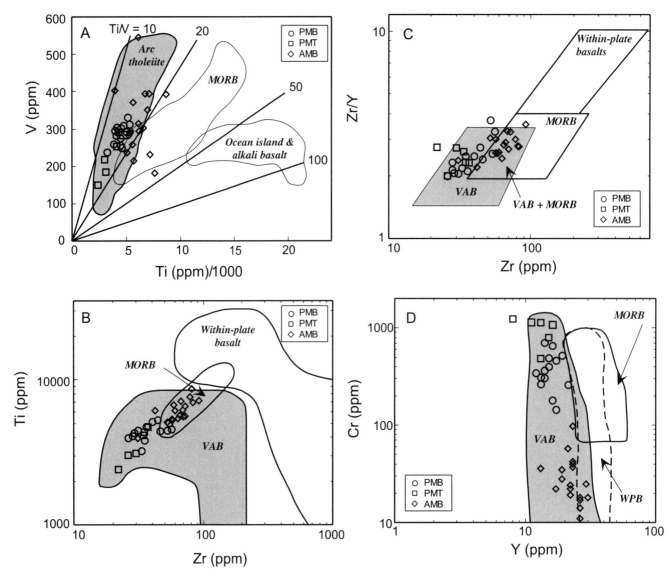

Figure 8. Representative geochemical discrimination diagrams for the Villa de Cura metabasalts. (A) Incompatible element discrimination diagram of Shervais (1982). (B) Incompatible element discrimination diagram of Pearce (1982). (C) Incompatible element discrimination diagram of Pearce (1983). (D) Incompatible element discrimination diagram of Pearce (1982). AMB—andesitic metabasalt; MORB—mid-oceanic-ridge basalt; VAB—volcanic arc basalt; PMB—pyroxene metabasalt; PMT—picritic metatuff; WPB—within-plate basalts.

pyroxene metabasalt, and 1.4–6.0 in andesitic metabasalt. LREE concentrations are greatest in andesitic metabasalt (9.6–54.9 times chondrite) and lowest in picritic metatuff (7.3–14.7 times chondrite). Relative enrichment of andesitic metabasalt relative to pyroxene metabasalt and picritic metatuff further supports the evolved nature of this suite. Sample 98-83 (picritic metatuff from El Caño Formation) appears to have a LREE depleted pattern similar to N-MORB; however, its La/Yb ratio is positive at 1.2. Sample 98-83 may represent the most primitive initial melt composition of a newly formed island-arc. The enrichment in LREE is a feature of calc-alkaline suites elsewhere in the Caribbean such as Puerto Rico (Donnelly and Rogers, 1978). In contrast, typical IATs usually show flat REE patterns.

Metasedimentary Rocks

SiO_2 values for metasedimentary rocks range from 67.2 to 79.5 wt%; the lowest value occurs in the graphitic schist from the El Caño Formation, and the highest value occurs in the metachert from the Santa Isabel Formation. Variation diagrams of compatible and incompatible elements plotted relative to Zr show similar trends. Sample 98-64 (metachert) is consistently the most depleted. All other samples show a trend toward enrichment, though no clear pattern of enrichment related to metamorphic grade, rock type, or formation is indicated.

REE diagrams. Figure 11A shows the REE patterns of analyzed metasedimentary rocks. Sample 98-64 (metachert) is depleted relative to chondrite and has a La/Yb ratio of 2.4. All

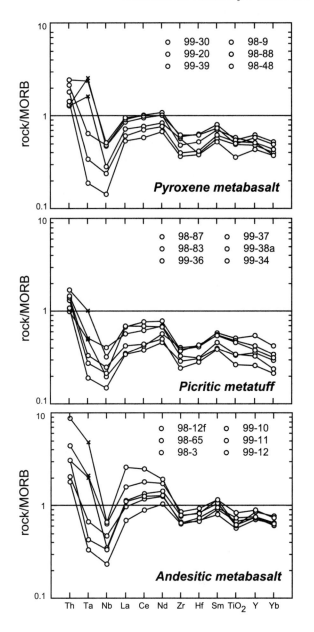

Figure 9. Multi-element diagrams for Villa de Cura group metabasalts group according to Pearce (1983). Ta is marked with an "x" to indicate processing contamination.

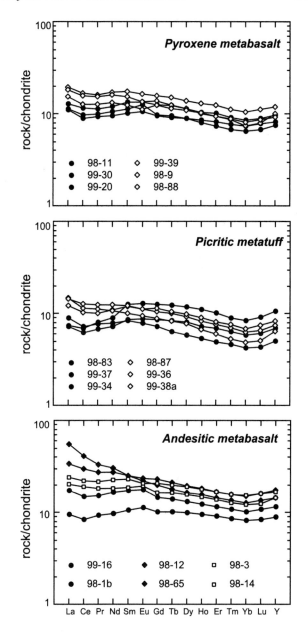

Figure 10. Rare earth element data for Villa de Cura group metabasalts normalized to the chondrite values of Sun and McDonough (1989).

other samples have a pronounced Eu anomaly, indicating presence of plagioclase in the sediment provenance. La/Yb ratios of these sediments average 4.7 in the Santa Isabel Formation (excluding chert sample), 2.7 in the El Carmen Formation, and 7.6 in the El Caño Formation. The enrichment of LREE–heavy REE (HREE) supports an island-arc provenance for these metasedimentary rocks. Sample 98-64 (metachert) could have been formed in an island-arc or mid-oceanic ridge environment.

Multi-element diagrams. The multi-element diagram in Figure 11B again supports an island-arc provenance for these metasedimentary rocks. La/Nb ratios range from 1.8 to 3.0 in all samples except 98-64, where the La/Nb ratio is 0.7. Sample 98-64 is also depleted relative to MORB, while all other samples are enriched relative to MORB. A significant TiO_2 anomaly is seen in all samples but 98-64 (metachert).

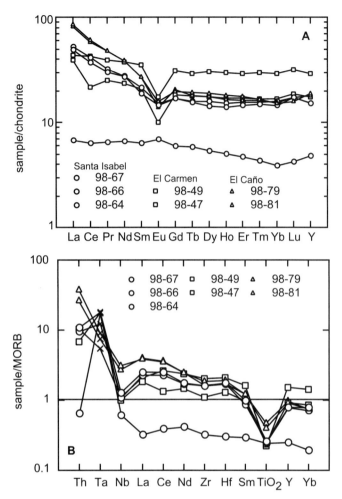

Figure 11. Representative geochemical plots for metasedimentary rock samples in the Villa de Cura group. (A) Rare earth element data normalized to the chondrite values of Sun and McDonough (1989). (B) Multi-element plot of trace element data from metasedimentary rock samples. MORB—mid-oceanic-ridge basalt. Ta values are represented by an "x" to indicate contamination during sample processing. Normalization values from Pearce (1983).

OTHER ALLOCHTHONOUS BASALTS IN THE CARIBBEAN REALM

The circum-Caribbean realm and the associated Caribbean plate are represented by four distinct igneous rock series: (1) Jurassic MORB, (2) Early and Late Cretaceous IATs (equivalent to primitive island-arc [PIA] of Donnelly and Rogers [1978] and Beets et al. [1984]), (3) Early to Late Cretaceous calc-alkaline (CA), and (4) Early to Late Cretaceous oceanic plateau.

The Caribbean plate is built upon Jurassic oceanic basement that originated in a Pacific mid-oceanic spreading center (e.g., Montgomery et al., 1994; Kerr et al., 2003). Mauffret and Leroy (1997) use thermal subsidence rates to determine a 160 Ma maximum age for oceanic crust in the Venezuela, Colombia, and Haitian basins. A 152 Ma age determined from sediment accu-

mulation rates in the Venezuela basin appears to corroborate these results (Mauffret and Leroy, 1997). Intercalated Jurassic radiolarian chert have been found in the Siquisique ophiolite of northern Venezuela (Bartok et al., 1985), the Duarte Formation of Hispaniola (Lewis and Jiménez, 1991), the Bermeja complex of Puerto Rico (Schellekens, 1998), the Santa Elena–Nicoya complex of Costa Rica (e.g., Sinton et al., 1997; Beccaluva et al., 1999; Hoernle et al., 2004) and the northern ophiolitic mélange of Cuba (Iturralde-Vinent et al., 1996).

The IATs, or PIA association (e.g., Donnelly and Rogers, 1978), are products of the Cretaceous Great Arc of the Caribbean. Aptian (121–112 Ma) to Albian (112–99 Ma) age IATs (Fig. 2) are found in the Washikemba Formation of Bonaire (Donnelly and Rogers, 1978; Beets et al., 1984; Thompson et al., 2004b); the Tobago Volcanic Group and North Coast Schist of Tobago (Frost and Snoke, 1989; Snoke et al., 2001); the pre-Robles complex of Puerto Rico (Schellekens, 1998); the Maimón Formation, Los Ranchos Formation, and Guamira basalts of Hispaniola (Lebrón and Perfit, 1994); the Water Island Formation of the Virgin Islands; and the Cretaceous Volcanic Arc of Cuba (e.g., Iturralde-Vinent, 1996; Kerr et al., 1999; Blein et al., 2003). Some of these, the Maimón Formation (Hispaniola), Los Pasos (Cuba), and Water Island Formation (Virgin Islands), are bimodal suites with low HFSE concentrations in mafic rocks (Lewis et al., 2002; Blein et al., 2003). These are the oldest and most primitive island-arc volcanics in the Greater Antilles. Blein et al. (2003) proposed that there are two juxtaposed arc sequences in Cuba: one is related to the Cretaceous Greater Antilles island-arc and the other is a Jurassic to Early Cretaceous island-arc suite with a Pacific provenance. The Los Ranchos Formation (Hispaniola) and pre-Robles units (Puerto Rico) are more evolved than the Maimón and Water Island Formations (Jolly et al., 2001). In fact, there is no sharp stratigraphic break between the tholeiitic and calc-alkaline suites in Puerto Rico (E.G. Lidiak, 2002, personal commun.).

The CA series of the Great Arc of the Caribbean are generally younger than the IAT series. In Aruba, the 85–82 Ma tonalitic Aruba batholith intrudes the Turonian (93.5–89 Ma) Aruba Lava Formation (Beets et al., 1984; White et al., 1999). The ca. 86 Ma calc-alkaline El Salado granite of Margarita Island (Venezuela) intrudes >105 Ma high-pressure rocks of the Juan Griego and La Rinconada Groups (Stöckhert et al., 1995). In Puerto Rico, calc-alkaline assemblages include the upper Albian to Campanian Robles–Río Orocovis Formations, as well as Cenomanian to Lower Santonian and upper Santonian to Maastrichtian calc-alkaline and shoshonitic volcanic phases (Donnelly et al., 1990; Jolly et al., 1998; Schellekens, 1998; Jolly et al., 2001). Calc-alkaline rocks in Hispaniola include the Tiero Formation, the Loma la Vega Formation, and the Las Guajabas tuffs (Lebrón and Perfit, 1994; Lewis et al., 2002). In Cuba, a Santonian to Campanian calc-alkaline assemblage is found within the Cretaceous Volcanic Arc belt (Diaz de Villalvilla, 1997).

The Cretaceous Caribbean-Colombian oceanic plateau is thought to have formed by the initial plume head of the ancestral Galápagos hot spot (Duncan and Hargraves, 1984; Burke,

1988; Kerr et al., 1996; Mauffret and Leroy, 1997; Thompson et al., 2004a). However, Pindell et al. (this volume), among others, suggest that the Caribbean plateau originated elsewhere. Terranes thought to be related to the Cretaceous Caribbean-Colombian oceanic plateau include the Gorgona Island komatiites, the Western Cordillera and Serranía de Baudo in Colombia, the Curaçao Lava Formation, the Aruba Lava Formation, the Lower Duarte complex and Dumisseau Formation of Hispaniola, and the Nicoya complex of Costa Rica (Kerr et al., 1997a; Lapierre et al., 1997; Sinton et al., 1998; Beccaluva et al., 1999; White et al., 1999).

A significant number of $^{40}Ar/^{39}Ar$ age dates from Cretaceous Caribbean-Colombian oceanic plateau basalts have been published that highlight the primary phases of volcanism within the province as 92–88 Ma and 76–72 Ma (see Kerr et al., 2003, and references therein). However, this may not represent the initial eruption of the plume, as Mauffret and Leroy (1997) identified three distinct plateaus, which are found on the lower Nicaragua rise, the western Colombia basin, and the Beata ridge. They estimate that the initial volcanic phase of the Cretaceous Caribbean-Colombian oceanic plateau occurred in the late Aptian (113 Ma), followed by two more widespread eruptive events in the Turonian (93.5–89.0 Ma) and Campanian (83.5–71.3 Ma). Recently, Hoernle et al. (2004) reported 139 Ma ages for basalts in Nicaragua related to the Cretaceous Caribbean-Columbian oceanic plateau.

DISCUSSION

Fragments of igneous terranes are found throughout the entire Caribbean margin. The information that can be gleaned from correlating these assemblages and interpreting their petrotectonic histories is essential for understanding Caribbean tectonic history. The geochemistry, geochronology, and in some cases metamorphic history of emplaced oceanic crust provide information on the origin of the Caribbean plate and timing of arc polarity reversal.

Geochemical Comparison of the Villa de Cura and Circum-Caribbean Basalts

As previously stated, allochthonous basaltic terranes in the Caribbean are represented by four main rock series: MORB, IAT, CA and shoshonitic basalt and andesite, and oceanic plateau basalts (Fig. 12). MORB fields are not shown in Figure 11 in order to maintain clarity; however, geochemical characteristics of Caribbean MORB include depleted LREE patterns, low concentrations of large ion lithophile elements (LILE), and the absence of more evolved intermediate and felsic rocks (Lebrón and Perfit, 1994).

Cretaceous IAT suites found throughout the Caribbean have several common characteristics. Most volcanic suites span a compositional range from basaltic to andesitic (Beets et al., 1984; Lebrón and Perfit, 1994). Typically, felsic rocks are volumetrically minor (Beets et al., 1984; Jolly et al., 1998). REE patterns are flat to only slightly LREE enriched relative to HREE (Beets et al., 1984; Frost and Snoke, 1989; Lebrón and Perfit, 1994; Jolly et al., 1998). LILE are enriched relative to HFSE as typical of island-arc

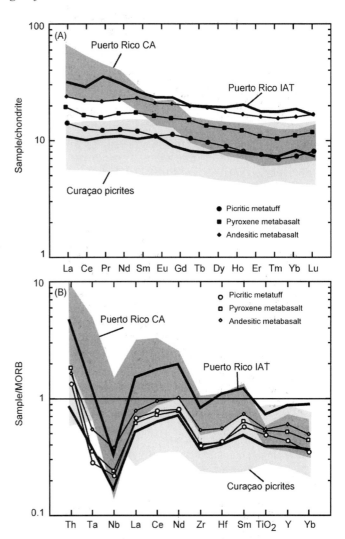

Figure 12. Comparative geochemical plots for various igneous and metaigneous suites in the Caribbean. (A) REE diagrams comparing representative Villa de Cura basalts with representative Caribbean island-arc tholeiites (IAT) and calc-alkaline (CA) rocks from Puerto Rico (Jolly et al., 1998) and representative oceanic plateau from the Curaçao Lava Formation (Révillon et al., 1999). Villa de Cura basalts are shown with lines connecting black symbols. IAT is shown as the field between two heavy black lines. CA is shown as a dark gray field. Oceanic plateau is shown as a light gray field. Mid-oceanic-ridge basalt (MORB) fields are not included in order to maintain clarity, but MORB characteristics are discussed in the text. Normalization values are from Sun and McDonough (1989). (B) Multi-element diagram after Pearce (1983) comparing representative Villa de Cura basalts with representative Caribbean IAT and CA rocks from Puerto Rico (Jolly et al., 1998) and representative oceanic plateau from the Curaçao Lava Formation (Révillon et al., 1999). Jolly et al. (1998) do not report Ta values, thus the fields shown for Ta have estimated Ta boundaries, which were estimated as the average between Th and Nb. Ta values in Villa de Cura basalts are from 1999 samples ground in a steel mill; thus, they are believed to be accurate. Villa de Cura basalts are shown with lines connecting white symbols. IAT is shown as the field between two heavy black lines. CA is shown as a dark gray field. Oceanic plateau is shown as a light gray field. MORB fields are not included in order to maintain clarity, but MORB characteristics are discussed in the text. Normalization values are from Pearce (1983).

basalts, but LILE/HFSE ratios are significantly lower than those found in the calc-alkaline rock suites (Beets et al., 1984; Frost and Snoke, 1989; Lebrón and Perfit, 1994; Jolly et al., 1998).

The calc-alkaline and shoshonitic suites of the Caribbean often include basalts, andesites, rhyodacites, and rhyolites, as well as diorite and tonalite and associated volcaniclastic sedimentary rocks (Donnelly et al., 1990; Lebrón and Perfit, 1994). In the Greater Antilles, they are characterized by high concentrations of K_2O, Ba, Rb, and Sr, as well as more extreme enrichment of LILE relative to HFSE and LREE-HREE (Lebrón and Perfit, 1994; Jolly et al., 1998; Jolly et al., 2001; Lewis et al., 2002).

Cretaceous Caribbean-Colombian oceanic plateau basalts are chemically and lithologically distinct from other basalts of oceanic affinity in the Caribbean realm. The primary lithologies incorporated in accreted portions of the Cretaceous Caribbean-Colombian oceanic plateau are picrites, pillow basalts, dolerites, and komatiites (Kerr et al., 1997a, 2003; White et al., 1999; Hauff et al., 2000). These rocks are characterized by high MgO (up to 30 wt% in picrites), flat REE patterns, ratios of La/Nb (normalized to primitive mantle) ≤ 1, and lack of Nb and Ta depletion (Kerr et al., 1998, 2003; Hauff et al., 2000). It is often difficult to uniquely determine the petrotectonic setting of basalts. For example, Kerr et al. (2003) note that a portion of the El Carmen Formation has geochemical signatures similar to oceanic plateaus with flat REE patterns and $La_{pmn}/Nb_{pmn} = 1$. However, all of our samples have $La_{pmn}/Nb_{pmn} > 1$. In addition, field evidence for metatuffs within the El Carmen Formation and the gradational boundary with the El Chino Formation both support our interpretation of an island-arc protolith.

Figure 12 compares the REE and incompatible multi-element patterns of three representative samples from the Villa de Cura (including picritic metatuff, pyroxene metabasalt, and andesitic metabasalt) with those in the Curaçao picrites (of the Curaçao Lava Formation; Révillon et al., 1999) and Puerto Rico IAT and CA assemblages (Jolly et al., 1998). All members of the Villa de Cura, including the more evolved andesitic metabasalt of the Santa Isabel Formation, overlap the field of Puerto Rico IAT. These samples are represented by an overall LREE enrichment relative to HREE with average La/Yb ratios of 2.4, compared with almost twice that (La/Yb = 5.3) in the CA field (Fig. 12A). REE patterns of oceanic plateau rocks from Curaçao are relatively flat (La/Yb = 1.6).

Figure 12B again illustrates the overlap between Villa de Cura basalts and IAT basalts from Puerto Rico. Villa de Cura basalts show depletion of HFSE relative to N-MORB and a distinct Nb anomaly consistent with that of IAT. IAT and CA rocks from Puerto Rico have values of La/Nb = 5.4 and 5.8, respectively, while La/Nb = 0.8 in Cretaceous Caribbean-Colombian oceanic plateau basalts from Curaçao.

Timing of Arc Polarity Reversal in the Caribbean

The timing of arc polarity reversal along the Great Arc of the Caribbean has been controversial (e.g., Lebrón and Perfit, 1994; Draper et al., 1996; Kerr et al., 1999; Lapierre et al., 1999; Lewis et al., 1999; Pindell et al., this volume). One suggested mechanism of subduction polarity reversal is choking of the east-dip-ping subduction zone as a result of the arrival of overthickened, hot, buoyant oceanic lithosphere (i.e., the Cretaceous Caribbean-Colombian oceanic plateau).

Lebrón and Perfit (1994) demonstrated a temporal and geochemical evolution of the island-arc series in the Dominican Republic that argues for an Albian age polarity reversal. They suggested that an Aptian age tholeiitic island-arc overlying an east dipping subduction zone collided with the Cretaceous Caribbean-Colombian oceanic plateau in late Aptian to early Albian time, resulting in cessation of tholeiitic volcanism, regional uplift of the arc, and subsequent shallow water limestone deposition. This model also applies to the volcanic arc systems of Puerto Rico and Cuba (Lebrón and Perfit, 1994).

Draper et al. (1996) lend further support to Aptian–early Albian polarity reversal in the Caribbean. They documented north-directed thrust emplacement of the Loma Caribe peridotite (arc basement) over the Maimón Formation and Neocomian (144–121 Ma) Los Ranchos Formation. This event creates penetrative deformation in the Maimón Formation with deformation decreasing toward the northeast. Undeformed upper Albian limestone unconformably overlies the Los Ranchos Formation. Escuder Viruete et al. (2002) report $^{40}Ar/^{39}Ar$ results of 84.6 ± 0.5 Ma for exhumation and cooling during thrusting, consanguineous with the chemical changes in arc magmas described above.

Arc polarity reversal is also suggested in the Lesser and Leeward Antilles, in Tobago and Aruba (Beets et al., 1984; Frost and Snoke, 1989; White et al., 1999; Snoke and Noble, 2001; Snoke et al., 2001). In Tobago, the ca. 120 Ma North Coast Schist is deformed and metamorphosed at greenschist facies conditions. It structurally overlies the undeformed Tobago Volcanic Group, which is dated as Albian age by ammonite and radiolarian fossils, as well as $^{40}Ar/^{39}Ar$ (Snoke and Noble, 2001). Snoke and Noble (2001) concluded that subduction polarity reversal occurred sometime in the Albian before the eruption of the Tobago Volcanic Group (ca. 105 Ma), and that the North Coast Schist served as basement for deposition of younger arc sequences.

In Aruba, the 85–82 Ma tonalitic Aruba batholith intrudes the Aruba Lava Formation (Beets et al., 1984; White et al., 1999). The Aruba Lava Formation has not been successfully dated using $^{40}Ar/^{39}Ar$ methods (White et al., 1999). White et al. (1999) demonstrated the geochemical and isotopic similarity between the Aruba Lava Formation and the Curaçao Lava Formation. Thus, the Aruba Lava Formation was a part of the Cretaceous Caribbean-Colombian oceanic plateau. Conversely, the tonalitic Aruba batholith has island-arc affinity, broadly following a calc-alkaline trend. White et al. (1999) suggests that after arc polarity reversal, the Aruba batholith intruded the Cretaceous Caribbean-Colombian oceanic plateau.

Other authors do not support the idea that polarity reversal occurred before the main eruptive phase of the Cretaceous Caribbean-Colombian oceanic plateau, i.e., before ca. 91–88 Ma. Mauffret and Leroy (1997) use seismic evidence and sedimentation rates to state that there is likely an earlier event that began ca. 113 Ma (in the late Aptian).

Model: Formation and Subduction of the Villa De Cura Belt

The Villa de Cura Group (high-pressure blueschist unit) contains tholeiitic lavas with intercalated metavolcaniclastic sediments and metachert and was formed in an oceanic island-arc environment. The Villa de Cura Group rocks are geochemically similar to other IATs found throughout the Caribbean in Puerto Rico, Hispaniola, Cuba, Tobago, and Bonaire.

Smith et al. (1999) placed several constraints on subduction of the Villa de Cura blueschist belt. First, the barroisite belt experienced a different pressure-temperature-time (*P-T-t*) path than the glaucophane-epidote, glaucophane-lawsonite, and glaucophane-epidote belts. The *P-T-t* conditions experienced by the barroisite belt are interpreted by Smith et al. (1999) as representing the initiation of subduction after arc polarity reversal in an environment of an elevated geothermal gradient under non–steady-state conditions (e.g., Ernst, 1988; Wakabayashi, 1990). Peak metamorphic conditions for the barroisite belt were reached by ca. 96 Ma. Peak metamorphic conditions in the glaucophane-epidote, glaucophane-lawsonite, and pumpellyite-actinolite zones were reached sometime later, perhaps ca. 79 Ma (Smith et al., 1999). Smith et al. (1999) proposed a model for the subduction and exhumation of the Villa de Cura blueschist belt based on the above metamorphic and geochronologic constraints. However Smith et al. (1999) assumed a MORB origin for the glaucophane-epidote, glaucophane-lawsonite, and pumpellyite-actino-

lite zones. Thus, new evidence presented in this paper requires modification of the model of Smith et al. (1999).

We propose the following tectonic model for formation and later subduction of the Villa de Cura belt, with implications regarding timing of subduction polarity reversal along the Great Arc of the Caribbean:

Aptian (Fig. 13A)

Subduction of Pacific lithosphere continued beneath the Late Jurassic–Early Cretaceous Great Arc of the Caribbean. The arc erupted tholeiitic magmas that were contaminated by pelagic sediment derived from the Pacific (e.g., Lebrón and Perfit, 1994). The initial phase of the Cretaceous Caribbean-Colombian oceanic plateau formed a small oceanic plateau at either ca. 140 or 120 Ma. The Villa de Cura Group formed on the northeastern side of the arc. The protolith for the barroisite zone (BA; circle A in Fig. 13) lies near the recently (ca. 120 Ma; Pindell, 1993) extinct Proto-Caribbean spreading ridge; thus, it is probably hot relative to parts of the arc that are further away from the ridge, such as the protolith of the glaucophane-epidote (GE), glaucophane-lawsonite (GL), and pumpellyite-actinolite (PA) zones (circle B in Fig. 13). A left-lateral strike-slip fault separates circle A from circle B.

Albian (Fig. 13B)

The pre-Cretaceous Caribbean-Colombian oceanic plateau collided with the arc and choked the east-dipping subduction zone (it is also possible that increased spreading rates in the Atlantic

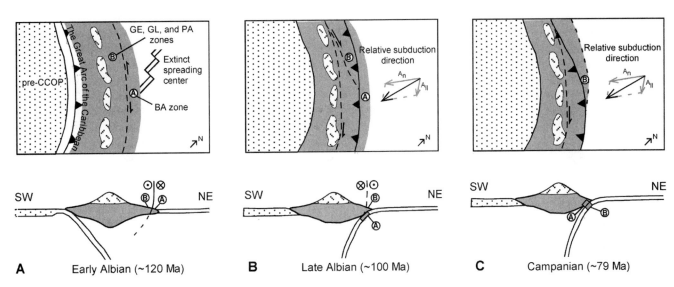

Figure 13. Possible tectonic scenario for the Villa de Cura Group. Dotted pattern represents the Cretaceous Caribbean oceanic plateau (CCOP) or pre-CCOP. Hatched pattern represents exposure of island arc above sea level, while gray represents extent of island arc below sea level. White is mid-oceanic-ridge basalt (MORB)–type oceanic crust. Circle A represents hypothetical location of the protolith of the barroisite (BA) zone through time, and circle B represents hypothetical location of the protolith of the glaucophane-epidote (GE), glaucophane-lawsonite (GL), and pumpellyite-actinolite (PA) zones through time. A_n and $A_{\parallel}$ represent the arc-normal and arc-parallel components, respectively, of the decomposed relative subduction direction vector (displacement partitioning of Avé Lallemant, 1996). Dashed lines are strike slip faults with corresponding relative motion vectors. (A) Map view and cross section of the Great Arc of the Caribbean and surrounding area in early Albian time (ca. 120 Ma) before subduction polarity reversal. (B) Map view and cross section of the Great Arc of the Caribbean in the late Albian (ca. 100 Ma) after polarity reversal and subduction of circle A. (C) Map view and cross section of the Great Arc of the Caribbean in Campanian time (ca. 79 Ma), after subduction of circle B. For more information, see description in text.

caused subduction polarity reversal [Pindell, 1993]). Continued northeastward motion of the Caribbean relative to the Americas resulted in the formation of a southwest-dipping subduction zone in which Proto-Caribbean crust was consumed beneath the island-arc. Subduction initiated within the arc along the former left-lateral strike-slip fault. Circle A (BA zone protolith) is now part of the downgoing plate and was subducted beneath the arc while it was still hot. Peak metamorphism in the BA zone (circle A) occurred at about ca. 96 Ma. Relative subduction direction was oblique to the trench (Pindell, 1993) resulting in displacement partitioning (Avé Lallemant, 1996) along the arc. The arc-normal vector component (A_n) caused subduction and arc-perpendicular thrusting, while the arc-parallel vector component ($A_{\parallel}$) caused right-lateral displacement in the forearc. A series of anastomosing strike-slip faults formed in the forearc over the west dipping subducting plate. Right-lateral motion along a NW-SE–trending strike slip fault moved circle B (PA, GL, and GE zones) southward to the former location of circle A.

Campanian (Fig. 13C)

As west-dipping subduction continued, terrigenous sediment derived from the Americas contaminated the mantle wedge, resulting in eruption and intrusion of calc-alkaline magma over and/or into the tholeiitic basement. The Cretaceous Caribbean-Colombian oceanic plateau began its main eruptive phase in the Turonian (93.5–88 Ma). Southward movement and overall geometry of the wedge that contains circle B caused initiation of subduction along the former NW-SE–striking right-lateral strike-slip fault. As a result, circle B became part of the downgoing plate and was subducted beneath the arc. Decoupling of circle A from Proto-Caribbean lithosphere occurred sometime before subduction of circle B. For further information regarding the metamorphic and exhumation history of the Villa de Cura belt after initial subduction see Smith et al. (1999).

This tectonic model is a variant of many others for the Caribbean such as that proposed by Pindell (1993) and Pindell et al. (this volume). It is also similar to model C of Giunta et al. (2003). The major difference is that we propose that the Villa de Cura Group represents two forearc slivers within the Great Arc of the Caribbean. Subsequent strike-slip motion juxtaposes these two slivers and they are amalgamated in the subduction zone and exhumed as a coherent unit.

CONCLUSIONS

Metavolcanic rocks of the Villa de Cura Group were classified into three rock types: pyroxene metabasalt, picritic metatuff, and andesitic metabasalt. These are all part of a high-pressure subduction-related metamorphic sequence. Pyroxene metabasalt is blue-green and typically massive, with large clinopyroxene phenocrysts that make up 1–15% of the rock volume. The characteristic assemblage of pyroxene metabasalt is clinopyroxene ± chlorite ± amphibole (either glaucophane, barroisite, and/or actinolite) ± epidote ± albite ± white mica. Picritic metatuff is light green, finely laminated, and occurs in thin layers. It is generally aphanitic with a matrix of chlorite + white mica + lawsonite ± amphibole ± clinopyroxene ± quartz, although small, rare clinopyroxene phenocrysts are found. Andesitic metabasalt is light blue-green, well foliated, and lacks phenocrysts. Andesitic metabasalt is the most siliceous of the three metavolcanic rock types and is typically composed of chlorite + amphibole (either barroisite or glaucophane) + albite + quartz + epidote ± white mica ± lawsonite ± calcite.

New major and trace element geochemical data show that all subbelts of the Villa de Cura belt have an oceanic island-arc composition. All rock types are tholeiitic, and an evolutionary trend (from more to less mafic) is seen from picritic metatuff, to pyroxene metabasalt, to andesitic metabasalt. Trace element discrimination diagrams show a very consistent correlation of Villa de Cura metavolcanics with island-arc tholeiite fields. MORB-normalized multi-element diagrams exhibit typical arc signatures, including a strongly negative Nb anomaly and depletion of HFSE relative to N-MORB. Chondrite-normalized REE diagrams show that Villa de Cura metabasalts are LREE enriched and have positive LREE/HREE ratios in all samples. Island-arc tholeiites of the Villa de Cura Group are similar to other Aptian-Albian arc tholeiites found throughout the Caribbean in Cuba, Puerto Rico, Hispaniola, Tobago, and Aruba.

The Villa de Cura (and other Caribbean) island-arc tholeiites may have formed above an east-dipping Benioff zone as Pacific lithosphere was consumed beneath the Great Arc of the Caribbean. An early phase of the Cretaceous Caribbean-Colombian oceanic plateau collided with the subduction zone and choked it with hot, buoyant lithosphere. A late Albian arc polarity reversal resulted in subduction of Proto-Caribbean lithosphere beneath the Great Arc of the Caribbean. Subduction of continentally derived sediment contaminated the mantle wedge and began a new calc-alkaline eruptive phase of the Great Arc of the Caribbean. Subduction of the Villa de Cura belt occurred after the arc polarity reversal. The protolith of the barroisite subbelt of the Villa de Cura belt was subducted shortly after arc polarity reversal. The protoliths of the pumpellyite-actinolite, glaucophane-lawsonite, and glaucophane-epidote subbelts were carried southward in a forearc sliver along a series of anastomosing strike-slip faults where they were incorporated into Proto-Caribbean lithosphere and subducted in Campanian time under cool subduction zone conditions. These two forearc slivers were then amalgamated in the subduction zone and exhumed onto the northern Venezuela margin.

ACKNOWLEDGMENTS

This work was supported by National Science Foundation grant EAR-9706521 to VBS and HGAL. We are grateful to Diego Sanabria and Brian Locke for field assistance. Helpful and thorough reviews by John Lewis and an anonymous reviewer helped clarify this manuscript.

REFERENCES CITED

Avé Lallemant, H.G., 1996, Displacement partitioning and arc-parallel extension: Example from the southeastern Caribbean plate margin, *in* Bebout, G.E., Scholl, D.W., Kirby, S.H., and Platt, J.P., eds., Subduction top to bottom: American Geophysical Union Monograph 96, p. 113–118.

Bartok, P.E., Renz, O., and Westermann, G.E.G., 1985, The Siquisique ophiolites, northern Lara State, Venezuela: A discussion on their Middle Jurassic ammonites and tectonic implications: Geological Society of America Bulletin, v. 96, p. 1050–1055, doi: 10.1130/0016-7606(1985)96<1050:TSONLS>2.0.CO;2.

Bebout, G.E., Ryan, J.G., Leeman, W.P., and Bebout, A.E., 1999, Fractionation of trace elements by subduction zone metamorphism: Effect of convergent-margin thermal evolution: Earth and Planetary Science Letters, v. 171, p. 63–81, doi: 10.1016/S0012-821X(99)00135-1.

Beccaluva, L., Coltori, M., Giunta, G., Iturralde-Vinent, M., Navarro, E., Siena, F., and Urbani, F., 1996, Cross sections through the ophiolitic units of the southern and northern margins of the Caribbean plate in Venezuela (northern Cordilleras) and central Cuba: Ofioliti, v. 21, p. 85–103.

Beccaluva, L., Chinchilla-Chaves, A.L., Coltorti, M., Giunta, G., Sierra, F., and Vaccaro, C., 1999, Petrological and structural significance of the Santa Elena–Nicoya ophiolitic complex in Costa Rica and geodynamic implications: European Journal of Mineralogy, v. 11, p. 1091–1107.

Beck, C., 1985. La chaine Caraïbe au merideien de Caracas: geologie, tectogenese, place dans l'evolution geodynamique Mesozoique-Cenozoique des Caraïbes Meridionales [Ph.D. dissertation], Lille, France, L'Universite des Sciences et Techniques de Lille, 462 p.

Becker, H., Jochum, K.P., and Carlson, R.W., 1999, Constraints from high-pressure veins in eclogites on the composition of hydrous fluids in subduction zones: Chemical Geology, v. 160, p. 291–308, doi: 10.1016/S0009-2541(99)00104-7.

Beets, D.J., Maresch, W.V., Klaver, G.T., Mottana, A., Bocchio, R., Beunk, F.F., and Monen, H.P., 1984, Magmatic rock series and high-pressure metamorphism as constraints on the tectonic history of the southern Caribbean, *in* Bonini, W.E., Hargraves, R.B., and Shagam, R., eds., The Caribbean–South American plate boundary and regional tectonics: Geological Society of America Memoir 162, p. 95–130.

Bellizzia, A., and Dengo, C., 1990, The Caribbean mountain system, northern South America: A summary, *in* Dengo, C., and Case. J.E., eds., The Caribbean region: Boulder, Colorado, Geological Society of America, The Geology of North America, v. H, p. 167–176.

Bellizzia, A., Pimental, N., and Bajo, R., 1976, Mapa geológico estructural de Venezuela: Caracas, Foninves, scale 1:500,000.

Blein, O., Guillot, S., Lapierre, J., Mercier de Lépinay, B., Lardeaux, J.-M., Millan Trujillo, G., Campos, M., and Garcia, A., 2003, Geochemistry of the Mabujina Complex, central Cuba: Implications on the Cuban Cretaceous arc rocks: Journal of Geology, v. 111, p. 89–101, doi: 10.1086/344666.

Burke, K., 1988, Tectonic evolution of the Caribbean: Annual Reviews in Earth and Planetary Science, v. 16, p. 201–230, doi: 10.1146/annurev.ea.16.050188.001221.

Burke, K., Fox, P.J., and Şengör, A.M.C., 1978, Buoyant ocean floor and the origin of the Caribbean: Journal of Geophysical Research, v. 83, p. 3949–3954.

Diaz de Villalvilla, L., 1997, Caracterización geológica de las formaciones volcánicas y volcano-sedimentarias en Cuba Central, Provincias Cienfuegos–Villa Clara–Sancti Spiritus, *in* Furrazola-Bermudez, G., and Nuñez Cambra, K.E., eds., Estudios sobra la Geologia de Cuba: Ciudad de la Habana, Cuba, Instituto de Geologia y Paleontologia, p. 325–344.

Donnelly, T.W., and Rogers, J.J.W., 1978, The distribution of igneous rock suites throughout the Caribbean: Geologie en Mijnbouw, v. 57, p. 151–162.

Donnelly, T.W., Beets, D., Carr, M.J., Jackson, T., Klaver, G., Lewis, J., Maury, R., Schellekens, H., Smith, A.L., Wadge, G., and Westercamp, D., 1990, History and tectonic setting of Caribbean magmatism, *in* Dengo, G., and Case, J.E., eds., The Caribbean region: Boulder, Colorado, Geological Society of America, The Geology of North America. v. H, p. 339–374.

Draper, G., Gutiérrez, G., and Lewis, J.R., 1996, Thrust emplacement of the Hispaniola peridotite belt: Orogenic expression of the mid-Cretaceous Caribbean arc polarity reversal?: Geology, v. 24, p. 1143–1146.

Duncan, R.A., and Hargraves, R.B., 1984, Plate tectonic evolution of the Caribbean region in the mantle reference frame, *in* Bonini, W.E., Hargraves, R.B., and Shagam, R., eds., The Caribbean–South America plate boundary and regional tectonics: Geological Society of America Memoir 162, p. 81–93.

Ernst, W.G., 1988, Tectonic history of subduction zones inferred from retrograde blueschist P-T paths: Geology, v. 16, p. 1081–1084, doi: 10.1130/0091-7613(1988)016<1081:THOSZI>2.3.CO;2.

Escuder Viruete, J., Hernaiz Huerta, P.P., Draper, G., Gutierrez, G., Lewis, J.F., and Pérez-Estaún, A., 2002, Metamorfismo y estructura de la Formación Maimón y los Complejos Duarte y Río Verde, Cordillera Central Dominicana: Implicaciones en la estructura y la evolución del primitivo Arco Isla Caribeño: Acta Geológica Hispanica, v. 37, p. 123–162.

Frost, C.D., and Snoke, A.W., 1989, Tobago, West Indies, a fragment of a Mesozoic oceanic island arc: Petrochemical evidence: Journal of the Geological Society of London, v. 146, p. 953–964.

Giunta, G., Beccaluva, L., Coltorti, M., Siena, F., and Vaccaro, C., 2002, The southern margin of the Caribbean plate in Venezuela: Tectono-magmatic setting of the ophiolite units and kinematic evolution: Lithos, v. 63, p. 19–40, doi: 10.1016/S0024-4937(02)00120-2.

Giunta, G., Marroni, M., Padoa, E., and Pandolfi, L., 2003, Geological constraints for the geodynamic evolution of the southern margin of the Caribbean plate, *in* Bartolini, C., Buffler, R.T., and Blickwede, J., eds., The Circum-Gulf of Mexico and Caribbean region: Hydrocarbon habitats, basin formation, and plate tectonics: American Association of Petroleum Geologists Memoir 79, p. 104–125.

Hauff, F., Hoernle, K., Tilton, G., Graham, D.W., and Kerr, A.C., 2000, Large volume recycling of oceanic lithosphere over short time scales: Geochemical constraints from the Caribbean Large Igneous Province: Earth and Planetary Science Letters, v. 174, p. 247–263, doi: 10.1016/S0012-821X(99)00272-1.

Hernaiz Huerta, P.P., Lewis, J.J., Escuder Viruete, J., Gutierrez, G., Mortensen, J., Hames, W., Solé, J., Martinez, A., and Draper, G., 2000, Memoria explicativa del Mapa Geológica a escala 1:50,000 de Villa Altagracia (6172-II): Dirección General de Minería, Santo Domingo, Proyecto de Cartografia Geotemática de la República Dominicana, scale 1:50,000.

Hoernle, K., Hauff, F., and van den Bogaard, P., 2004, 70 m.y. history (139–69 Ma) for the Caribbean large igneous province: Geology, v. 32, p. 697–700, doi: 10.1130/G20574.1.

Humphris, S.E., and Thompson, G., 1978, Trace-element mobility during hydrothermal alteration of oceanic basalts: Geochimica et Cosmochimica Acta, v. 42, p. 127–136, doi: 10.1016/0016-7037(78)90222-3.

Iturralde-Vinent, M.A., 1996, Cuba: El arco de islas volcanicas del Cretacico, *in* Iturralde-Vinent, M.A., ed., Cuban ophiolites and volcanic arcs: Miami, Florida, International Geological Correlation Programme 364, p. 79–189.

Iturralde-Vinent, M.A., Millán. G., Korpás, E., Nagy, E., and Pajón, J., 1996, Geological interpretation of the Cuban K-Ar database, *in* Iturralde-Vinent, M.A., ed., Cuban ophiolites and volcanic arcs: Miami, Florida, International Geological Correlation Programme 364, p. 48–69.

Johnson, D.M., Hooper, P.R., and Conrey, R.M., 1999, XRF analysis of rocks and minerals for major and trace elements on a single low dilution Li-tetraborate fused bead: Advances in X-ray Analysis, v. 41, p. 843–867.

Jolly, W.T., Lidiak, E.G., Dickin, A.P., and Wu. T.-W., 1998, Geochemical diversity of Mesozoic island-arc tectonic blocks in eastern Puerto Rico, *in* Lidiak, E.G., and Larue, D.K., eds., Tectonics and Geochemistry of the Northeastern Caribbean: Geological Society of America Special Paper 322, p. 67–98.

Jolly, W.T., Lidiak, E.G., Dickin, A.P., and Wu, T.-W., 2001, Secular geochemistry of central Puerto Rican island arc lavas: Constraints on Mesozoic tectonism in the eastern Greater Antilles: Journal of Petrology, v. 42, p. 2197–2214, doi: 10.1093/petrology/42.12.2197.

Kerr, A.C., Marriner, G.F., Arndt, N.T., Tarney, J., Nivia, A., Saunders, A.D., and Duncan, R.A., 1996, The petrogenesis of komatiites, picrites and basalts from the Isle of Gorgona, Colombia: New field, petrographic and geochemical constraints: Lithos, v. 37, p. 245–260.

Kerr, A.C., Tarney, J., Marriner, G.F., Nivia, A., and Saunders, A.D., 1997a, The Caribbean-Colombian Cretaceous igneous province: The internal anatomy of an oceanic plateau, *in* Mahoney, J.J., and Coffin. M., eds., Large igneous provinces: Continental, oceanic and planetary flood volcanism: American Geophysical Union Monograph 100, p. 123–144.

Kerr, A.C., Marriner, G.F., Tarney, J., Nivia, A., Saunders, A.D., Thirlwall, M.F., and Sinton, C.W., 1997b, Cretaceous basaltic terranes in western Colombia: Elemental, chronological and Sr-Nd constraints on petrogenesis: Journal of Petrology, v. 38, p. 677–702, doi: 10.1093/petrology/38.6.677.

Kerr, A.C., Tarney, J., Nivia, A., Marriner, G.F., and Saunders, A.D., 1998, The internal structure at oceanic plateaus: Inferences from obducted Cretaceous terranes in western Colombia and the Caribbean: Tectonophysics, v. 292, p. 173–188, doi: 10.1016/S0040-1951(98)00067-5.

Kerr, A.C., Iturralde-Vinent, M.A., Saunders, A.D., Babbs, T.L., and Tarney, J., 1999, A new plate tectonic model of the Caribbean: Implications from a geochemical reconnaissance of Cuban Mesozoic volcanic rocks: Geological Society of America Bulletin, v. 111, p. 1581–1599, doi: 10.1130/0016-7606(1999)111<1581:ANPTMO>2.3.CO;2.

Kerr, A.C., White, R.V., Thompson, P.M.E., Tarney, J., and Saunders, A.D., 2003, No oceanic plateau—no Caribbean plate? The seminal role of oceanic plateau in Caribbean plate evolution, *in* Bartolini, C., Buffler, R.T., and Blickwede, J., eds., The Circum-Gulf of Mexico and Caribbean region: Hydrocarbon habitats, basin formation, and plate tectonics: American Association of Petroleum Geologists Memoir 79, p. 126–168.

Kerr, A.C., Tarney, J., Kempton, P.D., Pringle, M.S., and Nivia, A., 2004, Mafic pegmatites intruding oceanic plateau gabbros and ultramafic cumulates from Bolívar, Colombia: Evidence for a "wet"' mantle plume: Journal of Petrology, v. 45, p. 1877–1906, doi: 10.1093/petrology/egh037.

Kesler, S.E., Sutter, J.F., Barton, J.M., and Speck, R.C., 1991, Age of intrusive rocks in Northern Hispaniola, *in* Mann, P., Draper, G., and Lewis. J.F., eds. Geologic and tectonic development of the North America–Caribbean plate boundary in Hispaniola: Geological Society of America Special Paper 262, p. 165–172.

Knaack, C., Cornelius, S., and Hooper, P., 1994, Trace element analyses of rocks and minerals by ICP-MS: GeoAnalytical Laboratory, Washington State University, updated 1 Sept. 1997, http://www.wsu.edu/~geology/Pages/Services/ICP.html (Accessed April 2000).

Lapierre, H., Dupuis, V., de Lepinay, B.M., Ruiz, J., Tardy, M., Maury, R.C., Hernandez, J., and Loubet, M., 1997, Is the lower Duarte igneous complex (northern Hispaniola) a remnant of the Caribbean plume-generated oceanic plateau?: Journal of Geology, v. 105, p. 111–120.

Lapierre, H., Dupuis, V., de Lépinay, B.M., Bosch, D., Monié, P., Tardy, M., Maury, R.C., Hernandez, J., Polvé, M., Yeghicheyan, D., and Cotton, J., 1999, Late Jurassic oceanic crust and upper Cretaceous Caribbean plateau picritic basalts exposed in the Duarte igneous complex, Hispaniola: Journal of Geology, v. 107, p. 193–207, doi: 10.1086/314341.

Lebrón, M.C., and Perfit, M.R., 1994, Petrochemistry and tectonic significance of Cretaceous island-arc rocks. Cordillera Oriental, Dominican Republic: Tectonophysics, v. 229, p. 69–100, doi: 10.1016/0040-1951(94)90006-X.

Lewis, J.F., and Jiménez, G., 1991, Duarte Complex in the La Vega–Jarabacoa–Janico area, central Hispaniola: Geologic and geochemical features of the seafloor during the early stages of arc volcanism, *in* Mann, P., Draper, G., and Lewis. J.F., eds., Geologic and tectonic development of the North America–Caribbean plate boundary in Hispaniola: Geological Society of America Special Paper 262, p. 115–141.

Lewis, J.F., Hames, W.E., and Draper, G., 1999, Late Jurassic oceanic crust and upper Cretaceous Caribbean plateau picritic basalts exposed in the Duarte igneous complex. Hispaniola: A discussion: Journal of Geology, v. 107, p. 505–508, doi: 10.1086/314358.

Lewis, J.F., Excuder Viruete, J., Hernaiz Huerta, P.P., Gutierrez, F., Draper, G., and Pérez-Estaún, A., 2002, Subdivisión geoquímica del arco Isla Circum-Caribeño, Cordillera Central Dominicana: Implicaciones para la formación, acrecion y crecimineto cortical en un ambiente intraoceánico: Acta Geologica Hispanica, v. 37, p. 81–122.

Loubet, M., Montigny, B., Chachati, B., Duarte, N., Lambert, B., Martín, C., and Thuizat, M., 1985, Geochemical and geochronological constraints on the geodynamical development of the Caribbean chain of Venezuela, *in* Masce, A., ed., Symposium Geodynamique des Caraïbes: Technip, Paris, v. 1, p. 553–566.

Mattson, P.H., and Pessagno, E.A., Jr., 1979, Jurassic and Early Cretaceous radiolarians in Puerto Rican ophiolites: Tectonic implications: Geology, v. 7, p. 440–444, doi: 10.1130/0091-7613(1979)7<440:JAECRI>2.0.CO;2.

Mauffret, A., and Leroy, S., 1997, Seismic stratigraphy and structure of the Caribbean igneous province: Tectonophysics, v. 283, p. 61–104, doi: 10.1016/S0040-1951(97)00103-0.

Montgomery, H., Pessagno, E.A., Lewis, J., and Schellekens, J.H., 1994, Paleogeography of Jurassic fragments in the Caribbean: Tectonics, v. 13, p. 725–732, doi: 10.1029/94TC00455.

Murray, C.G., 1973, Estudios petrológicos de complejos ultramáficos zonados en Venezuela y Alaska: Caracas, Boletín Geológico, v. 12, p. 173–279.

Navarro, E., 1983, Petrología y petrogénesis de las rocas metavolcánicas del Grupo Villa de Cura: Cararcas, Geos, v. 28, p. 170–317.

Oxburgh, E.R., 1966, Geology and metamorphism of Cretaceous rocks in eastern Carabobo State, Venezuela Coast Ranges, *in* Hess, H.H., ed., Caribbean Geological Investigations: Geological Society of America Memoir 98, p. 241–310.

Pearce, J.A., 1982, Trace element characteristics of lavas from destructive plate boundaries, *in* Thorpe, R.E., ed., Andesites: Chichester, Wiley, p. 525–548.

Pearce, J.A., 1983, Role of the sub-continental lithosphere in magma genesis at active continental margins, *in* Hawkesworth, C.J., and Norry, M.J., eds., Continental basalts and mantle xenoliths: Nantwich, Shiva Press, p. 230–249.

Pettijohn, F.J., 1963, Chemical composition of sandstones—excluding carbonate and volcanic sands: United States Geological Survey Professional Paper 400-S, 19 p.

Pindell, J.L., 1993, Regional synopsis of Gulf of Mexico and Caribbean evolution, *in* Pindell, J.L., and Perkins, B.F., eds., Mesozoic and early Cenozoic development of the Gulf of Mexico and Caribbean region—A context for hydrocarbon exploration, Proceedings, Gulf Coast Section, SEPM Foundation 13th Annual Research Conference: Houston, Texas, SEPM (Society for Sedimentary Geology) Foundation, p. 251–274.

Pindell, J.L., and Barrett, S.F., 1990, Geological evolution of the Caribbean region: A plate tectonic perspective, *in* Dengo, C., and Case. J.E., eds., The Caribbean region: Geological Society of America, The Geology of North America, v. H, p. 405–432.

Pindell, J.L., Cande, S.C., Pitman, W.C., Rowley, D.B., Dewey, J.F., LaBrecque, J., and Haxby, W., 1988, A plate-kinematic framework for models of Caribbean evolution: Tectonophysics, v. 155, p. 121–138, doi: 10.1016/0040-1951(88)90262-4.

Priem, H.N.A., Beets, D.J., and Verdurmen, E.A.T., 1986, Precambrian rocks in an early Tertiary conglomerate on Bonaire, Netherlands Antilles (southern Caribbean borderland): Evidence for a 300 km eastward displacement relative to the South American mainland?: Geologie en Mijnbouw, v. 65, p. 35–40.

Révillon, S., Arndt, N.T., Hallot, E., Kerr, A.C., and Tarney, J., 1999, Petrogenesis of picrites from the Caribbean Plateau and the North Atlantic magmatic province: Lithos, v. 49, p. 1–21, doi: 10.1016/S0024-4937(99)00038-9.

Schellekens, J.H., 1998, Geochemical evolution and tectonic history of Puerto Rico, *in* Lidiak, E.G., and Larue, D.K., eds., Tectonics and geochemistry of the northeastern Caribbean: Geological Society of America Special Paper 322, p. 35–60.

Shagam, R., 1960, Geology of the central Aragua State, Venezuela: Geological Society of America Bulletin, v. 71, p. 249–302.

Sharp, W.D., and Snoke, A.W., 1988, Tobago, West Indies; geochronological study of a fragment of a composite Mesozoic oceanic island-arc: Geological Society of America Abstracts with Programs, v. 20, no. 7, p. 60.

Shervais, J.W., 1982, Ti-V plots and the petrogenesis of modern and ophiolitic lavas: Earth and Planetary Science Letters, v. 59, p. 101–118, doi: 10.1016/0012-821X(82)90120-0.

Sinton, C.W., Duncan, R.A., and Denyer, P., 1997, Nicoya Peninsula, Costa Rica: A single suite of oceanic plateau magmas: Journal of Geophysical Research, v. 102, p. 15,507–15,520, doi: 10.1029/97JB00681.

Sinton, C.W., Duncan, R.A., Storey, M., Lewis, J., and Estrada, J.J., 1998, An oceanic flood basalt province within the Caribbean plate: Earth and Planetary Science Letters, v. 155, p. 221–235, doi: 10.1016/S0012-821X(97)00214-8.

Smith, C.A., Sisson, V.B., Avé Lallemant, H.G., and Copeland, P., 1999, Two contrasting pressure-temperature paths in the Villa de Cura blueschist belt, Venezuela: Possible evidence for Late Cretaceous initiation of subduction in the Caribbean: Geological Society of America Bulletin, v. 111, p. 831–848, doi: 10.1130/0016-7606(1999)111<0831:TCPTTP>2.3.CO;2.

Snoke, A.W., and Noble, P.J., 2001, Ammonite-radiolarian assemblage, Tobago Volcanic Group, Tobago, West Indies; implications for the evolution of the Great Arc of the Caribbean: Geological Society of America Bulletin, v. 113, p. 256–264, doi: 10.1130/0016-7606(2001)113<0256:ARATVG>2.0.CO;2.

Snoke, A.W., Yule, J.D., Rowe, D.W., Wadge, G., and Sharp, W.D., 1990, Stratigraphic and structural relationships on Tobago, West Indies, and some tectonic implications, *in* Larue, D.K., and Draper, G., eds., Transactions of the 12th Caribbean geological conference, St. Croix, U.S. Virgin Islands: Miami, Florida, Miami Geological Society, v. 12, p. 389–402.

Snoke, A.W., Rowe, D.W., Yule, J.D., and Wadge, G., 2001, Petrologic and structural history of Tobago, West Indies: A fragment of the accreted Mesozoic oceanic-arc of the southern Caribbean: Geological Society of America Special Paper 354, 54 p.

Sorensen, S.S., and Grossman, J.N., 1989, Enrichment of trace elements in garnet amphibolites from a paleo-subduction zone: Catalina Schist, southern California: Geochimica et Cosmochimica Acta, v. 53, p. 3155–3177, doi: 10.1016/0016-7037(89)90096-3.

Sorensen, S.S., and Grossman, J.N., 1993, Accessory minerals and subduction zone metasomatism: a geochemical comparison of the Shuksan Suite, Washington and the Catalina Schist, California: Chemical Geology, v. 110, p. 269–297, doi: 10.1016/0009-2541(93)90258-K.

Sorensen, S.S., Grossman, J.N., and Perfit, M.R., 1997, Phengite-hosted LILE enrichment in eclogite and related rocks: implications for fluid-mediated mass transfer in subduction zones and arc magma genesis: Journal of Petrology, v. 38, p. 3–34, doi: 10.1093/petrology/38.1.3.

Staudigel, H., Plank, T., White, B., and Schmincke, H.-U., 1996. Geochemical fluxes during seafloor alteration of the basaltic upper oceanic crust: DSDP sites 417 and 418, *in* Bebout, G.E., Scholl, D.W., Kirby, S.H., and Platt, J.P., eds., Subduction top to bottom: American Geophysical Union Monograph 96, p. 19–36.

Stöckhert, B., Maresch, W.V., Brix, M., Kaiser, C., Toetz, A., Kluge, R., and Krückhans-Lueder, G., 1995, Crustal history of Margarita Island (Venezuela) in detail: Constraint on the Caribbean plate-tectonic scenario: Geology, v. 23, p. 787–790, doi: 10.1130/0091-7613(1995)023<0787:CHOMIV>2.3.CO;2.

Sun, S.-S., and McDonough, 1989, Chemical and isotopic systematics of oceanic basalts: implications for mantle composition and processes, *in* Saunders, A.D., and Norry, M.J., eds., Magmatism in the ocean basins: London, Geological Society Special Publication 42, p. 313–345.

Thompson, P.M.E., Kempton, P.D., White, R.V., Kerr, A.C., Tarney, J., Saunders, A.D., Fitton, J.G., and McBirney, A., 2004a, Hf-Nd isotope constraints on the origin of the Cretaceous Caribbean plateau and its relationship to the Galápagos plume: Earth and Planetary Science Letters, v. 217, p. 59–75, doi: 10.1016/S0012-821X(03)00542-9.

Thompson, P.M.E., Kempton, P.D., White, R.V., Saunders, A.D., Kerr, A.C., Tarney, J., and Pringle, M.S., 2004b, Elemental Hf-Nd isotopic and geochronological constraints on an island arc sequence associated with the Cretaceous Caribbean plateau: Bonaire, Dutch Antilles: Lithos, v. 74, p. 91–116, doi: 10.1016/j.lithos.2004.01.004.

Wakabayashi, J., 1990, Counterclockwise *P-T-t* paths from amphibolites, Franciscan complex, California: Relics from the early stages of subduction zone metamorphism: Journal of Geology, v. 98, p. 657–680.

Walker, R.J., Storey, M.J., Kerr, A.C., Tarney, J., and Arndt, N.T., 1999, Implications of [187]Os isotopic heterogeneities in a mantle plume: Evidence from Gorgona and Curaçao: Geochimica et Cosmochimica Acta, v. 63, p. 713–728, doi: 10.1016/S0016-7037(99)00041-1.

Wiedmann, J., 1978, Ammonites from the Curaçao Lava Formation, Curaçao, Caribbean: Geologie en Mijnbouw, v. 57, p. 361–364.

White, R.N., Tarney, J., Kerr, A.C., Saunders, A.D., Kempton, R.D., and Klaver, G.T., 1999, Modification of an oceanic plateau, Aruba, Dutch Caribbean: Implications for the generation of continental crust: Lithos, v. 46, p. 43–68, doi: 10.1016/S0024-4937(98)00061-9.

MANUSCRIPT ACCEPTED BY THE SOCIETY 5 APRIL 2005

Geological Society of America
Special Paper 394
2005

Thrust belt interpretation of the Serranía del Interior and Maturín subbasin, eastern Venezuela

Enrique J. Hung*

Department of Earth Science, MS-126, Rice University, Houston, Texas 77251-1892, USA

ABSTRACT

The Cordillera of eastern Venezuela is a south-vergent fold-thrust belt of Neogene age formed on the South American plate and its Atlantic passive margin series by right-lateral transpression during the relative eastward migration of the Caribbean plate. Together with the topographically high Serranía del Interior, the Maturín subbasin is the easternmost onshore segment of the Venezuelan Cordillera, its foothills, and its foreland. Oilfields and data coverage of the Maturín subbasin abundantly document the compound sediment wedge, its structure, and its sedimentary and tectonic evolution.

In the Monagas foothills, décollements at the base of the Miocene are responsible for the formation of a complex accretionary wedge. Deeper structures in the Monagas foothills involve the Mesozoic assemblages that were emplaced by thrusting following the emplacement of the Carapita accretionary wedge. Apparent "out of sequence" relations at the surface of the Serranía del Interior and in the shallow subsurface of the Maturín subbasin are due to the interference of late deeper structures with the earlier structures of the accretionary wedge. Six alternative structural interpretations range from basement-involved to non–basement-involved décollement tectonics. These hypotheses imply varying amounts of shortening along the Serranía to foreland ranging from 9% to 66% or 15–115 km oblique component of the El Pilar fault.

Keywords: Maturín Basin, Serranía del Interior, thrust and fold belt, out-of-sequence.

INTRODUCTION

The Eastern Venezuela Basin (Fig. 1) is associated with the eastward migration of the Caribbean plate along the El Pilar strike slip fault zone and other unnamed offshore faults (Stephan et al., 1990; Pindell, 1993; Erlich and Barrett, 1990; Lugo and Mann, 1995). South of the El Pilar Fault, the Serranía del Interior, a Cretaceous to Paleogene passive margin sequence, was folded and faulted as a result of Neogene transpression resulting in a N70°E striking fold and thrust trend (e.g., Gutiérrez, 1986; Lil-

liu, 1990; Chevalier, 1993). This trend continues to the south into the Monagas foothills where large compressional structures are traps for major oil fields (Carnevali, 1989; Aymard et al., 1990). A 6–8-km-thick Neogene foreland basin, the Maturín subbasin, overlies northward-dipping Cretaceous to Paleogene sedimentary rocks as well as Precambrian crystalline basement of the Guyana Shield to the south (Fig. 1; Di Croce et al., 1999).

The region beneath the Serranía del Interior lacks subsurface data and has relatively poor seismic resolution of deep structures in the Monagas foothills. The main purpose of this study is to present

*Present address: Calle Zamora Las Trinitarias D-129, Nueva Barcelona, Barcelona, 6001 Anzoategui, Venezuela; enriquejosehung@yahoo.com or EnriqueHung@chevron.com

Hung, E.J., 2005, Thrust belt interpretation of the Serranía del Interior and Maturín subbasin, eastern Venezuela, *in* Avé Lallemant, H.G., and Sisson, V.B., eds., Caribbean–South American plate interactions, Venezuela: Geological Society of America Special Paper 394, p. 251–270, doi: 10.1130/2005.2394(10). For permission to copy, contact editing@geosociety.org. ©2005 Geological Society of America.

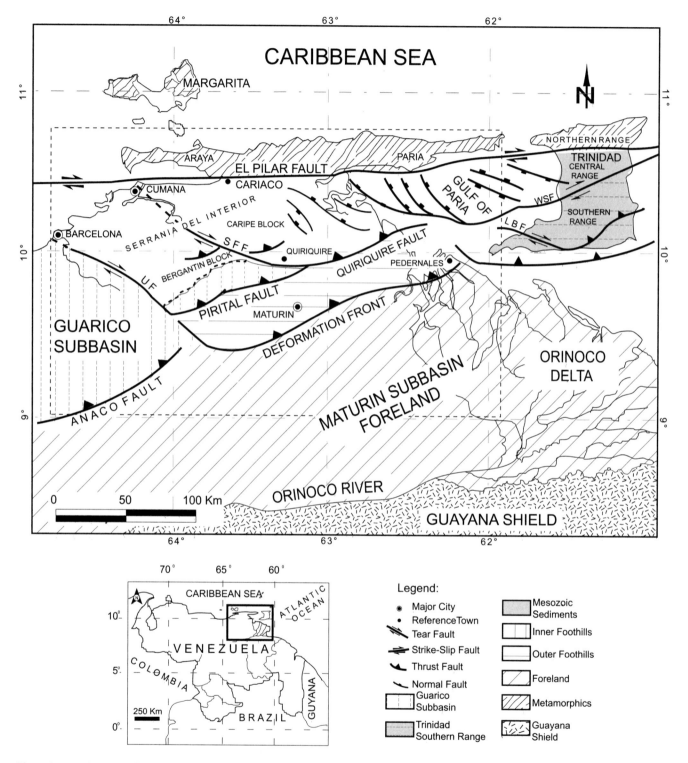

Figure 1. Location map of the Eastern Venezuela Basin. Relevant structures in the basin after Bellizzia et al. (1976) and Robertson and Burke (1989). LBF—Los Bajos Fault; SFF—San Francisco Fault; UF—Urica Fault; WSF—Warm Spring Fault.

internally consistent admissible cross sections that best define the geologic problems of this fold and thrust belt. Cross sections were constructed using line drawings of seismic profiles and well log correlations. The line drawings were converted from time to depth sections in order to construct six different interpretations.

REGIONAL SETTING

Geologic and geophysical studies define the Caribbean plate, which is surrounded by four rigid plates: the North American, South American, Cocos, and Nazca plates (e.g., Mann et al., 1990). Relative eastward movement of the Caribbean plate with respect to North and South American plates dominates the tectonics of northern South America (Mann et al., 1990, Ostos et al., this volume, Chapter 2). The southern boundary of the Caribbean is a wide and complex zone that extends along the Venezuelan and Colombian coastal margin and includes the Boconó and the San Sebastian–El Pilar right lateral strike slip fault zones. In addition, this boundary zone is characterized by thrusting and rifting (Stephan et al., 1990; Biju-Duval et al., 1978, 1983; Schubert, 1984; Mann and Burke, 1984; Mann et al., 1990; Lugo and Mann, 1995). Southeast vergent thrusting in the Serranía del Interior coeval with right-lateral strike-slip along the El Pilar fault are results of strain partitioning along this plate boundary (Avé Lallemant, 1997).

Studies of earthquake focal mechanisms and seismic tomography of the southern boundary of the Caribbean plate suggest subduction beneath the South American plate (Van der Hilst, 1990; Van der Hilst and Mann, 1994). Avé Lallemant (1997) describes the transpressive orogenic belt in terms of incipient subduction of the Caribbean plate beneath the South American plate. In his model, east-west strike-slip faults are coeval with thrust faults and they share the same décollement surface. Another interpretation by Russo et al. (1993) suggests that oceanic lithosphere originally attached to South America subducts underneath the Caribbean plate toward the northwest.

Tectonic Evolution of the Eastern Venezuela Basin

The Eastern Venezuelan Basin formed as the result of the complex interaction between the South American, North American, and Caribbean lithospheric plates (e.g., Stephan et al., 1990; Pindell, 1993; Erlich and Barrett, 1990, 1992). Three major tectonic stages are commonly identified (e.g., Di Croce et al., 1999):
1. Triassic to Late Jurassic rift phase (breakup of Pangea);
2. Late Jurassic–Oligocene passive margin phase;
3. Early Miocene to present active transpressive margin phase.

The North and South American plates separated near the end of the Jurassic. Basaltic rocks in the Espino graben (Guárico sub-basin) dated at 162 Ma indicate that rifting occurred at least at that time (Feo-Codecido et al., 1984). The rifting was followed by subsidence of the northern South America passive margin. Cessation of seafloor spreading between North and South America occurred around Campanian time as the Great Arc of the Caribbean, an island arc, collided with the passive margin of North America (Yucatán block–Cuba–Hispaniola) and South America. From late Paleocene to the Present, transpressional deformation advanced diachronously along the northern border of South America as the Caribbean plate migrated eastward with respect to South and North America (Pindell and Barrett, 1990; Lugo and Mann, 1995).

In western Venezuela, transpression occurred during the early to middle Eocene. Volcanism in the Lesser Antilles arc and the development of the "Lara Nappes" in western Venezuela took place in the Eocene (Pindell and Barrett, 1990; Stephan et al., 1990). Progressively younger transpression eventually affected eastern Venezuela and Trinidad during late Oligocene–middle Miocene (Locke and Garver, this volume). Thrust sheets and associated foredeep basins override the former Cretaceous passive margin sequence as a result of the eastward migration of the Caribbean plate. The Oligocene is a tectonically quiet period and perhaps reflects a slowdown of the eastward Caribbean relative motion (Stephan et al., 1990).

The Eastern Venezuela Basin may be divided into three structural provinces: (1) Serranía del Interior, (2) Monagas foothills, and (3) Maturín Foreland. Major geologic faults between these provinces are the El Pilar, Urica, San Francisco, Pirital, and Los Bajos faults, and the deformation front itself (Fig. 1).

The Serranía del Interior includes a southeast-verging fold belt with folds and thrusts orientated roughly N70°E (e.g., Rossi, 1985; Gutiérrez, 1986). Surface maps show the lengths of the folds to be ~70 km with wavelengths of 5 km. There are four faults bordering the Serranía including the east-striking El Pilar strike-slip fault to the north, the N70°E striking Pirital thrust fault complex to the south, the northwest-striking Urica fault zone, and the Los Bajos fault zone to the east. The San Francisco right lateral tear fault dissects the Serranía into two blocks: the Bergantín block to the west and the Caripe block to the east, and merges with the Quiriquire fault to the south (González de Juana et al., 1980). The segmentation of the folds and thrusts by the Urica, San Francisco, and Los Bajos tear faults suggests west to east diachronous deformation analogous to the north to south thrust propagation, thus showing significant strain partitioning (Passalacqua et al., 1995; Avé Lallemant, 1997).

To the south of the Pirital and Quiriquire thrusts, the fold belt continues in the subsurface and terminates at the deformation front (Lilliu, 1990). On the surface, shale-cored anticlines parallel the thrust fault orientation (Subieta et al., 1987; Chevalier, 1993). These shale anticlines formed during Neogene time. This alignment on the surface and its statement on seismic profiles in the subsurface define the deformation front throughout the Eastern Venezuelan Basin. North of the deformation front, the Monagas foothills include giant oil fields with medium- to light-grade oil (e.g., El Tejero, El Carito, El Furrial, Corozo, and Boquerón; Aymard et al., 1990; Parnaud et al., 1995; Gallango and Parnaud, 1995).

The foreland is bounded by the deformation front to the north-northwest, by the Guyana Shield to the south, and by the Atlantic Ocean to the northeast. The southern margin of the foreland is characterized by basement-involved normal faults that define the prolific oil-bearing structures. Discordantly overlying these normal faulted blocks, listric growth faults deform Neogene sedimentary rocks. In the Mapirito area of the foreland, NS-striking listric faults dip toward the east-northeast (Di Croce et al., 1999).

Stratigraphy

The stratigraphy of the Eastern Venezuelan Foreland Basin is subdivided in five units: (1) crystalline Precambrian basement, (2) Paleozoic, (3) Jurassic, (4) passive margin sequence (Cretaceous to Oligocene), and (5) Neogene foredeep (Fig. 2; Di Croce et al., 1999).

Basement

The crystalline Precambrian basement crops out to the south in the Guyana Shield, where it is dated between 3600 and 800 Ma (Martín-Bellizzia, 1974; Mendoza, 1977; and González de Juana et al., 1980). It consists mainly of metasedimentary and meta-igneous rocks.

Paleozoic

Sedimentary rocks in the Guárico subbasin have been reported in some wells. For example, the Carrizal well west of the Maturín subbasin penetrated 1827 m (5990 ft) of Cambrian Hato Viejo and overlying Cambrian Carrizal formations (Feo-Codecido et al., 1984). These rocks may correspond to prominent reflectors seen on the seismic profiles in the Maturín subbasin.

The Jurassic Espino graben has been described from the Machete-Zuata field (González de Juana et al., 1980), west of the Maturín subbasin; it trends southwest. The graben is filled with redbeds and intercalated basalt flows (Feo-Codecido et al., 1984). The width of these half grabens is on the order of 5–10 km.

Cretaceous to Paleogene

The Eastern Venezuela Basin merges to the southeast with the Atlantic passive margin of South America. The passive margin sequence consists of Cretaceous to Oligocene marine clastics. During the Oligocene, the passive margin was a thick wedge thinning toward the south with onlap terminations against the Precambrian rocks of the Guyana Shield (e.g., Hedberg, 1950; Rosales, 1973; González de Juana et al., 1980; Erlich and Barrett, 1992).

Stratigraphic correlations in the Serranía were done by Rossi (1985), Vivas (1985), Chevalier (1993), and Aguasuelos Ingeniería-Lagoven (1994). Di Croce et al. (1999) correlated the stratigraphy from the offshore Orinoco platform to the Serranía del Interior and to the Maturín subbasin.

Paleogeography of the Eastern Venezuela Basin shows a southern sediment source for the Cretaceous clastic rocks (González de Juana et al., 1980; Rohr, 1991; Erlich and Barrett, 1992) in the Serranía del Interior. The lower Cretaceous is composed of Barremian sedimentary rocks that grade upward from continental facies at the base into shelf to shallow marine carbonates for the Lower Aptian sediments at the Serranía del Interior. The Cenomanian to Coniacian sequence of sedimentary rocks overlies the Albian transgressive shale. Reducing conditions terminate with a globally recognized regression of Coniacian age (Schlanger and Jenkins, 1976).

Within this interval, the Querecual Formation was deposited; this is the most important source rock of the Eastern Venezuelan Basin (Hedberg, 1937; González de Juana et al., 1980; Aymard et al., 1990; Gallango and Parnaud, 1995; Parnaud et al., 1995). The absence of the upper Maastrichtian preceding the Paleocene suggests a hiatus corresponding to the lower Paleocene and part of the Maastrichtian in the Serranía (Hedberg and Pyre, 1944; González de Juana et al., 1980). The Paleocene section of the Maturín subbasin represents a shallow water facies.

Eocene fossils indicate a transgression in the neritic domain in the uppermost portion of the Vidoño Formation. Paleogeographic reconstructions of the eastern Venezuela and Trinidad passive margin show a broad shelf edge that merged into a slope toward Trinidad during Eocene time (Di Croce, 1995).

In the Monagas foothills, the Oligocene is the most productive reservoir of the basin. Reservoirs occur in the Naricual and Los Jabillos Formations (e.g., González de Juana et al., 1980; Arnstein et al., 1985; Carnevali, 1989). These were deposited in shelf to shallow water. Seismic data offshore of the Orinoco delta suggest a progradation probably associated with Oligocene lowstand deltas (Di Croce et al., 1999). To the south and west, coeval sedimentary rocks in the foredeep are included in the Merecure Formation. The absence of Oligocene faunas in this formation and the orientation of the passive margin suggest that the Oligocene sedimentary rocks are truncated by erosion.

Foredeep Basin Fill

Neogene-age sediments fill the Maturín Subbasin. Wells in the basin have up to 6100 m (~20,000 ft) of Neogene sedimentary rocks. A north-south correlation of key wells along the Maturín subbasin illustrates the position of the Maturín subbasin axis marked by the deepest point of the section (Fig. 3). In addition, this axis roughly coincides with the deformation front. Three sedimentary transport directions are noted: an important longitudinal west to east transport, a southerly sediment source from the adjacent Guyana Shield, and a limited northwesterly sediment supply from the emergent folded belt of the Serranía del Interior, which is deposited in small satellite basins (Di Croce et al., 1999).

In the Monagas foothills, lower to middle Miocene sedimentary rocks are involved in an accretionary wedge. Faunas from lower to middle Miocene rocks are similar to the "normal Carapita fauna" defined by Stainforth (1971). The lower to middle Miocene can be divided into depositional sequences with back-stepping cycles at the bottom and fore-stepping to aggradational cycles toward the top. These packages were deposited in a littoral to shallow marine setting with coastal bars that prograded mainly from west to east (Di Croce et al., 1999) in map view. These cycles fill a v-shaped basin that in map view narrows westward and widens eastward toward the Atlantic Ocean.

The upper Miocene is characterized by coarsening upward sequences. Overall, this is a regressive system that may be divided from bottom to top into two different lithofacies: (1) a shallow

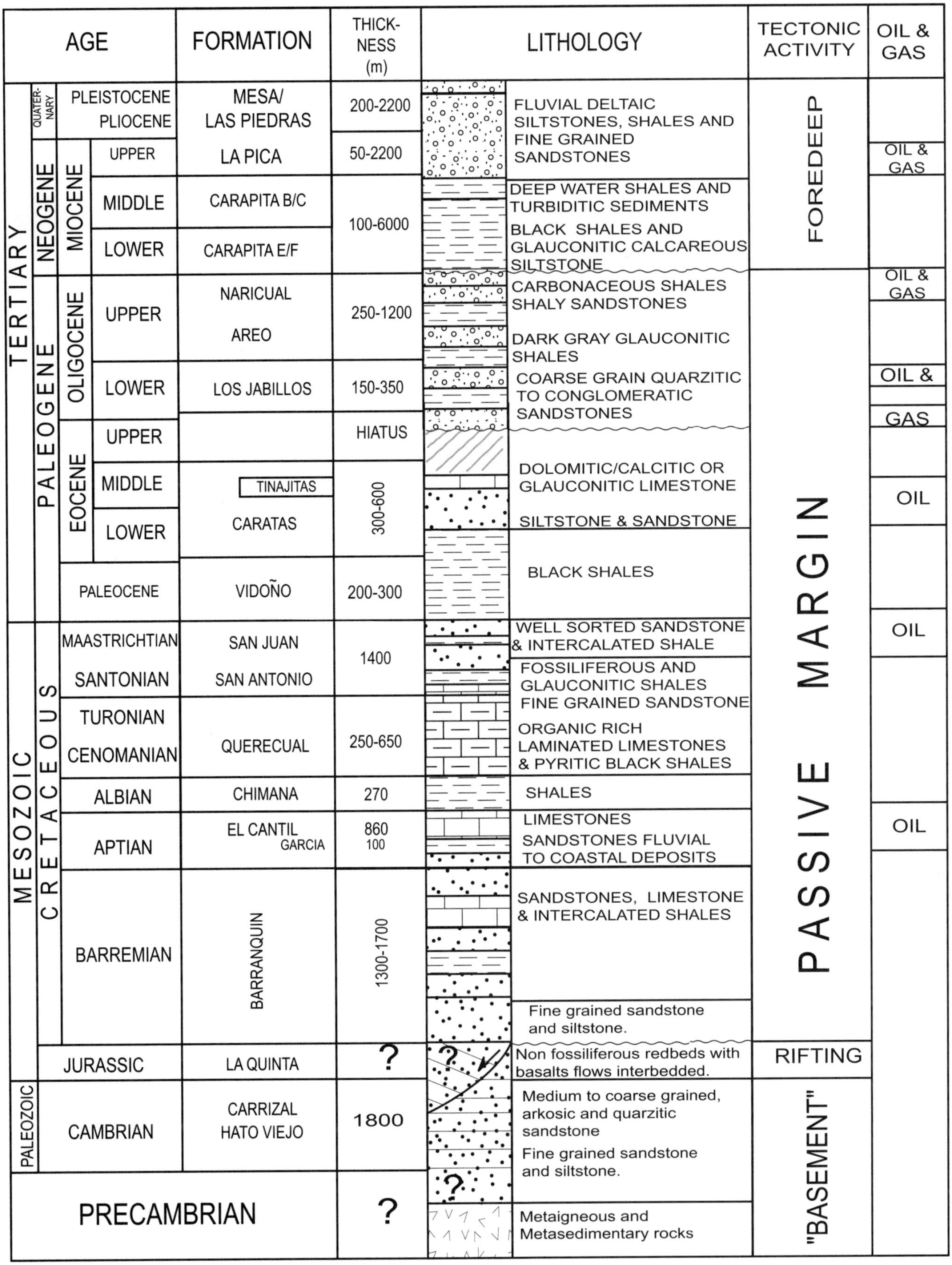

AGE			FORMATION	THICKNESS (m)	LITHOLOGY	TECTONIC ACTIVITY	OIL & GAS
TERTIARY	NEOGENE	QUATERNARY · PLEISTOCENE / PLIOCENE	MESA/ LAS PIEDRAS	200-2200	FLUVIAL DELTAIC SILTSTONES, SHALES AND FINE GRAINED SANDSTONES	FOREDEEP	
		MIOCENE UPPER	LA PICA	50-2200			OIL & GAS
		MIOCENE MIDDLE	CARAPITA B/C	100-6000	DEEP WATER SHALES AND TURBIDITIC SEDIMENTS		
		MIOCENE LOWER	CARAPITA E/F		BLACK SHALES AND GLAUCONITIC CALCAREOUS SILTSTONE		
	PALEOGENE	OLIGOCENE UPPER	NARICUAL AREO	250-1200	CARBONACEOUS SHALES SHALY SANDSTONES / DARK GRAY GLAUCONITIC SHALES	PASSIVE MARGIN	OIL & GAS
		OLIGOCENE LOWER	LOS JABILLOS	150-350	COARSE GRAIN QUARZITIC TO CONGLOMERATIC SANDSTONES		OIL & GAS
		EOCENE UPPER		HIATUS	DOLOMITIC/CALCITIC OR GLAUCONITIC LIMESTONE		OIL
		EOCENE MIDDLE	TINAJITAS	300-600			
		EOCENE LOWER	CARATAS		SILTSTONE & SANDSTONE		
		PALEOCENE	VIDOÑO	200-300	BLACK SHALES		
MESOZOIC	CRETACEOUS	MAASTRICHTIAN	SAN JUAN	1400	WELL SORTED SANDSTONE & INTERCALATED SHALE		OIL
		SANTONIAN	SAN ANTONIO		FOSSILIFEROUS AND GLAUCONITIC SHALES FINE GRAINED SANDSTONE		
		TURONIAN	QUERECUAL	250-650	ORGANIC RICH LAMINATED LIMESTONES & PYRITIC BLACK SHALES		
		CENOMANIAN					
		ALBIAN	CHIMANA	270	SHALES		
		APTIAN	EL CANTIL / GARCIA	860 / 100	LIMESTONES / SANDSTONES FLUVIAL TO COASTAL DEPOSITS		OIL
		BARREMIAN	BARRANQUIN	1300-1700	SANDSTONES, LIMESTONE & INTERCALATED SHALES / Fine grained sandstone and siltstone.		
		JURASSIC	LA QUINTA	?	Non fossiliferous redbeds with basalts flows interbedded.	RIFTING	
PALEOZOIC		CAMBRIAN	CARRIZAL HATO VIEJO	1800	Medium to coarse grained, arkosic and quarzitic sandstone / Fine grained sandstone and siltstone.	"BASEMENT"	
PRECAMBRIAN				?	Metaigneous and Metasedimentary rocks		

Figure 2. Summary of stratigraphy of the Eastern Venezuela Basin.

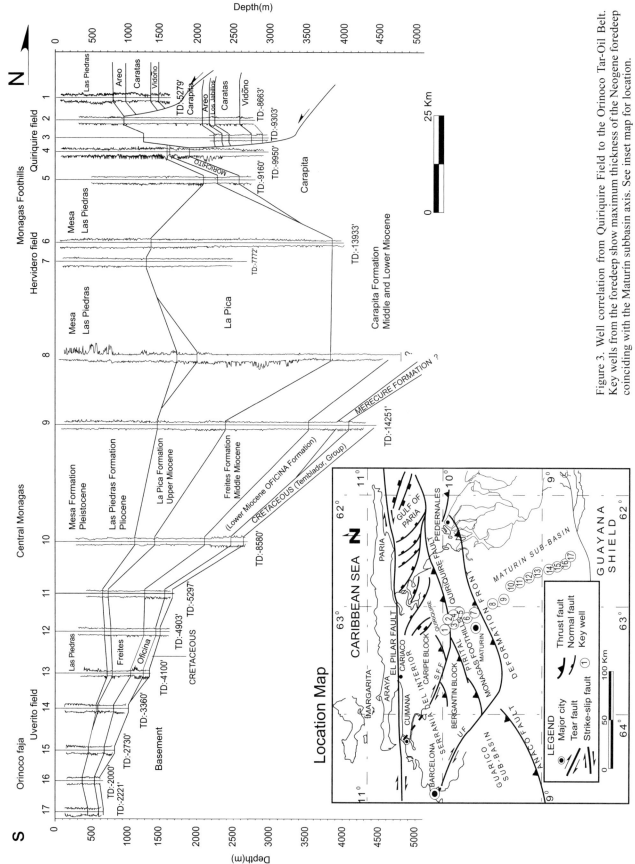

SELECTED WELL CORRELATION OF THE MATURIN SUB-BASIN

Figure 3. Well correlation from Quiriquire Field to the Orinoco Tar-Oil Belt. Key wells from the foredeep show maximum thickness of the Neogene foredeep coinciding with the Maturin subbasin axis. See inset map for location.

water to outer shelf–upper bathyal setting, and (2) a continental to coastal plain environment dominated by highstand sequences.

The Plio-Pleistocene unit is a widely correlated sequence recognizable on seismic and well data. To the west and northwest, the sequence onlaps against the emerging folded belt. Lithology and fossils from wells indicate facies ranging from littoral and marginal marine to mostly continental.

Serranía–Maturín Subbasin Transect

Data

A selection of subsurface data (wells and seismic) from the Monagas foothills and the Maturín subbasin were made available by Lagoven, S.A. The seismic data consists of 1000 km of time-migrated two-dimensional seismic profiles assembled into six regional strike and five regional dip profiles across the Monagas foothills. The available well data set consisted of 50 control wells containing complete formational descriptions and seismic time-depth functions (Fig. 4). The surface geology on the Serranía del Interior includes structures involving Barremian to Tertiary rocks. This was interpreted using updated stratigraphic columns, cross sections, and geologic maps from Rossi (1985), Vivas (1985), Chevalier (1993), and Aguasuelos Ingeniería-Lagoven (1994). The final result is a 170 km long N-S transect through the Maturín subbasin derived from 90 km of seismic profiles, 12 key wells, and an 80-km-long surface cross section (Fig. 5).

Methods

Line drawings of seismic profiles trace the most relevant reflectors. They emphasize robust data and neglect artifacts. Representative seismic profiles were selected to cover the area, and short profiles were combined to form a grid of regional profiles. Key wells were selected to correlate the major stratigraphic units. From bottom to top, these units are Lower Cretaceous, Upper Cretaceous, Paleogene, lower and middle Miocene, upper Miocene, Pliocene, and Pleistocene. This resulted in eleven profiles in a regional grid, which involves ~1000 km of seismic data and consists of five north-trending and six east-trending profiles.

Depth conversion of the line drawings was done using interval velocities obtained from wells. The results of the typical interval velocities and density ranges are listed in Table 1. The resulting velocities are applied to each profile to estimate the depth of every horizon. Depth calculations are made every 5 km along all the profiles, defining some 250 distributed control points.

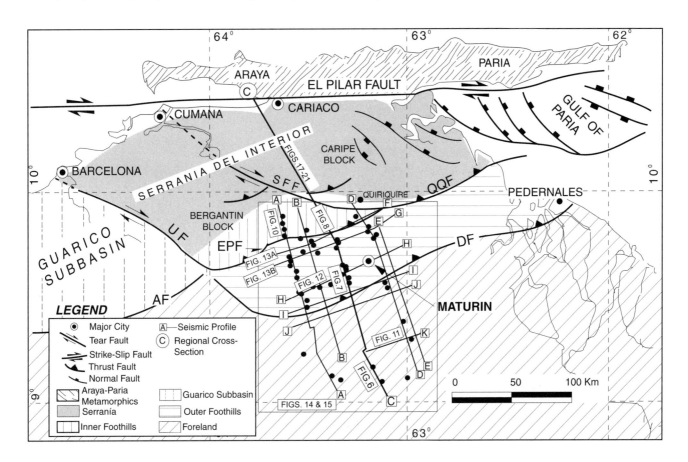

Figure 4. Index map showing available data: 1000 km of seismic profiles, 50 key wells, and 13 stratigraphic sections. Profile C is the regional cross section. AF—Anaco fault; DF—deformation front; EPF—El Pirital fault; QQF—Quiriquire fault; SFF—San Francisco fault; UF—Urica fault.

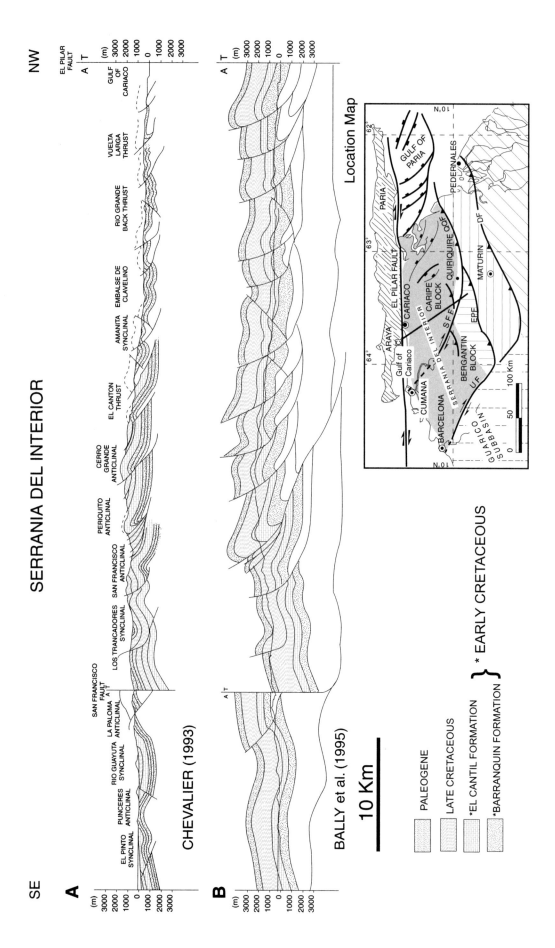

Figure 5. (A) Surface section across the Serranía del Interior (from Chevalier, 1993). (B) Interpreted thickness and basal décollement surface on the Serranía del Interior cross section (Bally et al., 1995). Suggested thickness is provided from updated stratigraphic columns (Aguasuelos Ingeniería-Lagoven, 1994). Location map: DF—deformation front; EPF—El Pirital fault; QQF—Quiriquire fault; SFF—San Francisco fault; UF—Urica fault.

TABLE 1. VELOCITY AND DENSITY VALUES
USED FOR DEPTH CONVERSION

Interval	Velocity (m/s)	Density (g/cm³)
Pleistocene	2100	2.17–2.24
Pliocene	2400	2.17–2.30
Upper Miocene	2700	2.23–2.28
Middle and lower Miocene	2800	2.31–2.40
Paleogene	3600	2.48–2.5
Upper Cretaceous	3900	2.5–2.58
Lower Cretaceous	4400	2.56–2.75

Note: Values from Bonini (1978); Lilliu (1990); Vierbuchen (1984); Martín and Espinoza (1990); Carnevali (1991); Passalacqua et al. (1995); and Martinez (1995).

Selected Previous Work

Balanced cross sections assume simple geometries to permit a palinspastic restoration (e.g., Dahlstrom, 1969; Boyer and Elliot, 1982; Suppe, 1983). The profiles and balanced cross sections are oriented approximately parallel to the assumed tectonic transport direction, ~N70°W (Carnevali, 1989). Some published interpretations (Carnevali, 1989) assume basement is not involved in the deformation as indicated by the gentle northerly dip of seismic reflectors on the basement, which can be extrapolated far toward the north. The absence of basement involvement is compatible with previous interpretations (e.g., Feo-Codecido et al., 1984). The limited amount of available information was utilized to construct a basement map to provide internal consistency for the profiles. This interpretation implies the basement is overlain by a wedge of northward thickening Cretaceous-Paleogene sequences (see Rosales, 1973; Chevalier, 1993; Roure et al., 1994; Passalacqua et al., 1995). The estimated total thickness for the Cretaceous is compatible with the thickness derived from surface geology (e.g., Rossi, 1985; Aguasuelos Ingeniería-Lagoven, 1994). The base of the lowermost Miocene probably coincides with the basal

foredeep unconformity that formed in response to the inception of the fold belt. In this context, the datum utilized for the restorations is the top of the Oligocene and base of the lower Miocene boundary. In some interpretations, the top of the basement coincides with the interpreted basal décollement surface for the thrust faults of the area. Alternative interpretations that involve the basement will be discussed later.

Interpretation

The subsurface interpretations in this study are mostly based on line drawings of seismic profiles across the Monagas foothills (Figs. 6–13). The surface profile across the Serranía del Interior (i.e., Chevalier, 1993) was simplified and reduced to the same scale as the subsurface data (Fig. 5) to provide restorable geometries for both the foreland and the Serranía del Interior.

The subsurface interpretation of the Monagas foothills will be discussed in the following, first by describing the NNW dip profiles, second by describing the ENE strike profiles, and third by extracting the structural styles from the Serranía del Interior surface maps and cross sections. Finally, the analysis of six different interpretations of the Foreland–Serranía section will be presented.

Dip Profiles

From south to north, the following provinces are differentiated (Figs. 1 and 4): (1) the foreland is the area south of the deformation front; (2) the outer foothills are north of the foreland and south of the Pirital thrust fault in the north; and (3) the inner foothills correspond to the area north of the Pirital thrust fault and south of the Neogene onlap against the Serranía outcrops.

The Pirital high located in the inner foothills is a duplex structure bordered to the south by the Pirital basal thrust. North of the Pirital high, the Morichito satellite basin occupies the northern flank and syncline of this anticlinal complex.

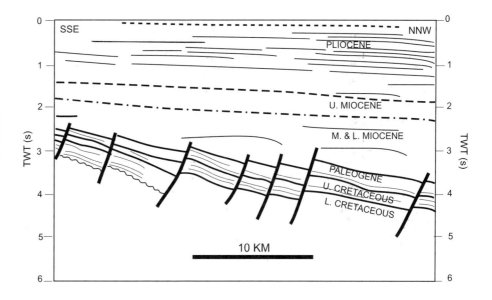

Figure 6. Line drawing from a foreland portion shows south dipping normal faults (2–3 s) overlain by northward thickening Neogene sedimentary rocks. See Figure 4 for location. TWT—two-way traveltime.

E.J. Hung

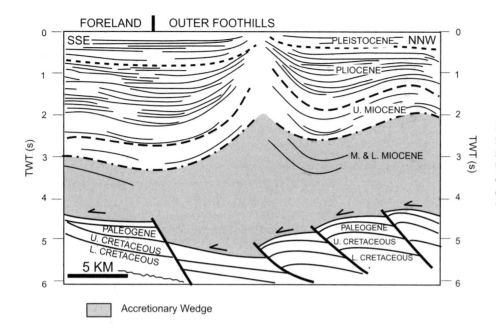

Figure 7. Line drawing showing how reflectors diverge from the apex of the shale anticline. The near surface reflectors are truncated. The axis of the southern syncline corresponds to the southern edge of the outer foothills. TWT—two-way traveltime.

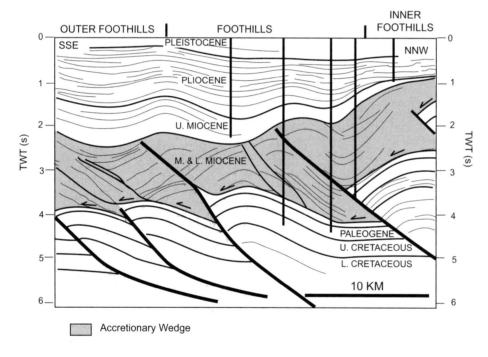

Figure 8. The figure shows the outer foothills thrust and folds. Note the Neogene disharmonic folds overlying the Cretaceous to Oligocene folds. See Figure 4 for location. Tick marks on top show intersection with strike profiles. TWT—two-way traveltime.

Seismic profiles show the foreland basement dipping gently to the north. High angle normal faults offset the basement and the overlying Cretaceous to Paleogene sequence. The fault planes are interpreted mostly as dipping to the north and occasionally to the south (Fig. 6). The sedimentary cover overlying the basement thickens toward the north. To the south, these sediments gradually wedge out, permitting the Precambrian rocks to crop out on the Guyana Shield (González de Juana et al., 1980; Di Croce, 1995; Di Croce et al., 1999).

At the southern edge of the outer foothills, reflectors representing upper Miocene and younger sedimentary rocks dip steeply and define frontal anticlines. Listric thrust faults and associated imbricates form the main structures of the outer foothills. The thrust faults are generally interpreted to flatten with depth and to merge on top of the basement (Fig. 7).

Note that structures involving middle to lower Miocene sedimentary rocks often appear to be disharmonic with the underlying structures (e.g., upper Miocene synclines coincide with anticlines involving Oligocene–lower Miocene sediments) (Fig. 8). The data are not sufficient to resolve the structural details within this interval; however, well tops often indicate repeated Miocene sections (intra-Carapita deformation). In addition, these Miocene

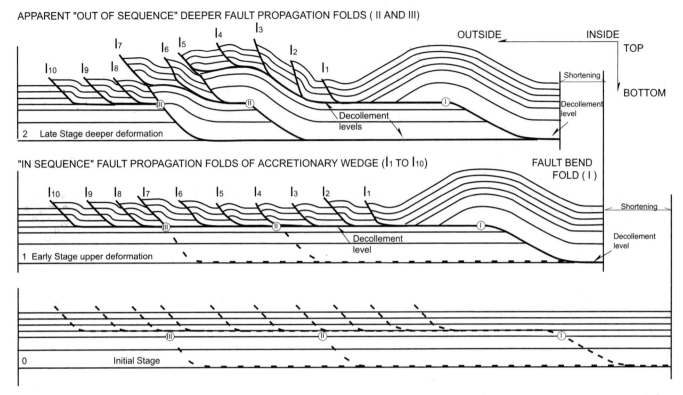

APPARENT "OUT OF SEQUENCE" DEEPER FAULT PROPAGATION FOLDS (II AND III)

"IN SEQUENCE" FAULT PROPAGATION FOLDS OF ACCRETIONARY WEDGE (I1 TO I10)

Figure 9. Two-stage deformation with thrusts using fault bend folds. This sketch mimics the interpretation for the early deformation of the higher Carapita accretionary wedge and later and deeper deformation involving Mesozoic folds of the Monagas foothills. Numbers follow the sequence of deformation. I5 and I7 represent "out of sequence."

sediments show high pore pressure, an ideal condition for internal decoupling within the Carapita (Roure et al., 1994).

It is suggested here that deformation occurred in sequence; i.e., with an early phase of deformation involving only the higher Carapita shale followed by later deformation involving Cretaceous to Oligocene sedimentary rocks (Fig. 8). Commonly the definition of "in sequence" is not given. In the context of this study, "in sequence" refers to succession of deformation proceeding toward the foreland (e.g., Boyer and Elliot, 1982). Here, as in many other folded belts, multiple décollement levels are involved (Fig. 9).

The inner foothills consist of imbricates that repeat the Cretaceous to Paleogene section, placing the thrusts and related folds close to the surface. These duplex structures override the outer foothills folds. The Carapita section that originally formed the cover of the lower units is now accumulated in the form of the accretionary wedge complex described earlier from the outer foothills. Minor decoupling surfaces are also interpreted at the base of the upper Cretaceous. Intra-Miocene unconformities converge onto the Pirital high; to the north, perched and sometimes tilted satellite basins are often developed (e.g., Morichito Basin). Figure 10 is a portion of seismic profile across the Morichito satellite basin. The base of this basin is interpreted to be middle Miocene and the top of these isolated basins is upper Miocene (see also Lilliu, 1990; Chevalier, 1993; Linares, 1992; Passalac-

qua et al. 1995). To the north, this unconformity truncates the crest of the anticlines, suggesting continued growth for the near surface blocks of the inner foothills.

Miocene sedimentary rocks forming satellite basins on the sides of the Pirital high show lower Miocene onlapping on Paleogene strata to the west and a conformable contact to the east (Fig. 10). See also the three-dimensional seismic images from the same area in Rigatti et al. (2001).

Several generalizations can be made from the dip profiles: (1) Anticlines with crests can be found at depths typically between 6 and 7 km. The wavelength of the structures varies between 4 and 5 km, and the total width of the ramps is ~7–10 km. The anticlines are fault propagation folds (e.g., Suppe, 1983); (2) the level of décollement reaches depths on the order of 10–12 km; (3) the Paleogene top of the structures is ~5 km deep and the structures are 8 km wide; (4) well-developed anticlines with Paleogene crests are less than 5 km deep with ramps underlying the Pirital thrust fault. These hydrocarbon-bearing structures are part of the El Furrial trend described earlier.

Strike Profiles

The description of the strike profiles also involves the lateral correlation of the structures previously examined on the north-south balanced cross sections.

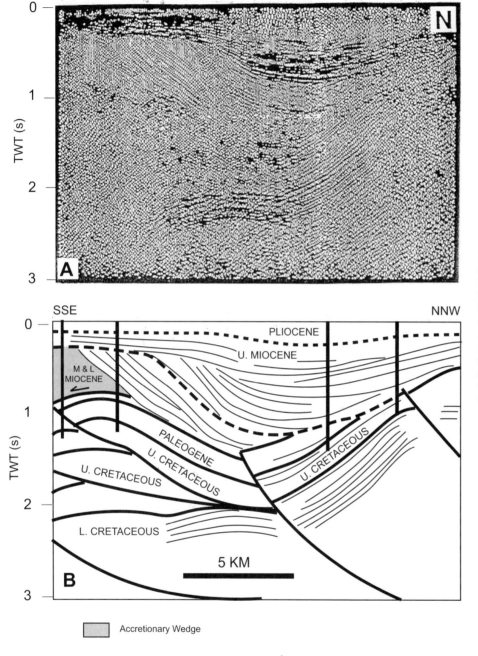

Figure 10. (A) Uninterpreted seismic data from the inner foothills. Strong reflectors in the center (2 s) describe the fold geometry. Note the offset of the upper reflectors (>2 s) and the high-dip reflectors converging to the south. (B) Interpreted line drawing showing the inner foothills thrust and folds. Crests of some folds underneath appear eroded, showing lower Miocene in contact with upper Cretaceous. See Figure 4 for location. TWT—two-way traveltime.

The Foreland

The foreland area is characterized by basement-involved normal faults and flat Neogene reflectors. Seismic profiles show the foreland basement plunging to the east. High-angle normal faults offset the basement and the overlying Cretaceous to Paleogene sequence. The orientation of these normal faults is not well known. They are here interpreted mostly as dipping to the west and occasionally to the east (Fig. 11). In addition to the basement-involved normal faults, this profile also shows the northerly striking Miocene listric faults dipping to the east.

The Neogene sedimentary cover thickens toward the east. The eastward thickening of the Neogene is associated with the regional eastward progradation of these units (e.g., Di Croce et al., 1999).

The Foothills

The transition between the foreland and the outer foothills is shown on Figure 12. Figure 13 is a depth conversion of a strike profile across the El Furrial and Boquerón oil fields. The top of the structures is ~5 km deep with a length along strike of 15–20 km. Frontal ramps, lateral ramps, and imbricates form the main structures of this portion of the foothills. The arcuate

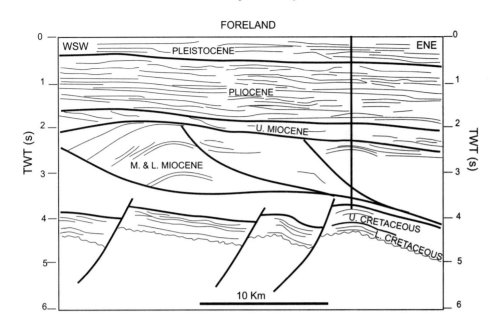

Figure 11. Line drawing showing west-dipping normal faults (4–5 s) overlain by east-thickening Neogene sediments. Note east-dipping normal faults involving middle to lower Miocene. See Figure 4 for location. TWT—two-way traveltime.

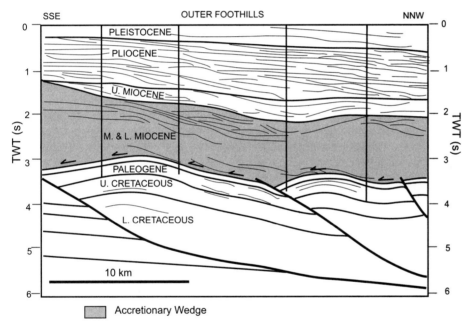

Figure 12. Line drawing showing the outer foothills thrust and folds. Deep structures not evident on the seismic profiles are supported from N-S intersections and wells. See Figure 4 for location. TWT—two-way traveltime.

faults flatten with depth and parallel the top of the basement. On these strike profiles, thrusts are gentle, deep structures with crests at typical depths between 6 and 7 km. The length along strike of these structures varies between 20 and 25 km, and the total length of the lateral ramps is ~30 km (profiles J, east half, and I; Fig. 14). The level of décollement reaches depths on the order of 10–12 km. In the outer foothills, structures typically plunge to the east. Minor blocks along the lateral ramps show the possible repetition of the Cretaceous to Paleogene sequence. Pliocene to Recent formations thicken toward the east.

The inner foothills consist of imbricates that place Mesozoic sedimentary rocks on top of Oligocene to Mesozoic sedi-

mentary rocks. The basal décollement at the top of the basement is consistently shown plunging to the east, and all major thrust ramps are connected to the basal décollement as shown on the cross section (Fig. 11). Some detachments bring lower Cretaceous on top of lower Miocene.

Depth Slice Maps

Depth converted profiles were used to construct "depth slices." These slices represent the map view of horizontal planes cutting across the depth converted data set. Two depth slices (5 km and 7 km) were selected to summarize the inter-

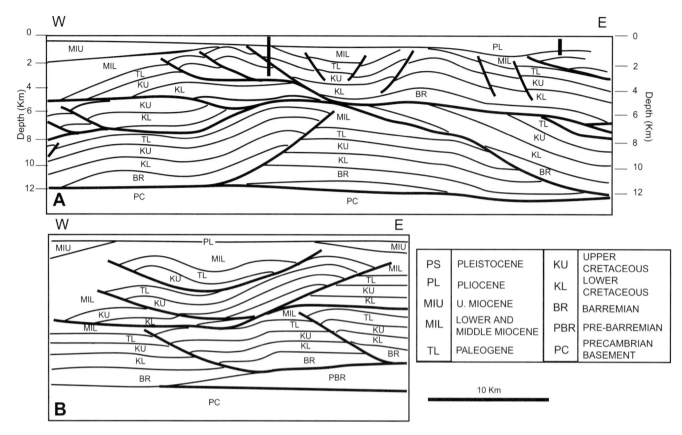

Figure 13. Depth conversion for ENE-WSW inner foothills strike profiles. The figure shows the interpreted basal décollement surface plunging to the east (12 km deep) on top of the basement and minor décollements on lower Miocene (6 km deep) and Lower Cretaceous (4 km deep). Thickness of the overthrusted higher units is greater than the lower units of the outer foothills. See Figure 4 for location.

pretation of the subsurface (Figs. 14 and 15). Note that this presentation is analogous to the time slices of three-dimensional seismic surveys.

A depth slice at 5 km (Fig. 14) illustrates the complex thrust faults and the relationship between the inner and outer foothills. The widespread distribution of the lower to middle Miocene represents the accretionary wedge of the foothills and a large part of the foreland. In the foreland, the depth slice shows the distribution of the Cretaceous to Paleogene sedimentary rocks.

A deeper slice at 7 km shows the connection of the thrust faults and correspondence of structures underlying the Pirital imbricates and the complete outer foothills (Fig. 15). The lower Miocene is distributed around deep structures and forms narrow wedges along some thrusts (Figs. 14 and 15). In the foreland, both the lower Cretaceous rocks and the basement are shown with interpreted orientation of the normal faults and distribution of Cretaceous and Paleogene sedimentary rocks.

Serranía del Interior

The style of the folds of the Serranía del Interior contrasts with the foothills and their complex duplex structures that involve the Mesozoic (e.g., Jusepín and Quiriquire For-

mations). The Serranía del Interior is characterized by a set of décollement folds and faults similar to those described in the Jura Mountains (e.g., Sommaruga, 1997) or Melville Island (e.g., Harrison and Bally, 1988) (see Fig. 6). The San Francisco tear fault has a pronounced right lateral offset (Rod, 1956; Rosales, 1973; Rossi, 1985). The fault is nearly vertical along its NW trend and offsets a fold axis (Fig. 16). To the south, the San Francisco tear fault emerges and joins the Quiriquire thrust fault. The Quiriquire thrust probably continues in the subsurface as the décollement of the major thrust faults of the area (cf. Rigatti et al. 2001).

The Neogene is eroded over the Serranía del Interior. The map shows an erosional pattern involving Barremian rocks to the north and gradually younger Late Cretaceous and Paleogene outcrops to the south and west of the map. Near the El Pilar strike slip fault, erosion exposes the oldest rocks of the Serranía del Interior, the Barranquín Formation. Further south, the outcropping folds and thrusts strike N70°E with gradually younger strata exposed up to the San Francisco tear fault, where Oligocene sedimentary rocks are on the surface. To the south of the San Francisco fault, early Cretaceous rocks are exposed again. A similar pattern is shown on the 5-km-depth slice (Fig. 16).

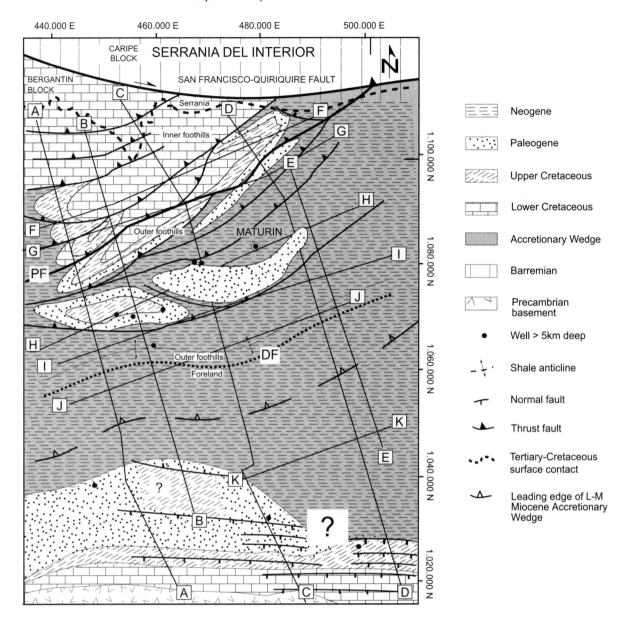

Figure 14. Depth slice 5 km deep illustrating the connection of thrust faults and the correspondence of structures from the foothills. DF—deformation front; PF—Pirital fault. The deformation front, the Pirital fault, and the Tertiary-Cretaceous contact are the boundaries for the foreland, outer foothills, and inner foothills, respectively. See Figure 4 for location.

DISCUSSION

Different interpretations can be made of the deep structures beneath the Serranía and their relation to the subsurface structure of the foothills. The most significant problem is how to fill the space available between an extrapolated foreland basement top and the outcrops. The greatest uncertainty is the nature and thickness of the rocks underlying the Lower Cretaceous of the Serranía (i.e., the section below the oldest outcropping stratigraphy shown on Fig. 17[1]). Several authors have drawn cross sections from the Serranía del Interior to the foreland (Rosales, 1973; Rossi, 1985; Roure et al., 1994; Passalacqua et al., 1995; Chevalier, 1993; Martínez, 1995) and all have proposed unique solutions.

[1]Figures 17–20 are on loose sheets accompanying this volume and in the GSA Data Repository as item 2005180, available online at www.geosociety.org/pubs/ft2005.htm, or on request from editing@geosociety.org or Documents Secretary, GSA, P.O. Box 9140, Boulder, CO 80301, USA.

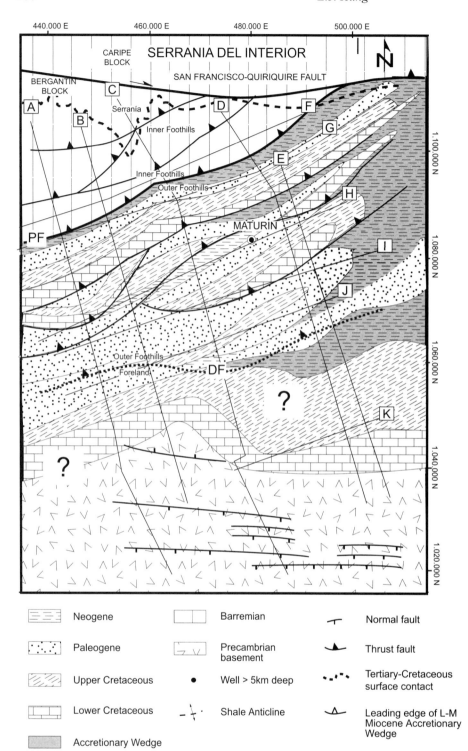

Figure 15. Depth slice 7 km deep illustrates the connection of thrust faults and the correspondence of structures from the foothills. DF—deformation front; PF—Pirital fault. The deformation front, the Pirital fault, and the Tertiary-Cretaceous contact are the boundaries for the foreland, outer foothills, and inner foothills, respectively. See Figure 4 for location.

Our profile ties the modified surface section of the Serranía del Interior (Fig. 5) to the foothills and foreland. Six different hypotheses will be examined, as follows (see also Table 2):
1. Basement-involved structures across the whole area;
2. Basement-involved structures only underneath the Serranía;

3. Paleozoic sediment wedge underlying the foothills but involved in the Serranía;
4. Inversion of Jurassic half-grabens underneath the Serranía;
5. Multiple décollement surfaces; and
6. Extensive duplex structures beneath the Serranía.

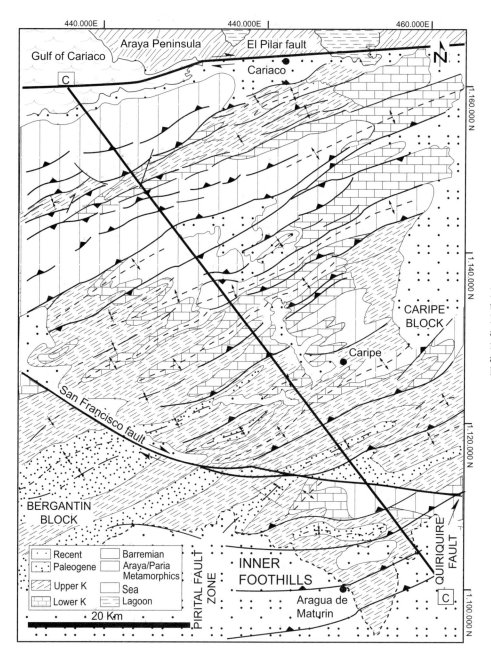

Figure 16. Simplified geologic map of the Serranía del Interior, modified from Bellizzia et al. (1976), Rossi (1985), and Chevalier (1993). Location of surface cross section C and surface data are illustrated (Aguasuelos Ingeniería-Lagoven, 1994).

The "basement-involved" hypothesis (hypothesis 1; Fig. 18, top [see footnote 1] assumes high angle reverse faults throughout the fold belt. The basement forms a regional synform, with its deepest portion coinciding with the basin axis. The southern portion of the synform is characterized by normal faults, whereas the north portion involves north-dipping reverse faults, and the top of the basement ranges between 4 km and 6 km deep. Intrabasement décollement is assumed to be on a crustal scale. Minimum shortening of ~35 km (20%) is distributed between all reverse faults.

The main problem with this interpretation is the presence of a shallow, presumably magnetic basement. Magnetic data published so far do not show corresponding uplift with an abrupt relief of some 8 km at the south margin of the Serranía (e.g., Potié, 1989).

An alternative to this model (hypothesis 2) is that basement is involved only under the Serranía del Interior (Fig. 18, bottom). In this model, beneath the Serranía, a thick wedge of Precambrian rocks is juxtaposed to the décollement structures of the foothills. Intrabasement regional décollement surfaces suggest that these autochthonous basement rocks occur at least 30 km north of the present day section. In addition, the base of the pre-Barranquín section and Miocene (Carapita base) are shown as minor décollements. The Quiriquire thrust fault juxtaposes Precambrian crystalline basement and sediments of the foothills. The Quiriquire thrust is shown to be the frontal ramp of a large structure associated with the San Francisco tear fault as previously suggested from the

TABLE 2. SIX DIFFERENT HYPOTHESES FOR REGIONAL PROFILE

Hypothesis	Minimum shortening	Décollement horizons	Comments
Basement-involved deformation	9%—16 km	Intra-basement	High angle reverse faults throughout the folded belt. Basement controls a regional synform.
Basement-involved deformation beneath the Serranía del Interior; in the foothills, only sediments are involved	20%—35 km	Intra-basement base pre-Barranquín and Miocene (Carapita base)	Thick wedge of Precambrian is juxtaposed next to sediment-involved structures in the foothills. Regional basement ramp surface deepens to the north to join the El Pilar at 35 km depth.
Paleozoic sedimentary wedge	21%—37 km	Intra-Paleozoic base pre-Barranquín, lower Miocene	A wedge of Paleozoic sediments underlies the folded belt. Regional low angle ramp detaches Paleozoic sediments from the basement, thus decoupling the whole Serranía.
Graben inversion	21%—37 km	Intra-basement Locally: top of Jurassic, lower Miocene	Serranía high inverted half grabens.
Imbricates with multiple long décollements	63%—110 km	Base pre-Barranquín, lower Miocene, top of Barremian (in Serranía)	Ramps emerging on high angle thrusts. Greater thickness for pre-Barranquín sediments assumed.
Duplex beneath the Serranía del Interior	66%—115 km	Base pre-Barranquín, lower Miocene	Duplication of the passive margin sequence. Multiple anticline structures beneath the Serranía.

surface map. Here again the published magnetic data do not show obvious magnetic basement uplift.

The third hypothesis assumes a regional low angle ramp detaching Paleozoic sedimentary rocks from the basement (Fig. 19, top). The ramp decouples the whole Serranía from the undeformed basement. The slope of the top of the basement increases beneath the foothills and can be estimated to reach depths of ~35 km. Relatively undeformed Paleozoic sedimentary rocks in the basin have been reported from wells to the west in the Guárico subbasin. This interpretation suggests a distribution to the northeast of the Paleozoic sediments beneath the eastern Venezuela folded belt (e.g., Feo-Codecido et al., 1984). Evidence to support this interpretation will only come with better pre-Cretaceous seismic resolution and drilling.

A fourth possible interpretation (Fig. 19, bottom [see footnote 1]) assumes that inversion of Jurassic half grabens is combined with Late Jurassic–Early Cretaceous evaporites that may coincide with local décollements (e.g., Roure et al., 1994). Syn-rift sequences may correspond to a Triassic to Late Jurassic rift phase (e.g., Burke, 1988; Stephan et al., 1990; Pindell and Barrett, 1990; Di Croce, 1995). The presence of Triassic to Upper Jurassic rift fill is supported by wells from the Espino Graben to the west, where the Late Jurassic La Quinta Formation overlies thick Paleozoic rocks of the Hato Viejo and Carrizal Formations (Hedberg, 1950; Beck, 1978; Feo-Codecido et al., 1984; Bartok, 1993). This interpretation agrees in principle with Roure et al. (1994) and Chevalier et al. (1995); however, here the assumed thickness of the synrift deposits is much larger. This fourth interpretation is weak because seismic reflection lines in the foreland show only very limited Triassic-Jurassic extension. However, conclusive mapping of the Jurassic of the Espino Graben to the east could strengthen this interpretation. To the northeast, in the Gulf of Paria and Trinidad folded belt, three wells have penetrated into evaporites of Late Jurassic–Early Cretaceous age, suggesting the possible detachment of the overlying rocks (Arnstein et al., 1985; Chiock, 1985).

The fifth interpretation shows imbricates associated with high angle thrusts (Fig. 20, bottom [see footnote 1]). The greater thickness of pre-Barranquín sediments corresponds to a northward passive margin thickening. Similar but smaller imbricate structures characterize the foothills. Reconstruction of this interpretation implies substantial shortening estimated to be on the order of 110 km. Well data from the Gulf of Paria and Trinidad have shown Late Jurassic to Early Cretaceous evaporites as a possible décollement level (Roure et al., 1994). On the other hand, shale-rich formations such as the Querecual Formation may serve as an additional décollement surface (Chevalier et al., 1995). In the same way it is conceivable that shale-rich formations like the García and Chimana Formations are potential detachment surfaces involved in the highly imbricated structures cited in this interpretation. This interpretation, like the preceding versions, needs to be tested by gravity and magnetic models. However, ultimately much better seismic reflection lines that cross the foothills and deep seismic reflection data across the Serranía calibrated with wells will convincingly constrain this interpretation.

The final possible interpretation suggests extensive shortening and repetition of Cretaceous-Oligocene passive margin sequence beneath the Serranía and part of the foothills (Fig. 20, top). Complex duplex structures are assumed to occur beneath the Serranía. Notice that a decoupling surface occurs on top of the lower Miocene (Carapita Formation), part of which is now represented by an accretionary wedge in the foothills. Sediments in this accretionary wedge are over-pressured (Betancour et al., 1993; Octavio et al., 1996), an ideal condition for decoupling within the Carapita (e.g., Gretener, 1981). The overriding imbricated blocks are evidently thicker than the underlying units because the Cretaceous-Paleogene passive margin sequence is assumed to thicken toward the north. The autochthonous Precambrian basement remains undeformed and possibly continues to the north coinciding with the regional décollement. The El Pilar strike-slip fault also merges into this major detachment, which as a whole can be viewed as the basis of a transpressional orogenic float (Oldow, et al., 1990; Bally et al., 1995).

CONCLUSIONS

Assuming little or no basement involvement in the structures of the Monagas foothills, the top of the basement may be extrapolated at least to the southern edge of the Serranía del Interior. However, the top of the basement could also dip farther north and extend all the way to the El Pilar strike-slip fault. Extrapolation of a gently northward dipping foreland basement top creates a significant space problem.

Basement-involved interpretations suggest shortening on the order of 15–30 km for a point near the El Pilar fault. Interpretations that do not involve the basement have the largest amount of shortening, implying a northward displacement of the El Pilar fault in excess of 100 km. Thus, alternative hypotheses imply that shortening across the Serranía to foreland transect may range from 9% to 66% (Table 2).

The foreland-verging thrust system appears to be "in sequence" as the deformation proceeds toward the foreland with thrust décollements getting progressively deeper with time.

In the Monagas foothills, décollements at the base of the Miocene are responsible for the formation of the complex Carapita accretionary wedge. The deeper structures of the Monagas foothills involve the Mesozoic and were formed after the Carapita accretionary wedge. Apparent "out of sequence" relations at the surface and in the shallow subsurface are due to the interference of late lower structures with the earlier structures of the Carapita accretionary wedge.

The choice between the various interpretations given in this paper is important because basement involvement under the Serranía leaves no prospects for hydrocarbon, whereas the duplex interpretation leaves room for sizable gas exploration targets.

ACKNOWLEDGMENTS

Data for this study were kindly provided by Lagoven, S.A., a subsidiary of Petróleo de Venezuela, S.A., and by the staff of the Instituto de Ingeniería Simón Bolívar. Comments by Dick Biscke and especially Bert Bally are greatly appreciated. Special thanks to formal reviewers Carlos Dengo and Dietrich Roeder from whom I learned and experienced their distinguished point of view.

REFERENCES CITED

Aguasuelos Ingeniería-Lagoven, 1994, Levantamiento Geológico de la Superficie en la Serranía del Interior Cuenca Oriental de Venezuela: Internal Report. v. 1, 185 p.

Arnstein, R., Cabrera. E., Russomano, F., and Sánchez, H., 1985, Revisión Estratigráfica de la Cuenca de Venezuela Oriental: VI Venezuelan Geological Conference, v. 1, p. 41–69.

Avé Lallemant, H.G., 1997, Transpression, displacement partitioning and exhumation in the eastern Caribbean–South America plate boundary zone: Tectonics, v. 16, p. 272–289, doi: 10.1029/96TC03725.

Aymard, R., Pimentel, L., Eitz, P., Lopéz, P., Chaouch, A., Navarro, J., Mijares, J., and Pereira, J.G., 1990, Geological integration and evaluation

of northern Monagas, Eastern Venezuelan Basin, in Brooks, J., ed., Classic petroleum provinces: London, Blackwell, Geological Society Special Publication 50, p. 37–53.

Bally, A.W., Di Croce, J., Ysaccis, R., and Hung, E., 1995, The structural evolution of the east Venezuela transpressional orogen and its sedimentary basins: Geological Society of America Abstracts with Programs, v. 27, no. 6, p. A-154.

Bartok, P., 1993, Pre-breakup geology of the Gulf of Mexico–Caribbean: Its relation to Triassic and Jurassic rift systems of the region: Tectonics, v. 12, p. 441–459.

Beck, C., 1978, Poliphasic Tertiary tectonics of the interior range in the central part of the western Caribbean chain, Guárico state, Northern Venezuela, in MacGillavry, H.J., and Beets B.J., eds., The 8th Caribbean Geological Conference, Willemstad, 1977: Geologie en Mijnbouw, v. 57, p. 99–104.

Bellizzia, A., Pimental, N., and Bajo, R., 1976, Mapa geológico estructural de Venezuela: Caracas, Minesterio de Minas e Hidrocarburos, escala 1:500,000.

Betancour, R.I., Vellez, F., and Gonzales, A., 1993, Assessing the impacts of geopressure on exploration using integrated geological log analysis (abs.): AAPG Bulletin, v. 77, p. 308.

Biju-Duval, B., Mascle, A., Montadert, L., and Wanneson, J., 1978, Seismic investigation in the Colombia, Venezuela and Grenada Basins, and on the Barbados Ridge for future IOPD drilling, in MacGillavry, H.J., and Beets B.J., eds.: The 8th Caribbean Geological Conference, Willemstad, 1977: Geologie en Mijnbouw, v. 57, p. 105–116.

Biju-Duval, B., Mascle, A., Rosales, H., and Young, G., 1983, Episutural Oligomiocene basins along the Venezuelan margin, in Watkins, J.S., and Drake, C.L., eds., Studies in continental margin geology: American Association of Petroleum Geologists Memoir 34, p. 347–358.

Bonini, W.E., 1978, Anomalous crust in the eastern Venezuela Basin and the Bouguer gravity anomaly field of northern Venezuela and the Caribbean borderland: Geologie en Mijnbouw, v. 57, p. 151–162.

Boyer, S., and Elliot, D., 1982, Thrust systems: AAPG Bulletin, v. 66, p. 1196–1230.

Burke, K., 1988, Tectonic evolution of the Caribbean: Annual Reviews of Earth and Planetary Sciences, v. 16, p. 201–230.

Carnevali, J., 1989, Geology of new giant oil fields in mountain front of northeastern Venezuela: Proceedings, 28th International Geological Congress, Washington, 9–19 July, v. 1, p. 1240–1241.

Carnevali, J.O., 1991, Monagas thrust fold belt in the Eastern Venezuela Basin: Anatomy of a giant discovery in the 1980s, in Proceedings, Thirteenth World Petroleum Congress: Buenos Aires, Argentina, v. 2, p. 47–58.

Chevalier, Y., 1993, A cross section from the oil-rich Maturín subbasin to Margarita island: The geodynamic relations between South American and Caribbean plates: Tectonics and stratigraphy: American Association of Petroleum Geologists–Sociedad Venezolana de Geólogos Field Trip Guide, 165 p.

Chevalier, Y., González, G., Mata, S., Santiago, N., and Spano, F., 1995, Estratigrafía secuencial y tectonica del transecto El Pilar–Cerro Negro, Cuenca Oriental de Venezuela: VI Congreso Colombiano del Petróleo, p. 115–125.

Chiock, M., 1985, Cretáceo y Paleógeno en el subsuelo del norte de Monagas, in Espejo, A., Ríos, J.H., Bellizzia, N.P., and de Pardo, A., Memoria, VI Congreso Geológico Venezolano: Caracas, Sociedad Venezolano de Geólogos, v. 1, p. 350–383.

Dahlstrom, C.D., 1969, Balanced cross sections: Canadian Journal of Earth Sciences, v. 6, p. 743–757.

Di Croce, J., 1995, Eastern Venezuela Basin: Sequence stratigraphy and structural evolution [Ph.D. Thesis]: Houston, Rice University, 225 p.

Di Croce, J., Bally, A., and Vail, P., 1999, Sequence stratigraphy of the Eastern Venezuela Basin, in Mann, P., ed., Caribbean basins of the world: Amsterdam, Elsevier, p. 419–476.

Erlich, R.N., and Barrett, S.F., 1990, Cenozoic plate tectonic history of the northern Venezuela-Trinidad area: Tectonics, v. 9, p. 161–184.

Erlich, R.N., and Barrett, S.F., 1992, Petroleum geology of the Eastern Venezuela Foreland Basin, in Macqueen, R.W., and Leckie, D.A., eds., Foreland basins and fold belts: American Association of Petroleum Geologists Memoir 55, p. 341–362.

Feo-Codecido, G., Smith, F.D., Aboud, N.N., and Giacomo, E., 1984, Basement and Paleozoic rocks of the Venezuelan Llanos Basin, in Bonini, W.E., Hargraves, R.V., and Shagam, R., eds., The Caribbean–South American plate boundary and regional tectonics: Geological Society of America Memoir 162, p. 175–187.

Gallango, O., and Parnaud, F., 1995, Two-dimensional computer modeling of oil generation and migration in a transect of the Eastern Venezuela Basin: American Association of Petroleum Geologists Memoir 62, p. 727–740.

González de Juana, C., Arozena, J., and Picard-Cadillat, X., 1980, Geología de Venezuela y de sus cuencas petrolíferas: Caracas, Fonives, 2 volumes, 1051 p.

Gretener, P.E., 1981, Pore pressure, discontinuitites and overthrusts, in McClay, K.R., and Price, N.J., eds., Thrust and nappe tectonics: London, Geological Society Special Publication 9, p. 335–352.

Gutiérrez, R., 1986, Nuevas espectativas en la subcuenca de Maturín, Cuenca Oriental de Venezuela: Caracas, Boletín de la Sociedad Venezolana de Géologos, v. 42, p. 33–43.

Harrison, J.C., and Bally, A.W., 1988, Cross sections of the Parry Islands fold belt on Melville Island, Canadian Artic Islands: Implications for the timing and kinematic history of some thin-skinned décollement systems: Bulletin of Canadian Petroleum Geology, v. 36, p. 311–332.

Hedberg, H.D., 1937, Stratigraphy of the Rio Querecual section of Northeastern Venezuela: Geological Society of America Bulletin, v. 48, no. 12, p. 1972–2024.

Hedberg, H.D., 1950, Geology of the Eastern Venezuela Basin (Anzoátegui-Monagas-Sucre-Easter Guárico portion): Geological Society of America Bulletin, v. 61, no. 11, p. 1173–1216.

Hedberg, H.D., and Pyre, A., 1944, Stratigraphy of northeastern Anzoátegui, Venezuela: AAPG Bulletin, v. 20, p. 1–128.

Lilliu, A., 1990, Geophysical interpretation of Maturín Foreland, Northeastern Venezuela [M.S. Thesis]: Houston, University of Houston, 124 p.

Linares, L.M., 1992, Sequence stratigraphy of late Miocene–Pleistocene of Northern Monagas, Eastern Venezuela Basin [M.A. Thesis]: Austin, University of Texas at Austin, 84 p.

Lugo, J., and Mann, P., 1995, Jurassic-Eocene tectonic events of Maracaibo Basin, Venezuela, in Tankard, A.J., Suárez, R, and Welsink, H.J., eds., Petroleum Basins of South America: American Association of Petroleum Geologists Memoir 62, p. 699–725.

Mann, P., and Burke, K., 1984, Neotectonics of the Caribbean: Review of Geophysics and Space Physics, v. 22, p. 309–362.

Mann, P., Schubert, C., and Burke, K., 1990, Review of Caribbean neotectonics, in Dengo, G., and Case, J.E., eds., The Caribbean region: Geological Society of America, The Geology of North America, v. H, p. 307–338.

Martín, N., and Espinoza, E., 1990, Integración de la información gravimétrica del flanco noreste de la cuenca oriental de Venezuela, in Memoria, V Congreso Venezolano de Geofísica: Caracas, Sociedad Venezolana de Ingeniería Geofísica, p. 78–85.

Martín-Bellizzia, C., 1974, Paleotectónica del escudo de Guayana, in Conferencia Geológica Inter-Guyanas IX, Ciudad Guayana, Venezuela, Mayo, 1972: Caracas, Memoria Boliviana de Geólogos, Publicación Especial, v. 6, p. 251–305.

Martínez, J.A., 1995, A geological and geophysical study of structural style along a transect of the Maturín subbasin, Eastern Venezuela Basin [M.S Thesis]: Columbia, South Carolina, University of South Carolina, 141 p.

Mendoza, V., 1977, Evolución tectónica del escudo de Guayana, in Congreso Latinoamericano de Geología, II: Caracas, Memoria, Boletín Geológico, Publicación Especial, v. 7, no. 3, p. 2237–2270.

Octavio, D.A., Gonzalez, G., and Ortega, L., 1996, Ocurencia de intervalos turbidíticos en la Formación Carapita: AAPG Bulletin, v. 80, p. 1319.

Oldow, J.S., Bally, A.W., and Avé Lallemant, H.G., 1990, Transpression, orogenic float, and lithospheric balance: Geology, v. 18, p. 991–994, doi: 10.1130/0091-7613(1990)018<0991:TOFALB>2.3.CO;2.

Parnaud, F., Gou, Y., Pascual, J.-C., Tuskowski, I., Gallango, O., Passalacqua, H., and Roure, F., 1995, Petroleum geology of the central part of the Eastern Venezuelan Basin, in Tankard, A.J., Suárez, R., and Welsink, H.J., eds., Petroleum basins of South America: American Association of Petroleum Geologists Memoir 62, p. 741–756.

Passalacqua, H., Fernandez, F., Gou, Y., and Roure, F., 1995, Crustal architecture and strain partitioning in the eastern Venezuelan ranges, in Tankard, A.J., Suárez, R., and Welsink, H.J., eds., Petroleum basins of South America: American Association of Petroleum Geologists Memoir 62, p. 667–679.

Pindell, J.L., 1993, Regional synopsis of Gulf of Mexico and Caribbean evolution, in Pindell, J.L., and Perkins, B.F., eds., Mesozoic and early Cenozoic development of the Gulf of Mexico and Caribbean region—A context for hydrocarbon exploration, Proceedings, Gulf Coast Section, SEPM Foundation 13th Annual Research Conference: Houston, Texas, Society for Sedimentary Geology (SEPM) Foundation, p. 251–274.

Pindell, J.L., and Barrett, S.F., 1990, Geological evolution of the Caribbean region: A plate-tectonic perspective, in Dengo, G., and Case, J.E., eds., The Caribbean Region: Geological Society of America, The Geology of North America, v. H, p. 405–432.

Potié, G., 1989, Contribution á l'étude géologique de la frontière sud-est de la plaque Caraibe: La Serranía del Interior Oriental sur le transect Cumaná-Urica et le basin de Maturín Venezuela [Ph.D. Thesis]: Brest, Université de Bretagne Occidentale, 240 p.

Rigatti, V., Fox, A., Roden, R., Danahey, L., Gajkdwski, W., Mali, E., and Vigh, D., 2001, 3D PSDM case history in a thrust belt: Quirirque block, Eastern Venezuela Basin: The Leading Edge, v. 20, p. 514–518, doi: 10.1190/1.1438982.

Robertson, P., and Burke, K., 1989, Evolution of southern Caribbean plate boundary, vicinity of Trinidad and Tobago: American Association of Petroleum Geologists Bulletin, v. 73, p. 490–509.

Rod, E., 1956, Strike slip faults of northern Venezuela: AAPG Bulletin, v. 40, p. 457–476.

Rohr, G., 1991, Paleogeographic maps, Maturín Basin of eastern Venezuela and Trinidad: Port Spain, Trinidad, Transactions of the 2nd Geological Conference of the Geological Society of Trinidad and Tobago, p. 88–105.

Rosales, H., 1973, Excursion #5: Venezuela nororiental–Serranía del Interior: Maturín, Muelle de Cariaco: Caracas, Segundo Congreso Latinoamericano de Geología, p. 470–493.

Rossi, T., 1985, Contribution á l'ètude géologique de la frontière sud-est de la plaque Caraibe: Etude géologique de la Serranía del Interior Oriental (Venezuela) sur le transect Cariaco-Maturín syntheses paléogéographique et géodynamique [Ph.D. thesis]: Brest, Université de Bretagne Occidentale, 340 p.

Roure, F., Carnevali, J., Gou, Y., and Subieta, T., 1994, Geometry and kinematics of the North Monagas thrust belt (Venezuela): Marine and Petroleum Geology, v. 11, no. 3, p. 347–362, doi: 10.1016/0264-8172(94)90054-X.

Russo, R.M., Speed, R.C., Okal, E.A., Shepherd, J.B., and Rowley, K.C., 1993, Seismicity and tectonics of the southeastern Caribbean: Journal of Geophysical Research, v. 98, p. 14,299–14,516.

Schubert, C., 1984, Basin formation along Boconó–Morón–El Pilar fault system, Venezuela: Journal of Geophysical Research, v. 89, p. 5711–5718.

Schlanger, S.O., and Jenkins, H.C., 1976, Cretaceous oceanic anoxic events: Causes and consequences: Geologie en Mijnbouw, v. 55, no. 3–4, p. 179–184.

Sommaruga, A., 1997, Geology of the central Jura and the molasse basin: New insight into an evaporite-based foreland fold and thrust belt: Mémoire de la Sociêtè de Neuchâtel, Science Natural, v. 12, 176 p.

Stainforth, R.M., 1971, La formación Carapita de Venezuela Oriental: Caracas, Memoria IV Congreso Venezolano, v. 1, p. 433–463.

Stephan, J.F., Mercier de Lepinay, B., Calais, E., Tardy, M., Beck, C., Carfantan, J.C., Olivet, J.L., Villa, J.M., Bouyesse, P., Mauffret, A., Bourgois, J., Thery, J.M., Tounor, J., Blanchet, R., and Decourt, J., 1990, Paleogeodynamic maps of the Caribbean: 14 steps from Lias to present: Bulletin Société Géologique de France, serie 8, v. VI, p. 915–919.

Subieta, T., Carnevali, J., and Hunter, V., 1987, Evolución tectonoestratigráfica de la Serranía del Interior y de la subcuenca de Maturín, in Bellizzia, A, Escoffery, A.L., and Bass. I., eds., Memoria del III Simposio Bolivariano: Caracas, Sociedad Venezolana de Geólogos, v. 2, p. 549–578.

Suppe, J., 1983, Geometry and kinematics of fault bend folding: American Journal of Science, v. 283, p. 684–721.

Van der Hilst, R.D., 1990, Tomography with P, PP and pP delay-time data and the three-dimensional mantle structure below the Caribbean region: Geologica Utraiectina, v. 67, 250 p.

Van der Hilst, R.D., and Mann, P., 1994, Tectonic implication of tomographic images of subducted lithosphere beneath northwestern South America: Geology, v. 22, p. 451–454, doi: 10.1130/0091-7613(1994)022<0451:TIOTIO>2.3.CO;2.

Vierbuchen, R.C., 1984, The geology of the El Pilar fault zone and adjacent areas in northeastern Venezuela, in Bonini, W.E., Hargraves, R.B., and Shagam, R., eds., The Caribbean–South American plate boundary and regional tectonics: Geological Society of America Memoir 162, p. 189–212.

Vivas, V., 1985, Contribución al estudio de la Serranía Oriental (Venezuela), estratigrafía y tectónica de la región de Bergantín–Santa Ines [Tèse 3d cycle]: Brest, France, Université de Bretagne Occidentale, 480 p.

MANUSCRIPT ACCEPTED BY THE SOCIETY 5 APRIL 2005

Geological Society of America
Special Paper 394
2005

Tectonic and thermal history of the western Serranía del Interior foreland fold and thrust belt and Guárico basin, north-central Venezuela: Implications of new apatite fission-track analysis and seismic interpretation

Jaime Pérez de Armas

Department of Earth Science, MS-126, Rice University, Houston, Texas 77005, USA

ABSTRACT

Structural analysis, interpretation of seismic reflection lines, and apatite fission-track analysis in the western Serranía del Interior fold and thrust belt and in the Guárico basin of north-central Venezuela indicate that the area underwent Mesozoic and Tertiary to Recent deformation. Mesozoic deformation, related to the breakup of Pangea, resulted in the formation of the Espino graben in the southernmost portion of the Guárico basin and the formation of the Proto-Caribbean lithosphere between the diverging North and South American plates. The northern margin of Venezuela became a northward-facing passive margin. Minor normal faults formed in the Guárico basin.

The most intense deformation took place in the Neogene when the Leeward Antilles volcanic island arc collided obliquely with South America. The inception of the basal foredeep unconformity in the late Eocene–early Oligocene marks the formation of a perisutural basin on top of a buried graben system. It is coeval with minor extension and possible reactivation of Cretaceous normal faults in the Guárico basin. It marks the deepening of the foredeep. Cooling ages derived from apatite fission-tracks suggest that the obduction of the fold and thrust belt in the study area occurred in the late Oligocene through the middle Miocene. Field data and seismic interpretations suggest also that contractional deformation began during the Neogene, and specifically during the Miocene.

The most surprising results of the detrital apatite fission-track study are the ages acquired in the sedimentary rocks of the easternmost part of the study area in the foreland fold and thrust belt. They indicate an Eocene thermal event. This event may be related to the Eocene NW-SE convergence of the North and South American plates that must have caused the Proto-Caribbean lithosphere to be shortened. This event is not related to the collision of the arc with South America, as the arc was far to the west during the Eocene.

Keywords: Caribbean tectonics, apatite fission-tracks, Guárico basin, Venezuela, western Serranía del Interior.

Pérez de Armas, J., 2005, Tectonic and thermal history of the western Serranía del Interior foreland fold and thrust belt and Guárico basin, north-central Venezuela: Implications of new apatite fission-track analysis and seismic interpretation, *in* Avé Lallemant, H.G., and Sisson, V.B., eds., Caribbean–South American plate interactions, Venezuela: Geological Society of America Special Paper 394, p. 271–314, doi: 10.1130/2005.2394(11). For permission to copy, contact editing@geosociety.org. ©2005 Geological Society of America.

INTRODUCTION

The western Serranía del Interior foreland fold and thrust belt and the Guárico basin in north-central Venezuela are part of the complex Caribbean–South American plate boundary zone that includes different Mesozoic-Cenozoic orogenic cycles and records obduction of allochthonous terranes onto the continental plate. The Caribbean–South American plate boundary zone can be considered as a megasuture (Bally and Snelson, 1980) that developed since the Late Cretaceous in western Venezuela and migrated to eastern Venezuela until Recent times (Lugo and Mann, 1995) (Fig. 1).

The convergence between the Caribbean and South American plates may have been NW-SE for most of the time and, thus, with respect to the E-W–trending continental margin of South America, the convergence was highly right-oblique. Thus, collision of the Caribbean plate and the Leeward Antilles volcanic island arc with the South American continent is highly diachronous: it happened in Paleocene-Eocene time in western Venezuela, in the Oligocene in north-central Venezuela, and in the Miocene in eastern Venezuela (Lugo and Mann, 1995).

Convergence between North and South America started during the Paleocene (e.g., Pindell, 1993). One important question is whether, in north-central and eastern Venezuela, the convergence caused Eocene deformation in the area before formation of the collisional deformation structures. Pindell (1997) suggests that contraction between the North and South American plates may have deformed the Proto-Caribbean crust, forming an incipient subduction zone and subsequent early uplift of the Northern Range of Trinidad and possibly the northern Serranía.

The present study was undertaken in order to determine how many deformation phases occurred in north-central Venezuela and how these structures relate to the plate tectonic history of the Caribbean. The study included mapping along four N-S–trending transects through the area, structural analysis, interpretation of seismic reflection lines, and fission-track analysis. Fieldwork was carried out in 1995, 1996, and 1997.

Peirson (1963, 1965), Menéndez (1966), Bell (1968), and Beck (1978, 1985a, 1985b) mapped the area previously. In this study, the interpretations of these were utilized for checking the stratigraphy and the structure in the field. Changes were made

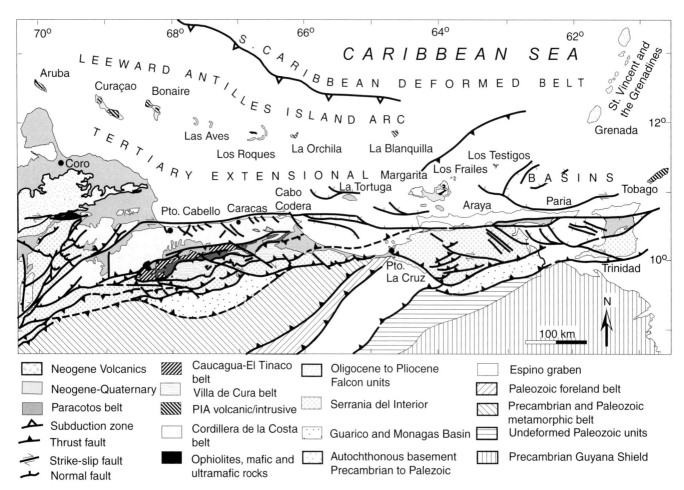

Figure 1. Tectonostratigraphic map of northern Venezuela and southern Caribbean showing the main tectonic belts and lithological units. From Ysaccis (1997).

when deemed necessary, in view of the relatively new concept of displacement partitioning (e.g., Fitch, 1972; Oldow et al., 1989; Cashman et al., 1992). Generally, in plate boundary zones where the convergence rate vector is oblique, the normal component causes the development of folds and thrust faults (sub) parallel to the boundary, and the parallel component results in displacements along margin-parallel strike-slip faults (Avé Lallemant and Guth, 1990; Tikoff and Teyssier, 1994; Avé Lallemant, 1996, 1997).

Fission-track analysis of detrital apatites was performed to determine thermal effects associated with the uplift and denudation of the western Serranía del Interior. The primary goal of this analysis was to find out whether the area had been deformed during one or two events.

REGIONAL TECTONICS OF NORTH-CENTRAL VENEZUELA

The Caribbean–South American plate boundary in north-central Venezuela is a megasuture that includes different complex Mesozoic-Cenozoic orogenic cycles. It records the exhumation and obduction of an accretionary fold and thrust belt that includes high pressure–low temperature (HP-LT) metamorphic rocks (blue-schist and eclogite), ophiolite, greenschist, island-arc igneous rocks, passive-margin–derived metamorphic rocks, volcanogenic turbidites, and passive-margin derived sedimentary rocks of different ages and tectonic history. Paleogene north-dipping subduction associated with the obduction of the Lara nappes was followed by the development of a south-dipping Neogene Benioff zone with no associated volcanism. Both the north-dipping and the south-dipping subduction were previously inferred by tomographic studies and gravimetric and magnetic modeling (Van der Hilst, 1990; Bosch and Rodríguez, 1992; Van der Hilst and Mann, 1994).

The regional tectonics of the area must be understood within the South American and Caribbean plate tectonic context (for a more detailed discussion, see Pindell, 1993; Summa et al., 2003; Pindell et al., this volume; and Pérez de Armas, 2005). The northern part of the South American plate consists mainly of the Precambrian Guyana Shield and three allochthonous belts, two accreted in the Paleozoic and one in the Cenozoic (e.g., Feo-Codecido et al., 1984).

In Early Jurassic time, the supercontinent of Pangea started to break up, and subsequently, North and South America drifted apart, and the Proto-Caribbean lithosphere was formed between the two Americas. The northern margin of South America became a passive continental margin. Since mid-Cretaceous time, the Farallon plate (later the Caribbean plate) moved first northeastward (120 Ma to ca. 55 Ma) and subsequently, eastward (55 Ma to Recent), inserting itself between the North and South American plate (e.g., Pindell 1993). Convergence between the latter two plates started at ca. 55 Ma (e.g., Pindell, 1993). The relative eastward passage of the Caribbean plate resulted in diachronous deformation of the northern margin of South America.

The Caribbean–South American plate boundary zone consists of many allochthonous and parautochthonous belts that

approximate a general E-W trend (Fig. 1). From north to south, these belts are (1) the South Caribbean deformed belt, (2) the Leeward Antilles volcanic island arc, (3) a zone of Tertiary pull-apart basins, (4) the Caribbean Mountain system, and (5) a belt of foreland basins (Ostos et al., this volume, Chapter 2). Most of these belts are separated by major fault systems (Figs. 1 and 2).

The Caribbean Mountain system is subdivided into several subbelts (e.g., Menéndez, 1966; Ostos et al., this volume, Chapter 2). The two most southern subbelts are the Villa de Cura complex in the north and the western Serranía del Interior fold and thrust belt in the south (Fig. 1). The two are separated by the Cantagallo fault, a low-angle, north-dipping thrust fault that is the southernmost limit of the allochthonous metamorphic belts. The western Serranía del Interior is a south-facing foreland fold and thrust belt that has been subdivided into four belts, which are, from north to south: (1) the "Piedmont belt," (2) the "Belt of thrust faults," (3) the "Belt of overturned beds," and (4) the "Belt of gently dipping beds." The western Serranía del Interior and the Guárico foreland basin in the south are the subject of the present study (Figs. 1 and 2).

GUÁRICO BASIN

Seismic Stratigraphy of the Guárico Basin

Introduction

The stratigraphy of the Guárico basin and the Serranía is shown in Figures 3 and 4. Although very little structure of the Guárico basin is seen at the surface ("Belt of gently dipping beds," Bell, 1968), larger deformation structures are recognized on seismic reflection profiles (Aymard et al., 1985; Blanco et al., 1988; Daal and Lander, 1993). The oldest structures in the region are NE-SW–trending normal faults related to the divergence of the North and South American plates (e.g., Espino graben). Several tectonic pulses have been defined previously in the Guárico basin and are summarized here: (1) Triassic-Jurassic extension associated with the breakup of Pangea forming the Espino graben, (2) Cretaceous extension and syntectonic sedimentation possibly extending to the late Eocene, (3) middle to late Eocene uplift of the El Baúl arch generating a regional unconformity, (4) Oligocene subsidence and formation of a deep basin, and (5) a middle to late Miocene compressional event resulting in south-vergent structures, reactivation of Cretaceous normal faults, and loading of the thrust sheets onto Oligo-Miocene stratigraphic sequences (e.g., González and Lander, 1980; Aymard et al., 1985; Blanco et al., 1988).

Data Set

A regional grid of 1400 km of industry two-dimensional seismic reflection profiles, shot in the mid-1980s, well data, time-velocity surveys, and synthetic seismograms were used to interpret the tectonic evolution of the Guárico basin. Location of the seismic grid is shown in Figure 5. Petróleos de Venezuela (PDVSA) kindly provided the data set. The seismic grid is denser in hydrocarbon producing areas, such as the Yucal-Placer field

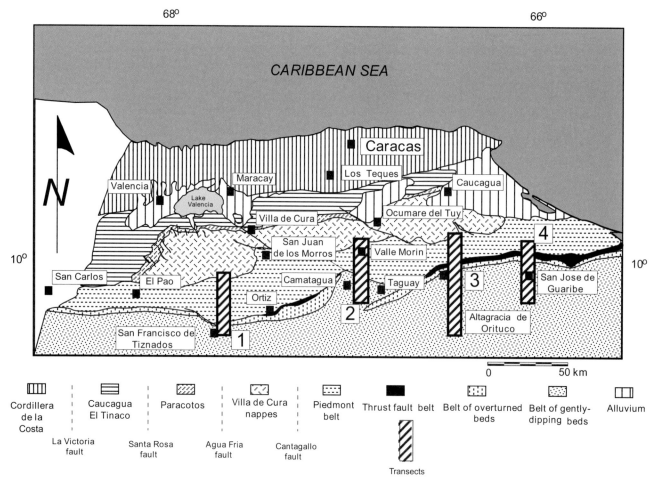

Figure 2. Map of tectonic belts in the north-central Caribbean Mountain system as defined by Menéndez (1966), Peirson (1965), Bell (1968), and Beck (1978). The dashed areas represent the studied transects: (1) Platillón-Tiznados, (2) Camatagüita–Valle Morín, (3) Altagracia de Orituco, and (4) and San José de Guaribe.

(Daal and Lander, 1993). Published biostratigraphic reports on the area are scarce. This paper uses the biostratigraphy of Fasola et al. (1985) as a guide to determine the ages of the different stratigraphic units.

Methodology

Interpretation and subdivision of seismic units into correlatable entities throughout the Guárico basin are based on the principles established by Vail et al. (1977) and Vail (1987). In the present study, subdivisions in stratigraphic units and their regional correlation were based on Fasola et al. (1985).

Synthetic seismograms generated from transit time well logs in conjunction with biostratigraphy for the same wells studied by Fasola et al. (1985) and previously published papers (e.g., Daal and Lander, 1993) were used to calibrate the seismic sections. In this project, six regional seismic transects were studied, five oriented northwest-southeast and one oriented east-northeast–west-southwest (Figs. 5–12). Velocity surveys allowed converting time sections into depth sections (Figs. 7–11).

On the basis of the interpreted two-dimensional seismic reflection lines, the Guárico basin was subdivided into five major seismic sequences or megasequences bounded by sequence boundaries: (1) Precambrian-Paleozoic pre-rift (Pre-K); (2) Triassic-Jurassic synrift (T-J); (3) Cretaceous post-rift (K); (4) Oligocene-Miocene Roblecito-Chaguaramas foredeep, which includes two seismic sequences (OA, OB, OC, OM, N1); and (5) Neogene Roblecito-Chaguaramas foredeep (N2) (Figs. 3 and 6–12).

Precambrian-Paleozoic Pre-Rift Rock Units

In north-central Venezuela, the pre-Cretaceous basement consists of Precambrian crystalline rocks that are in tectonic contact with Paleozoic metamorphic and sedimentary rocks (Feo-Codecido et al., 1984). Previously interpreted well logs indicate the presence of sedimentary Paleozoic units in the area, but it was not possible to recognize them on the available seismic lines. Cambrian to Lower Ordovician siliciclastic rocks may be preserved in the Espino graben. In this study, all undifferentiated Precambrian and Paleozoic rocks are combined and labeled Pre-K (pre-Cretaceous) (Figs. 7–12).

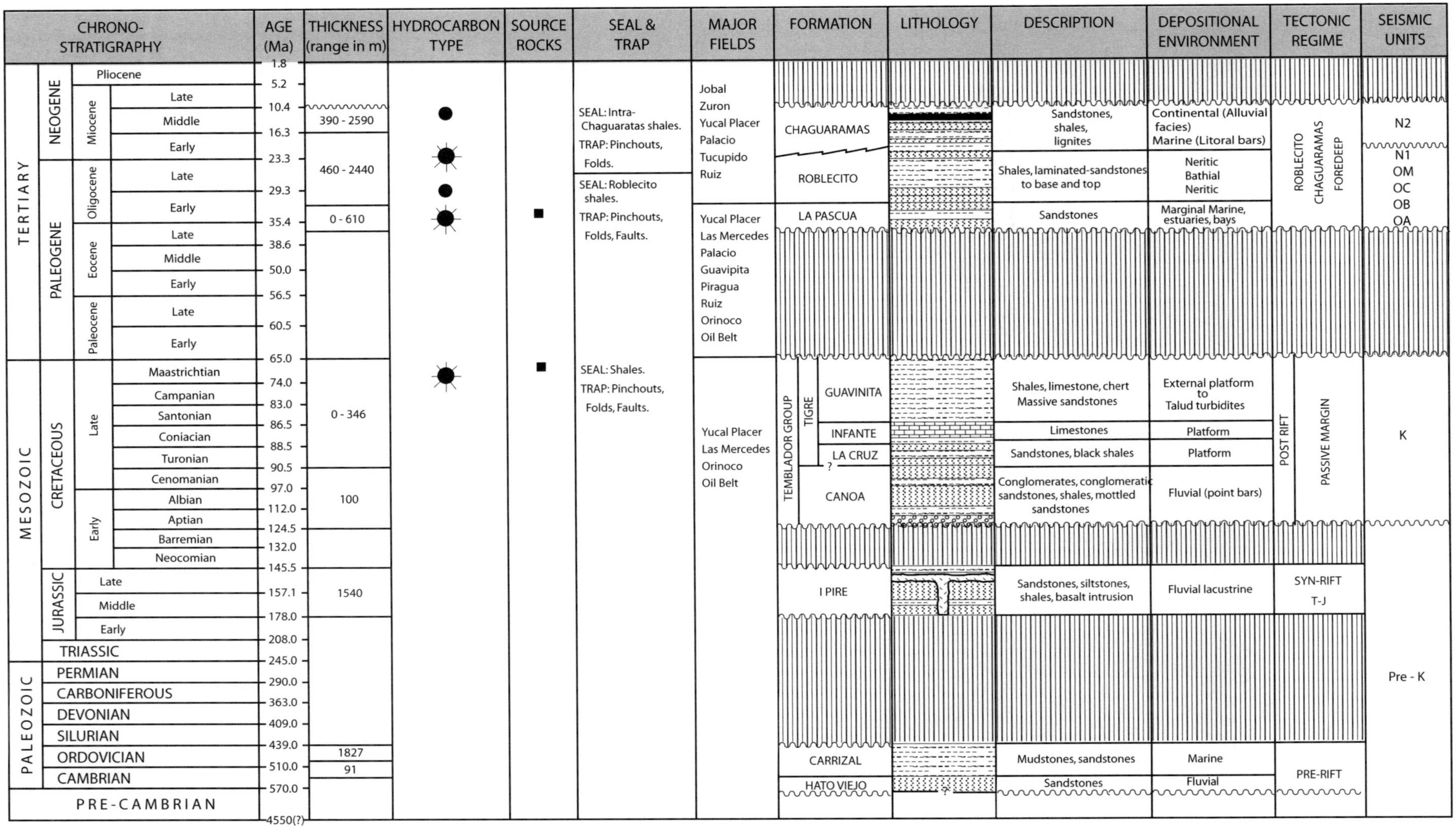

Figure 3. Stratigraphy of Guárico basin, north-central Venezuela, compiled from several authors (e.g., González de Juana et al., 1980; Fasola et al., 1985; Aymard et al., 1985; Erlich and Barrett, 1992; Daal and Lander, 1993).

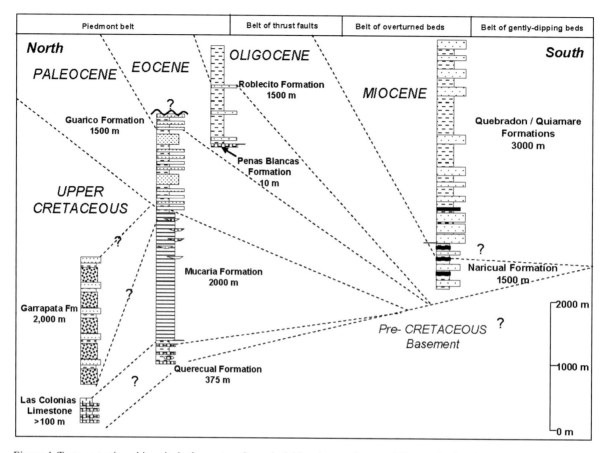

Figure 4. Tectonostratigraphic units in the western Serranía del Interior, north-central Venezuela, showing their relationship with the tectonic belts, thicknesses of the units measured from cross sections, and their lateral relationships.

Triassic-Jurassic Synrift Sequence

This seismic unit is recognized in the Espino graben and includes thick Triassic-Jurassic (T-J) sedimentary rocks, but may include Paleozoic (Cambrian-Ordovician) sedimentary units as well. The graben is located in the southernmost portion of the basin. In the interpreted seismic section (Fig. 11), units tend to expand toward the faults that bound the graben and are in fault contact with the Precambrian and Paleozoic basement.

The Triassic-Jurassic Espino graben is a rift system that probably formed during the breakup of Pangea and the subsequent North and South America plate divergence (e.g., Pindell and Dewey, 1982; Summa et al., 2003). In the Guárico basin, the Espino graben trends NE-SW. It extends to the NE toward the Eastern Venezuela basin and to the SW toward the Venezuelan and Colombian Llanos (Feo-Codecido et al., 1984). This rift developed on older accreted Paleozoic metamorphic and Precambrian igneous-metamorphic terranes of the Guyana craton. The Triassic to Jurassic units contain an intraformational volcanic flow dated at 157 and 162 Ma (K-Ar; Feo-Codecido et al., 1984).

In some areas, the Paleozoic sedimentary deposits are not present. Instead, underlying the Cretaceous and younger deposits, there is either an accreted Paleozoic metamorphic terrane or the Guyana crystalline basement. Ysaccis (1997) presented a

tectonic map of northern Venezuela that depicts the subsurface extension of the Precambrian and Paleozoic metamorphic folded belts, Paleozoic foreland folds, Espino graben deposits, and undeformed Paleozoic and Precambrian Guyana Shield (Fig. 1).

Post-Rift Sequences

Passive margin sequence—Cretaceous (K). The Cretaceous seismic unit in the Guárico basin (K) is bound at its base by a regional unconformity that marks the encroachment of the Cretaceous seas onto continental South America (Figs. 3 and 7–12) (González de Juana et al., 1980). The top of this unit represents a late Eocene–early Oligocene basal foredeep unconformity that marks the beginning of the loading of the Lara nappes onto the South American craton in north-central Venezuela (Fasola et al., 1985; Kiser, 1997). This unit thickens toward the east of the basin and is thinner to the south toward the Guyana craton and also thinner to the west toward the El Baúl high (Figs. 7–12). The westward thinning of the K unit could be due to erosion, which might have occurred during the uplift of the El Baúl high in middle to late Eocene time (Blanco et al., 1988). In the present study, analysis of two-dimensional seismic lines suggests that a minor extensional phase occurred during the sedimentation of the Cretaceous sequence. These structures were reactivated during

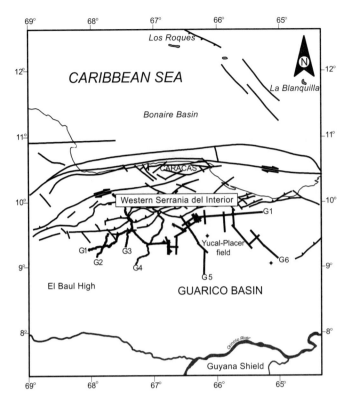

Figure 5. Location map of seismic sections (G) used in this study and field transects.

LEGEND FOR SEISMIC LINES
GUARICO BASIN
North-Central Venezuela

SYMBOLS

⚒	Key
⌒	Normal fault
⌒	Reverse fault
⌒	Reactivated fault
G1 ▾	Intersection with transect G1
G4	2D seismic line location
··········	Late Eocene-Early Oligocene basal foredeep unconformity

STRATIGRAPHY

☐	NA-NG	Neogene
☐	OM	Oligocene-Miocene
☐	OA-OC	Oligocene
☐	K	Cretaceous
☐	T-J	Triassic-Jurassic
☐	Pre-K	Pre-Cretaceous
☐	KT	Cretaceous-Tertiary terranes
☐	VdC	Cretaceous Villa de Cura nappes

Figure 6. Legend for interpreted two-dimensional seismic lines in Figures 7–12.

the loading of the Lara nappes onto South America in the early Oligocene (Figs. 7–12).

Roblecito-Chaguaramas Foredeep

Late Eocene–early Oligocene to Miocene (OA to OM, N1). The seismic stratigraphic unit that onlaps the Cretaceous sequence (OA) and marks the inception of the foredeep in north-central Venezuela is late Eocene–early Oligocene (González de Juana et al., 1980; Fasola et al., 1985; Kiser, 1997). In the present study, this seismic sequence includes four late Eocene–early Oligocene to early Miocene seismic units. They are correlated on the basis of the report by Fasola et al. (1985). The units, from older to younger, are OA, OB, OC, and OM (Figs. 7–12).

In the northern parts of the Guárico basin, the base of the unit OA is represented by the transgressive La Pascua Formation (late Eocene–early Oligocene) and its transition to the Roblecito Formation. The units OB and OC (Oligocene) represent the deepening phase of the basin represented solely by the Roblecito Formation. The unit OM (Oligocene-Miocene) represents the basal units of the filling and capping phase of the foredeep by the Roblecito and Chaguaramas Formations (Fasola et al., 1985).

Deposition of the units OA and OB is coeval with the development or reactivation of extensional structures during the inception of the Guárico foredeep in the late Eocene–early Oligocene (Figs. 7–12). Some normal faults were possibly inverted during the middle Miocene tectonic event (Fig. 9).

In the Guárico basin, two Neogene stratigraphic sequences are divided by a regional unconformity (Figs. 3, 11, and 12). These units are named in this study Neogene 1 and Neogene 2 (Figs. 11 and 12). The Neogene 1 seismic unit was divided into three subunits for the purpose of seismic correlation: NA, NB, and NC (Figs. 11 and 12). There is no biostratigraphic control of these units since they are near-shore marine to continental deposits

Neogene Roblecito-Chaguaramas Foredeep

Neogene N2. This seismic unit, Neogene 2 (N2), represents the capping and filling of the foredeep basin. It is divided into four seismic packages: ND, NE, NF, and NG (Figs. 11 and 12). These subdivisions were constructed solely on seismic characteristics in order to allow regional correlation. Seismic units NA to NG correspond to the Neogene Chaguaramas Formation in the Venezuelan geological literature (Fig. 3). Figure 12 shows how the basin was uplifted and tilted to the east by a post-Miocene tectonic event (Fig. 12).

278   *J. Pérez de Armas*

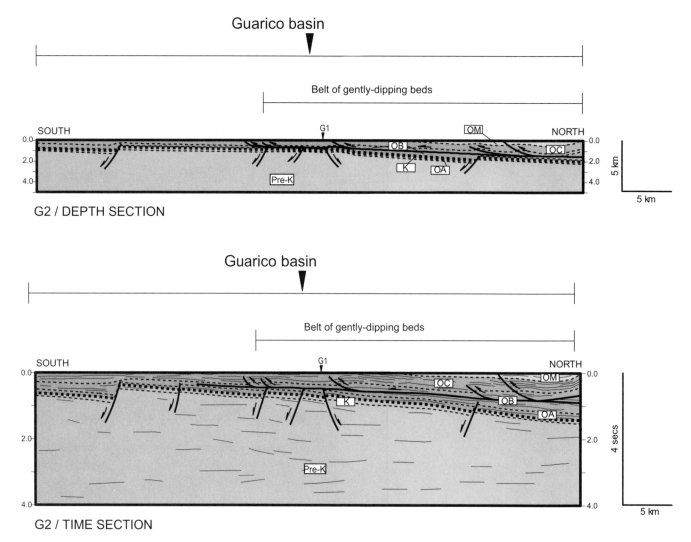

Figure 7. Time and depth-converted composite line drawings of seismic section G2, south of the Platillón-Tiznados transect. For legend, see Figure 6.

Deformation History of the Guárico Basin

There are two quite distinctive structural styles observed in the seismic sections. First, the Neogene décollement or decoupling level along OB (Roblecito Formation) serves as a relative "boundary" for this structural architecture. Below the décollement, there is an extensional regime initiated in the Mesozoic with the opening of the Espino graben. A younger extensional regime occurred during the Tertiary in response to the tectonic loading of the Lara nappes that generated the Roblecito foredeep. Secondly, Neogene contraction in the Guárico basin (Figs. 7–12) resulted in imbricate thrust faults merging into the décollement.

Based on the analysis of 1400 km of two-dimensional seismic reflection profiles and other interpretations from the literature, it is suggested here that there are, at least, five separate deformation episodes in the Guárico basin and the Serranía del Interior foreland fold and thrust belt. Deformation phases 1 and 2 are related to the rifting and drifting of the Americas since the

Triassic-Jurassic. Phases 3 through 5 are related to the continuous interaction between the Caribbean and South American plates since late Eocene–early Oligocene time.

(1) Formation of a Triassic-Jurassic Rift

Extension and opening of the Espino graben system occurred in the southernmost portion of the Guárico basin (Fig. 11). The formation of this extensional system was related to the opening of the Atlantic Ocean. The graben-bounding faults crosscut sedimentary and metamorphic Paleozoic rocks and Precambrian crystalline basement of the Guyana craton. This structure may extend beneath the eastern Serranía del Interior and to the Apure and Colombian Llanos in the west (e.g., Feo-Codecido et al., 1984).

(2) Passive Margin

In the Cretaceous, a north-facing passive margin was formed that subsequently underwent thermal subsidence (e.g., Pindell, 1993). This is the time of the encroachment of the proto-Carib-

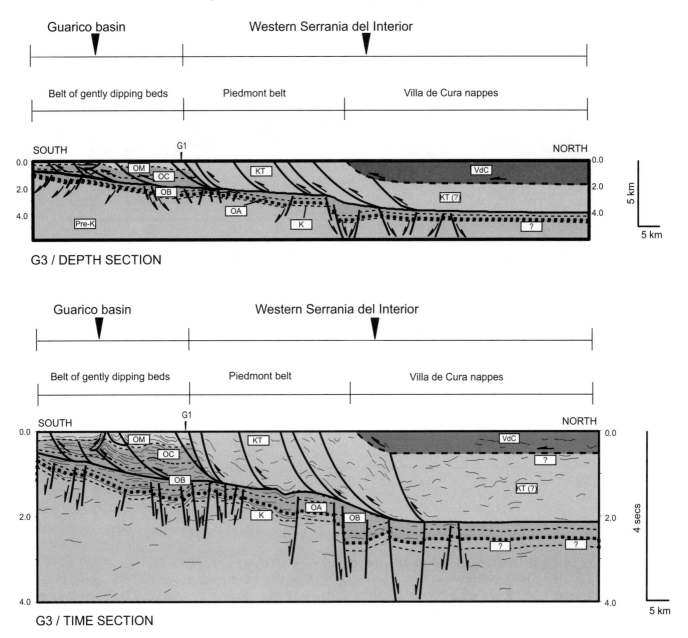

Figure 8. Time and depth-converted composite line drawings of seismic section G3, south of the city of San Juan de Los Morros, in the Guárico basin. For legend, see Figure 6.

bean seas onto continental South America and the formation of normal faults (Figs. 7–12).

(3) Foredeep Unconformity

A basal foredeep unconformity formed in the late Eocene–early Oligocene (González de Juana et al., 1980; Fasola et al., 1985; Kiser, 1997). It was coeval with minor extension in the Guárico basin. In late Eocene–early Oligocene, during the deposition of units OA and OB, normal faults were either reactivated or developed newly in the autochthonous terranes of the South American plate (Figs. 7–12). They extend well south into the

basin and could have been formed in response to the flexure due to loading of the Lara nappes onto the Guyana craton and the peneplaned Paleozoic folded belt during the early stages of the formation of the foredeep (e.g., Summa et al., 2003)

(4) Contraction

In north-central Venezuela, contractional structures formed during the Miocene. The Guárico basin is decoupled along marine shales of the stratigraphic sequence OB of the Roblecito Formation. From this sole thrust or detachment level, south-vergent thrust imbricates emerged in the Oligocene-Miocene sedimen-

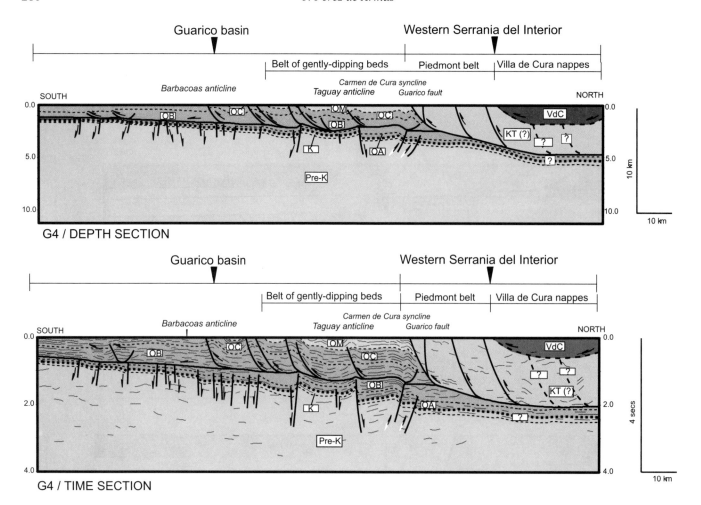

Figure 9. Time and depth-converted composite line drawings of seismic section G4, south of the Camatagüita–Valle Morín transect, in the Guárico basin. For legend, see Figure 6.

tary sequences of the Guárico foredeep. Several small triangle zones developed within the basin. Deformation of sub-sequence ND by thrust imbrication might mark the end of contractional deformation within the basin (Fig. 11). Seismic resolution is very poor within the "Piedmont belt" and beneath both the "Piedmont belt" and the Villa de Cura nappes, allowing room for a wide range of structural interpretations (Figs. 8 and 9).

Two of the interpreted two-dimensional seismic lines cut across the contact of the "Piedmont belt" with the Villa de Cura complex (Figs. 8 and 9). Modeling based on gravimetric and magnetic data supports the idea that the Villa de Cura nappe is a klippe (Bosch and Rodríguez, 1992; Smith et al., 1999). The klippe might be very thin, possibly between 1 and 2 km (Figures 3 and 4 of Bosch and Rodríguez, 1992).

Projection of the proximal passive margin and its basement suggests that the interpreted Cretaceous sequence K and, probably, the late Eocene-Oligocene units OA and OB may extend northward beneath the Serranía del Interior and the Villa de Cura nappes (Figs. 8 and 9).

(5) Regional Uplift

A post-Miocene tectonic event uplifted, peneplaned, and tilted the Guárico basin to the east (Fig. 12). Minor Neogene and younger extension is observed throughout the basin deforming Oligocene sedimentary sequences as well (Figs. 10 and 11). The available seismic data do not constrain the orientation of the latter extensional structures. Based on analysis of two-dimensional seismic data, Blanco et al. (1988) and Daal and Lander (1993) suggest that these normal faults are NE-SW–trending.

WESTERN SERRANÍA DEL INTERIOR

Stratigraphy

In this study, the stratigraphy of the western Serranía del Interior, also known as the Guárico mountain front (Bell, 1968; Bellizzia, 1972; González and Picard, 1972), is complicated because of severe deformation. South of the Villa de Cura blueschist unit, the western Serranía del Interior consists of a series

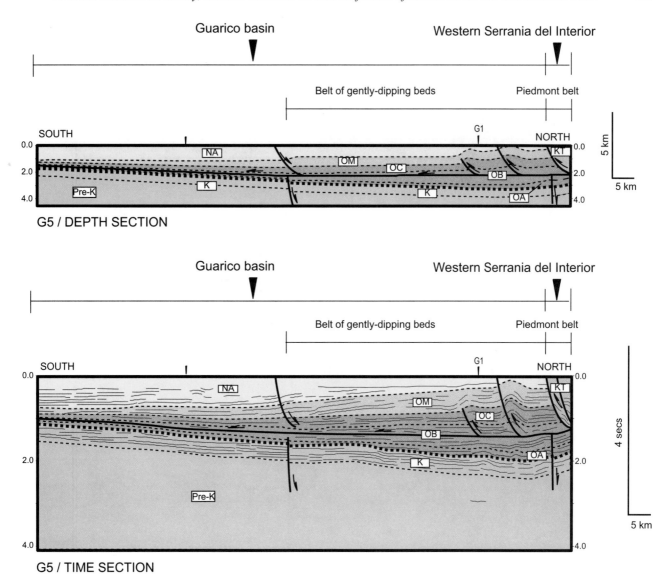

Figure 10. Time and depth-converted composite line drawings of seismic section G5, south of the Altagracia de Orituco transect, in the Guárico basin. For legend, see Figure 6.

of Cretaceous-Tertiary tectonic belts of different origin (Figs. 1 and 2). Beck (1978) subdivided the area into several belts and units, but in this paper I will follow the structures described by Peirson (1965) and Bell (1968). These belts are, from north to south: (1) "Piedmont belt," (2) "Belt of thrust faults" (Chacual complex), (3) "Belt of overturned beds," and (4) "Belt of gently dipping beds" (Fig. 2). Table 1 shows thickness of the different sedimentary units estimated from the transects in the western Serranía del Interior.

The oldest rocks in the Serranía del Interior are Lower to Upper Cretaceous shelfal limestones of the Querecual Formation and siltstones of the Mucaria Formation. They constitute the remnant of the Cretaceous passive margin included in the accretionary wedge (Fig. 4). Mapable volcanogenic turbidites

with olistoliths of mafic and ultramafic rocks of the Garrapata Formation are considered of Coniacian-Santonian age (Bell 1968), but age and stratigraphic relationships are still in debate (Fig. 4) (Albertos et al., 1989). The Mucaria Formation sequence grades upward into Upper Cretaceous–Paleocene turbidites of the Guárico Formation (Fig. 4). The Guárico Formation is equivalent to other turbidite facies found in western Venezuela; i.e., the Río Guache, Trujillo, and Moran Formations (e.g., Blin, 1989). Dismembered limestone blocks of Cretaceous-Paleocene age are embedded within the Garrapata and Guárico Formation along the Serranía del Interior foreland fold and thrust belt (Fig. 4) (Platillón Limestone, Las Colonias Limestone, Morros de San Juan, Morros de Macaira). The stratigraphic top of the Guárico Formation in the Camatagua

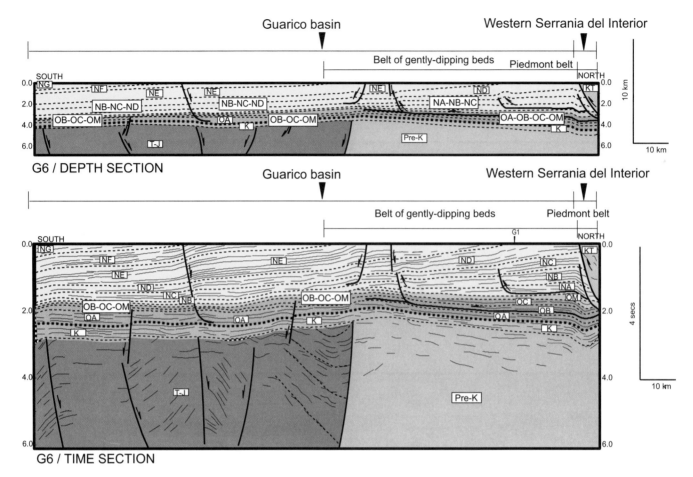

Figure 11. Time and depth-converted composite line drawings of seismic section G6, south of the San José de Guaribe transect, in the Guárico basin. For legend, see Figure 6.

area has been removed by erosion and is overlain unconformably by the upper Eocene Peñas Blancas carbonates (Fig. 4) (Peirson, 1965; Bell, 1968). The Oligocene-Miocene foredeep stratigraphic sequence involved in the Serranía is composed of a regressive unit of open marine shales to terrestrial deposits (Roblecito, Quebradón, Naricual, and Quiamare Formations). (For more detail, see Ostos et al., this volume, Chapter 2; and Pérez de Armas, 2005).

Deformation History of the Western Serranía del Interior

(1) "Piedmont Belt"

The first and northernmost belt is the Piedmont belt. It is separated from the Villa de Cura complex to the north by the Cantagallo fault and to the south either by the "Belt of thrust faults" or by the "Belt of overturned beds" (Figs. 1 and 2). The "Piedmont belt" is characterized by south-vergent, tight-to-isoclinal folds and south-vergent thrust and reverse faults.

(2) "Belt of Thrust Faults"

This belt crops out discontinuously along the Serranía del Interior between the "Piedmont belt" and the "Belt of overturned beds" (Fig. 2). This structural province is intensely deformed by south-vergent, imbricate thrust faults that juxtapose Cretaceous, Paleogene, and Neogene sedimentary units. Beck (1978, 1985a, 1985b) suggested that the sedimentary cover that forms the Serranía is detached along an Albian or pre-Albian horizon. This belt probably represents a detachment zone that has been unroofed.

(3) "Belt of Overturned Beds"

This belt consists of a southward overturned syncline. It possibly is cut by a fault parallel to the fold-axial plane.

(4) "Belt of Gently Dipping Beds"

The "Belt of gently dipping beds" is the most southerly zone and includes a mildly deformed rock sequence of the Guárico basin (Figs. 1 and 2). Open folds and a few south-vergent thrust faults occur, but with minor displacement.

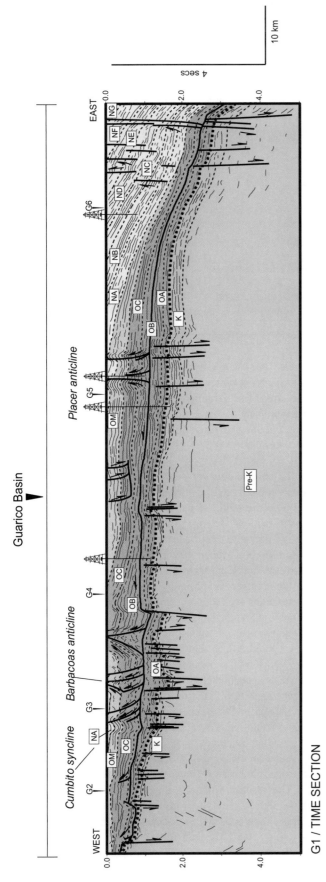

Figure 12. Time line drawing of an east-west two-dimensional seismic line composite section across the Guárico basin (G1) showing uplift and peneplanation of the Guárico basin during Pliocene-Pleistocene times. For legend, see Figure 6.

Regional Geological Transects

Four N-S–trending regional transects (Figs. 1 and 2) were selected for study based on maps (Creole Petroleum Corporation, 1961a, 1961b, 1961c, 1961d; Peirson, 1965; Bell, 1968, Albertos et al., 1989), and previous geological papers and dissertations (Peirson, 1965; Bell, 1968; Bellizzia et al., 1976; Beck, 1985a, 1985b; Albertos et al., 1989; Blin, 1989; Bellizzia and Dengo, 1990). The four transects are, from west to east: (1) Platillón-Tiznados, (2) Camatagüita–Valle Morín, (3) Altagracia de Orituco, and (4) San José de Guaribe (Figs. 1, 2, and 13–17).

Structural analysis of the four study transects (Creole Petroleum Corporation, 1961a, 1961b, 1961c, 1961d; Peirson, 1965; Bell, 1968; Beck, 1978; Beck 1985a, 1985b; Albertos et al., 1989) suggest that the Serranía del Interior fold and thrust belt can be subdivided into an internal (northern) and external (southern) zone. Beck (1978, 1985a, 1985b) recognized that the northern portion of the "Piedmont belt" consists of an olistolith complex embedded in a Paleocene–lower Eocene matrix. The internal (northern) zone is the belt of rocks that lies near the tectonic contact with the Villa de Cura nappes along the Cantagallo fault and includes the "Piedmont belt" of Bell (1968). It consists of a chaotic suite of olistoliths embedded in a coarse matrix of rocks of varied provenance (Figs. 14–16a and 16b). It has been correlated with the Garrapata Formation and the chaotic facies of the Guárico Formation (e.g., Bell, 1968). The olistoliths seen in the study areas are light gray platform limestones (Platillón-Tiznados limestone, Morros de San Juan; Peirson et al., 1966), black carbonates, serpentinites, greenstones, and diorites (Platillón-Tiznados and Camatagüita–Valle Morín). The heterogeneity in rock composition suggests a sedimentary environment of feeder channels at the toe of a turbidite system (Albertos et al., 1989; Yoris, 1999, personal commun.). In the easternmost San José de Guaribe transect, the contact of this innermost belt with the Villa de Cura nappes is not observed (Fig. 17). The contact between the external and internal zones is always of structural origin. In all four transects, the external (southern) zone comprises of several units: (1) Cretaceous parautochthonous platformal carbonates of the Querecual Formation and siliciclastics of the Mucaria Formation, (2) allochthonous-parautochthonous Cretaceous-Paleogene mid-to-external facies turbidites, (3) the Guárico Formation, and (4) the foredeep Oligocene-Miocene siliciclastic rocks of the Roblecito, Naricual, Quebradón, and Quiamare Formations (Figs. 14–17).

The interpreted structure of the "Piedmont belt" is a hinterland dipping thrust with imbricates or unroofed duplexes with south-vergent folds, bounded by south-vergent high-angle reverse faults (Figs. 14–17). The northeast-striking high-angle faults are displaced by northwest-southeast–striking dextral tear faults (e.g., Guárico fault). The latter faults may correspond to unroofed lateral ramps.

TABLE 1. THICKNESS OF SEDIMENTARY UNITS IN THE WESTERN SERRANÍA DEL INTERIOR
ESTIMATED FROM THE TRANSECTS

Formation/ transect	Stratigraphic age	Platillón Tiznados thickness (m)	Camagüita Valle Morín thickness (m)	Altagracia de Orituco thickness (m)	San José de Guaribe thickness (m)
Quiamare	Miocene	N/A	N/A	N/A	650
Quebradón	upper Miocene–middle Miocene	1500 with Quiamare	N/A	3000 with Quiamare	700
Naricual	Oligocene–lower Miocene	N/A	N/A	N/A	650
Roblecito	upper Eocene–lower Miocene	N/A	1500	N/A	N/A
Peñas Blancas	middle Eocene	N/A	10*	N/A	N/A
Guárico	Cretaceous-Paleocene	1500	2500	1500	500
Mucaria	Cretaceous	2000	810	2000	400
Querecual	Cretaceous	180	375	125	N/A
Garrapata	Cretaceous-Paleocene (?)	2000	500	1500	700

Note: N/A—non-applicable/not measured.
*Estimated by Bell (1968).

The lack of pre-Cretaceous rocks involved in the deformation suggests that the relatively high-angle faults of the imbricates have to flatten out and merge with a detachment surface located at some level within the autochthonous platformal Cretaceous carbonates and whose surface expression is interpreted to be the "Belt of thrust faults" (Chacual complex) (Figs. 16a, 16b, and 17).

Mesoscopic Structures

Ductile and brittle mesoscopic structures were analyzed for two reasons. First, they might reveal whether displacement partitioning occurred. Second, they might indicate whether or not more than one orogenic event occurred.

Ductile Deformation Structures

The orientations of bedding planes (S_o), fold axial planes (S_{ap}), cleavage (S), and fold axes (F) were determined. The data were plotted on lower-hemisphere, equal-area diagrams (Ramsay and Huber, 1987) using the Stereonet program (Allmendinger, 1995a).

Bedding planes (S_o), fold-axial planes (S_{ap}), and axial-plane cleavages (S) generally strike ENE-WSW and dip moderately to the north in the three westerly transects (Figs. 14–16 and 18). However, in the San José de Guaribe transect (Figs. 17 and 18), they strike E-W and dip moderately to the north. Fold axes occur in a moderately NNW-dipping great-circle girdle with an ENE-WSW–trending maximum in the three westerly domains (Fig. 18); they are steeply N-plunging in the Guaribe area (Fig. 18).

The structures in the west are compatible with SSE-directed tectonic transport, and in the Guaribe domain, they are compatible with S-directed thrusting. The steep attitude of the fold axes in the Guaribe transect indicates that this domain has undergone much larger contractional strain and strain rotation than the other three areas. Mesoscopic ductile structures indicating more than one deformation event were not observed. However, Neogene rocks are much less deformed than Cretaceous-Paleogene rocks. This may indicate that at least two phases of deformation have occurred, but due to a similar displacement field, it is likely that similar deformation structures may have formed.

Brittle Deformation Structures

Mesoscopic faults and slickenside striations were measured to determine the mode of deformation as well as the tectonic transport direction. Determination of the sense of slip on the faults was based on established techniques (Petit, 1987; Gamond, 1987; Ramsay and Huber, 1987). Data (Figs. 19 and 20) were plotted using FaultKin (Marrett and Allmendinger, 1990, 1991, 1992; Allmendinger, 1995b).

Thrust faults in all four domains are compatible with a NW- to NNW-trending contraction axis (major principal contraction axis Z) and a subvertical extension axis (minor principal extension axis X) (Figs. 19 and 20). In the Guaribe domain, some thrust faults indicate NNE-SSW shortening (Fig. 20). Mesoscopic left- and right-lateral strike-slip faults in all domains are compatible with N-S contraction and E-W extension (Figs. 19 and 20). Several sets of mesoscopic normal faults occur in the region. They are compatible with NW-SE and NE-SW to ENE-WSW extension (Figs. 19 and 20). Crosscutting relationships suggest that the mesoscopic thrust faults formed simultaneously with the tear faults. These tear faults may be associated with regional lateral ramps (Figs. 1, 2, 6, and 14–17). The youngest structures are the normal faults.

In the allochthonous belts north of the right-lateral La Victoria fault (Schubert, 1988), displacement partitioning has clearly occurred (e.g., Avé Lallemant, 1997). However, south of the La Victoria fault, only N-S to NW-SE contraction has occurred.

Timing of the Deformation

A summary of the timing of the structures studied in the field is shown in Figure 21. Based on structural data gathered in the field and previously discussed, there are at least three important contractional phases that affected the foreland fold belt: (1) a middle Eocene NW-SE contraction responsible for the accretion of the Cretaceous-Tertiary turbidites and passive margin deposits into the accretionary wedge, Lara nappes, in the west; (2) a middle to late Miocene contractional event with a very similar strain field as that of the Eocene that involves the Oligocene-Miocene deposits in the deformation; and (3) a N-S Pliocene-Pleistocene contractional event that involves the molasse in the foreland fold belt.

Integrated Geological Transects

An attempt to merge the geological information obtained from field work along the four studied transects, and along the depth-converted two-dimensional seismic lines, was made to assess the structural geometry of both allochthonous and autochthonous stratigraphic units and to postulate a tectonic evolution for the area (Figs. 22–25). On the first three integrated transects, the structural relationships are shown between the allochthonous blueschists of the Villa de Cura nappes, the allochthonous-parautochthonous sequences of the western Serranía del Interior, and the autochthonous sequences of the Guárico foredeep (Figs. 22–24). The last transect does not show the contact of the Villa de Cura nappes and the "Piedmont belt" (Fig. 25). The structural contact between the western Serranía del Interior and the Guárico foredeep occurs along the Guárico frontal thrust (Figs. 22–25). The Villa de Cura nappes are interpreted as a klippe based on gravimetric and magnetic models (Bosch and Rodríguez, 1992). They are in structural contact with the western Serranía del Interior along the Cantagallo thrust (Figs. 14–16 and 22–24). In the integrated Tiznados-Platillón transect, the "Piedmont belt" overrides the autochthonous sequences of the perisutural Guárico foredeep, forming a triangle-zone in the vicinity of the San Francisco de Tiznados village (Fig. 22).

The general structure consists of south-vergent hinterland-dipping imbricates that merge to a sole thrust or décollement along the basinal Oligocene horizon deforming the western Serranía del Interior and the Guárico foredeep (Figs. 22–26[1]). This detachment level probably ramps down farther north since Cretaceous sequences are included in the deformation ("Piedmont belt").

Surface expression of this decoupling level is found in the "Belt of thrust faults" or Chacual complex, where Cretaceous and Tertiary rocks are intensely deformed (Fig. 25). In summary, deformation and strain are more intense in the north, within the Cretaceous-Paleogene rocks of the "Piedmont belt," suggesting a north-south strain gradient. This intense deformation could have taken place in the middle Eocene, prior to the final

Neogene emplacement of the nappes to the south. Minor faults formed during the Cretaceous and were later reactivated during the inception of the basal foredeep unconformity due to flexure of the South American continental crust during the emplacement of the nappes. The "Piedmont belt" is projected to extend beneath the Villa de Cura nappes, and in turn the Cretaceous-Paleogene basinal deposits are interpreted to extend beneath both the "Piedmont belt" and the Villa de Cura nappes. Some Neogene reverse faults are observed in the Camatagüita–Valle Morín integrated transect, affecting the Pre-Cretaceous, Cretaceous, and Paleogene rocks of the Guárico basin.

On the basis of the four integrated seismic transects, and the E-W–trending seismic line, a hypothetical NS-trending cross section was constructed through the Caribbean–South American plate boundary zone (Fig. 26) that included interpre-

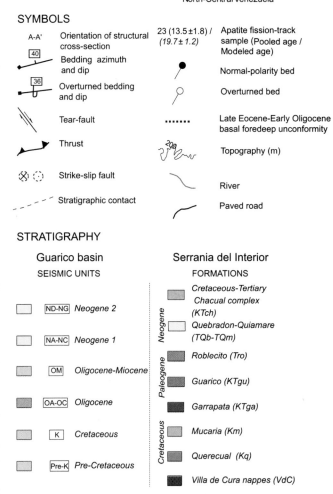

Figure 13. Legend for maps and transects used in this study, as shown on Figures 14–17 and 22–25.

---

[1]Figure 26 is on a loose sheet accompanying this volume and in the GSA Data Repository as item 2005181, available online at www.geosociety.org/pubs/ft2005.htm, or on request from editing@geosociety.org or Documents Secretary, GSA, P.O. Box 9140, Boulder, CO 80301, USA.

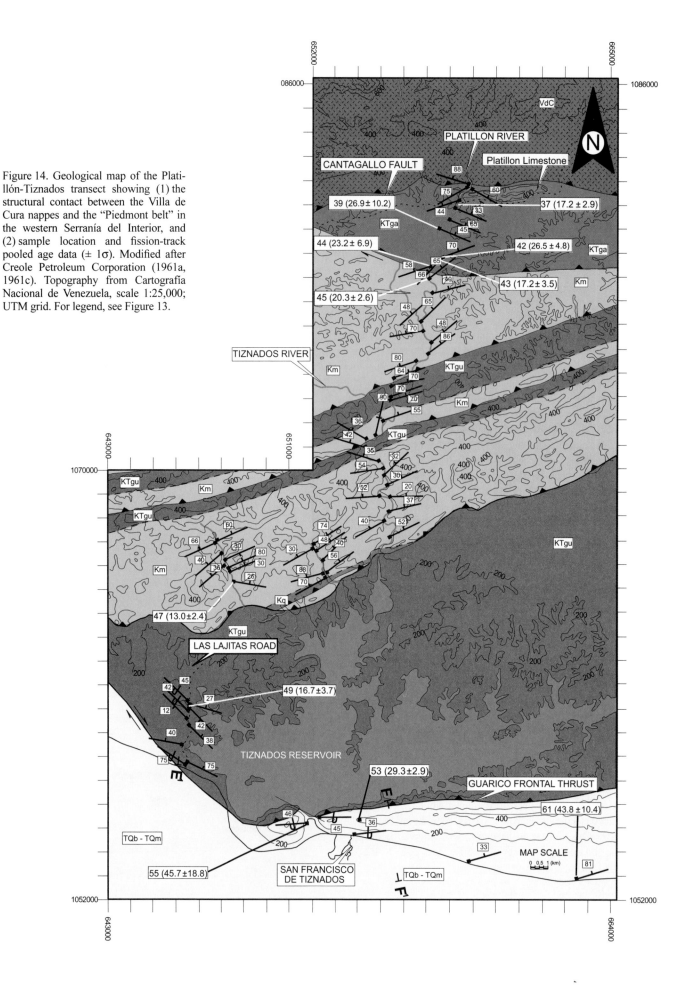

Figure 14. Geological map of the Platillón-Tiznados transect showing (1) the structural contact between the Villa de Cura nappes and the "Piedmont belt" in the western Serranía del Interior, and (2) sample location and fission-track pooled age data (± 1σ). Modified after Creole Petroleum Corporation (1961a, 1961c). Topography from Cartografía Nacional de Venezuela, scale 1:25,000; UTM grid. For legend, see Figure 13.

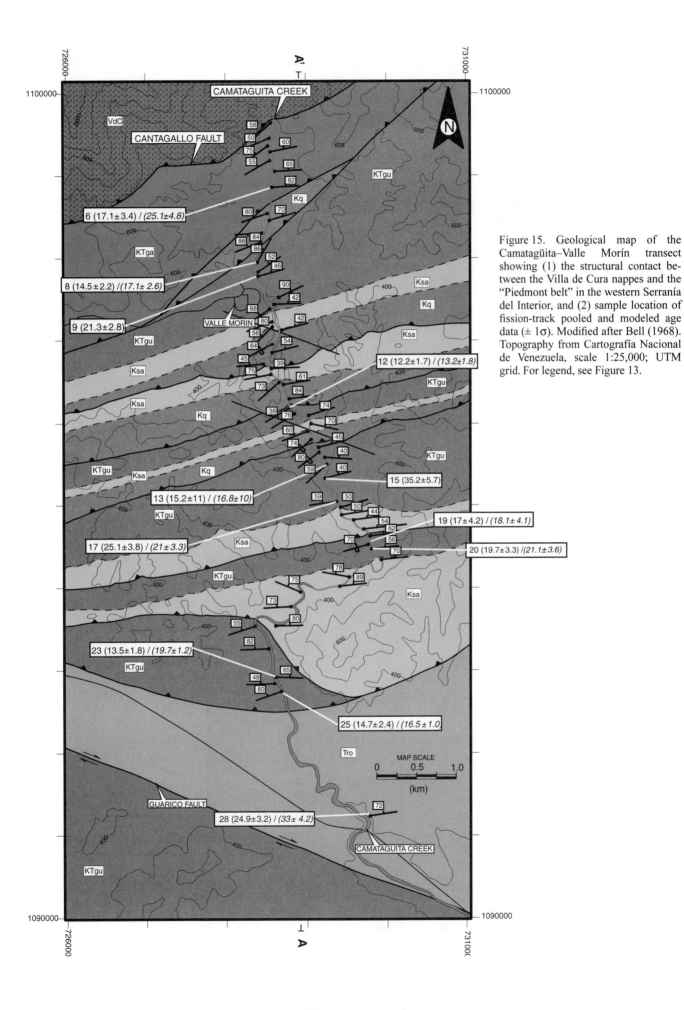

Figure 15. Geological map of the Camatagüita–Valle Morín transect showing (1) the structural contact between the Villa de Cura nappes and the "Piedmont belt" in the western Serranía del Interior, and (2) sample location of fission-track pooled and modeled age data (± 1σ). Modified after Bell (1968). Topography from Cartografía Nacional de Venezuela, scale 1:25,000; UTM grid. For legend, see Figure 13.

Figure 16 (*on this and following page*). (A and B) Geological map of the Altagracia de Orituco transect showing the structural "Belt of gently-dipping beds" in the western Serranía del Interior. Modified after Albertos et al. (1989). Topography from Cartografía Nacional de Venezuela, scale 1:25,000; UTM grid. For legend, see Figure 13.

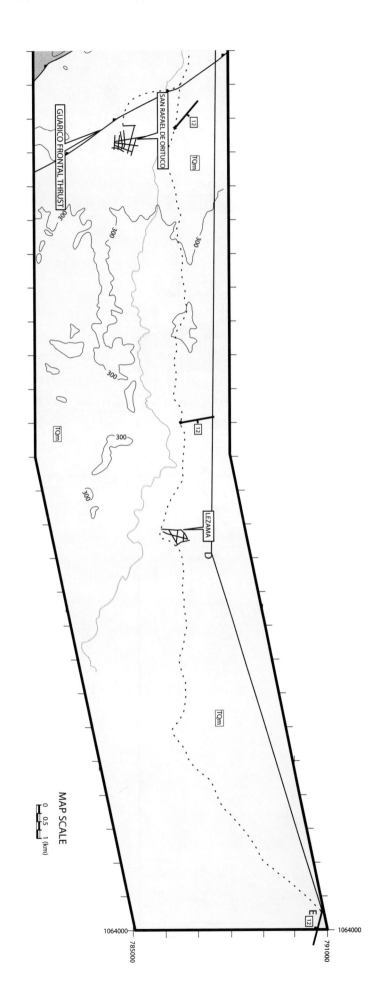

B

GUARICO FRONTAL THRUST

SAN RAFAEL DE ORITUCO

LEZAMA

MAP SCALE

0   0.5   1 (km)

Figure 16 (*continued*).

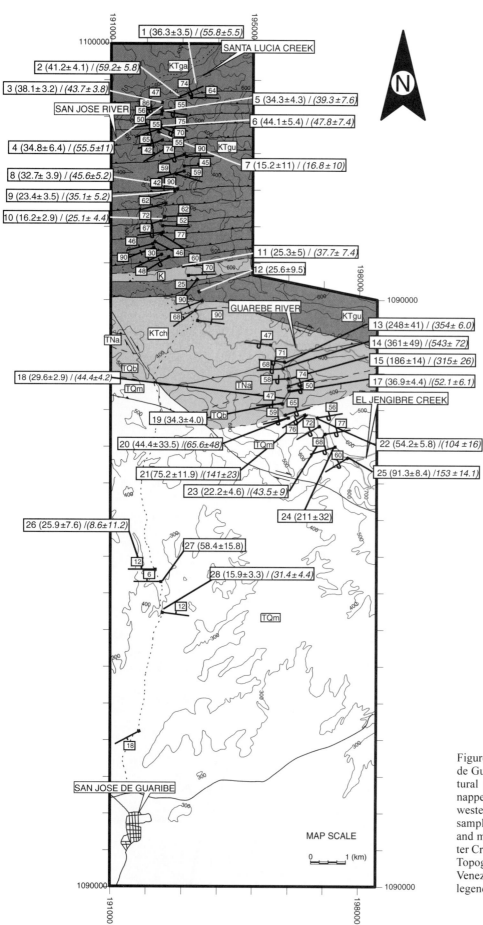

Figure 17. Geological map of the San José de Guaribe transect showing (1) the structural contact between the Villa de Cura nappes and the "Piedmont belt" in the western Serranía del Interior, and (2) sample location of fission-track pooled and modeled age data (±1σ). Modified after Creole Petroleum Corporation (1961d). Topography from Cartografía Nacional de Venezuela, scale 1:25,000; UTM grid. For legend, see Figure 13.

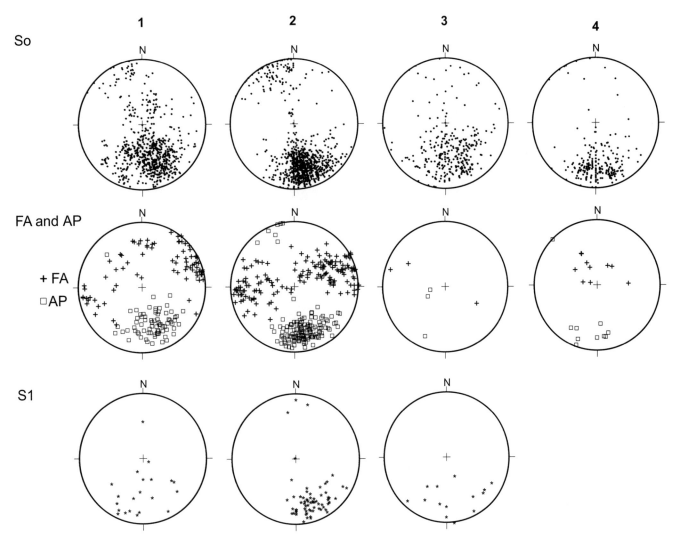

Figure 18. Equal-area, lower-hemisphere projection of ductile structural elements measured in the following regional transects: (1) Platillón-Tiznados, (2) Camatagüita–Valle Morín, (3) Altagracia de Orituco, and (4) San José de Guaribe. In (1): 678 poles to bedding plane (So), 81 poles to fold axial planes (AP), 81 fold axes (FA), and 21 poles to axial plane clevages (S1). In (2): 915 poles to bedding plane (So), 156 poles to old axial planes (AP), 180 fold axes (FA), and 68 poles to axial plane clevages (S1). In (3): 356 poles to bedding plane (So), 3 poles to fold axial planes (AP), 3 fold axes (FA), and poles to 14 axial plane clevages (S1). In (4): 233 poles to bedding plane (So), 10 poles to fold axial planes (AP) and 10 fold axes (FA). See Figure 2 for location of transects.

tation of previous work in offshore Venezuela by Biju-Duval et al. (1982), in the Cordillera de la Costa and Villa de Cura belts by Ostos (1990), and in the Villa de Cura nappes by Smith et al. (1999). Figure 26 [see footnote 1] shows a southward-dipping Neogene subduction zone in the north, where the Caribbean is subducting beneath the South American plate and a northward dipping Paleogene subduction zone in the south, where the allochthons were obducted onto South American continental crust. These terranes are detached along deep décollement levels and can be considered as an orogenic float as defined by Oldow et al. (1989, 1990). The allochthonous terranes are, from north to south: (1) Cretaceous-Oligocene (K-OL) in the Venezuela basin; (2) Neogene (N) sediments in the Los Roques

trough, Curaçao ridge, and Venezuela; (3) crystalline basement of the Bonaire Basin (Mz-T) that includes the Leeward islands; (4) Eocene-Miocene (E-M) and Miocene-Pliocene sediments (M-P) in the Bonaire basin; (5) obducted Mesozoic metasediments and Paleozoic metaigneous rocks of the Caracas Group in the Cordillera de la Costa Belt (Mz) and Cretaceous Villa de Cura nappe (VDC); (6) platform and basinal parautochthonous sedimentary rocks of the Serranía del Interior (K-T); (7) Tertiary autochthonous sequences (foredeep deposits) above décollement level in the Guárico basin (T), and (8) autochthonous Cretaceous-Tertiary sequences in the Guárico basin (K-T).

Reconstruction and balancing of the integrated Caribbean–South America geological cross section uses a combination of

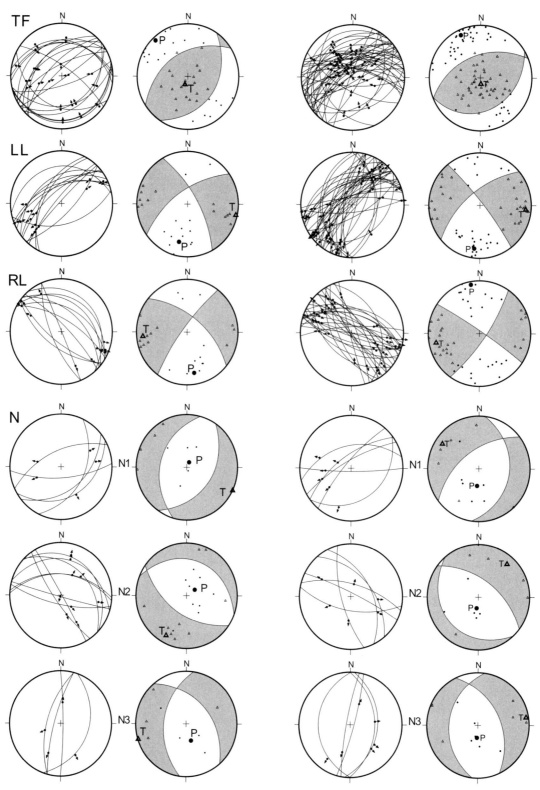

Figure 19. Equal-area, lower-hemisphere projection of brittle structural elements measured in the following regional transects: (1) Platillón-Tiznados and (2) Camatagüita–Valle Morín. Arrows indicate relative movement of missing block. Beach balls represent lower-hemisphere moment tensor solutions for the respective group of family faults. P and T represent strain axes: P—contractional; T—extensional. In (1): 19 thrust faults (TF), 13 left-lateral faults (LL), 11 right-lateral faults (RL), 5 normal faults (N1), 9 normal faults (N2), and 4 normal faults (N3). In (2): 41 thrust faults (TF), 29 left-lateral faults (LL), 26 right-lateral faults (RL), 6 normal faults (N1), 5 normal faults (N2), and 5 normal faults (N3). See Figure 2 for location of transects.

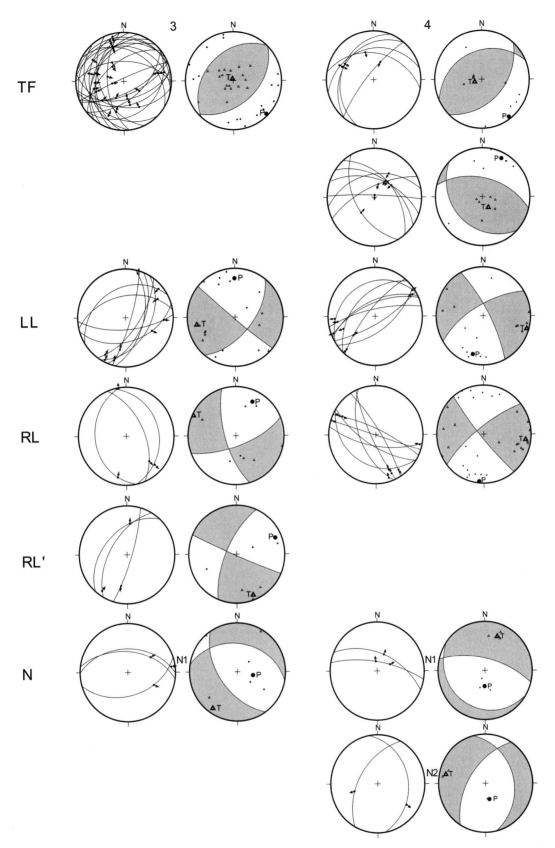

Figure 20. Equal-area, lower-hemisphere projection of brittle structural elements measured in the following regional transects: (3) Altagracia de Orituco and (4) San José de Guaribe. Arrows indicate relative movement of missing block. Beach balls represent lower-hemisphere moment tensor solutions for the respective group of family faults. P and T represent strain axes: P—contractional; T—extensional. In (3): 18 thrust faults (TF), 9 left-lateral faults (LL), 3 right-lateral faults (RL), 3 right-lateral faults (RL'). In (4): (LL), 8 right-lateral faults (RL), 3 normal faults (N1), and 2 normal faults (N2). See Figure 2 for location of transects.

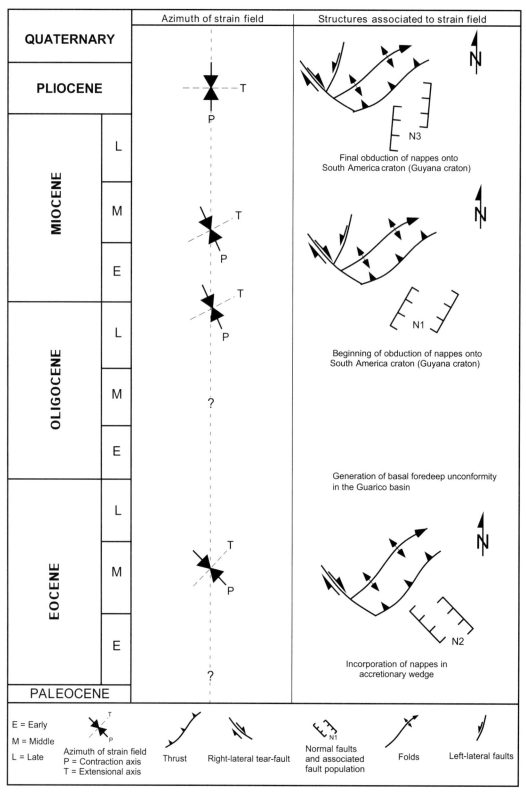

Figure 21. Summary of timing of deformation for the western Serranía del Interior.

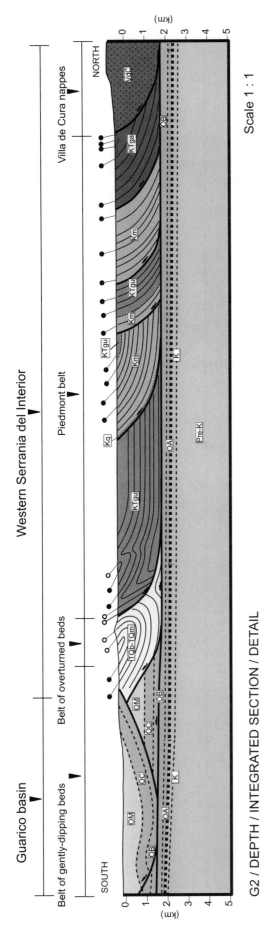

Figure 22. Integrated geological cross section using seismic line G2 and geological cross section from the Platillón-Tiznados transect. For legend, see Figure 13.

line length and area conservation that although not unique is consistent with the geology and its structural style (e.g., Dalstrom, 1969). The datum utilized for this restoration is the level OB (Oligocene, ca. 32 Ma). Pinning the Caribbean–South America geological cross section to the south, in the Guárico basin, the calculated minimum shortening obtained from its reconstruction is ~200 km since Oligocene time (32 Ma). A minimum calculated strain rate would be 0.6 cm/yr.

APATITE FISSION-TRACK ANALYSIS

Introduction

Apatite fission-track (AFT) analysis and modeling can yield important thermochronometric data, which can constrain several variables associated with low-temperature (~110 °C) geological events occurring at shallow levels in the earth crust, such as basin subsidence, sedimentary provenance, and mountain-building processes (e.g., Gallagher et al., 1998). Depth of burial, peak burial temperature, and timing of peak burial temperature can be assessed, as well as cooling events associated with uplift, exhumation, and erosion of buried rocks (e.g., Andriessen, 1995). The technique has been in use since the early 1960s, but, relatively recently, advances have been made to aid understanding of fission-track annealing such as its relationship with temperature and chemistry (Naeser and Faul, 1969; Laslett et al., 1987; Carlson et al., 1999; Donelick et al., 1999; Ketcham et al., 1999) and the derivation of time-temperature paths when combined with track length data (e.g., Green et al., 1989). In this study, detrital AFT data yield new information that helps in interpreting the history of the accretionary wedge obducted onto the Guyana craton.

Previous Work

Relatively few zircon and apatite fission-track ages have been published for north-central Venezuela. Zircon fission-track ages for samples from the Cordillera de la Costa belt are 19.7 ± 2.1 Ma (Kohn et al., 1984) and 19.8 ± 1.2 Ma and 19.8 ± 1.2 Ma (Sisson et al., this volume, Chapter 3). AFT ages from the Cordillera de la Costa belt are 16.3 ± 1.6 Ma, 15.0 ± 1.4 Ma, and 14.1 ± 1.6 Ma (Sisson et al., this volume, Chapter 3).

AFT ages for samples of the Serranía del Interior in north-central Venezuela are 15.8 ± 2.8, 14.2 ± 2.0 Ma, and 123.5 ± 1.8 Ma (Sisson et al., this volume, Chapter 3). In the Eastern Serranía del Interior, Locke (2001) acquired 19 AFT ages of which 13 were between ca. 35 and 18 Ma with peak ages decreasing from north to south and six were between ca. 13 and 3 Ma, indicating that two thermal events had occurred (see Locke and Garver, this volume).

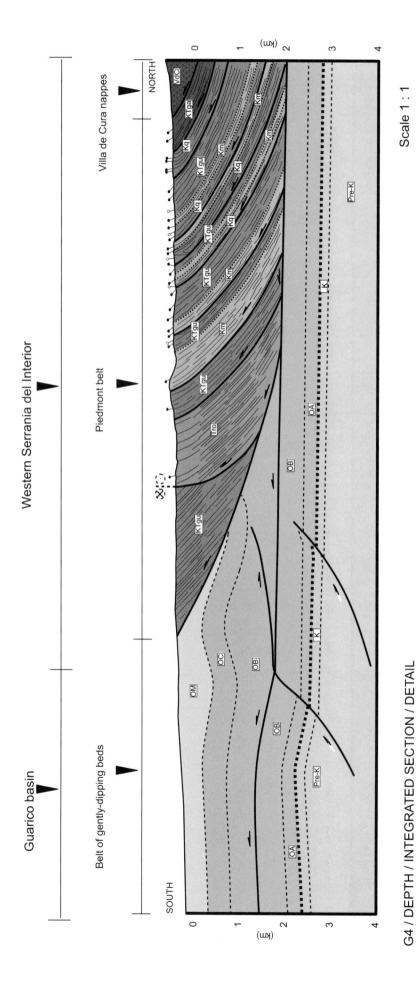

Figure 23. Integrated geological cross section using seismic line G4 and geological cross section from the Camatagüita–Valle Morín transect. For legend, see Figure 13.

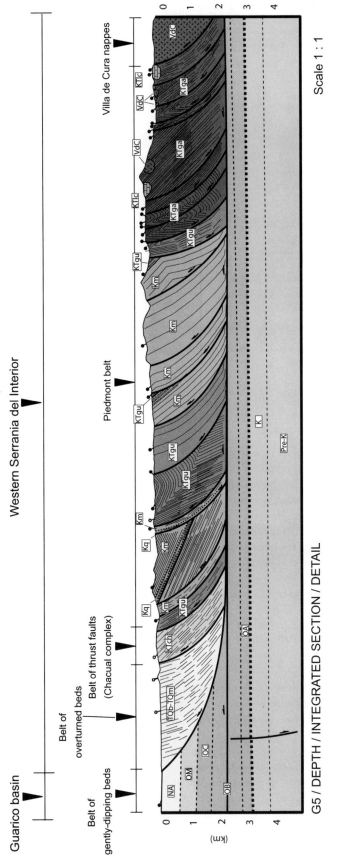

Figure 24. Integrated geological cross section using seismic line G5 and geological cross section from the Altagracia de Orituco transect. For legend, see Figure 13.

Methods

Sampling

Thirty samples were collected along each of the four regional transects (Platillón-Tiznados, Camagüita–Valle Morín, Altagracia de Orituco, and San José de Guaribe) through the western Serranía del Interior and the Guárico foreland basin. Each transect cut across the allochthonous, parautochthonous, and autochthonous terranes.

Laboratory Analysis

Preparation of samples for AFT analysis followed the procedures listed in Pérez de Armas (2005). Fission-track ages of apatite grains were obtained using the external detector method of Naeser and Faul (1969) and a zeta calibration factor (Fleischer et al., 1975; Hurford and Green, 1983) of $\xi = 128.5 \pm 7.9$ (Pérez de Armas, 2005) relative to U-standard glass (Corning Glass, CN-1). Irradiation was done at the Texas A&M University Radiation Center. Polished mounts were etched to reveal fission-tracks by immersing the mounts in a 5.5 M HNO_3 solution for 20 seconds at 21 °C. The zeta (ξ) calibration factor used in the apatite fission-track age equation is a weighted mean of ξ values calculated for the Durango de Mercado and Fish Canyon Tuff apatites relative to Corning Glass CN-1.

Following Donelick and Miller (1991), AFT wafer mounts for track length population analysis were irradiated with a 50 µCi [252]Cf radioactive source in a vacuum chamber. Samples were immersed in a 5.5 M HNO_3 solution for 20 seconds at 21 °C to etch horizontal and fully confined fission-tracks within apatite crystals. AFT lengths in Fish Canyon Tuff (14.91 ± 0.15 µm) and Durango de Mercado (15.03 ± 0.15 µm) apatites were measured for calibration purposes. Sample preparation and AFT data measurement and analysis were performed by the author of the present study at Rice University and at Donelick Analytical in Houston, Texas (now Apatite to Zircon, Inc., in Moscow, Idaho).

Age Determination

The chemical composition of apatite is correlated with fission-track annealing kinetics (Carlson et al., 1999; Ketcham et al., 1999). Apatites with high fluorine concentration anneal faster at lower temperatures than their relatively more chlorinated counterparts (Green et al., 1986; Donelick et al., 1999). AFT analysis was performed using AFTSolve (Ketcham et al., 2000). AFTSolve allows grouping of populations of apatite crystals into kinetic classes, usually correlated with etch pit dimensions (R. Donelick, 1993, U.S. Patent Number 5,267,274; R. Donelick, 1995, Australian Patent Number 658,800). There is also a correlation between the chemical composition of apatite and the diameter of the etch figure parallel to crystallographic *c*-axis (e.g., Burtner and Nigrini, 1994; Burtner et al., 1994).

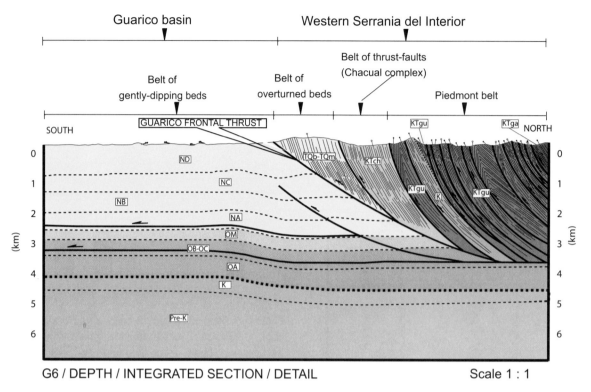

Figure 25. Integrated geological cross section using seismic line G6 and geological cross section from the San José de Guaribe transect. For legend, see Figure 13.

Likewise, AFTSolve includes several laboratory-derived calibrations that predict fission-track response to either heating or cooling (e.g., Carlson et al., 1999). AFTSolve generates thermal histories (time-temperature paths) for a given sample by performing Monte Carlo simulations.

The resultant thermal history of a sedimentary sample depends on three factors: (1) provenance (monotonically cooling from the source to deposition in sedimentary environment); (2) burial (monotonically heating; reflecting the path from time of deposition to time of peak burial temperature); and (3) exhumation (monotonically cooling; from time of peak of burial temperature to present day conditions; Ketcham et al., 2000). The provenance segment is included in the thermal history since apatites can preserve non-reset predepositional fission tracks. The stratigraphic age (age of deposition) used in the determination of the time-temperature history path in all studied samples was obtained from the Códico Geológico de Venezuela (PDVSA, 2004) and from González de Juana et al. (1980). The burial segment can be calibrated against independent geological and geochemical data; i.e., stratigraphic age and vitrinite reflectance, respectively.

Using AFTSolve, forward models for each sample are made using the measured AFT age and length to determine timing of peak temperature and peak of burial temperature. Timing of peak temperature is then used as a constraint in the overall time-temperature history in the Monte Carlo simulations. The exhumation segment can be calibrated with geochemical data

as well. Time-temperature paths converge to a range of possible solutions and are (1) acceptable (acceptable fit: a broad range of solutions within a dark gray band; Figs. 27 and 28) when both the model fission-track age and the model fission-track length distribution fit the measured fission track age and length with a level of confidence (Kolmogorov-Smirnov [K-S] test and age goodness-of-fit [GOF]) of 0.05 or greater; (2) good (good fit: a range of solutions within a light gray band; Figs. 27 and 28) when both the model fission-track age and the model fission-track length distribution fit the measured fission track age and length with a level of confidence (K-S test and age GOF) of 0.5 or greater; and (3) best fit (black line; Figs. 27 and 28).

AFTSolve gives an estimate of the vitrinite reflectance or maturity of the rock following the EasyRo method of Sweeney and Burnham (1990). Quality of output and its interpretation are dependent on the quality of age and track length measurements, accuracy of stratigraphy age of sample, and independent geochemical studies. A pooled fission-track age is based on a statistical procedure that assumes that a population of apatite crystals within a sample underwent the same thermal history and has the same kinetics. The age of the oldest fission track denotes the earliest-formed track population in a simulation that is not fully annealed by model's end. It marks the earliest time constrained by the fission-track data. If it postdates the onset of final cooling as set by model constraints, it indicates that the peak reheating temperature is not constrained by the

AFT data. Conversely, if it predates the provenance age, then it indicates that the fission-track data may contain an inherited (predepositional) component.

Depth of burial (z) and uplift rate (Ur) were calculated only in the Camatagüita–Valle Morín and San José de Guaribe transects. The former follows this relationship:

$$z = (T_{max} - 25\ °C)/G,$$

where z = maximum burial depth, T_{max} = peak burial temperature, and G = geothermal gradient, assuming a present day temperature of 25 °C. Two geothermal gradients of 27 °C/km and 39 °C/km, the latter value estimated in the Yucal-Placer field (Daal and Lander, 1993) were used in the calculations. It is assumed that the geothermal gradient has been constant since the emplacement of the tectonic slivers in the Neogene, since there is no data regarding paleogradients in the area.

The uplift rate (Ur) follows this relationship:

$$Ur = z/t_c,$$

where Ur = uplift rate, z = burial depth, and t_c = timing of cooling event.

As discussed above, the timing of the cooling event is not given by the oldest track but by the model constraints. If the oldest track is younger than the reheating time constraint, then t_c should be the time of this constraint, as it is the time at which T_{max} was reached. Conversely, if the oldest track is younger than the reheating time constraint, then the peak temperature is basically unconstrained. In this case, T_{max} should be the temperature at the time given by the oldest track, not the time of the reheating constraint.

Results of Present Study

One hundred and twenty samples were collected: 30 in each of the four transects. The samples from the Altagracia de Orituco area are still pending future analysis. Of the 90 remaining samples, 56 yielded enough apatite to obtain fission-track ages. Of the latter group, only 37 samples had enough good quality track lengths for apatite fission-track modeling. Table 2 shows a summary of the apatite fission-track ages. Table 3 summarizes apatite fission-track length data for all apatite grains. A summary of thermal histories and implications of the AFT data for 37 samples is presented in Table 4. Pooled AFT ages, oldest track ages, and calculated vitrinite reflectance for selected samples are shown in Figures 27 and 28.

Stratigraphic ages for the units of the Serranía were obtained from previously published reports (e.g., González de Juana et al., 1980).

Platillón-Tiznados Transect

In the Platillón-Tiznados area (Fig. 14), siliciclastic samples yielded enough apatite for fission-track age analysis (PFT-37 to PFT-65). No mounts for AFT length analysis were prepared.

Therefore, no estimates of peak burial temperatures, time of peak burial, and depth of burial could be assessed.

In the Platillón-Tiznados area, pooled AFT ages obtained in samples of the Mucaria, Garrapata, and Guárico Formations in the "Piedmont belt" (allochthonous-parautochthonous terranes) range from 26.5 ± 4.8 to 13 ± 2.4 Ma (late Oligocene to middle Miocene; Table 3, PFT-37 to PFT-49). These ages are younger than the stratigraphic ages of the sampled units (Tables 2 and 3), suggesting a cooling event associated with mountain building processes that started in the area in the late Oligocene (i.e., the emplacement the Serranía del Interior nappes onto the South American autochthonous terranes). In the "Piedmont belt" along this transect, there is an apparent cooling age gradient (Fig. 14): near the Cantagallo fault, within the Garrapata Formation, AFT ages are mainly late Oligocene with two middle Miocene ages (PFT-37 and PFT-43). To the south, samples from the Mucaria and Guárico Formations yielded AFT ages of 13.0 ± 2.4 Ma and 16.7 ± 3.7 Ma, respectively.

AFT ages from the Galera Member of the Quebradón and Quiamare Formations in the "Belt of overturned beds" (autochthonous-parautochthonous terrane) are as old as or older than their estimated stratigraphic age (PFT-53, PFT-55, and PFT-61), suggesting influence from provenance, in this case Eocene-Oligocene (Tables 2 and 4).

Camatagüita–Valle Morín Transect

In the "Piedmont belt" of the Camatagüita–Valle Morín transect (Fig. 15), samples collected from the Cretaceous-Tertiary units (Garrapata-Guárico Formations) clearly show reset AFT ages (stratigraphic age is greater than the fission-track age; Tables 2 and 4). Pooled AFT ages range from 21.3 ± 2.8 to 14.5 ± 2.2 Ma (early to middle Miocene; PFT-6 to PFT-25). Modeling of AFT data and track length using AFTSolve suggests that the time of the cooling event ranges from late Oligocene to middle Miocene where peak temperatures reached well above ~110 °C, enough to reset all previous/older cooling events (Figs. 15 and 27; Table 4).

Estimates of vitrinite reflectance or EasyRo calculated by AFTSolve, following Sweeney and Burnham (1990), suggest that all samples are mature to overmature (>0.65 ± 0.01% in all study samples). No independent vitrinite reflectance analysis was undertaken in the samples to constrain such estimates. Estimates of cooling rates for the samples range from 4 to 8 °C/m.y., with values clustering between 7 and 8 °C/m.y. for four samples and 4 and 5 °C/m.y. for three samples.

The best temperature of burial calculated from the modeling algorithm AFTSolve provides an estimate of maximum depth of burial given a particular geothermal gradient. Table 5 shows such estimates for modeled samples of the track-reset Cretaceous-Tertiary Garrapata and Guárico Formations, assuming two geothermal gradients of 27 °C/km and 39 °C/km as estimated for the Yucal-Placer field (Daal and Lander, 1993).

Results suggest that depth of burial for the samples range from 3 km to 5 km for a geothermal gradient of 27 °C/km, and from 2 to 4 km when the geothermal gradient is 39 °C/km. These

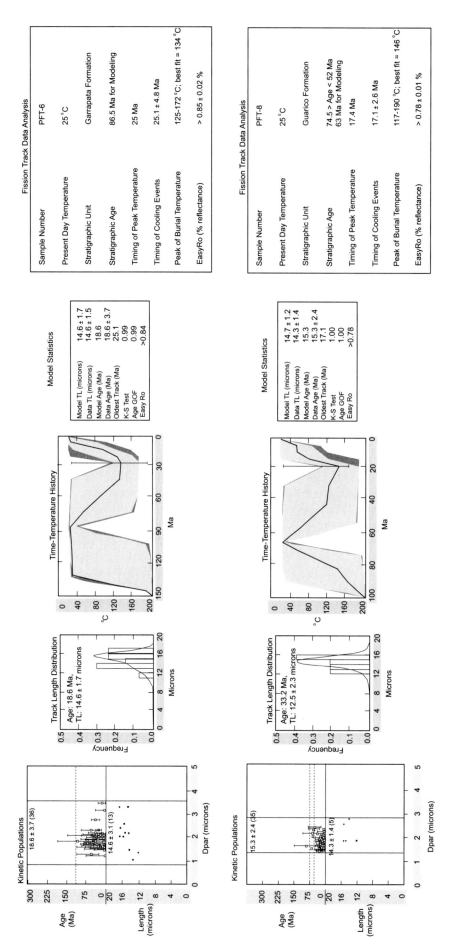

Figure 27. Modeling of apatite fission-track data for samples PFT-6 and PFT-8 in the Camatagüita–Valle Morín transect, suggesting a relatively rapid cooling that initiated at 25.1 ± 4.8 Ma (late Oligocene) and 17.1 ± 2.6 Ma (early Miocene), respectively. These ages correspond to the time of generation and preservation of the first fission-tracks once the sample cooled and reached temperatures below ~110 °C. GOF—goodness-of-fit; K-S—Kolmogorov-Smirnov test; TL—track length.

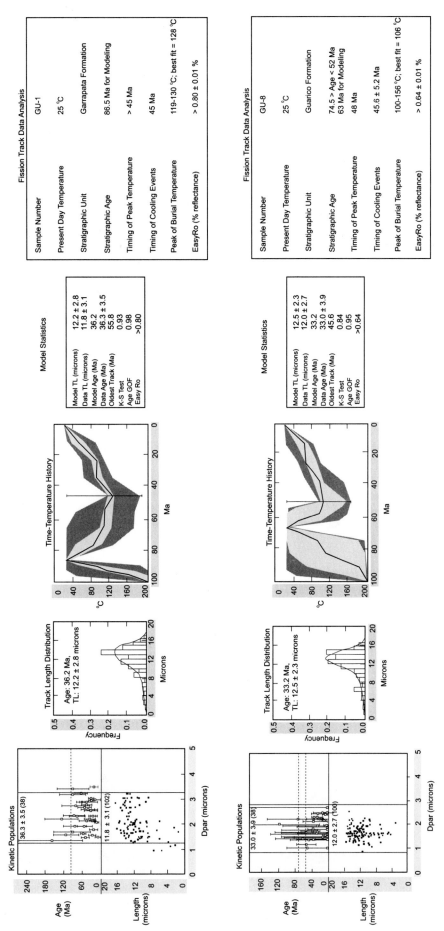

Figure 28. Modeling of apatite fission-track data for samples GU-1 and GU-8 in the San José de Guaribe transect, suggest cooling that initiated at 55.8 ± 5.5 Ma (Paleocene-Eocene) and 43.7 ± 5.2 Ma (early to middle Eocene), respectively. GOF—goodness-of-fit; K-S—Kolmogorov-Smirnov test; TL—track length.

TABLE 2. SUMMARY OF APATITE FISSION-TRACK AGE DATA

Sample	Sample location	ρ_s (10^6 tracks/cm^2)	N_s (tracks)	ρ_i (10^6 tracks/cm^2)	N_i (tracks)	ρ_d (10^6 tracks/cm^2)	N_d (tracks)
PFT-2	CAM	0.671	530	2.182	1725	4.174	4094
PFT-6	CAM	0.021	31	0.334	487	4.19	4094
PFT-8	CAM	0.026	53	0.479	986	4.207	4094
PFT-9	CAM	0.066	80	0.835	1018	4.224	4094
PFT-12	CAM	0.067	68	1.495	1518	4.258	4094
PFT-13	CAM	0.056	2	1.004	36	4.275	4094
PFT-15	CAM	0.132	50	1.035	391	4.292	4094
PFT-17	CAM	0.163	62	2.214	843	4.308	4094
PFT-19	CAM	0.142	23	2.192	355	4.359	4094
PFT-20	CAM	0.274	46	3.859	647	4.376	4094
PFT-21	CAM	0.101	183	1.767	3209	4.393	4094
PFT-23	CAM	0.064	82	1.158	1491	3.822	4349
PFT-25	CAM	0.055	47	0.922	781	3.816	4349
PFT-28	CAM	0.091	88	0.896	862	3.81	4349
PFT-29	CAM	0.148	190	1.555	1991	3.805	4349
PFT-37	PTZ	0.074	45	1.049	635	3.781	4349
PFT-39	PTZ	0.035	8	0.315	72	3.775	4349
PFT-42	PTZ	0.035	38	0.323	346	3.763	4349
PFT-43	PTZ	0.056	29	0.783	406	3.758	4349
PFT-44	PTZ	0.072	13	0.748	135	3.752	4349
PFT-45	PTZ	0.061	86	0.723	1017	3.746	4349
PFT-47	PTZ	0.04	35	0.748	647	3.74	4349
PFT-49	PTZ	0.079	24	1.134	344	3.734	4349
PFT-53	PTZ	0.261	193	2.562	1894	4.486	4009
PFT-55	PTZ	0.144	7	0.905	44	4.483	4009
PFT-61	PTZ	0.286	22	1.875	144	4.476	4009
PFT-65	PTZ	0.705	74	7.146	750	4.468	4009
GU-1	SJG	0.137	203	1.204	1783	4.983	3917
GU-2	SJG	0.162	188	1.248	1452	4.966	3917
GU-3	SJG	0.163	357	1.355	2969	4.949	3917
GU-4	SJG	0.229	37	2.075	336	4.932	3917
GU-5	SJG	0.229	94	2.104	863	4.915	3917
GU-6	SJG	0.211	102	1.688	818	5.522	4200
GU-7	SJG	0.139	19	2.193	299	5.586	4200
GU-8	SJG	0.105	108	1.146	1179	5.575	4200
GU-9	SJG	0.169	57	2.582	871	5.564	4200
GU-10	SJG	0.21	37	4.614	812	5.554	4200
GU-11	SJG	0.105	30	1.478	422	5.543	4200
GU-12	SJG	0.192	8	2.668	111	5.533	4200
GU-13	SJG	1.605	75	2.076	97	5.083	3917
GU-14	SJG	2.463	145	2.174	128	5.1	3917
GU-15	SJG	1.221	779	2.127	1357	5.117	3917
GU-16	SJG	0.237	24	1.721	174	5.134	3917
GU-17	SJG	0.269	108	2.403	966	5.151	3917
GU-18	SJG	0.182	194	2.038	2170	5.168	3917
GU-19	SJG	0.145	116	1.403	1124	5.184	3917
GU-20	SJG	0.056	2	0.419	15	5.201	3917
GU-21	SJG	0.996	58	4.413	257	5.218	3917
GU-22	SJG	0.215	159	1.331	982	5.235	3917
GU-23	SJG	0.391	28	5.915	424	5.252	3917
GU-24	SJG	3.163	83	4.992	131	5.268	3917
GU-25	SJG	0.628	290	2.321	1071	5.285	3917
GU-26	SJG	0.197	13	2.473	163	5.067	3917
GU-27	SJG	0.422	17	2.331	94	5.05	3917
GU-28	SJG	0.131	27	2.667	548	5.033	3917
GU-29	SJG	0.748	89	4.318	514	5.016	3917

Continued

TABLE 2. SUMMARY OF APATITE FISSION-TRACK AGE DATA (continued)

Sample	Sample location	Grains (dmnls)	Q (dmnls)	Dpar (μm)	Dper (μm)	Pooled FT Age (Ma)	Mean FT Age (Ma)
PFT-2	CAM	22	0	1.66	0.23	81.9 ± 6.6	110 ± 29
PFT-6	CAM	41	0.815	1.87	0.41	17.1 ± 3.4	18.6 ± 4
PFT-8	CAM	43	0.237	1.88	0.36	14.5 ± 2.2	15.9 ± 3.5
PFT-9	CAM	36	0.36	1.82	0.38	21.3 ± 2.8	19.6 ± 4.4
PFT-12	CAM	28	0.035	1.82	0.29	12.2 ± 1.7	14.8 ± 5.2
PFT-13	CAM	2	0.565	1.66	0.14	15.2 ± 11.1	18.0 ± 9.9
PFT-15	CAM	14	0.002	1.58	0.21	35.2 ± 5.7	25.8 ± 11.5
PFT-17	CAM	15	0	1.75	0.22	20.3 ± 3	97.3 ± 81.4
PFT-19	CAM	7	0.266	2.03	0.55	18.1 ± 4.1	16.6 ± 8.1
PFT-20	CAM	9	0.001	1.59	0.27	20.0 ± 3.3	27.1 ± 8.6
PFT-21	CAM	62	0	1.45	0.21	16.1 ± 1.6	25.9 ± 4.3
PFT-23	CAM	39	0.474	1.72	0.34	13.5 ± 1.8	13.7 ± 1.9
PFT-25	CAM	28	0	1.8	0.33	14.7 ± 2.4	28.5 ± 14
PFT-28	CAM	25	0	1.63	0.28	24.9 ± 3.2	34.2 ± 10.2
PFT-29	CAM	27	0	1.72	0.28	23.3 ± 2.3	36.9 ± 10.8
PFT-37	PTZ	16	0	1.76	0.33	17.2 ± 2.9	27.9 ± 15.3
PFT-39	PTZ	8	0.61	1.82	0.33	26.9 ± 10.2	32.9 ± 15.4
PFT-42	PTZ	27	0.434	1.61	0.36	26.5 ± 4.8	37.4 ± 10.3
PFT-43	PTZ	18	0.936	1.64	0.37	17.2 ± 3.5	15.7 ± 4.2
PFT-44	PTZ	10	0.014	1.85	0.39	23.2 ± 6.9	30.7 ± 15
PFT-45	PTZ	30	0.109	1.88	0.43	20.3 ± 2.6	19.4 ± 4.1
PFT-47	PTZ	33	0.442	1.77	0.28	13.0 ± 2.4	13.3 ± 2.7
PFT-49	PTZ	11	0.002	1.72	0.24	16.7 ± 3.7	56.9 ± 44.5
PFT-53	PTZ	21	0	1.78	0.26	29.3 ± 2.9	33.7 ± 7.8
PFT-55	PTZ	2	0.863	1.51	0.15	45.7 ± 18.8	44.4 ± 5.6
PFT-61	PTZ	2	0.328	1.72	0.28	43.8 ± 10.4	35.6 ± 18
PFT-65	PTZ	3	0.559	2.03	0.21	28.3 ± 3.9	28.6 ± 3.9
GU-1	SJG	38	0	2.33	0.81	36.3 ± 3.5	50.7 ± 6.6
GU-2	SJG	38	0.104	2.19	0.73	41.2 ± 4.1	49.3 ± 7.2
GU-3	SJG	58	0.168	2.44	0.6	38.1 ± 3.2	45.3 ± 7
GU-4	SJG	9	0.9	2.05	0.32	34.8 ± 6.4	31.5 ± 6.8
GU-5	SJG	37	0.005	1.88	0.68	34.3 ± 4.3	46.8 ± 8
GU-6	SJG	36	0.048	2.07	0.47	44.1 ± 5.4	54.7 ± 13.9
GU-7	SJG	8	0.073	1.77	0.3	22.8 ± 5.6	43 ± 16.6
GU-8	SJG	41	0.333	1.76	0.34	32.7 ± 3.9	36.1 ± 6.6
GU-9	SJG	23	0.004	1.88	0.57	23.4 ± 3.5	27.8 ± 6.3
GU-10	SJG	11	0	1.8	0.49	16.2 ± 2.9	28.5 ± 12.3
GU-11	SJG	19	0	1.56	0.46	25.3 ± 5	94.2 ± 45.1
GU-12	SJG	4	0.821	1.68	0.53	25.6 ± 9.5	30.9 ± 11.4
GU-13	SJG	6	0	2.08	0.39	248.0 ± 41	305.0 ± 130
GU-14	SJG	6	0	1.8	0.31	361.0 ± 49	302.0 ± 191
GU-15	SJG	31	0	1.92	0.33	186.0 ± 14	216.0 ± 34
GU-16	SJG	16	0.356	1.73	0.3	45.3 ± 10.3	71.5 ± 24.1
GU-17	SJG	33	0.184	2.04	0.34	36.9 ± 4.4	39.4 ± 6.3
GU-18	SJG	47	0	1.92	0.39	29.6 ± 2.9	27 ± 5.3
GU-19	SJG	44	0	1.91	0.38	34.3 ± 4	62.3 ± 14.5
GU-20	SJG	2	0.787	2.19	0.2	44.4 ± 33.5	46.2 ± 13.4
GU-21	SJG	9	0.089	2.48	0.52	75.2 ± 11.9	136.0 ± 54
GU-22	SJG	40	0.001	1.83	0.33	54.2 ± 5.8	81.9 ± 22.4
GU-23	SJG	6	0.261	1.97	0.34	22.2 ± 4.6	30.7 ± 9.1
GU-24	SJG	2	0.031	2.03	0.35	211.0 ± 32	148.0 ± 121
GU-25	SJG	23	0	1.96	0.34	91.3 ± 8.4	55.2 ± 15.9
GU-26	SJG	7	0.458	1.93	0.43	25.9 ± 7.6	32.8 ± 18.5
GU-27	SJG	3	0.009	2.41	0.41	58.4 ± 15.8	50.5 ± 42.5
GU-28	SJG	7	0.602	1.94	0.43	15.9 ± 3.3	15.3 ± 9.4
GU-29	SJG	10	0	1.92	0.38	55.6 ± 7.3	74.7 ± 31.2

Note: standard and induced track densities measured on mica external detectors and spontaneous track density on internal mineral surfaces. Ages determined using zeta = 128 ± 7.9 for dosimeter glass CN-1. N_s (tracks): ρ_s (10^6 tracks/cm^2); s—spontaneous (natural) tracks: N_i (tracks): ρ_i (10^6 tracks/cm^2); i—induced (reactor) tracks; N_d (tracks): ρ_d (10^6 tracks/cm^2); d—dosimeter glass (reactor) tracks. Grains (number of grains); dmnls—dimensionless; Q (dimensionless; probability of greater chi^2); Dpar—etch pit diameter parallel to crystallographic c-axis (microns); Dper—etch pit diameter perpendicular to crystallographic c-axis (microns); pooled FT age in Ma ± 1σ; mean FT age in Ma ± 1σ.

TABLE 3. SUMMARY OF APATITE FISSION-TRACK LENGTH DATA

Sample	Sample ID	Sample location	Tracks	Mean length (μm)	s.d. (μm)	Dpar (μm)	Dper (μm)	0–1 (μm)	1–2 (μm)	2–3 (μm)	3–4 (μm)	4–5 (μm)
1	PFT-02	CAM	–	–	–	–	–	–	–	–	–	–
2	PFT-06	CAM	13	13.49 ± 0.53	1.84	2.22	0.63	–	–	–	–	–
3	PFT-08	CAM	5	13.09 ± 0.88	1.76	2.18	0.57	–	–	–	–	–
4	PFT-09	CAM	–	–	–	–	–	–	–	–	–	–
5	PFT-12	CAM	3	14.43 ± 0.89	1.26	2.39	0.74	–	–	–	–	–
6	PFT-13	CAM	7	13.23 ± 1.32	3.23	2.01	0.36	–	–	–	–	–
7	PFT-15	CAM	–	–	–	–	–	–	–	–	–	–
8	PFT-17	CAM	3	11.22 ± 2.89	4.08	1.71	0.39	–	–	–	–	–
9	PFT-19	CAM	33	12.64 ± 0.58	3.27	2.3	0.63	–	–	–	–	2
10	PFT-20	CAM	5	13.2 ± 0.63	1.26	1.8	0.55	–	–	–	–	–
11	PFT-21	CAM	–	–	–	–	–	–	–	–	–	–
12	PFT-23	CAM	29	12.29 ± 0.61	3.24	2.06	0.52	–	–	1	–	–
13	PFT-25	CAM	12	13.53 ± 1.2	3.98	2.25	0.46	–	1	–	–	–
14	PFT-28	CAM	27	12.88 ± 0.49	2.49	1.81	0.45	–	–	–	–	–
15	PFT-29	CAM	64	11.81 ± 0.38	3	2.04	0.42	–	–	–	–	2
16	PFT-37	PTZ	–	–	–	–	–	–	–	–	–	–
17	PFT-39	PTZ	–	–	–	–	–	–	–	–	–	–
18	PFT-42	PTZ	–	–	–	–	–	–	–	–	–	–
19	PFT-43	PTZ	–	–	–	–	–	–	–	–	–	–
20	PFT-44	PTZ	–	–	–	–	–	–	–	–	–	–
21	PFT-45	PTZ	–	–	–	–	–	–	–	–	–	–
22	PFT-47	PTZ	–	–	–	–	–	–	–	–	–	–
23	PFT-49	PTZ	–	–	–	–	–	–	–	–	–	–
24	PFT-53	PTZ	–	–	–	–	–	–	–	–	–	–
25	PFT-55	PTZ	–	–	–	–	–	–	–	–	–	–
26	PFT-61	PTZ	–	–	–	–	–	–	–	–	–	–
27	PFT-65	PTZ	–	–	–	–	–	–	–	–	–	–
28	GU-01	SJG	102	11.77 ± 0.31	3.13	2.05	0.74	–	1	2	2	–
29	GU-02	SJG	100	11.82 ± 0.32	3.16	2.01	0.74	–	–	3	–	6
30	GU-03	SJG	101	13.35 ± 0.2	2.03	2.23	0.87	–	–	–	–	–
31	GU-04	SJG	17	9.48 ± 0.9	3.59	1.61	0.45	–	–	1	1	1
32	GU-05	SJG	103	11.69 ± 0.3	3.06	1.92	0.65	–	–	2	1	1
33	GU-06	SJG	100	11.87 ± 0.29	2.84	1.91	0.59	–	–	–	3	2
34	GU-07	SJG	80	10.98 ± 0.35	3.1	1.51	0.44	–	–	2	2	1
35	GU-08	SJG	100	12.04 ± 0.27	2.72	1.68	0.47	–	–	–	1	2
36	GU-09	SJG	18	12.22 ± 0.47	1.92	1.57	0.49	–	–	–	–	–
37	GU-10	SJG	107	11.71 ± 0.28	2.88	1.64	0.44	–	–	1	–	2
38	GU-11	SJG	58	11.62 ± 0.37	2.82	1.59	0.45	–	–	–	–	2
39	GU-12	SJG	–	–	–	–	–	–	–	–	–	–
40	GU-13	SJG	29	10.04 ± 0.43	2.26	1.73	0.47	–	–	–	1	–
41	GU-14	SJG	10	9.19 ± 0.63	1.9	1.77	0.3	–	–	–	–	–
42	GU-15	SJG	97	9.93 ± 0.19	1.86	1.66	0.41	–	–	1	–	–
43	GU-16	SJG	–	–	–	–	–	–	–	–	–	–
44	GU-17	SJG	8	10.04 ± 0.95	2.5	1.5	0.42	–	–	–	–	–
45	GU-18	SJG	64	10.82 ± 0.37	2.94	1.72	0.5	–	–	1	1	1
46	GU-19	SJG	44	10.97 ± 0.32	2.07	1.67	0.4	–	–	–	–	1
47	GU-20	SJG	30	10.22 ± 0.56	2.99	1.8	0.46	–	–	–	1	1
48	GU-21	SJG	6	8.62 ± 0.64	1.44	1.53	0.39	–	–	–	–	–
49	GU-22	SJG	114	10.9 ± 0.19	2.03	1.43	0.4	1	–	1	–	–
50	GU-23	SJG	34	10.52 ± 0.3	1.75	1.69	0.47	–	–	–	–	–
51	GU-24	SJG	6	9.63 ± 1.11	2.48	1.72	0.47	–	–	–	–	–
52	GU-25	SJG	10	10.61 ± 0.69	2.06	1.76	0.42	–	–	–	–	–
53	GU-26	SJG	1	9.85 ± 1.39	0.34	–	–	–	–	–	–	–
54	GU-27	SJG	–	–	–	–	–	–	–	–	–	–
55	GU-28	SJG	2	9.4 ± 2.95	2.95	1.75	0.94	–	–	–	–	–
56	GU-29	SJG	22	10 ± 0.5	2.27	1.85	0.43	–	–	–	1	–

Continued

TABLE 3. SUMMARY OF APATITE FISSION-TRACK LENGTH DATA *(continued)*

Sample	Sample ID	5–6 (µm)	6–7 (µm)	7–8 (µm)	8–9 (µm)	9–10 (µm)	10–11 (µm)	11–12 (µm)	12–13 (µm)	13–14 (µm)	14–15 (µm)	15–16 (µm)	16–17 (µm)	17–18 (µm)
1	PFT-02	–	–	–	–	–	–	–	–	–	–	–	–	–
2	PFT-06	–	–	–	–	–	–	4	3	–	3	1	2	–
3	PFT-08	–	–	–	–	–	1	–	1	1	2	–	–	–
4	PFT-09	–	–	–	–	–	–	–	–	–	–	–	–	–
5	PFT-12	–	–	–	–	–	–	–	–	1	1	1	–	–
6	PFT-13	–	–	1	–	–	1	–	–	–	3	2	–	–
7	PFT-15	–	–	–	–	–	–	–	–	–	–	–	–	–
8	PFT-17	–	1	–	–	–	–	–	–	2	–	–	–	–
9	PFT-19	1	–	1	1	1	1	2	6	4	5	6	3	–
10	PFT-20	–	–	–	–	–	–	1	1	1	2	–	–	–
11	PFT-21	–	–	–	–	–	–	–	–	–	–	–	–	–
12	PFT-23	1	–	1	1	2	2	1	2	6	10	2	–	–
13	PFT-25	–	–	–	–	–	–	–	1	3	3	2	1	1
14	PFT-28	1	–	1	–	2	1	1	2	10	6	2	1	–
15	PFT-29	3	1	3	3	3	6	6	11	10	9	5	2	–
16	PFT-37	–	–	–	–	–	–	–	–	–	–	–	–	–
17	PFT-39	–	–	–	–	–	–	–	–	–	–	–	–	–
18	PFT-42	–	–	–	–	–	–	–	–	–	–	–	–	–
19	PFT-43	–	–	–	–	–	–	–	–	–	–	–	–	–
20	PFT-44	–	–	–	–	–	–	–	–	–	–	–	–	–
21	PFT-45	–	–	–	–	–	–	–	–	–	–	–	–	–
22	PFT-47	–	–	–	–	–	–	–	–	–	–	–	–	–
23	PFT-49	–	–	–	–	–	–	–	–	–	–	–	–	–
24	PFT-53	–	–	–	–	–	–	–	–	–	–	–	–	–
25	PFT-55	–	–	–	–	–	–	–	–	–	–	–	–	–
26	PFT-61	–	–	–	–	–	–	–	–	–	–	–	–	–
27	PFT-65	–	–	–	–	–	–	–	–	–	–	–	–	–
28	GU-01	2	2	1	7	4	10	14	10	25	13	7	2	–
29	GU-02	–	1	2	3	3	10	8	21	19	17	6	1	–
30	GU-03	1	1	–	1	6	4	4	13	28	29	10	4	–
31	GU-04	1	1	–	1	2	4	1	1	1	2	–	–	–
32	GU-05	5	2	1	4	8	10	14	9	21	15	10	–	–
33	GU-06	–	3	3	3	10	7	7	16	30	10	4	1	1
34	GU-07	3	2	3	5	4	10	12	15	10	8	2	1	–
35	GU-08	1	6	1	2	5	6	13	20	16	21	6	–	–
36	GU-09	–	1	–	–	1	2	2	5	4	3	–	–	–
37	GU-10	3	5	2	5	9	6	8	21	25	13	5	2	–
38	GU-11	1	2	3	4	2	3	7	12	13	6	3	–	–
39	GU-12	–	–	–	–	–	–	–	–	–	–	–	–	–
40	GU-13	1	–	2	2	9	4	2	6	2	–	–	–	–
41	GU-14	–	2	1	1	2	2	1	1	–	–	–	–	–
42	GU-15	1	1	9	10	33	18	11	9	2	1	1	–	–
43	GU-16	–	–	–	–	–	–	–	–	–	–	–	–	–
44	GU-17	1	1	–	–	–	1	4	1	–	–	–	–	–
45	GU-18	1	4	5	1	7	9	6	11	10	7	–	–	–
46	GU-19	–	1	2	2	6	9	9	8	4	2	–	–	–
47	GU-20	1	3	1	1	3	7	6	3	–	–	2	1	–
48	GU-21	–	2	–	–	3	1	–	–	–	–	–	–	–
49	GU-22	–	1	3	6	16	35	24	8	13	6	–	–	–
50	GU-23	–	1	1	1	11	8	5	3	4	–	–	–	–
51	GU-24	–	1	–	1	2	1	–	–	1	–	–	–	–
52	GU-25	1	–	–	–	1	3	2	2	1	–	–	–	–
53	GU-26	–	–	–	–	–	–	–	–	–	–	–	–	–
54	GU-27	–	–	–	–	–	–	–	–	–	–	–	–	–
55	GU-28	–	–	1	–	–	–	1	–	–	–	–	–	–
56	GU-29	–	–	2	2	5	7	1	2	1	1	–	–	–

Note: Dpar—maximum length of fission track etch pits parallel to the crystallographic *c*-axis at their intersections with the polished and etched apatite surface; Dper—maximum diameter of fission track etch pits perpendicular to the *c*-axis at their intersections with the polished and etched apatite surface; s.d.—standard deviation.

TABLE 4. SUMMARY OF THERMAL HISTORY OF APATITE FISSION-TRACK DATA FOR SELECTED SAMPLES

Sample no.	Formation	Age (Ma)	Transect	Surface temp. (°C)	Time of peak temp. (Ma)	Time of cooling events (Ma)	Time of cooling events central value (Ma)	Peak burial temp.	Peak Burial Temp. (best)	Cooling rate (°C/m.y.)	EasyRo (% reflectance)
PFT-6	Garrapata	86	CAM	25	25.0	25.1 ± 4.8	25.1	125–172 °C; best = 134 °C	134.0	4.3	>0.85 ± 0.02
PFT-8	Guárico	63	CAM	25	17.4	17.1 ± 2.6	17.1	117–190 °C; best = 146 °C	146.0	7.1	>0.78 ± 0.01
PFT-12	Guárico	63	CAM	25	12.8	13.2 ± 1.8	13.2	102–179 °C; best = 127 °C	127.0	7.7	>0.67 ± 0.01
PFT-13	Guárico	63	CAM	25	15.0	16.8 ± 10	16.8	105–184 °C; best = 120 °C	120.0	5.7	>0.70 ± 0.01
PFT-17	Guárico	63	CAM	25	26.0	25.1 ± 3.8	25.1	97–187 °C; best = 115 °C	115.0	3.6	>0.65 ± 0.01
PFT-19	Guárico	63	CAM	25	20.0	17.0 ± 4.2	17.0	104–187 °C; best = 164 °C	164.0	8.2	>0.65 ± 0.01
PFT-20	Guárico	63	CAM	25	24.0	21.1 ± 3.6	21.1	94–184 °C; best = 162 °C	162.0	6.5	>0.65 ± 0.01
PFT-23	Guárico	63	CAM	25	21.0	19.7 ± 1.2	19.7	106–183 °C; best = 117 °C	117.0	4.7	>0.70 ± 0.01
PFT-25	Guárico	63	CAM	25	16.7	16.5 ± 1.0	16.5	103–198 °C; best = 136 °C	136.0	6.7	>0.68 ± 0.01
PFT-28	Roblecito	32	CAM	25	29.0	33.0 ± 4.2	33.0	108–160 °C; best = 124 °C	124.0	3.0	>0.77 ± 0.01
PFT-29	Guárico	63	CAM	25	23.0	21.8 ± 2.2	21.8	123–147 °C; best = 128 °C	128.0	4.7	>0.77 ± 0.01
GU-1	Garrapata	86	SJG	25	45.0	55.8 ± 5.5	55.8	119–130 °C; best = 128 °C	128.0	1.8	>0.80 ± 0.01
GU-2	Garrapata	86	SJG	25	59.0	59.2 ± 5.8	59.2	120–142 °C; best = 129 °C	129.0	1.8	>0.79 ± 0.01
GU-3	Guárico	63	SJG	25	43.0	43.7 ± 3.8	43.7	127–169 °C; best = 139 °C	139.0	2.6	>0.82 ± 0.01
GU-4	Guárico	63	SJG	25	58.0	55.5 ± 11	55.5	91–183 °C; best = 107 °C	107.0	1.5	>0.63 ± 0.01
GU-5	Guárico	63	SJG	25	42.0	39.3 ± 7.6	39.3	143–167 °C; best = 162 °C	162.0	3.5	>1.43 ± 0.01
GU-6	Guárico	63	SJG	25	56.0	47.8 ± 7.4	47.8	86–168 °C; best = 144 °C	144.0	2.5	>1.00 ± 0.02
GU-7	Guárico	63	SJG	25	54.0	49.3 ± 7.4	49.3	94–151 °C; best = 144 °C	144.0	2.4	>1.00 ± 0.02
GU-8	Guárico	63	SJG	25	48.0	45.6 ± 5.2	45.6	100–156 °C; best = 106 °C	106.0	1.8	>0.64 ± 0.01
GU-9	Guárico	63	SJG	25	45.0	35.1 ± 5.2	35.1	98–175 °C; best = 102 °C	102.0	2.2	>0.64 ± 0.00
GU-10	Guárico	63	SJG	25	28.0	25.0 ± 4.4	25.0	101–135 °C; best = 109 °C	109.0	3.4	>0.63 ± 0.00
GU-11	Guárico	63	SJG	25	40.0	37.7 ± 7.4	37.7	96–173 °C; best = 106 °C	106.0	2.1	>0.63 ± 0.00
GU-13	Naricual	23	SJG	25	14.8	354.0 ± 60	354.0	99–119 °C; best = 107 °C	107.0	0.2	>0.75 ± 0.02
GU-14	Naricual	23	SJG	25	14.5	543.0 ± 72	543.0	59–110 °C; best = 90 °C	90.0	0.1	>0.75 ± 0.02
GU-15	Naricual	23	SJG	25	14.5	315.0 ± 2	315.0	91–108 °C; best = 93 °C	93.0	0.2	>0.63 ± 0.01
GU-17	Quebradón	20	SJG	25	14.5	52.1 ± 6.1	52.1	90–130 °C; best = 108 °C	108.0	1.6	>0.78 ± 0.01
GU-18	Quebradón	20	SJG	25	14.5	44.4 ± 4.2	44.4	102–122 °C; best = 104 °C	104.0	1.8	>0.78 ± 0.01
GU-19	Quebradón	20	SJG	25	14.5	49.4 ± 5.8	49.4	93–113 °C; best = 104 °C	104.0	1.6	>0.69 ± 0.01
GU-20	Quiamare	20	SJG	25	14.5	65.6 ± 48	65.6	101–127 °C; best = 104 °C	104.0	1.2	>0.69 ± 0.01
GU-21	Quiamare	20	SJG	25	14.5	141 ± 23	141.0	105–131 °C; best = 124 °C	124.0	0.7	>0.80 ± 0.01
GU-22	Quiamare	20	SJG	25	14.5	104 ± 16	104.0	81–99 °C; best = 81 °C	81.0	0.5	>0.63 ± 0.01
GU-23	Quiamare	20	SJG	25	14.5	43.5 ± 9	43.5	87–112 °C; best = 97 °C	97.0	1.7	>0.64 ± 0.01
GU-24	Quiamare	20	SJG	25	14.5	289 ± 43.9	289.0	72–105 °C; best = 98 °C	98.0	0.3	>0.65 ± 0.01
GU-25	Quiamare	20	SJG	25	14.5	153 ± 14.1	153.0	81–108 °C; best = 96 °C	96.0	0.5	>0.65 ± 0.01
GU-26	Quiamare	20	SJG	25	14.5	38.6 ± 11.2	38.6	54–120 °C; best = 109 °C	109.0	2.2	>0.68 ± 0.01
GU-28	Quiamare	20	SJG	25	14.5	31.4 ± 4.4	31.4	104–125 °C; best = 120 °C	120.0	3.0	>0.69 ± 0.01
GU-29	Quiamare	20	SJG	25	14.5	91 ± 11	91.0	101–117 °C; best = 104 °C	104.0	0.9	>0.69 ± 0.01

Note: Timing of peak temperature, timing of cooling events, peak burial temperature, and estimated Easy Ro (% reflectance) obtained by modeling apatite fission–track age and length data in AFTSolve.

depths of burial values may be equivalent to the thickness of the sedimentary section eroded since the onset of the deformation. Thus, erosion may have removed up to 5 km of sediment.

A summary of calculated uplift rates for the Garrapata and Guárico formation samples is shown in Table 6. Uplift rates vary from 0.11 to 0.30 mm/yr for a geothermal gradient of 27 °C/km, and from 0.08 to 0.21 mm/yr for a geothermal gradient of 39 °C/km. One sample collected in the Neogene Galera Member of the Quebradón Formation in the "Belt of overturned beds" yields an apatite fission-track age (PFT-2, 81.9 ± 6.6 Ma) that is older than its stratigraphic age (Table 4). This AFT age suggests that burial, subsidence, and subsequent heating of this sample was not enough to completely anneal any previous thermal events. The latter age is influenced by the provenance.

No evident age-gradient is observed from north to south along the Camatagüita–Valle Morín transect. Almost all ages are similar within a small statistical error.

San José de Guaribe Transect

AFT data in samples collected along the San José de Guaribe transect show cooling ages that are older than those of the previously studied transects but still younger than the stratigraphic ages (Figs. 17 and 28; Table 4). They do not seem to fit previous models for the interaction of the Caribbean–South American plates in northern Venezuela and the subsequent mountain building process. Samples collected along the "Piedmont belt" in the siliciclastic units of the Guárico Formation and in a unit lithologically similar to the Garrapata Formation yield pooled AFT ages that range from 44.1 ± 5.4 Ma to 16.2 ± 2.9 Ma (early Eocene to middle Miocene; GU-1 to GU-11; Tables 2 and 4). Thermal histories for 24 out of 26 studied samples have K-S tests and age GOF of 0.5 or greater, indicating a high level of confidence. The time of cooling events for the Garrapata and the Guárico Formations obtained from the models is ca. 45 Ma.

The Venezuelan geological literature (e.g., González de Juana et al., 1980) suggests that the age of the Guárico Formation ranges from Late Cretaceous to early Eocene. However, Erlich and Barrett (1992) and Ostos et al. (this volume, Chapter 2) suggest that the formation is as young as late Paleocene. Thus, the stratigraphic age of the samples may be older than the cooling events. Table 5 shows paleodepth or burial depth estimates for modeled samples of the track-reset Cretaceous-Tertiary Garrapata and Guárico Formations assuming two geothermal gradients, 27 °C/km and 39 °C/km, as estimated for the Yucal-Placer field (Daal and Lander, 1993). As in the Camatagüita–Valle Morín transect, the geothermal gradient is assumed constant since the emplacement of the tectonic slivers in the Neogene.

As in the Camatagüita–Valle Morín transect, results suggest that depth of burial for the samples range from 3 to 5 km for a geothermal gradient of 27 °C/km, and from 2 to 4 km for a geothermal gradient of 39 °C/km. Depth of burial values may be equivalent to the thickness of the sedimentary section eroded since the onset of the deformation. Thus, the maximum thickness of sedimentary rocks removed by erosion could be as high as 5 km. Uplift rates

vary from 0.07 0.13 mm/yr for a geothermal gradient of 27 °C/km, and from 0.05 to 0.09 mm/yr for a geothermal gradient of 39 °C/km. These calculated uplift rates are small because the time of the cooling events (Eocene) is considered in the calculations.

Samples of the Neogene Naricual, Quebradón, and Quiamare Formations collected along the "Belt of thrusts faults," "Belt of overturned beds," and "Belt of gently dipping beds," yield AFT ages influenced by provenance, since their stratigraphic ages are younger than their estimated cooling ages. The provenance of these rocks might have had many sources, varying from the Guyana craton in the south to the emerging mountain range to the north. Samples from the Naricual Formation yielded both Paleozoic and Eocene AFT cooling ages (Tables 2 and 4). Thus, the sampled sedimentary rocks of the Neogene Naricual, Quebradón, and Quiamare Formations involved in the "Belt of thrust faults," "Belt of overturned beds," and "Belt of gently dipping beds" (Guárico basin) never reached temperatures higher than 110–150 °C, necessary to completely obliterate evidence of former thermal events. Therefore, for thermal gradients 27 °C/km and 39 °C/km, the maximum depth of burial varies between 2–4 km and 1–3 km, respectively (Table 5). AFTSolve analysis indicates that for the model to converge to an acceptable or good time-temperature path solution, the non-reset samples of the "Belt of thrust faults," "Belt of overturned beds," and "Belt of gently dipping beds" should have had an approximate timing of cooling events at ca. 15 Ma.

Pooled AFT ages and oldest track ages suggest a north-south cooling age gradient within the "Piedmont belt" of the San José de Guaribe section (Fig. 17). Pooled AFT ages range from middle Eocene in the north to late Oligocene in the south. Likewise, oldest track ages range from middle Eocene in the north to late Oligocene in the south. This suggests that the uplift, cooling, and exhumation of the accretionary wedge occurred in the middle Eocene. Thus, the emplacement of a southward-vergent folded foreland belt may have started in the middle Eocene.

As previously mentioned, Locke (2001) suggested that in eastern Serranía del Interior, there is a middle Eocene–early Miocene north-south AFT cooling age gradient. Although Locke (2001) sampled units that differ in age and depositional environment from those analyzed in this work, it is interesting to note that there is a younging of events from west to east and from north to south beginning in San José de Guaribe and continuing to Locke's (2001) regional transect in the eastern Serranía del Interior. The middle Eocene–late Oligocene pooled AFT north-south age gradient in the "Piedmont belt" of the Guaribe transect compares well to the middle Eocene–early Miocene pooled AFT north-south age gradient in Locke's (2001) regional transect.

Discussion of the AFT Study

Fission-track data generated and analyzed in this study suggest that an important mountain building process was active in north-central Venezuela from, at least, late Oligocene time and throughout the Neogene. Middle Miocene AFT ages are related to the final obduction of the Lara and western Serranía del Interior

TABLE 5. DEPTH OF BURIAL

Sample no.	Formation	Transect	Surface temp. (°C)	Peak burial temp. from AFTSolve modeling (°C)	Depth of burial, geothermal gradient 27 °C/km	Depth of burial, geothermal gradient 39 °C/km	EasyRo (% reflectance)
PFT-6	Garrapata	CAM	25	134	4	3	>0.85 ± 0.01%
PFT-8	Guárico	CAM	25	146	4	3	>0.78 ± 0.01%
PFT-12	Guárico	CAM	25	127	4	3	>0.67 ± 0.01%
PFT-13	Guárico	CAM	25	120	4	2	>0.70 ± 0.01%
PFT-17	Guárico	CAM	25	115	3	2	>0.65 ± 0.01%
PFT-19	Guárico	CAM	25	164	5	4	>0.65 ±0.01%
PFT-20	Guárico	CAM	25	164	5	4	>0.65 ± 0.01%
PFT-23	Guárico	CAM	25	117	3	2	>0.70 ± 0.01%
PFT-25	Guárico	CAM	25	136	4	3	>0.68 ± 0.01%
PFT-28	Guárico	CAM	25	124	4	3	>0.77 ± 0.01%
PFT-29	Guárico	CAM	25	128	4	3	>0.67 ± 0.01%
GU-1	Garrapata	SJG	25	128	4	3	>0.80 ± 0.01%
GU-2	Garrapata	SJG	25	129	4	3	>0.79 ± 0.01%
GU-3	Guárico	SJG	25	139	4	3	>0.82 ± 0.01%
GU-4	Guárico	SJG	25	107	3	2	>0.63 ± 0.01%
GU-5	Guárico	SJG	25	162	5	4	>1.43 ± 0.01%
GU-6	Guárico	SJG	25	144	4	3	>1.00 ± 0.02%
GU-7	Guárico	SJG	25	144	4	3	>1.00 ± 0.02%
GU-8	Guárico	SJG	25	106	3	2	>0.64 ± 0.01%
GU-9	Guárico	SJG	25	102	3	2	>0.64 ± 0.00%
GU-10	Guárico	SJG	25	109	3	2	>0.63 ± 0.00%
GU-11	Guárico	SJG	25	106	3	2	>0.63 ± 0.00%
GU-13	Naricual	SJG	25	107	3	2	>0.75 ± 0.02%
GU-14	Naricual	SJG	25	90	2	2	>0.75 ± 0.02%
GU-15	Naricual	SJG	25	93	3	2	>0.63 ± 0.01%
GU-17	Quebradón	SJG	25	108	3	2	>0.78 ± 0.01%
GU-18	Quebradón	SJG	25	104	3	2	>0.69 ± 0.01%
GU-19	Quebradón	SJG	25	104	3	2	>0.69 ± 0.01%
GU-20	Quiamare	SJG	25	104	3	2	>0.69 ± 0.01%
GU-21	Quiamare	SJG	25	124	4	3	>0.80 ± 0.01%
GU-22	Quiamare	SJG	25	81	2	1	>0.63 ±0.01%
GU-23	Quiamare	SJG	25	97	3	2	>0.64 ± 0.01%
GU-24	Quiamare	SJG	25	98	3	2	>0.65 ± 0.01%
GU-25	Quiamare	SJG	25	96	3	2	>0.65 ± 0.01%
GU-26	Quiamare	SJG	25	109	3	2	>0.68 ± 0.01%
GU-28	Quiamare	SJG	25	120	4	2	>0.69 ± 0.01%
GU-29	Quiamare	SJG	25	104	3	2	>0.69 ± 0.01%

Note: Depth of burial given peak burial temperatures calculated from AFTSolve, and possible geothermal gradients, for samples in the Camagüita–Valle Morín and San José de Guaribe transects.

nappes. The Cordillera de la Costa belt was rising and eroding as well, as indicated by several middle Miocene AFT ages (Avé Lallemant and Sisson, 1993). It is possible that the final obduction of the allochthonous nappes onto continental South America in the middle Miocene is related to a flip in subduction polarity from north- to south-dipping. The stratigraphic record and structural analysis of this study suggest that the mountain building process did not stop during the middle Miocene. Instead, it continued possibly until the Plio-Pleistocene, as the early-late Miocene Quiamare Formation is included in the Serranía del Interior foreland fold and thrust belt and the Guárico basin was tilted to the east, marking the inception of a foredeep in northeastern South America.

The late Oligocene–middle Miocene signatures observed in the apatite grains (Pérez de Armas, 1998; Pérez de Armas, 2005)

TABLE 6. UPLIFT RATES

Sample no.	Formation	Transect	Time of cooling event (Ma)	Time of cooling event central value (Ma)	Depth of burial geothermal gradient 27 °C/km	Uplift rate (mm/yr) geothermal gradient 27 °C/km	Depth of burial geothermal gradient 39 °C/km	Uplift rate (mm/yr) geothermal gradient 39 °C/km
PFT-6	Garrapata	CAM	25.1 ± 4.8	25.1	4	0.16	3	0.11
PFT-8	Guárico	CAM	17.1 ± 2.6	17.1	4	0.26	3	0.18
PFT-12	Guárico	CAM	13.2 ± 1.8	13.2	4	0.29	3	0.20
PFT-13	Guárico	CAM	16.8 ± 10	16.8	4	0.21	2	0.14
PFT-17	Guárico	CAM	25.1 ± 3.8	25.1	3	0.13	2	0.09
PFT-19	Guárico	CAM	17.0 ± 4.2	17	5	0.30	4	0.21
PFT-20	Guárico	CAM	21.1 ± 3.6	21.1	5	0.24	4	0.17
PFT-23	Guárico	CAM	19.0 ± 1.2	19	3	0.18	2	0.12
PFT-25	Guárico	CAM	16.5 ± 1.0	16.5	4	0.25	3	0.17
PFT-28	Guárico	CAM	33.0 ± 4.2	33	4	0.11	3	0.08
PFT-29	Guárico	CAM	21.8 ± 2.2	21.8	4	0.17	3	0.12
GU-1	Garrapata	SJG	55.8 ± 5.5	55.8	4	0.13	3	0.05
GU-2	Garrapata	SJG	59.2 ± 5.8	59.2	4	0.07	3	0.05
GU-3	Guárico	SJG	43.7 ± 3.8	43.7	4	0.10	3	0.07
GU-4	Guárico	SJG	55.5 ± 11	55.5	3	0.05	2	0.04
GU-5	Guárico	SJG	39.3 ± 7.6	39.3	5	0.13	4	0.09
GU-6	Guárico	SJG	47.8 ± 7.4	47.8	4	0.09	3	0.06
GU-7	Guárico	SJG	49.3 ± 7.4	49.3	4	0.09	3	0.06
GU-8	Guárico	SJG	45.6 ± 5.2	45.6	3	0.07	2	0.05
GU-9	Guárico	SJG	35.1 ± 5.2	35.1	3	0.08	2	0.06
GU-10	Guárico	SJG	25.0 ± 4.4	25	3	0.12	2	0.09
GU-11	Guárico	SJG	37.7 ± 7.4	37.7	3	0.08	2	0.06

Note: Calculation of uplift rates given depth of burial and timing of cooling events calculated from AFTSolve, and possible geothermal gradients, for samples in the Camatagüita–Valle Morín and San José de Guaribe transects.

suggest that the Roblecito foredeep was involved in deformation during the late Oligocene cooling event. The Oligocene time of peak burial, peak burial temperature, and depth of burial of the allochthonous-parautochthonous accretionary wedge (Querecual, Garrapata, and Guárico Formations) in the Camatagüita–Valle Morín area and possibly the Platillón-Tiznados area can be associated with the arrival of the Villa de Cura nappes in north-central Venezuela. Clearly, AFT data from the Villa de Cura nappes are needed to support this statement. Ongoing contraction between the North and South American plates and their westward motion with respect to the Caribbean plate caused the subsequent south-directed tectonic transport of the nappes of the western Serranía del Interior in the Miocene. This is the time of the inception of the foredeep in eastern Venezuela (Hung, 1997).

The cooling ages obtained in rocks of the "Piedmont belt" in the easternmost San José de Guaribe transect do not follow the same pattern observed in the western transects and also do not fit with recent models proposed for the Caribbean–South America plate boundary (e.g., Pindell et al., 1998). AFT ages were not reset during the Miocene, and there is a north-south apatite fission-track cooling age gradient from middle Eocene to late Oligocene. One possible explanation for these Eocene cooling ages is that in eastern Venezuela deformation began during the middle Eocene due to North and South American plate convergence (Pin-

dell, 1997; Pindell et al., 1998). Therefore, it is possible that eastern Venezuela was no longer a passive margin at that early time. Convergence between North and South America started during the Paleocene, and by middle Eocene time shortening could have been ~70 km (e.g., Pindell, 1997). Pindell (1997) and Pindell et al. (1998) suggest that contraction between the North and South American plates could have deformed the Proto-Caribbean crust. A subduction zone may have formed already in the Eocene causing subsequent early uplift of the Cordillera de la Costa and possibly of the northern Serranía as early as the early Paleocene.

The recognition of deformation in eastern Venezuela since the Paleogene does not preclude the generation of a roughly N-S oriented forearc basin in northwestern Venezuela as a result of the interaction of the Caribbean and South American plates. Therefore, it is possible that there was an evolving south-vergent foreland fold and thrust belt and associated foredeep along northern Venezuela during most of the Paleogene (Lugo and Mann, 1995).

Alternatively, AFT ages in the Garrapata and Guárico Formations along the San José de Guaribe transect may reflect the influence of provenance. Non-reset AFT age values may suggest that the cooling event represents a thermal event of the provenance rock, possibly caused by the emplacement of the Lara nappes in western Venezuela. However, a question still lingers as to how these cooling ages were preserved in the rocks within the Piedmont zone in the San José de Guaribe transect while the same rock types to the west, in the Camatagüita–Valle Morín and Platillón-Tiznados transects, underwent burial, causing the previous thermal events to be reset.

TECTONIC MODEL

According to most plate tectonic models for the Proto-Caribbean and Caribbean lithosphere (e.g., Pindell et al., 1998; Pindell et al., this volume), the North and South American plates rifted apart during Jurassic and Lower Cretaceous time as a result of the breakup of the supercontinent Pangea (Bartok, 1993). Upper Jurassic and Lower Cretaceous sediments were deposited on the passive continental margin of South America. In Paleocene-Eocene time, North and South America started to converge again. As a result of this convergence, the northern margin of South America evolved from a passive margin to a foredeep, as suggested by Pindell et al. (1998).

Beck (1978) suggested on the basis of sedimentary structures that the Serranía del Interior fold and thrust belt and the Guárico basin underwent two phases of contraction: first in the Eocene and subsequently in the Miocene. The Eocene cooling ages derived from the AFT data in the eastern part of the study area (San José de Guaribe) are consistent with Beck's model and with the N-S convergence. New $^{40}Ar/^{39}Ar$ ages record exhumation of the Cordillera de la Costa belt in the Eocene as well (Sisson et al., this volume, Chapter 3). The Cretaceous-Paleogene sedimentary rocks were probably incorporated in the accretionary wedge and deformed in the Eocene. The Cretaceous-Paleogene rocks of the "Piedmont belt" in the north are more intensely deformed than the rocks in the south. The deformation that affected the younger rock sequences started in the Neogene and continued through the Plio-Pleistocene.

The Cretaceous and Paleogene rocks in the western part of the study area were uplifted, eroded, and exhumed, and they went through the AFT annealing temperature of 110 °C in the late Oligocene through the middle Miocene (Fig. 29). Initiation of mountain building occurred in the late Oligocene, west of the site of its final emplacement, which occurred in the middle Miocene. This is the time that the Leeward Antilles and the allochthonous Caribbean terranes collided with South America (e.g., Pindell et al., this volume). The final obduction of the allochthonous nappes onto continental South America in middle Miocene time marks the flip in the polarity of the subduction from a north-dipping Paleogene subduction to a south-dipping Benioff subduction zone (e.g., Figure 9 of Avé Lallemant, 1997). Likewise, the inception of the basal foredeep unconformity in the Eastern Venezuela basin occurred in the early Miocene. An early to middle Miocene tectonic event is recorded as well, offshore of north-central Venezuela. Here, Paleogene extensional structures north of the Margarita–Los Testigos high, La Tortuga, La Blanquilla basins, and Cubagua subbasin were inverted (Ysaccis, 1997). Biological evidence suggests that major divergence in marine species of stingrays

occurred in northern South America as a result of physiographical isolation during the Miocene (Lovejoy et al., 1998). Freshwater stingray species can be observed in the Platillón and Tiznados Rivers today.

Any pre-Oligocene fission tracks in the Cretaceous-Paleogene rocks from the Platillón-Tiznados and Camatagüita–Valle Morín transects must have been completely annealed prior to the late Oligocene–middle Miocene events. Only in the San José de Guaribe area, AFT ages were not reset. Here, the rocks in the Paleogene accretionary wedge did not get hot enough for the fission tracks to be completely annealed. The accretionary wedge may have formed as the result of N-S convergence of the Americas. Pindell et al. (1998) suggested that a sutural basin might have formed along the margin of central and eastern Venezuela prior to the emplacement of the nappes. The collision of the Leeward Antilles volcanic arc caused the Villa de Cura nappes to be obducted and thrust to the south. Final emplacement of the nappes uplifted the entire northern margin, resetting the apatite thermochronometer and resulting in the middle Miocene ages observed in the Cordillera de la Costa belt. More AFT data of rocks along the Villa de Cura nappes are needed to better constrain its cooling history and to corroborate the hypothesis that the final obduction of this allochthonous terrane occurred in the middle Miocene (Fig. 29). The thrust faults along which the allochthonous belts (inclusive of the Villa de Cura nappes) were emplaced can be considered as out-of sequence or envelopment thrusts, but, of course, there is considerable time between the two events.

As noted, during the early to middle Miocene, metamorphic rocks of the accretionary wedge, specifically in the Cordillera de la Costa belt, experienced cooling below ~110 °C (Sisson et al., this volume, Chapter 3). Likewise, middle Miocene AFT age data are widespread in the study area, in particular in the "Piedmont belt." Presence of blueschists along the Venezuelan coast and in the Villa de Cura nappes (klippe; Avé Lallemant and Sisson, 1993) and the antiformal structure of the Cordillera de la Costa rock suite (Ostos, 1990) suggest also that regional uplift occurred during the Pliocene-Pleistocene. All these arguments suggest that a regional tectonic pulse or rebound took place in the middle Miocene to Recent times, due to the interaction of the Caribbean and South American plates.

SUMMARY AND CONCLUSIONS

The E-W–trending Caribbean–South American plate boundary zone in north-central Venezuela consists of several E-W–trending belts, from north to south: the North Caribbean deformed belt, the Leeward Antilles volcanic island arc, a zone of Neogene extension, the Caribbean Mountain system, and the Guárico foreland basin. The Caribbean Mountain system consists of several belts of which the Serranía del Interior foreland fold and thrust belt is the most southern. The Serranía is divided into four belts, the northernmost of which is the "Piedmont belt," tectonically underlying the Villa de Cura blueschist nappes (klippe). The present study involves only the Serranía and the Guárico foreland basin.

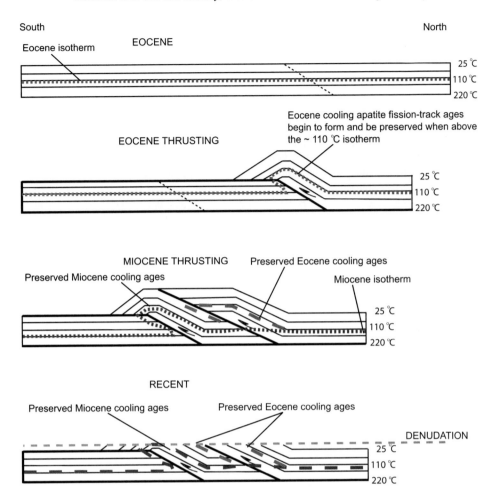

Figure 29. Tectonic model for north-central Venezuela. This cartoon shows how an Eocene apatite fission-track age can be preserved. Fission tracks form continuously within a ^{238}U-bearing host crystal (e.g., apatite). All fission tracks within a detrital apatite at temperatures well above ~110 °C will anneal. As soon as there is a geological event (e.g., generation of a perisutural foreland fold and thrust belt) the apatite fission tracks in the rocks that are uplifted and cooled below ~110 °C will be preserved and therefore will time the thrusting event. Subsequent younger events can be preserved in this very same manner. However, loading of an allochthonous terrane on top of the hinterland portion of the belt (i.e., the one preserving an Eocene cooling event) could cause the preserved Eocene cooling ages to anneal at temperatures above ~110 °C.

Cenozoic deformation and thermal histories of the Serranía del Interior foreland fold and thrust belt in north-central Venezuela were studied by applying structural analysis, interpretation of seismic lines, and apatite fission-track (AFT) analysis. Four N-S–trending transects were investigated. They are, from west to east: (1) Platillón-Tiznados, (2) Camatagüita–Valle Morín, (3) Altagracia de Orituco, and (4) San José de Guaribe. Analysis of regional two-dimensional seismic lines and field data suggests that the South American plate in north-central Venezuela underwent several phases of deformation:

1. NW-SE Extension

Extension and the opening of the Espino graben in the southernmost portion of the Guárico basin occurred in Triassic-Jurassic time. The graben-bounding faults displace sedimentary and metamorphic Paleozoic rocks and Precambrian crystalline basement of the Guyana Shield. The graben may extend beneath the eastern Serranía del Interior to the east and to the Apure and Colombia Llanos in the west.

2. Passive Margin

In the Cretaceous, a north-facing passive margin formed that subsequently subsided due to cooling (e.g., Pindell, 1993). This is the time of sea level rise, transgression, and encroachment of the proto-Caribbean seas onto continental South America.

3. Contraction I

In the Paleocene-Eocene, the North and South American plates started to converge in a NW-SE direction. The trend of the plate boundary zone was E-W; thus, convergence was highly oblique. This caused displacement partitioning in the northernmost allochthonous terranes of the Caribbean Mountains (Avé Lallemant, 1997). Thrusting and folding were the result of N-S shortening related to the boundary-normal component of convergence, and the boundary-parallel component was expressed by displacements along EW-trending right-lateral strike-slip faults and shear zones. However, the deformation structures in the Serranía del Interior fold and thrust belt formed only by N-S shortening. The La Victoria fault zone, north of the Serranía del Interior, may be the most southern structure along which major strike-slip displacements have occurred.

As contraction was highly right-oblique, collision of the Leeward Antilles arc with South America was strongly diachronous: it happened in Paleocene and Eocene time in the west (Lara nappes), in the Oligocene and Miocene in the western Serranía del Interior of north-central Venezuela, and in the eastern Serranía del Interior, during the Miocene, Pliocene, and Pleistocene. The AFT ages in the western Serranía as presented here support the model of diachronous collision.

During the middle Miocene, a major regional event occurred that caused the inverted basins in the Venezuelan platform and resulted in uplift of the entire area. It is possible that the final obduction of the allochthonous nappes onto continental South America in the middle Miocene was caused by the change in the polarity of the subduction from north-dipping in the Paleogene to south-dipping in the Neogene.

4. Foredeep

Late Eocene–early Oligocene inception of the basal foredeep unconformity in the study area was coeval with extension in the Guárico basin. Normal faults in the autochthonous terranes of the South American plate were either reactivated older faults or they were newly formed. They extend well south into the basin and may have formed during early stages of the development of the foredeep in response to the loading of the Lara nappes on the Guyana Shield and on the peneplaned Paleozoic folded belt.

During the contractional phase, the Guárico basin was decoupled along marine shales of the Roblecito Formation. From this sole thrust or detachment level, south-vergent thrust imbricates emerged, crosscutting Oligocene-Miocene sedimentary sequences of the Roblecito and Chaguaramas foredeep. Several small triangle zones developed within the basin. AFT shows that for most of the area the onset of uplift and cooling was late Oligocene–middle Miocene.

5. Guárico Basin

The Guárico basin was tilted to the east during a regional tectonic uplift that occurred in Pliocene-Pleistocene times. This caused the uplift and peneplanation of the Guárico basin. Field data support the hypothesis that during this time contractional tectonics occurred as the Miocene molasse was incorporated into the mountain range. Minor Neogene and younger extension is observed throughout the basin, affecting Oligocene sedimentary sequences as well (Figs. 18–20). The available seismic data do not constrain the orientation of the extensional structures. Even so, based on analysis of two-dimensional seismic data, Blanco et al. (1988) and Daal and Lander (1993) suggest that these normal faults are NE-SW–trending.

A NNE-SSW–trending two-dimensional composite seismic line through the Guárico basin shows the Pliocene-Pleistocene uplift and exhumation of the Guárico basin deposits (Fig. 12).

The latter deposits are much thinner in the east, and they are overlain by very thick sequences of the Chaguaramas Formation and lateral equivalents.

6. Contraction II

One of the most stunning results of the AFT analysis is the age of many samples from the easternmost transect (San José de Guaribe). This age is Paleogene and is younger than the stratigraphic age, suggesting that deformation had already begun in north-central Venezuela prior to the arrival of the Leeward volcanic island arc and the emplacement of the Serranía del Interior thrust sheets. Convergence of the North and South American plates in the Eocene may have been the driving force that generated the foreland basin in central-eastern Venezuela, involving the passive margin in the deformation since the middle Eocene.

7. Villa de Cura

Within the "Piedmont belt" and beneath it and the Villa de Cura nappes, the seismic resolution is quite poor, allowing for two contrasting structural interpretations: klippe or imbricate thrust sheet (Figs. 8 and 9). Two of the interpreted two-dimensional seismic lines cross the contact of the "Piedmont belt" with the Villa de Cura Group (Figs. 8 and 9), but the lines cannot resolve the question. Modeling of gravimetric and magnetic data suggests that the Villa de Cura nappes are very thin (between 1 and 2 km thick; Figures 3 and 4 of Bosch and Rodríguez, 1992) and, thus, may better be described as klippe. Projection of the proximal passive margin and its basement suggests that the interpreted Cretaceous sequence and probably the Lower Oligocene units may extend northward beneath the Serranía and the Villa de Cura nappes (Figs. 8, 9, and 22–26).

ACKNOWLEDGMENTS

I am deeply grateful to Hans Avé Lallemant for his infinite patience, openness, and support and for giving me the unique opportunity of being involved in this project. Likewise, I would like to express my gratitude to Raymond Donelick for being supportive, always accessible, and patient, and to Virginia Sisson for her invaluable help and kindness through my years at Rice University. I am also grateful to A.W. Bally, who improved greatly the content of this paper. I also thank Marino Ostos, Franklin Yoris, Robert Erlich, Jon Blickwede, and Stephen Barret for their technical advice and assistance in the field. I want to thank Carlos Rivero, who gave me a great deal of insight in reconstructing the cross section through the Caribbean–South American plate boundary zone. This project was funded by grants from Amoco, Apex, Conoco, Exxon, Mobil, Pérez-Companc, the National Science Foundation (grant EAR-9706521), and the American Chemical Society (ACS-PRF 27788-AC2) to Avé Lallemant.

REFERENCES CITED

Albertos, M., Yoris, F., and Urbani, F., 1989, Estudio geológico y análisis petrográfico-estadístico de la Formación Guárico y sus equivalentes en las secciones Altagracia de Orituco–Agua Blanca–San Francisco de Macaira, Estados Guárico y Miranda: VII Congreso Geológico Venezolano, Memorias, v. I, p. 289–314.

Allmendinger, R.W., 1995a, Stereonet: http://www.geo.cornell.edu/geology/faculty/RWA/RWA.html (Accessed: 1995).

Allmendinger, R.W., 1995b, FaultKin: http://www.geo.cornell.edu/geology/faculty/RWA/RWA.html (Accessed: 1995).

Andriessen, P.A., 1995, Fission-track analysis: Principles, methodology and implications for tectono-thermal histories of sedimentary basins, orogenic belts, and continental margins: Geologie en Mijnbouw, v. 74, p. 1–12.

Avé Lallemant, H.G., 1996, Displacement partitioning and arc-parallel extension in the Aleutian volcanic island arc: Tectonophysics, v. 256, p. 279–293, doi: 10.1016/0040-1951(95)00171-9.

Avé Lallemant, H.G., 1997, Transpression, displacement partitioning, and exhumation in the eastern Caribbean–South American plate boundary zone: Tectonics, v. 16, no. 2, p. 272–289, doi: 10.1029/96TC03725.

Avé Lallemant, H.G., and Guth, L.R., 1990, The role of extensional tectonics in exhumation of eclogites and blueschists in an oblique subduction setting: Northeastern Venezuela: Geology, v. 18, p. 950–953, doi: 10.1130/0091-7613(1990)018<0950:ROETIE>2.3.CO;2.

Avé Lallemant, H.G., and Sisson, V.B., 1993, Caribbean–South American plate interactions: Constraints from the Cordillera de la Costa Belt, Venezuela: A context for hydrocarbon exploration, Proceedings, Gulf Coast Section, SEPM Foundation 13th Annual Research Conference: Houston, Texas, Society for Sedimentary Geology (SEPM) Foundation, p. 211–219.

Aymard, R., Quijada, J., and Coriat, M., 1985, Campo Yucal-Placer trampa estratigráfica gigante de gas en la Cuenca Oriental de Venezuela: VI Congreso Geológico Venezolano, Memorias, v. IV, p. 2779–2803.

Bally, A.W., and Snelson, S., 1980, Realms of subsidence, *in* Miall, A.D. ed., Facts and principles of world petroleum occurrence: Canadian Society of Petroleum Geology, Memoir 6, p. 9–94.

Bartok, P., 1993, Prebreakup geology of the Gulf of Mexico–Caribbean: Its relation to Triassic and Jurassic rift systems of the region: Tectonics, v. 12, no. 2, p. 441–459.

Beck, C., 1978, Polyphase Tertiary tectonics of the interior range in the central part of the western Caribbean Chain, Guárico State, northern Venezuela: Geologie en Mijnbouw, v. 57, p. 99–104.

Beck, C.M., 1985a, Las napas de Aragua–Cadena Caribe central y la historia mesozóica del margen sur del Caribe a lo largo del meridiano de Caracas: Géodynamique des Caraïbes, Symposium, Paris, Edition Technip, p. 541–551.

Beck, C.M., 1985b, La Chaîne Caraïbe au meridien de Caracas: géologie, tectonogénèse, place dans l'évolution géodinamique Mésozoique-Cénozoique des Caraïbes Meridionales [Ph.D. dissertation]: Lille, France, Université de Sciences et Techniques de Lille, 462 p.

Bell, J.S., 1968, Geología de la region de Camatagua, Estado Aragua, Venezuela: Boletín de Geología, Venezuela Ministerio de Minas e Hidrocarburos, v. IX, p. 292–440.

Bellizzia, A., 1972, Sistema montañosos del Caribe, borde sur de la placa Caribe: Es una cordillera aloctona?: Caracas, Impreso por Cromotip, Transactions of the VI Caribbean Conference, p. 247–258.

Bellizzia, A., and Dengo, G., 1990, The Caribbean Mountain system, northern South America: A summary, *in* Dengo, G., and Case, J.E., eds., The Caribbean region: Geological Society of America, The Geology of North America, v. H, p. 167–175.

Bellizzia, A., Pimentel, N., and Bajo, R., 1976, Mapa geológico estructural de Venezuela: Caracas, Venezuela, Foninves, scale 1:500,000.

Biju-Duval, B., Mascle, A., Rosales, H., and Young, G., 1982, Episutural Oligo-Miocene basins along the north Venezuelan margin, *in* Watkins, J. and Drake, C., eds., Studies in continental margin geology: American Association of Petroleum Geologists Memoir 34, p. 347–358.

Blanco, B., Gomez, E., and Sanchez, H., 1988, Evolución tectónico-sedimentaria del norte de los estados Anzoátegui, Guárico, Cojedes y Portuguesa: IV Congreso Venezolano de Geofisica, p. 151–157.

Blin, B., 1989, Le front de la Chaîne Caraïbe Vénézuélienne entre la Serrania de Portuguesi et la region de Tiznados (surface et subsurface)—Apport des données paléomagnétiques—Interprétation géodynamique [Thèse Doct.]: Brest, France, Université de Bretagne Occidentale, 395 p.

Bosch, M., and Rodríguez, I., 1992, North Venezuelan collisional crustal block: The boundary between the Caribbean and South American plates: Journal of South American Earth Sciences, v. 6, no. 3, p. 133–143, doi: 10.1016/0895-9811(92)90003-H.

Burtner, R.L., and Nigrini, A., 1994, Thermochronology of the Idaho-Wyoming thrust belt during the Sevier Orogeny: A new, calibrated, multiprocess thermal model: AAPG Bulletin, v. 78, p. 1586–1612.

Burtner, R.L., Nigrini, A., and Donelick, R.A., 1994, Thermochronology of Lower Cretaceous source rocks in the Idaho-Wyoming Thrust Belt: AAPG Bulletin, v. 78, p. 1613–1636.

Carlson, W.D., Donelick, R.A., and Ketcham, R.A., 1999, Variability of apatite fission-track annealing kinetics I: Experimental results: American Mineralogist, v. 84, p. 1213–1223.

Cashman, S.M., Kelsey, H.M., Erdman, C.F., Cutten, H.N.C., and Berryman, K.R., 1992, Strain partitioning between structural domains in the forearc of the Hikurangi subduction zone, New Zealand: Tectonics, v. 11, p. 242–257.

Creole Petroleum Corporation, 1961a, Mapa D-8, escala 1:100,000.

Creole Petroleum Corporation, 1961b, Mapa D-9, escala 1:100,000.

Creole Petroleum Corporation, 1961c, Mapa E-8, escala 1:100,000.

Creole Petroleum Corporation, 1961d, Mapa E-9, escala 1:100,000.

Dalstrom, C.D., 1969, Balanced cross sections: Canadian Journal of Earth Sciences, v. 6, p. 743–757.

Daal, J.Q., and Lander, R., 1993, Yucal-Placer Field, Venezuela, Eastern Venezuela basin, Guárico basin, *in* Foster, N.H., and Beaumont, E.A., eds., American Association of Petroleum Geologists Treatise: Structural Traps VIII, p. 307–328.

Donelick, R.A., 1993, A method of fission-track analysis using bulk chemical etching of apatite: U.S. Patent 5,267,274.

Donelick, R.A., 1995, A method of fission-track analysis using bulk chemical etching of apatite: Australia Patent 658,800.

Donelick, R.A., and Miller, D.S., 1991, Enhanced TINT fission-track densities in low spontaneous track density apatites using ^{252}Cf-derived fission fragment tracks: A model and experimental observations: Nuclear Tracks and Radiation Measurements, v. 18, p. 301–307, doi: 10.1016/1359-0189(91)90022-A.

Donelick, R.A., Ketcham, R.A., and Carlson, W.D., 1999, Variability of apatite fission-track annealing kinetics II: Crystallographic orientation effects: American Mineralogist, v. 84, p. 1224–1234.

Erlich, R.N., and Barrett, S.F., 1992, Petroleum geology of the Eastern Venezuela basin, *in* Macqueen, R.W., and Leckie, D.A., eds., Foreland basins and folded belts: American Association of Petroleum Geologists Memoir 55, p. 341–362.

Fasola, A., Giffuni, G., Crespo, S., Paredes, I., and Euribe, A., 1985, Estudios bioestratigráficos del intervalo Cretaceo Superior (Maestrichtiense) a Miocene Inferior en el norte del Estado Guárico, Venezuela: VI Congreso Geológico Venezolano, Memorias, v. I, p. 588–645.

Feo-Codecido, G., Smith, F.D., Jr., Aboud, N., and de Di Giacomo, E., 1984, Basement and Paleozoic rocks of the Venezuelan Llanos basins, *in* Bonini, W.E., Hargraves, R.B., and Shagam, R., eds., The Caribbean–South American plate boundary and regional tectonics: Geological Society of America Memoir 162, p. 213–216.

Fitch, T.J., 1972, Plate convergence, transcurrent faults, and internal deformation adjacent to Southeast Asia and the western Pacific: Journal of Geophysical Research, v. 77, p. 4432–4469.

Fleischer, R.L., Price, P.B., and Walker, R.M., 1975, Nuclear tracks in solids: Berkeley, University of California Press, 605 p.

Gallagher, K., Brown, R., and Johnson, C., 1998, Fission-track analysis and its applications to geological problems: Annual Review of Earth and Planetary Science, v. 26, p. 519–572, doi: 10.1146/annurev.earth.26.1.519.

Gamond, J.F., 1987, Bridge structures as sense of displacement criteria in brittle fault zones: Journal of Structural Geology, v. 9, p. 609–620, doi: 10.1016/0191-8141(87)90146-5.

González, A., and Lander, R., 1980, Regímenes tectónicos desde el Triásico hasta el Neógeno en el area occidental de la cuenca oriental de Venezuela: Venezuelan Geophyiscal Congress, p. 134–141.

González, L., and Picard, X., 1972, Sedimentación y aloctonía en el frente de montañas de Guárico: Caracas, Impreso por Cromotip, Transactions of the VI Caribbean Conference, p. 83–88.

González de Juana, C., Iturralde de Arozena, J.M., and Picard, X., 1980, Geología de Venezuela y de sus cuencas petrolíferas: Caracas, Foninves, v. 1, 407 p.

Green, P.F., Duddy, I.R., Gleadow, A.J.W., Laslett, G.M., and Tingate, P.R., 1986, Thermal annealing of fission-tracks in apatite: 1. A quantitative description: Chemical Geology, v. 1, p. 285–317.

Green, P.F., Duddy, I.R., Laslett, G.M., Hegarty, K.A., Gleadow, A.J.W., and Lovering, J.F., 1989, Thermal annealing of fission tracks in apatite: Quantitative modeling techniques and extension to geological time scales: Chemical Geology, v. 79, p. 155–182.

Hung, E., 1997, Foredeep and thrust belt interpretation of the Maturín subbasin, Eastern Venezuela basin [M.A. Dissertation]: Houston, Rice University, 125 p.

Hurford, A.J., and Green, P.F., 1983, The zeta age calibration of fission-track dating: Chemical Geology, v. 77, p. 4432–4469.

Ketcham, R.A., Donelick, R.A., and Carlson, W.D., 1999, Variability of apatite fission-track annealing kinetics III: Extrapolation to geological times: American Mineralogist, v. 84, p. 1235–1255.

Ketcham, R.A., Donelick, R.A., and Donelick, M.A., 2000, AFTSolve: A program for multi-kinetic modeling of apatite fission-track data: Geological Materials Research, v. 2, no. 1, p. 1–32.

Kiser, G.D., 1997, La Pascua Formación; Eoceno Tardío–Oligoceno Temprano, Estado Guárico: PDVSA (Petroleos de Venezuela) Intevep, Código Geológico de Venezuela, www.pdv.com/lexico/l26w.htm (Accessed: 1997).

Kohn, B.P., Shagam, R., and Subieta, T., 1984, Results and preliminary implications of sixteen fission-track ages from rocks of the western Caribbean Mountains, Venezuela, *in* Bonini, W.E., Hargraves, R.B., and Shagam, R., eds., The Caribbean–South American plate boundary and regional tectonics: Geological Society of America Memoir 162, p. 415–421.

Laslett, G.M., Green, P.F., Duddy, I.R., and Gleadow, A.J.W., 1987, Thermal annealing of fission-tracks in apatite: 2. A quantitative analysis: Chemical Geology, Isotope Geoscience Section, v. 65, p. 1–13, doi: 10.1016/0168-9622(87)90057-1.

Locke, B.D., 2001, Thermal evolution of the eastern Serranía del Interior foreland fold and thrust belt, northeastern Venezuela, based on fission-track analyses [M.A. thesis]: Houston, Rice University, 167 p.

Lovejoy, N.R., Bermingham, E., and Martin, A.P., 1998, Marine incursion into South America: Nature, Scientific Correspondence, v. 396, p. 421–422.

Lugo, J., and Mann, P., 1995, Jurassic-Eocene tectonic evolution of Maracaibo Basin, Venezuela, *in* Tankard, A., Suárez, R., and Welsink, H.J., eds., Petroleum Basins of South America: American Association of Petroleum Geologists Memoir 62, p. 699–725.

Marrett, R.A., and Allmendinger, R.W., 1990, Kinematic analysis of fault data: Journal of Structural Geology, v. 12, no. 8, p. 973–986, doi: 10.1016/0191-8141(90)90093-E.

Marrett, R.A., and Allmendinger, R.W., 1991, Estimates of strain due to brittle faulting: sampling of fault population: Journal Structural Geology, Short Note, v. 13, no. 6, p. 735–738, doi: 10.1016/0191-8141(91)90034-G.

Marrett, R.A., and Allmendinger, R.W., 1992, Amount of extension on "small" faults: An example from the Viking graben: Geology, v. 20, p. 47–50, doi: 10.1130/0091-7613(1992)020<0047:AOEOSF>2.3.CO;2.

Menéndez, A., 1966, Tectónica de la parte central de las Montañas Occidentales del Caribe: Boletín de Geología, Caracas, v. 8, p. 116–139.

Naeser, C.W., and Faul, H., 1969, Fission-track annealing in apatite and sphene: Journal of Geophysical Research, v. 74, p. 705–710.

Oldow, J.S., Bally, A.W., Avé Lallemant, H.G., and Leeman, W.P., 1989, Phanerozoic evolution of the North American Cordillera, United States and Canada, *in* Bally, A.W., and Palmer, A.R., eds., The Geology of North America: An overview: Boulder, Colorado, Geological Society of America, The Geology of North America, v. A, p. 139–232.

Oldow, J.S., Bally, A.W., and Avé Lallemant, H.G., 1990, Transpression, orogenic float, and lithospheric balance: Geology, v. 18, p. 991–994, doi: 10.1130/0091-7613(1990)018<0991:TOFALB>2.3.CO;2.

Ostos, M., 1990, Tectonic evolution of the south-central Caribbean based on geochemical data [Ph.D. Dissertation]: Houston, Rice University, 441 p.

PDVSA (Petroleos de Venezuela), 2004, Código Geológico de Venezuela: http://www.pdv.com/lexico/ (Accessed: 2004).

Peirson, A.L., III, 1963, Galera Member of the Quebradón Formation: Asociación Venezolana de Geologia, Mineria y Petroleo, Boletín Informativo, v. 6, no. 5, p. 141–150.

Peirson, A.L., III, 1965, Geology of the Guárico mountain front: Asociación Venezolana de Geologia, Mineria y Petroleo, Boletín Informativo, v. 8, no. 7, p. 183–212.

Peirson, A.L., III, Salvador, A., and Stainforth, R.M., 1966, The Guárico Formation of north-central Venezuela: Asociación Venezolana de Geologia, Mineria y Petroleo, Boletín Informativo, v. 9, no. 7, p. 183–224.

Pérez de Armas, J.G., 1998, Thermal history of the Serranía del Interior foreland fold and thrust belt and Guárico foredeep, north-central Venezuela: Constraints from apatite fission-track modeling: Eos (Transactions, American Geophysical Union), v. 79, no. 45, p. F797.

Pérez de Armas, J.G., 2005, Tectonic and thermal evolution of the western Serranía del Interior Foreland fold and thrust belt and Guárico Foredeep, north-central Venezuela [Ph.D. Dissertation]: Houston, Rice University.

Petit, J.P., 1987, Criteria for the sense of movement on fault surfaces in brittle rocks: Journal of Structural Geology, v. 9, p. 597–608, doi: 10.1016/0191-8141(87)90145-3.

Pindell, J., 1993, Regional synopsis of Gulf of Mexico and Caribbean evolution, *in* Proceedings, Gulf Coast Section, SEPM Foundation 13th Annual Research Conference: Houston, Texas, Society for Sedimentary Geology (SEPM) Foundation, p. 251–274.

Pindell, J., 1997, Tectonic evolution and stratigraphic development of northern South America, VI Simposio Bolivariano: Petroleum exploration in the sub-Andean basins: American Association of Petroleum Geologists Short Course #2.

Pindell, J.L., and Dewey, J.F., 1982, Permo-Triassic reconstruction of western Pangean and the evolution of the Gulf of Mexico–Caribbean region: Tectonics, v. 1, p. 179–212.

Pindell, J.L., Higgs, R., and Dewey, J.F., 1998, Cenozoic palinspastic reconstruction, paleogeographic evolution and hydrocarbon setting of the northern margin of South America: Society for Sedimentary Geology (SEPM) Special Publication v. 58, p. 46–85.

Ramsay, J.G., and Huber, M., 1987, The techniques of modern structural geology, Volume 2: Folds and fractures: London, Academic Press, p. 309–700.

Schubert, C., 1988, Neotectonics of La Victoria Fault Zone, north-central Venezuela: Annales Tectonicae. v. II, p. 58–66.

Smith, C.A., Sisson, V.B., Avé Lallemant, H.G., and Copeland, P., 1999, Two contrasting pressure-temperature-time paths in the Villa de Cura blueschist belt, Venezuela: Possible evidence for Late Cretaceous initiation of subduction in the Caribbean: Geological Society of America Bulletin, v. 111, no. 6, p. 831–848, doi: 10.1130/0016-7606(1999)111<0831:TCPTTP>2.3.CO;2.

Summa, L.L., Goodman, E.D., Richardson, M., Norton, I.O., and Green, A.R., 2003, Hydrocarbon systems of northeastern Venezuela: Plate through molecular scale-analysis of the genesis and evolution of the Eastern Venezuela basin: Marine and Petroleum Geology, v. 20, p. 323–349, doi: 10.1016/S0264-8172(03)00040-0.

Sweeney, J.J., and Burnham, A.K., 1990, Evaluation of a simple model of vitrinite reflectance based on chemical kinetics: AAPG Bulletin, v. 74, p. 1559–1570.

Tikoff, B., and Teyssier, C., 1994, Strain modeling of displacement-field partitioning in transpressional orogens: Journal of Structural Geology, v. 16, no. 11, p. 1575–1588, doi: 10.1016/0191-8141(94)90034-5.

Vail, P.R., 1987, Seismic stratigraphy interpretation using sequence stratigraphy, *in* Bally A.W., ed., Atlas of Seismic Stratigraphy, volume 1: American Association of Petroleum Geologists Studies in Geology, v. 27, p. 1–10.

Vail, P.R., Mitchum, R.M., and Thompson, S., III, 1977, Seismic stratigraphy and global changes of sea level, part 3: Relative changes of sea level from coastal onlap, *in* Payton, C.W., eds., Seismic stratigraphy applications to hydrocarbon exploration: American Association of Petroleum Geology Memoir 26, p. 63–97.

Van der Hilst, R.D., 1990, Tomography with P, PP and pP delay-time data and the three-dimensional mantle structure below the Caribbean region: Geologica Utraiectina, v. 67, 250 p.

Van der Hilst, R., and Mann, P., 1994, Tectonic implications of tomographic images of subducted lithosphere beneath northwestern South America: Geology, v. 22, p. 451–454, doi: 10.1130/0091-7613(1994)022<0451:TIOTIO>2.3.CO;2.

Ysaccis, R., 1997, Tertiary evolution of the northeastern Venezuela offshore [Ph.D. Dissertation]: Houston, Rice University, 285 p.

Manuscript Accepted by the Society 5 April 2005

Geological Society of America
Special Paper 394
2005

Thermal evolution of the eastern Serranía del Interior foreland fold and thrust belt, northeastern Venezuela, based on apatite fission-track analyses

Brian D. Locke*

Department of Earth Science, MS-126, Rice University, Houston, Texas 77005-1892, USA

John I. Garver*

Department of Geology, Union College, Schenectady, New York 12308-2311, USA

ABSTRACT

The eastern Serranía del Interior foreland thrust belt in Venezuela consists of south-vergent thrusts that juxtapose Cretaceous and Paleogene passive margin units with less deformed Neogene basin strata. Apatite fission-track (AFT) ages, mainly from Cretaceous strata, are reset with distinct populations of grain ages that define two different cooling paths (CP). A number of samples have two reset ages that are apparently defined by apatite of different track retentiveness and they therefore record slightly different cooling events. CP1 has significant scatter, but populations of grain ages range from ca. 35–18 Ma, and peak ages decrease from north to south. Previous work estimated a total shortening of 115 km in the Serranía del Interior (Hung, 1997), and a two-stage model for the tectonic evolution of the eastern Serranía del Interior can be inferred. Stage 1 (45–20 Ma) involves in-sequence piggyback folding and imbricate thrusting propagating toward the south. Stage 2 (20–12 Ma) involves envelopment thrusting that doubled the thickness of the thrust sheets. Shortening within the main part of the Serranía del Interior thrust belt ceased at 12 Ma. CP2 is defined by low-retentive apatite. AFT peak ages are southward-younging between 13 and 3 Ma. Cooling ages of these low-retentive grains are only recognized in the northern part of the thrust belt near the El Pilar fault, and therefore these young cooling ages may represent reworking of the thrust belt due to transpression along the plate boundary. Deformation of the Serranía del Interior prior to Eocene and older collision of the Caribbean plate with South America is probably related to the convergence of the North and South American plates, which has been relatively constant since 50 Ma, but has been dominated by dextral transpression since late Miocene.

Keywords: Venezuela, Serranía del Interior, apatite fission track, foreland fold and thrust belt, thermal evolution.

*E-mails: brian_locke@anadarko.com; garverj@union.edu. Present address, Locke: Anadarko Petroleum, 1201 Lake Robbins Drive, The Woodlands, Texas 77380, USA.

Locke, B.D., and Garver, J.I., 2005, Thermal evolution of the eastern Serranía del Interior foreland fold and thrust belt, northeastern Venezuela, based on apatite fission-track analyses, *in* Avé Lallemant, H.G., and Sisson, V.B., eds., Caribbean–South American plate interactions, Venezuela: Geological Society of America Special Paper 394, p. 315–328, doi: 10.1130/2005.2394(12). For permission to copy, contact editing@geosociety.org. ©2005 Geological Society of America.

INTRODUCTION

The boundary between the South American and Caribbean plates in northern Venezuela is a wide zone of deformation resulting from a diachronous transcontractional collision and subduction of the Caribbean plate beneath the South American plate (Avé Lallemant, 1997; Pindell, 1993; Pindell et al., 1998, and this volume). Prior to this collision, the northern margin of Venezuela was a Cretaceous to Tertiary passive margin. The margin was then deformed as the Caribbean plate traveled to the east-southeast with respect to the South American plate. Deformation began in western Venezuela during the Eocene and becomes younger eastward. Consequently, the Leeward Antilles terrane and accretionary complexes were emplaced diachronously onto the northern margin of Venezuela. The collision resulted in the Caribbean Mountain system and the Serranía del Interior fold and thrust belt. The Serranía del Interior is subdivided into three portions: the eastern, central, and western. The eastern portion is the focus of this paper.

The eastern Serranía del Interior is a south-vergent foreland fold and thrust belt (Ostos et al., this volume, Chapter 2) with heavily deformed Cretaceous and Paleogene strata and less deformed Neogene sedimentary rocks (e.g., Case et al., 1984; Di Croce, 1995). The east-west–trending El Pilar fault separates the Caribbean Mountain system from the Serranía del Interior (Fig. 1).

Apatite fission-track data from sedimentary rocks in the central portion of the Serranía del Interior (in the state of Guárico) (Pérez et al., 1998; Pérez de Armas, this volume) indicated that two cooling events occurred. The first was a previously recognized late Oligocene to early Miocene event (ca. 34 Ma to ca. 12 Ma) that is inferred to be related to deformation in the central part of the Serranía del Interior. A previously unrecognized second event, ca. 40 Ma (middle Eocene), was recorded in the eastern part of the central Serranía del Interior. It is possible that this Eocene event is associated with convergence between the North and South American plates prior to the emplacement of the Caribbean plate.

Using global positioning system (GPS) velocity data, Dixon and Mao (1997) estimate that the North and South American plates are presently converging at the rate of 2.0 mm/yr. Other recent GPS studies (Weber et al., 2001; Pérez et al., 2001) find that the Caribbean plate is moving ~20 mm/yr in an easterly direction relative to South America. The rotation pole for convergence between North and South America is in the Atlantic Ocean at ~17°N latitude. Rates of shortening increase from east to west from 1 mm/yr to 8 mm/yr, and the shortening rate at the eastern Serranía del Interior is ~3.5 mm/yr. The pole of rotation and deformation rates of Dixon and Mao (1997) are similar to the Nuvel-1A prediction of DeMets et al. (1994) as well as four stage poles spanning the past 50 m.y. calculated by Müller and Smith (1993). Similarities between long-term average deformation rates and the stability of pole position suggest that the plate motions have been steady since ca. 50 Ma (e.g., Dixon and Mao, 1997; Summa et al., 2003). This important observation implies that deformation in the eastern portion of the Caribbean–South American plate boundary may have occurred prior to the passage of the Caribbean plate, and

the Eocene cooling event recorded by apatite fission-track may be the result of this plate convergence. The purpose of the present study is to use additional apatite fission-track data to determine the timing of exhumation of thrust sheets in the eastern Serranía del Interior fold and thrust belt and to relate these cooling ages to the tectonic evolution of the plate margin.

REGIONAL SETTING

Tectonic Setting

The north-central and northeastern boundary between the Caribbean and South American plates can be subdivided into three belts, from north to south: (1) the Leeward Antilles terrane; (2) the Caribbean Mountain system; and (3) central and eastern Serranía del Interior foreland fold and thrust belt. South of the eastern Serranía are the Monagas Foothills and the Maturín and Guárico subbasins of the Eastern Venezuela Basin (e.g., Case et al., 1984; Bellizzia and Dengo, 1990; Hung, 1997). The eastern Serranía del Interior is separated from the central Serranía del Interior by the Úrica fault. To the west of this fault is the Cariaco Basin, a pull-apart basin formed by a right step in the Morón–El Pilar fault zone (e.g., Erlich and Barrett, 1990). The El Pilar fault separates the Caribbean Mountain system from the eastern Serranía del Interior.

The Serranía del Interior is a south- to southeast-verging fold belt with major folds and thrust faults trending northeast to east and strike-slip faults trending northwest-southeast (e.g., Case et al., 1984; Chevalier et al., 1995). Upper Cretaceous and lower Tertiary rocks are exposed in the west and southwest, while older Cretaceous rocks, closer to the core of the structure, are exposed to the north and the east. The field area within the eastern Serranía del Interior (Figs. 1 and 2) is bounded to the north by the east-west–trending El Pilar right-lateral strike-slip fault, to the south and east by the 070°-trending subsurface Pirital fault, and to the west by the Úrica fault. The El Pilar right-lateral strike-slip fault extends east to west 700 km from the Cariaco Basin to northern Trinidad, with offset estimates ranging from 40 to 125 km (Burke et al., 1984; Mann et al., 1990). Motion on the fault began in the Miocene (Vierbuchen, 1984). The Pirital fault has ~20–30 km of horizontal displacement and 4–5 km of vertical displacement (Roure et al., 1994).

Stratigraphy

The stratigraphy of the eastern Serranía del Interior can be subdivided into five groups (Fig. 3): (1) Sucre Group (Neocomian–Albian), (2) Guayuta Group (Cenomanian–Campanian), (3) Santa Anita Group (Campanian–middle Eocene), (4) Merecure Group (lower Oligocene–early Miocene), and (5) Miocene to Recent deposits (Fig. 1). Stratigraphic work in the eastern Serranía del Interior was performed by Liddle (1928), Hedberg (1937, 1950), Hedberg and Pyre (1944), Rod and Maync (1954), Vierbuchen (1984), Yoris (1985, 1988, 1992), Chevalier (1993), Chevalier et al. (1995), and Ostos et al. (this volume; Chapter 2).

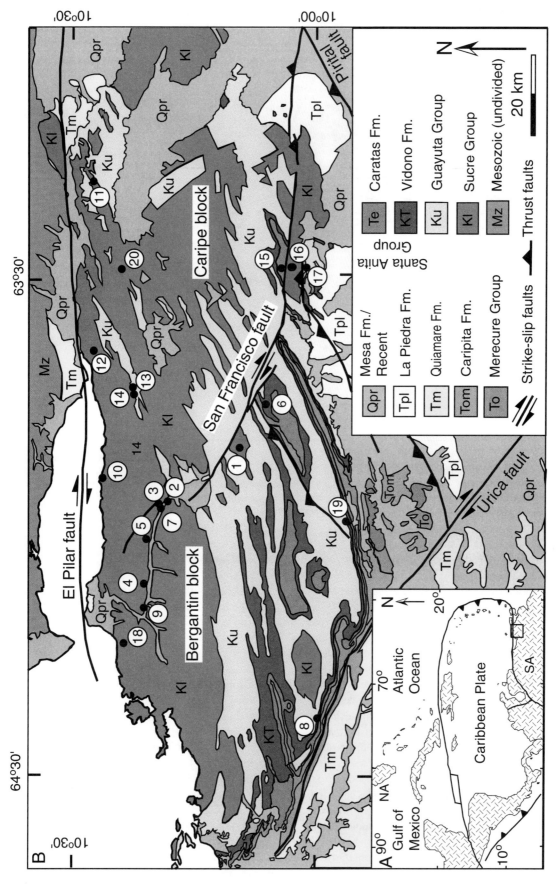

Figure 1. Simplified geologic and sample map of the eastern Serranía del Interior with insert for index map of the Caribbean plate (A). Black box is location of B. Based on map from Bellizzia et al. (1976). Qpr—Quaternary Pleistocene to Recent; Tpl—Tertiary Pliocene; Tm—Tertiary Miocene; Tmo—Tertiary Miocene-Oligocene; To—Tertiary Oligocene; Te—Tertiary Eocene; KT—Cretaceous-Tertiary; Ku—Upper Cretaceous; Kl—Lower Cretaceous; Mz—Mesozoic; NA—North American plate; SA—South American plate.

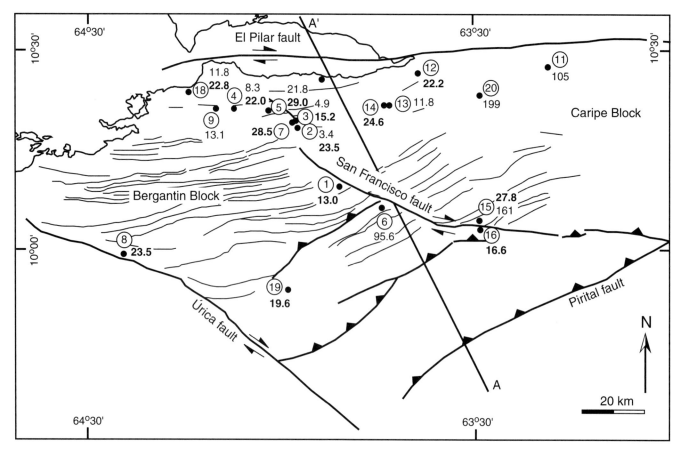

Figure 2. Simplified map of the eastern Serranía del Interior showing major faults, the location of apatite fission-track (AFT) samples, and main AFT ages. Circled numbers are the sample numbers from Table 1. Diagonal line represents transect A–A' on which fission-track ages are projected in Figure 4. Fold axes are shown as thin lines, thrust faults as thick lines with barbs, and strike-slip faults as thick lines with arrows showing motion direction. The most significant AFT age is shown on this map. Ages in boldface type contain the most significant percentage of grains. Very young peak ages (all P1 [young reset population]) and very old peak ages (Pd, which are non-reset and therefore depositional), are shown where significant.

González de Juana et al. (1980) summarized this information regarding the stratigraphic units.

The Upper Jurassic to Miocene units were deposited on a passive margin formed by the subsidence associated with the Mesozoic rifting and breakup of Pangea. Miocene to Recent units were deposited on an active margin during contraction between the Caribbean and South American plates as older rocks were uplifted, eroded, and redeposited. During this passive margin phase, the Sucre, Guayuta, and Santa Anita Groups, as well as the Los Jabillos and Areo Formations of the Merecure Group, were deposited with sediment input predominately derived from highlands to the south. During the active margin phase, the Naricual Formation of the Merecure Group and Neogene to Recent sediments were deposited as the Serranía del Interior was uplifted and eroded. Sediment input was from the north and south (Erlich and Barrett, 1990; Erikson and Pindell, 1993; Di Croce, 1995; Ostos et al., this volume, Chapter 2; F. Yoris, 2000, personal commun.). It is possible that the active margin began earlier during the middle Eocene as the Tinajitas Member of the Caratas Formation may have been deposited on the foredeep margin of northern Venezuela (Ostos et al., this volume, Chapter 2).

Structural Geology

Major thrust and lateral ramps (strike-slip faults) occur within the eastern Serranía del Interior. The Pirital thrust fault is a major tectonic feature in the subsurface, and Roure et al. (1994) propose that it has 20–30 km of horizontal displacement and 4–5 km of vertical displacement, but Pindell suggests it might have as much as 42 km of horizontal displacement (J. Pindell, 2000, personal commun.). Emplacement of the Pirital thrust sheet occurred during the middle Miocene along a décollement surface within shale of the Carapita Formation.

Previous structural work performed in the eastern Serranía del Interior includes Rod (1956), Rosales (1973), Vierbuchen, (1984), Rossi (1985), Carnevali (1988), Chevalier (1993), Roure et al. (1994), Chevalier et al. (1995), Di Croce (1995), Martinez (1995), Avé Lallemant (1997), Hung (1997), and Ysaccis (1997). Additionally, Creole Petroleum Company (1962) produced regional geologic maps.

Right-lateral, northwest-southeast–trending strike-slip fault systems within the eastern Serranía del Interior include, from west to east, the Úrica and San Francisco faults, dividing the eastern Ser-

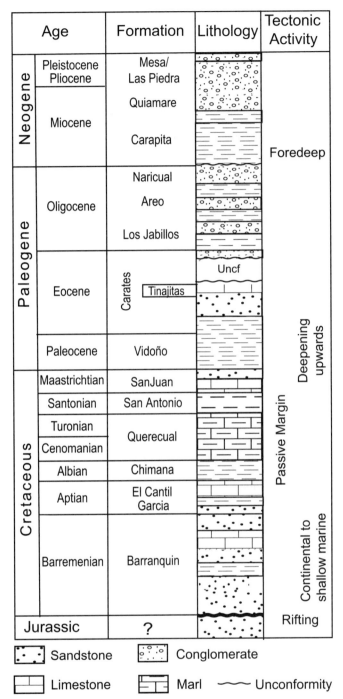

Figure 3. Composite stratigraphic column of the eastern Serranía del Interior (from Chevalier, 1995; Hung, this volume).

ranía del Interior from west to east into the Bergantín and Caripe blocks (Figs. 1 and 2; Roure et al., 1994; Chevalier et al., 1995). Dextral offset along the Úrica and San Francisco faults is less than 35 km and 25 km, respectively (Salvador and Stainforth, 1968; Rosales, 1972; Munro and Smith, 1984; Rossi, 1985).

One of the biggest controversies concerning the structure of the eastern Serranía del Interior is the interpretation of deep struc-

tures and basement faulting (Rosales, 1973; Rossi, 1985; Roure et al., 1994; Chevalier et al., 1995; Martinez 1995; Hung, 1997; Hung, this volume). The amount of deformation below the Lower Cretaceous rocks is unknown (Hung, 1997; Ysaccis, 1997). Hung (1997 and this volume) interpreted a cross section through the Caripe block of the eastern Serranía del Interior. He presents six possible reconstructions with estimates for shortening ranging from 9% (16 km) to 66% (115 km). Recent seismic data indicate that complex thrust structures exist beneath the eastern Serranía del Interior, and plate tectonic restorations (Pindell et al., 1998) suggest that ~115 km of shortening has occurred between the North American and South American plates. For our work here, we assume that this 115 km shortening estimate is reasonable.

APATITE FISSION-TRACK ANALYSIS

Fission tracks form by spontaneous fission of ^{238}U in a number of insulating solids, including several common rock-forming minerals. Fission-track (FT) ages are routinely determined for apatite and zircon, and these minerals have a relatively well-known response to thermal annealing (see Wagner and Van den Haute, 1992; Gallagher et al., 1998). A FT age corresponds to the time since cooling below a closure temperature or temperature range that is the effective limit of track retention. While the retention of fission tracks is temperature dependent, it is common practice to try to understand how this temperature relates to depth by assuming a typical geothermal gradient (typically 20–30 °C/km). Annealing temperatures in apatite mainly vary due to compositional variation (mainly Cl:F) (Carlson et al., 1999) and rate of cooling (Donelick, 1991; Crowley et al., 1990). Note that these annealing temperatures correspond to different effective closure temperatures, and as such, a rock that has a mixed population of grain compositions will have a complicated age spectrum because some grains record a low temperature and some record a slightly higher temperature. This situation is quite common in detrital suites that are cooled at relatively modest or low cooling rates (see Brandon et al., 1998).

The partial annealing zone (PAZ) is envisioned as being a zone of temperature ranges in which significant track fading occurs (see Gallagher et al., 1998). Below the PAZ, at high temperatures, tracks form but are annealed geologically instantly. Above the PAZ, the retention of tracks is nearly full, and virtually no track fading occurs. In the PAZ, tracks form, but are progressively annealed or shortened. For apatite, the effective closure temperature is ~110° ± 10 °C, but the practical bounds of the PAZ range from ~120 to 60 °C. Newly formed fission tracks in apatite are typically ~14 μm long. If these tracks are formed in high-level, long-cooled rock, the distribution of track lengths should reflect these original starting lengths. However, if tracks form and the rocks spend an appreciable time in the PAZ, we expect their mean length to shorten. Thus, in a general sense, we can use track-length distributions to understand how long a sample spent in the PAZ or how fast it passed through the PAZ.

The retention of fission-tracks in apatite is fundamentally controlled by composition of the grain, with Cl, F, and OH being the most widely recognized and best studied aspects of a grain, and it has long been appreciated that Cl-rich apatite is more resistant to annealing then F-rich apatite (see Gallagher et al., 1998). However, it is clear that other crystal-specific features affect the closure temperature and track retention. While composition of single grains is traditionally measured with an electron microprobe, it is also possible to measure chemical reactivity by analyzing etching features, such as track pits or track diameters. Note that to reveal tracks, the apatite grains are etched with HNO_3, and the disorder in the track allows preferential etching. The chemical composition (of apatite) and radiation damage (in zircon) are thought to be the basic control on solubility and how well tracks are revealed. By measuring solubility, grain populations with different chemical compositions can be distinguished. The parameter used to quantify solubility is called Dpar, which is the measurement of the maximum diameter of fission track etch pits parallel to the crystallographic *c*-axis (Burtner et al., 1994; Donelick 1993, 1995).

Complications arise in thermally altered samples that have a mix of apatite with different compositions. In this case, because the thermal response of an apatite is a function of composition, grains close at different temperatures and thus record different ages. This effect was highlighted by Brandon et al. (1998) in a study of reset, partly reset, and unreset apatite from the Olympic subduction complex in Washington State. In their study, all discordant samples were those with significant populations of grains younger than depositional age. They identified several types of single-sample resetting, which result from the distribution of grain composition and thermal history. Type R is a single concordant peak distribution that is totally reset. Type MR contains more than one peak, and all peaks are younger than the age of deposition, and as such, the differences in peak ages must be a function of apatite with slightly different track retention (i.e., they have slightly different effective closure temperatures). Type PR contains many peak ages, some older and some younger than depositional age, and in this case it is inferred that only some grains were reset. Finally, Type D has a population of grain ages older than depositional age. While Brandon et al. (1998) note that these sample types retain information about the cooling in the original source terrain, it is possible that the grains experienced heating to partially anneal tracks, so that the original cooling information is compromised, but the population of grain ages is still older than the age of deposition. By analyzing chlorine content in detrital grains, they were able to show that the youngest reset grains (Types R, MR, and PR) were dominated by fluor-apatite. However, their data do not show a clear relationship between Cl content and grain age in general, and therefore they conclude that there are other factors besides F:Cl ratio that contribute to grain age discordance. The conclusion from this work is that binomial peak fitting can resolve these geologically meaningful peak ages that correspond to grain populations with a similar retentiveness of tracks.

Experimental Techniques and Results

Samples of sedimentary rocks were collected for apatite fission-track analysis from the eastern Serranía del Interior (see Appendix Table A1 for details of sample locations). Apatite grains were separated from rock samples using conventional heavy liquid and magnetic separation techniques (Naeser, 1979). The standard fission-track age equation was used with a weighted mean zeta calibration factor based on the Durango apatite age standards (Hurford and Green, 1983). All measurements were done by B.D. Locke in the laboratory of R. Donelick, Apatite to Zircon, Inc. The grain-age distribution was fit using the binomial peak-fitting routine of Brandon (1996). A zeta calibration factor of 114 ± 9.3 was determined using apatite from Durango de Mercado, México.

In general, apatite grains from these units are difficult to work with due to low yield and poor grain quality. Individual apatite grains are severely corroded and dissolved, likely because of significant secondary porosity. Additionally, most grains typically have numerous inclusions. As a result of these limiting factors, relatively few grains represent some samples. In fact, we report four samples that were processed yet contained only a single countable grain (samples 6, 13, 17, and 20): We include these because they retain some information, but these results should be regarded with caution.

Fission-track results are summarized in Tables 1 and 2, and simplified results are shown on Figure 2 (for all analytical details, see Locke, 2001). Most samples fail χ^2 tests, indicating a heterogeneous population of grain ages (Table 2). Grain-age distributions were deconvolved into component populations; almost all samples have multiple populations of grain ages, and most samples have a young population of grain ages younger than depositional age. Samples that have multiple populations have old populations represented by very few grains, and in some cases just a single grain. As such, the estimate of the oldest population age is generally imprecise (Table 2). Note that in Table 2, the component populations are arranged in a practical way: the young reset population is P1 where it is younger than depositional age. In those samples that have two populations younger than depositional age, the second is placed under the second reset population column (all P2). Any population that is the same or older than deposition is placed in the non-reset column and is referred to as Pd for a "depositional" population age, which means it may retain provenance information at the time of deposition.

Most young populations of grain ages are between 28 and 13 Ma, but many ages fall between 19 and 25 Ma. The majority of samples were taken from the Lower Cretaceous Barranquín Formation (Ostos et al., this volume, Chapter 2), so the apparent ages are younger than depositional age. The northern part of the study area (Cumaná to Cumanacoa) has the youngest reset ages, which fall between 3.5 and 13 Ma, and older ages occur in this area as well.

TABLE 1. SUMMARY OF APATITE FISSION-TRACK AGE DATA

	Sample	ρ_s (10^6 tk)	N_s (tk)	ρ_i (10^6)	N_i (tk)	ρ_d (10^6)	N_d (tk)	Grains	Dpar (μm)	Dper (μm)	Track lengths (μm)	n	Pooled age (Ma)	Mean age (Ma)
1	BL-99-19a	0.149	124	2.439	2026	3.706	4315	32	1.79	0.65	13.45 ± 0.27	37	13.0 ± 1.6	12.3 ± 1.9
2	BL-99-2	0.192	211	2.089	2290	3.712	4315	38	1.81	0.66	12.98 ± 0.32	70	19.6 ± 2.1	23.8 ± 3.7
3	BL-99-5	0.171	135	2.404	1894	3.718	4315	35	1.86	0.66	13.45 ± 0.21	80	15.2 ± 1.8	16.1 ± 2.7
4	BL-99-16	0.174	120	1.678	1159	3.724	4315	22	1.79	0.66	12.36 ± 0.49	21	22.0 ± 2.8	29.9 ± 6.4
5	BL-99-9	0.246	79	1.808	581	3.730	4315	19	1.83	0.65	11.02 ± 0.99	23	29.0 ± 4.2	33.2 ± 11.5
6	BL-99-23	3.299	76	7.378	170	3.764	4315	1	2.08	0.69	nd	nd	95.6 ± 15.4	95.6 ± 15.4
7	BL-99-6	0.368	204	2.738	1516	3.773	4315	23	1.89	0.69	13.33 ± 0.24	49	29.0 ± 3.2	37.9 ± 13.0
8	BL-99-31	0.459	99	3.009	649	3.782	4315	10	1.75	0.71	nd	nd	32.9 ± 4.5	43.5 ± 16.4
9	BL-99-18	0.755	226	2.447	733	3.795	4315	5	2.09	0.78	14.22 ± 0.18	42	66.6 ± 7.5	46.0 ± 25.6
10	BL-00-21	0.670	60	7.109	637	3.350	4183	7	1.74	0.59	12.65 ± 0.39	13	18.0 ± 2.9	34.6 ± 17.8
11	BL-00-23	1.056	173	1.910	313	3.373	4183	7	1.81	0.65	nd	nd	106 ± 13	119 ± 20
12	BL-00-25	0.342	269	2.832	2229	3.389	4183	44	1.84	0.65	12.11 ± 0.73	33	23.4 ± 2.5	28.9 ± 4.8
13	BL-00-31	0.188	13	3.096	214	3.407	4183	1	2.11	0.66	12.83 ± 0.29	39	11.8 ± 3.5	11.8 ± 3.5
14	BL-00-32	0.373	127	2.961	1008	3.429	4183	22	1.90	0.75	13.88 ± 0.34	76	24.7 ± 3.1	27.2 ± 4.9
15	BL-00-38	0.848	728	1.171	1005	3.446	4183	24	1.89	0.79	11.56 ± 0.37	16	141 ± 14	159 ± 22
16	BL-00-44	0.393	112	3.750	1068	3.457	4183	17	2.00	0.79	14.04 ± 0.35	24	20.7 ± 2.7	28.5 ± 7.7
17	BL-00-48	0.122	5	0.537	22	3.475	4183	1	1.61	0.89	nd	nd	45.1 ± 22.6	45.1 ± 22.6
18	BL-00-72	0.597	170	5.242	1493	3.497	4183	18	1.87	0.79	14.13 ± 0.31	20	22.8 ± 2.6	39.0 ± 13.5
19	BL-00-81	0.503	119	5.165	1223	3.520	4183	16	1.98	0.82	13.66 ± 0.45	7	19.6 ± 2.5	28.0 ± .0
20	BL-00-92	0.260	4	0.260	4	3.542	4183	1	2.12	0.85	14.27 ± 0.20	45	200 ± 142	200 ± 142

Note: Track densities are given in tracks (tk) per square cm. Fission track ages were analyzed using the external detector method calibrated to standards of known age (Fish Canyon Tuff and Durango). Fission track ages were compared to measurements of the Fish Canyon tuff, Durango apatite, and the Tioga bentonite. Track lengths and Dpar/Dper measurements are based on repeated measurement of the Durango apatite. All ages were determined by B. Locke, under direction Ages were calculated using a zeta factor of 114 ± 9.3, which of R. Donelick, Apatite to Zircon, Inc. Track length measurements included on table only if we were able to make 5 or more measurements. Dpar—maximum length of fission track etch pits parallel to the crystallographic *c*-axis at their intersections with the polished and etched apatite surface; Dper—maximum diameter of fission track etch pits perpendicular to the *c*-axis at their intersections with the polished and etched apatite surface.

TABLE 2. BINOMIAL POPULATIONS FROM APATITE FISSION TRACK RESULTS

Sample	Map no.	Pooled Age (Ma)	Pooled 1 se	P(χ²)	Young reset population (P1) Age (Ma)	63% C.I.		N_r	Second reset population (P2) Age (Ma)	63% C.I.		N_r	Non-reset population (Pd) Age (Ma)	63% C.I.		N_r
BL-99-2	2	19.6	2.1	0	3.4	−1.2	+1.9	6	23.5	−2.3	+2.6	32				
BL-99-5	3	15.2	1.8	1	4.9	−2.1	+3.7	8	18.7	−2.6	+3.7	27				
BL-00-21	10	18.0	2.9	0	6.3	−1.7	+2.4	3	34.8	−6.1	+7.3	4				
BL-99-16	4	22.0	2.8	0	8.3	−2.1	+2.9	7	32.8	−4.6	+5.4	15				
BL-00-72	18	22.8	2.6	0	11.8	−1.9	+2.3	9	27.4	−4.0	+4.7	8	189.2	−42.7	+54.9	2
BL-99-19a	1	13.0	1.6	13	12.9	−1.5	+1.7	32								
BL-99-18	9	66.6	7.5	0	13.1	−3.0	+3.8	3					102.4	−11.4	+12.8	2
BL-00-44	16	20.7	2.7	0	16.6	−2.2	+2.5	16					121.9	−29.3	+38.5	1
BL-00-81	19	19.6	2.5	1	19.1	−2.3	+2.7	15					97.7	−50.5	+103.6	1
BL-00-25	12	23.4	2.5	0	22.2	−2.3	+2.5	42					118.0	−37.5	+54.8	2
BL-99-9	5	29.0	4.2	0	21.8	−3.5	+4.2	17					152.2	−45.0	+63.7	2
BL-99-31	8	32.9	4.5	0	23.5	−3.7	+4.4	7					80.0	−15.9	+19.80	3
BL-00-32	14	24.7	3.1	51	24.6	−2.9	+3.3	22								
BL-00-38*	15	141.0	14	0	27.8	−6.1	+7.8	3					161.2	−14.8	+16.3	21
BL-99-6	7	29.0	3.2	0	28.5	−3.0	+3.4	22					277.5	−171.8	+435.7	1
BL-99-23*	6	95.6	15.4	I.A.									95.3	−14.1	+16.5	1
BL-00-23*	11	106.0	13	12									105.4	−12.4	+14.1	7
BL-00-92*	20	200.0	142	I.A.									198.7	−100.5	+200.1	1

Note: $P(\chi^2) = \chi^2$ probability for concordance of grain ages. C.I.—confidence interval; I.A.—insufficient apatite for analysis; N_r—number of grains in peak; se—standard error. Number of grains per peak age rounded to the nearest whole number. All samples with less than 5 grains are excluded from this table, except the last two, which are included to indicate the fact that only an old, probably unreset grain was counted.

*Samples marked with asterisk have depositional ages as old or older than youngest peak.

Track length and Dpar measurements were not useful in identifying different grain populations because no correlation between grain age and Dpar was observed. Part of the problem is that the poor grain quality resulted in so few good grains for analysis. Note that the track-length distributions are mixed, and they represent track lengths measured from all populations. To understand the deconvolved data, we took the approach of Brandon et al. (1998) and determined whether we had Type R, MR, PR, or D samples (discussed above).

Discussion of FT Data

The age distribution of the FT data shows that there are multiple populations of grain ages younger than the depositional age. Peak-fitting methods were used to isolate populations with different annealing resistance (see Brandon, 1996). The age of the youngest population of grains is called the minimum age of the fission-track distribution (Galbraith and Laslett, 1993; Brandon et al., 1998). The minimum age corresponds to the age of grains with the least resistance to annealing: These grains will be the first to reset at the lowest temperatures within the PAZ and the last grains to begin to record a cooling event. Grains more resistant to annealing (i.e., older grain ages) will survive higher temperatures within the PAZ and may even retain provenance information.

Apatite grains presumably have a mixed provenance that includes variable compositions (Cl, F, or OH). The presence of this variable composition is apparent from the simple observation that we have multiple populations, most of which are younger than the depositional age of the samples. This observation suggests that the samples were derived from a heterogeneous source, deposited, and then heated to temperatures to fully reset some, but not all, apatite grains. It is probable that most samples with unreset older populations were not taken to temperatures higher than ~150 °C, because if they were, all grains would have been fully reset.

Using the nomenclature developed from the Olympic mountains (Brandon et al., 1998), we have Type MR, PR, and D samples. Of interest here are those populations that have been reset, so we focus on the reset part of all distributions. We can divide individual populations into three simple components (Table 2). The first is the young reset population, which represents grains that have a low retention of fission tracks, and is likely to be F-rich (Brandon et al., 1998). This population consists of grain ages between 3.4 and 28.5 Ma, and these ages presumably reflect the most recent cooling of individual rock samples in the area. The second reset population of grain ages only occurs in a few samples, but is well-defined by a number of grains for several samples. These are inferred to be reset ages, probably of more retentive apatite (Brandon et al., 1998). Finally, there are the non-reset populations of grain ages that are about equal to or older than the depositional age of the samples from which they were taken (Type D). It is possible that these grains retain some information about the original cooling history of the source region (i.e., Garver et al., 1999), but it is also possible that they have suffered a certain degree of annealing, and therefore they provide only a minimum estimate of those original cooling ages. These old populations are of limited utility because so few grains represent them and because the original track distribution may have been compromised due to heating.

Two samples may be entirely unreset such that all grains are older than depositional age (Type D; see samples 15 and 11, Table 2), but there is some uncertainty as to the original stratigraphic position because the rocks are deformed and difficult to distinguish in the area collected. Sample 15 was collected from either the Caratas Formation (middle Eocene) or the Los Jabillos Formation (lower Oligocene). Sample 11 was collected from the San Antonio Formation (Santonian), San Juan Formation (Maastrichtian), or Caratas Formation (middle Eocene). These are younger strata than the other samples, and because they have peak ages that can be older than depositional age, it is possible that these samples were not buried deep enough for complete resetting.

Note that sample 15 was part of a pair of samples taken on either side of the San Francisco fault. The sample on the north side of the fault is likely to be depositional (unreset), but the sample from the south side is ca. 17 Ma and from Cretaceous rocks, so it is likely that the San Francisco fault had some movement since 17 Ma.

GEOLOGIC INTERPRETATION OF APATITE FISSION-TRACK RESULTS

One of the most important observations with respect to the trend of the reset ages is that apatite fission-track (AFT) ages represented by the reset component populations (P1 and P2) young to the south (toward the foreland). AFT ages have been projected onto a northwest-southeast–trending transect (Fig. 4). The six P1 ages (open squares) are the youngest ages, and almost all of them are based on only a few grains (see Table 2; these are the first six ages in young reset column). The solid squares (generally P2 but P1 for those samples with no younger peak age) represent ages based on a significant number of grains. Each sample with a young age (open square) has a corresponding older age (solid square). A least-squares fit line has been drawn through the ages based on the majority of grains. The best-fit line for the reset ages shows those AFT ages become younger to the south. Note that we are in an interesting position of being able to interpret effectively two cooling age trends: one related to more retentive grains that presumably closed first (cooling path 1—CP1), and a younger population of grain ages (cooling path 2—CP2). These distinctive cooling paths result only from the fact that individual apatite grains had different retentiveness and closed at slightly different temperatures, so they record slightly different cooling ages. CP1 appears to record an early history of exhumation that progressed north to south across the thrust belt from ca. 35–18 Ma. CP2, which is only apparent in rocks in the northernmost part of the thrust belt, represents ~25 km of rock with ages that span ca. 3–13 Ma.

Geothermal Gradients

Based on numerous well logs, the present-day geothermal gradient within the eastern Serranía del Interior is 23 °C/km (A. Aleman, 2000, personal commun.). The surface temperature is assumed to be 25 °C. Using the geothermal gradient and surface temperature, it can be determined that the nominal closure temperature (110 ± 10 °C) occurs at a depth of ~3.7 km. We infer that all samples with partly reset or fully reset ages reached a temperature in excess of 110 °C. The Barranquín Formation is estimated to have been buried to a depth of ~5 km (i.e., ~140 °C; see Hung, 1997), well above the effective closure temperature for F-rich apatite, but still in the window for resetting Cl-rich apatite. This thermal gradient and burial depth are similar to that estimated by Summa et al. (2003). If this burial estimate can be applied regionally, ~1.3 km of overburden had to be removed before most apatite reached the PAZ.

Sequence of Thrusting

The south-vergent Serranía del Interior fold and thrust belt is inferred to have had Oligocene to Miocene deformation. Using seismic reflection data, both Roure et al. (1994) and Hung (1997) suggested that the eastern Serranía del Interior developed in two stages of deformation. The early stage was in-sequence with piggy-back thrusts. Shale of the Carapita Formation is inferred to have had high pore pressure and contains dewatering and compaction features such as mud diapirs that indicate that they would make a good décollement surface (Roure et al., 1994). Deformation

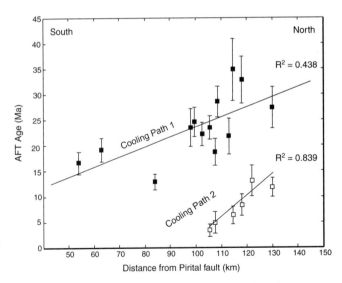

Figure 4. Graph of apatite fission-track reset ages projected on transect A–A′ in Figure 2. Open squares represent fission-track minimum ages from samples that have a second reset population or show full resetting (no grains unreset) (first six ages in young reset population [P1] in Table 2). Solid squares represent the fission-track minimum ages of the main reset population or older ages of partially reset populations (all other reset ages in Table 2).

probably began in the north during the deposition of the Narical Formation (upper Oligocene; see Fig. 3) and continued to the south during the deposition of the Carapita Formation (lower Miocene to lower middle Miocene). The early stage of deformation doubled the thickness of the thrust sheet and created the complex structure now recognized in the eastern Serranía del Interior. Late-stage deformation resulted in out-of-sequence faulting by reactivating older thrust faults such as the Pirital fault (Hung, this volume).

Pindell et al. (1998) attempted to reconstruct the Serranía del Interior fold and thrust belt to its original undeformed state in three steps working backward in time. The first step in this reconstruction is to remove ~20 km of right-lateral offset along the El Pilar fault and related strike-slip faults since ca. 12 Ma. The second step is to restore 40 km to 50 km on the thrust belt (horizontal shortening) using the Pirital thrust fault and similar faults south of the Pirital fault. The third step is to reconstruct ~40 km along the folds and thrusts of the Serranía del Interior to their undeformed state. The amount of shortening (80 km) in this model is slightly less than within the Serranía del Interior. In contrast, other workers have suggested shortening within the Serranía del Interior to be as high as ~110 km (i.e., Summa et al., 2003).

Shortening is inferred to have ceased at 12 Ma, and the initiation of deformation within the eastern Serranía del Interior began at ca. 45 Ma (middle Eocene). This time of onset corre-

sponds to the deposition of the Tinajitas Member of the Caratas Formation. As such, we can assume an average shortening rate of 3.5 mm/yr over the 33 m.y. required to shorten the eastern Serranía del Interior by 115 km.

Fission-track ages from the fold and thrust belt may be used to reconstruct the temporal evolution of deformation (see Locke, 2001, for full details). To do this, we assume that the fold and thrust belt evolved in a two-stage process as outlined above. We also assume that duplex structures uplift rock and that erosional exhumation occurs on the elevated part of the thrust belt. The tectonic model attempts to reconstruct the Serranía del Interior evolution from 45 Ma to the present at 30 Ma, 25 Ma, 20 Ma, and 12 Ma. The evolution of the eastern Serranía del Interior can be shown using a representative northwest-southeast–trending cross section (Fig. 5). The original locations of the 30 Ma, 25 Ma, and 20 Ma fission-track contours are shown on Figure 5 as black dots (Points A, B, and C, respectively). The effective closure temperature (110 °C, ~3.7 km) has been superimposed on the cross section with a dashed line. The irregular line represents the erosional surface. To simplify the model, each fission-track contour is located within one fault block. Within the individual fault block, internal deformation (faulting and folding) will thicken the block as shortening is accommodated. Slight displacement along the main fault will also occur.

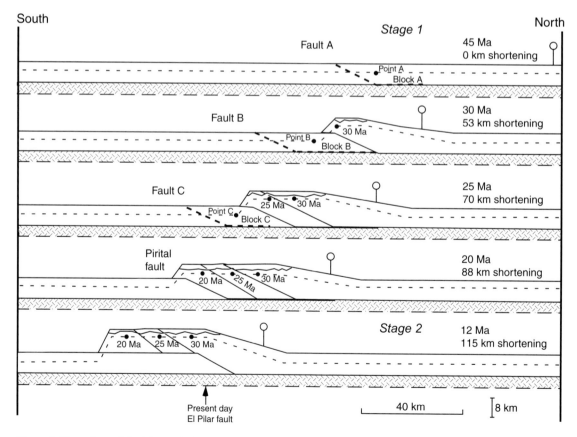

Figure 5. Tectonic model of the evolution of the eastern Serranía del Interior based on apatite fission-track data and balanced cross sections of Hung (this volume). See text for discussion.

Beginning at 45 Ma, with an initial shortening rate of 3.5 mm/yr, 52.5 km of shortening accumulated by 30 Ma. Some time between 45 Ma to 30 Ma, Point A was uplifted from ~5 km depth. Erosion of 1.3 km caused the temperature at Point A to decrease to the effective closure temperature where apatite began to record fission tracks within the PAZ, resulting in an AFT age of ca. 30 Ma. From 30 Ma to 25 Ma, Block B (Fig. 5) was activated in an in-sequence piggyback style, accumulating an additional 17.5 km of shortening. Uplift and deformation within Fault Block A was minimal. In a similar manner as Point A, Point B was uplifted to 3.7 km after 1.3 km of erosional exhumation drove cooling, and apatite fission-tracks accumulated at 25 Ma. With continued shortening (87.5 km), uplift, and erosion, Point C recorded FT cooling ages at 20 Ma. At 20 Ma, the second stage of deformation began with the emplacement of a long-undeformed thrust sheet by the Pirital envelopment thrust fault. Reasons for the change in deformation style may include (1) a change in the tectonic regime as the Caribbean plate interacts directly with the Serranía del Interior; (2) a decrease in the slope of the thrust wedge, which has sufficiently reduced the overburden to allow envelopment thrusting to occur; or (3) a pinch out of low-strength horizons hindering the propagation of additional in-sequence thrust faults. Roure et al. (1994) suggest that the Pirital thrust fault became active during the middle Miocene. Thus, using our estimated 3.5 mm/yr shortening, the Pirital envelopment fault accumulated 27.5 km of shortening. Pindell et al. (1998) estimate 40 km of shortening along the Pirital thrust fault. The envelopment thrusting doubled the thickness of the thrust sheet and increased uplift and erosion until Points A, B, and C reached their present day elevation.

From 12 Ma to Recent times, strike-slip motion occurred along the El Pilar and associated faults. Our second cooling path, defined by the least retentive apatite grains, appears to record cooling of rocks in the northern part of the thrust belt during this interval. It is possible that the very young cooling ages (3–13 Ma) record exhumation associated with this event. Interestingly, the youngest ages of CP1 (Fig. 4) are not closest to the fault, and the ages appear to get progressively younger within 30 km of the fault. It is possible that contractional deformation along the fault reworked thrust slices and in the process has progressively worked rocks forward (south) in the system. In this scenario, all ages related to CP2 (Fig. 4) are related to transpressive movement on the El Pilar fault.

Cooling and Exhumation Rates

Using this model, the cooling history of each deformation stage can be described independently. For Stage 1, the cooling history (and exhumation rate) from 30 to 25 Ma and 25 to 20 Ma is inferred to be the same because differences are not resolvable in the data. Therefore, in each 5 m.y. segment, cooling from 139 °C to 110 °C occurred, implying a cooling rate of ~6 °C/m.y. (exhumation rate of 0.2–0.3 km/m.y.) for each fault block during deformation and erosion. Assuming a constant exhumation rate from 20 Ma to the present, the cooling history of the second stage can be ~4.25 °C/m.y., with an exhumation rate from 20 Ma to the present of 0.2 km/m.y. The young P1 ages that define CP2 (13–3 Ma) imply that either the rocks were reheated or that they remained at relatively high temperatures until they were finally brought through closure in Miocene to Recent time.

Role of North and South American Convergence

Modeled deformation of the eastern Serranía del Interior began at ca. 45 Ma (González de Juana et al., 1980; Ostos et al., this volume, Chapter 2). At this time, the location of the Caribbean plate foredeep axis was far to the west: it intersected the northern margin of Venezuela in the Lake Maracaibo area, and the peripheral bulge was located near Caracas (Fig. 6; Pindell et al., 1998). The eastward-advancing Caribbean plate was not close enough to deform the Serranía del Interior, and as such, another mechanism

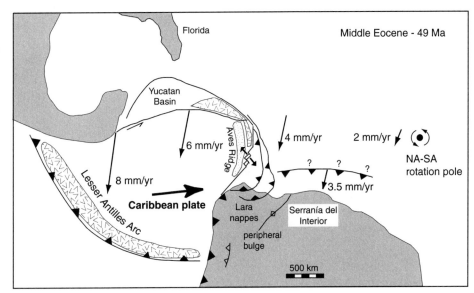

Figure 6. Middle Eocene paleography of the northern margin of South America showing location of the Caribbean plate with respect to the South American plate (from Pindell et al., 1998). Also shown are the relative motion of the Caribbean plate (thick arrow) and relative motions between the North and South American (NA-SA) plates (thin arrows; from Dixon and Mao, 1997). Rotation pole from Dixon and Mao (1997) is similar to that proposed by DeMets et al. (1994) and Summa et al. (2003). Stippled pattern indicates shallow marine regions; random "v" pattern indicates both active and inactive island-arc regions.

must have driven deformation in the thrust belt. The next obvious explanation for the deformation is the convergence between the North and South American plates (Fig. 6). Dixon and Mao (1997) estimated that this contraction occurred at a steady rate since ca. 50 Ma (see also Summa et al., 2003). Pindell et al. (1998) estimates that convergence began during the Maastrichtian and that Proto-Caribbean oceanic lithosphere might have been subducted beneath South American continental lithosphere. This subduction is referred to as the "Proto-Caribbean underthrust zone" (Pindell, 1993; Pindell et al., 1998). Pindell et al. (1998) estimate 70 km of convergence by the middle Eocene in eastern Venezuela. The Caribbean plate consumed the Proto-Caribbean seaway during its eastward movement causing deformation near plate boundaries. As the Caribbean plate advanced toward the Serranía del Interior (ca. 35 Ma), increasing amounts of shortening were taken up by the northern boundary of the Caribbean plate (i.e., Puerto Rico trench). The result was a cessation of shortening within the Serranía del Interior in response to North American and Caribbean plate convergence at ca. 12 Ma.

CONCLUSIONS

Apatite fission-track ages from the eastern Serranía del Interior show a gradual decrease in ages from north to south from ca. 30–15 Ma. This trend represents cooling of CP1, or the main cooling path, recorded by most samples. Based on cross sections by Hung (1997; this volume), a model for the tectonic evolution of the eastern Serranía del Interior suggests two stages of deformation. Assuming 115 km of total shortening at a rate of 3.5 mm/yr, deformation within the Serranía began at ca. 45 Ma. Stage 1 (45–20 Ma) involved internal deformation of fault blocks by folding and imbricate thrusting in an in-sequence piggyback style that advanced toward the south. Rocks were progressively uplifted and eroded from north to south. The amount of shortening during Stage 1 was ~88 km. Stage 2 (20–12 Ma) involved envelopment thrusting that doubled the thickness of the thrust sheet. The amount of shortening during Stage 2 was ~28 km. Erosion has continued to the present, which has brought the rocks to the surface. Overall shortening within the Serranía del Interior appears to have ceased at 12 Ma with the establishment of the El Pilar fault, but AFT ages of CP2 appear to reflect cooling related to the final stage of deformation. It is possible that transpression along the El Pilar reworked thrusts resulting in the 3–13 Ma southward-younging trend. The main phase of thrusting in the Serranía prior to the collision of the Caribbean plate with South America is probably related to the convergence of the North and South American plates, which has been relatively stable since 50 Ma. The last phase of deformation coincides with transpression on the El Pilar fault and transpression between the South American plate and the Caribbean plate.

ACKNOWLEDGMENTS

This work was supported by American Chemical Society Petroleum Research Fund #27788-AC2 grant to H.G. Avé Lallemant, as well as by funds from Conoco and a Sigma Xi Grant-In-Aid of Research. Ray and Margaret Donelick assisted with sample preparation and analysis at Apatite to Zircon, Inc. Richard Ketcham and Mark Brandon assisted in the modeling of the apatite fission-track data. Franklin Yoris and Estudios de Ingeniería Geológica Litos, S.A., assisted with field work and field work logistics. Paul O'Sullivan, Mary Roden-Tice, Hans Avé Lallemant, and Jinny Sisson provided thoughtful and thorough reviews. Garver acknowledges an Erskine Fellowship from the University of Canterbury (New Zealand) that supported him during the writing of this paper.

TABLE A1: DETAILS OF OUTCROP SAMPLES

Sample	Latitude (N)	Longitude (W)	Elev. (m)	Unit	Stage	Age (Ma)
BL-99-2	10°19'10"	63°57'50"	200	Barranquín (Taguarumo)	Aptian	113–124
BL-99-5	10°19'40"	63°57'90"	200	Barranquín (Taguarumo)	Aptian	113–124
BL-99-6	10°19'40"	63°57'90"	200	Barranquín (Taguarumo)	Aptian	113–124
BL-99-9	10°19'42"	63°58'32"	120	Barranquín (Taguarumo)	Aptian	113–124
BL-99-16	10°20'80"	64°06'87"	80	Barranquín (Taguarumo)	Aptian	113–124
BL-99-18	10°21'20"	64°90'23"	80	Barranquín (Taguarumo)	Aptian	113–124
BL-99-19a	10°09'92"	63°50'91"	800	Barranquín (Taguarumo)	Aptian	113–124
BL-99-23	10°06'77"	63°44'17"	100	San Juan	Maastrichtian	65–74
BL-99-31	09°59'68"	64°22'88"	220	San Juan	Maastrichtian	65–74
BL-00-21	10°26'58"	63°52'77"	5	Barranquín (Taguarumo)	Aptian	113–124
BL-00-23	10°27'10"	63°17'21"	200	San Antonio/San Juan/Caratas?	Santonian to Eocene	87-39
BL-00-25	10°27'73"	63°38'02"	320	Barranquín (Taguarumo)	Aptian	113–124
BL-00-31	10°23'16"	63°42'30"	400	Barranquín (Taguarumo)	Aptian	113–124
BL-00-32	10°23'05"	63°43'52"	400	Barranquín (Taguarumo)	Aptian	113–124
BL-00-38	10°03'91"	63°28'24"	800	Caratas/Los Jabillos?	M. Eocene–E. Oligocene	50–39–35–29
BL-00-44	10°02'06"	63°28'60"	560	Barranquín (Taguarumo)	Aptian	113–124
BL-00-48	10°00'15"	63°29'52"	400	Barranquín (Taguarumo)	Aptian	113–124
BL-00-72	10°22'85"	64°15'18"	80	Barranquín (Venados)	Barremian	131–124
BL-00-81	09°55'54"	64°04'91"	520	San Juan	Maastrichtian	65–74
BL-00-92	10°24'56"	63°29'45"	600	Barranquín (Picuda/Taguarumo?)	Aptian	113–124

Note: All units sampled are sandstones. Sample 00-23 is either from the San Antonio, the San Juan, or the Caratas Formations, and due to uncertainty in the stratigraphic position, it has a wide possible age range.

REFERENCES CITED

Avé Lallemant, H.G., 1997, Transpression, displacement partitioning, and exhumation in the eastern Caribbean–South American plate boundary zone: Tectonics, v. 16, p. 272–289.

Bellizzia, A., and Dengo, G., 1990, The Caribbean Mountain system, northern South America; A summary, *in* Dengo, G., and Case, J.E., eds., The Caribbean region: Boulder, Colorado, Geological Society of America, The Geology of North America, v. H, p. 167–175.

Bellizzia, A., Pimental, N., and Bajo, R., 1976, Mapa geológico estructural de Venezuela: Caracas, Foninves, escala 1:500,000.

Brandon, M.T., 1996, Probability density plot for fission-track ages of detrital zircon grain-age samples: Radiation Measurements, v. 26, p. 663–676.

Brandon, M.T., Roden-Tice, M., and Garver, J.I., 1998, Late Cenozoic exhumation of the Cascadia accretionary wedge in the Olympic Mountains, northwest Washington state: Geological Society of America Bulletin, v. 110, p. 985–1009.

Burke, K., Cooper, C., Dewey, J.F., Mann, P., and Pindell, L.J., 1984, Caribbean tectonics and relative plate motions, *in* Bonini, W.E., Hargraves, R.B., and Shagam, R., eds., The Caribbean–South American plate boundary and regional tectonics: Geological Society of America Memoir 162, p. 31–63.

Burtner, R.L., Nigrini, A., and Donelick, R.A., 1994, Thermochronology of lower Cretaceous source rocks in the Idaho-Wyoming thrust belt: AAPG Bulletin, v. 78, p. 1613–1636.

Carlson, W.D., Donelick, R.A., and Ketcham, R., 1999, Variability of apatite fission-track annealing kinetics: I. Experimental results: American Mineralogist, v. 84, p. 1213–1223.

Carnevali, J., 1989, Geology of new giant oil fields in mountain front of northeastern Venezuela: Proceedings, 28th International Geological Congress, Washington, 9–19 July, v. 1, p. 1240–1241.

Case, J.E., Holcombe, T.L., and Martin, R.G., 1984, Map showing major geologic provinces of the Caribbean region, *in* Bonini, W.E., Hargraves, R.B., and Shagam, R., eds., The Caribbean–South American plate boundary and regional tectonics: Boulder, Geological Society of America Memoir 162, p. 1–30.

Chevalier, Y., 1993, A cross section from the oil-rich Maturín sub-basin to Margarita Island: The geodynamic relations between South America and Caribbean plates, *in* Tectonics and stratigraphy: American Association of Petroleum Geologists/Sociedad Venezolana de Geólogos field trip, 11–14 March, 165 p.

Chevalier, Y., Alvarez, E., and Hernandez, G., 1995, A transverse section from the Orinoco Belt to the El Pilar fault system—Tectonics and stratigraphy: Caracas, IX Congreso Latinoamericano de Geología field trip, 9–10 November, 106 p.

Creole Petroleum Corporation, 1962, Mapas C-11 and D-11: Geología de Superficie, scale 1:100,000.

Crowley, K.D., Cameron, M., and McPherson, B.J., 1990, Annealing of etchable fission-track damage in F-, OH-, Cl- and Sr-apatite: 1. Systematics and preliminary interpretations: Nuclear Tracks and Radiation Measurements, v. 17, p. 409–410.

DeMets, C., Gordon, R.G., Argus, D.F., and Stein, S., 1994, Effect of recent revisions to the geomagnetic time scale on estimates of current plate motions: Geophysical Research Letters, v. 27, p. 2191–2194.

Di Croce, J., 1995, Eastern Venezuela Basin: Sequence stratigraphy and structural evolution [Ph.D. thesis]: Houston, Rice University, 225 p.

Dixon, T.H., and Mao, A., 1997, A GPS estimate of relative motion between North and South America: Geophysical Research Letters, v. 24, no. 5, p. 535–538.

Donelick, R.A., 1991, Crystallographic orientation dependence of mean etchable fission-track length in apatite: An empirical model and experimental observations: American Mineralogist, v. 76, p. 83–91.

Donelick, R.A., 1993, A method of fission-track analysis utilizing bulk chemical etching of apatite: U.S. Patent Number 6,267,274.

Donelick, R.A., 1995, A method of fission-track analysis utilizing bulk chemical etching of apatite: Australian Patent Number 658,800.

Erikson, J.P., and Pindell, J.L., 1993, Analysis of subsidence in northeastern Venezuela as a discriminator of tectonic models for northern South America: Geology, v. 21, p. 945–948.

Erlich, R.N., and Barrett, S.F., 1990, Cenozoic plate tectonic history of the northern Venezuela-Trinidad area: Tectonics, v. 9, no. 1, p. 161–184.

Galbraith, R.F., and Laslett, G.M., 1993, Statistical models for mixed fission track ages: Nuclear Tracks and Radiation Measurements, v. 21, p. 459–470.

Gallagher, K., Brown, R., and Johnson, C., 1998, Fission track analysis and its applications to geological problems: Annual Review of Earth and Planetary Science, v. 26, p. 519–572.

Garver, J.I., Brandon, M.T., Roden-Tice, M., and Kamp, P.J.J., 1999, Erosional denudation determined by fission-track ages of detrital apatite and zircon, *in* Ring, U., Brandon, M.T., Willett, S., and Lister, G., eds., Exhumation processes: Normal faulting, ductile flow, and erosion: Geological Society of London Special Publication 154, p. 283–304.

González de Juana, C., Iturralde, J.M., and Picard, X., 1980, Geología de Venezuela y de sus Cuencas Petrolíferas: Caracas, Ediciones Foninves, 1031 p.

Hedberg, H.D., 1937, Stratigraphy of the Río Querecual section of northeastern Venezuela: Geological Society of America Bulletin, v. 48, p. 1971–2024.

Hedberg, H.D., 1950, Geology of the Eastern Venezuela Basin (Anzoategui–Monagas–Sucre–eastern Guárico portion): Geological Society of America Bulletin, v. 61, p. 1173–1216.

Hedberg, H.D., and Pyre, A., 1944, Stratigraphy of northeastern Anzoategui, Venezuela: AAPG Bulletin, v. 28, p. 1–28.

Hung, E.J., 1997, Foredeep and thrust belt interpretation of the Maturín Sub-basin, Eastern Venezuela Basin [M.A. thesis]: Houston, Rice University, 125 p.

Hurford, A.J., and Green, P.F., 1983, The zeta age calibration of fission-track dating: Isotope Geoscience, v. 1, p. 285–317.

Liddle, R.A., 1928, The geology of Venezuela and Trinidad: Fort Worth, Mac Gowan Press, 522 p.

Locke, B.D., 2001, Thermal evolution of the eastern Serranía del Interior foreland fold and thrust belt, northeastern Venezuela, based on apatite fission track analyses [M.A. thesis]: Houston, Rice University, 167 p.

Mann, P., Schubert, C., and Burke, K., 1990, Review of Caribbean neotectonics, *in* Dengo, G., and Case, J.E., eds., The Caribbean region: Boulder, Colorado, Geological Society of America, p. 307–338.

Martinez, J.A., 1995, A geological and geophysical study of structural style along a transect of the Maturín Subbasin, Eastern Venezuela Basin [M.Sc. thesis]: Los Angeles, University of Southern California, 141 p.

Müller, R.D., and Smith, W.H.F., 1993, Deformation of the oceanic crust between the North American and South American plates: Journal of Geophysical Research, v. 98, p. 8275–8291.

Munro, S.E., and Smith, F.D., Jr., 1984, The Úrica fault zone, northeastern Venezuela, *in* Bonini, W.E., Hargraves, R.B., and Shagam, R., eds., The Caribbean–South American Plate boundary and regional tectonics: Geological Society of America Memoir 162, p. 213–215.

Naeser, C.W., 1979, Fission-track dating and geologic annealing of fission-tracks, *in* Jäger, E., and Hunziker, J.C., eds., Lectures in isotope geology: Heidelberg, Springer-Verlag, p. 154–169.

Pérez, J.G., Donelick, R., and Lallemant, H.G.A., 1998, Thermal history of the Serranía del Interior foreland fold and thrust belt and Guárico foredeep, north-central Venezuela: Constraints from apatite fission-track modeling: Eos (Transactions, American Geophysical Union), v. 79, p. F797.

Pérez, O.J., Bilham, R., Bendick, R., Velandia, J.R., Hernández, N., Moncayo, C., Hoyer, M., and Kozuch, M., 2001, Velocity field gradients across the southern Caribbean plate boundary and estimates of Caribbean–South American plate motion using GPS geodesy 1994–2000: Geophysical Research Letters, v. 28, p. 2987–2990.

Pindell, J.L., 1993, Regional synopsis of Gulf of Mexico and Caribbean evolution, *in* Pindell, J.L., and Perkins, R.F., eds., Mesozoic and early Cenozoic development of the Gulf of Mexico and Caribbean region—A context for hydrocarbon exploration, Proceedings, Gulf Coast Section SEPM Foundation 13th Annual Research Conference: Houston, Society for Sedimentary Geology (SEPM) Foundation, p. 251–274.

Pindell, J.L., Higgs, R., and Dewey, J.F., 1998, Cenozoic palinspastic reconstruction, paleogeographic evolution and hydrocarbon setting of the northern margin of South America, *in* Pindell, J.L., and Drake, C., eds., Paleogeographic evolution and non-glacial eustasy, northern South America: Society for Sedimentary Geology (SEPM) Special Publication 58, p. 45–86.

Rod, E., 1956, Strike-slip faults of northern Venezuela: AAPG Bulletin, v. 40, p. 457–476.

Rod, E., and Maync, W., 1954, Revision of Lower Cretaceous stratigraphy of Venezuela: AAPG Bulletin, v. 38, p. 193–283.

Rosales, H., 1972, La falla de San Francisco en el oriente de Venezuela: Caracas, Cuarto Congreso Geológico Venezalano, tomo IV, p. 2322–2336.

Rosales, H., 1973, Excursion #5: Venezuela nororiental–Serranía del Interior: Maturín, Muelle de Cariaco: Caracas, Segundo Congreso Latinoamericano de Geología, p. 470–493.

Rossi, T., 1985, Contribution á l'ètude géologique de la frontière sud-est de la plaque Caraibe: Etude géologique de la Serranía del Interior Oriental (Venezuela) sur le transect Cariaco-Maturín syntheses paléogéographique et géodynamique [Ph.D. thesis]: Brest, Université de Bretagne Occidentale, 340 p.

Roure, F., Carnevali, J.O., Gou, Y., and Subieta, T., 1994, Geometry and kinematics of the north Monagas thrust belt (Venezuela): Marine and Petroleum Geology, v. 11, no. 3, p. 347–362.

Salvador, A., and Stainforth, R.M., 1968, Clues in Venezuela to the geology of Trinidad and vice-versa: Trinidad, IV Caribbean Geology Conference, p. 31–40.

Summa, L.L., Goodman, E.D., Richardson, M., Norton, I.O., and Green, A.R., 2003, Hydrocarbon systems of Northeastern Venezuela: Plate through molecular-scale analysis of the genesis and evolution of the Eastern Venezuela Basin: Marine and Petroleum Geology, v. 20, p. 323–349.

Vierbuchen, R.C., 1984, The geology of the El Pilar fault zone and adjacent areas in northeastern Venezuela, *in* Bonini, W.E., Hargraves, R.B., and Shagam, R., eds., The Caribbean–South American plate boundary and regional tectonics: Geological Society of America Memoir 162, p. 189–212.

Wagner, G.A., and Van den Haute, P., 1992, Fission-track dating. Dordrecht, Kluwer Academic Publishers, 285 p.

Weber, J.C., Dixon, T.H., DeMets, C., Ambeh, W.B., Jansma, P., Mattioli, G., Saleh, J., Sella, G., Bilham, R., and Pérez, O., 2001, GPS estimate of relative plate motion between the Caribbean and South American plates, and geologic implications for Trinidad and Venezuela: Geology, v. 29, p. 75–78.

Yoris, F.G., 1985, Revision de la Estratigraphia del Cretaceo Inferior al sur y este de la Serranía del Interior, Venezuela nororiental: Caracas, VI Congress Geológico Venezolano, p. 1343–1393.

Yoris, F., 1988, Localidades tipo y secciones de referencia para los miembros de la Formation El Cantil en la Serranía del Interior, Venezuela nororiental: Boletín de la Sociedad Venezolana de Geólogos, v. 34, p. 52–70.

Yoris, F., 1992, Localidades tipo para los miembros de la Formacion Chimana en la Serranía del Interior, Venezuela nororiental: Caracas, Geos, v. 30, p. 295–324.

Ysaccis, R., 1997, Tertiary evolution of the northeastern Venezuela offshore [Ph.D. thesis]: Houston, Rice University, 285 p.

MANUSCRIPT ACCEPTED BY THE SOCIETY 5 APRIL 2005

Geological Society of America
Special Paper 394
2005

Epilogue

Hans G. Avé Lallemant*
Virginia B. Sisson*
Department of Earth Science, MS-126, Rice University, Houston, Texas 77251-1892, USA

INTRODUCTION

Several problems of the tectonic history of the Caribbean–South American plate boundary have been resolved as shown in the papers in this book. However, it seems that with each solution, several new questions arose, and still some old questions remain unanswered.

In October 1997, we organized a workshop dealing with the geology and tectonics of the southeastern Caribbean. This workshop was held at Rice University. Many geologists and geophysicists from all over the world participated. The goal of this meeting was to establish what was known of the southeastern Caribbean and what was not known and not understood. What kind of projects should be carried out to find answers to the questions? These discussions led to a proposal to the Continental Dynamics program of the National Science Foundation. The project was funded in 2001. The acronym of the project is BOLIVAR, which stands for Broadband Ocean-Land Investigations of Venezuela and the Antilles arc Region (Levander et al., 2004). In 2002, land-based studies started, but due to several problems, the marine part of the project was postponed to the spring of 2004. Very preliminary results were presented at the 2004 fall meeting of the American Geophysical Union.

In the following paragraphs, some of the questions dealing with the southeastern Caribbean are raised.

Southern Caribbean Deformed Belt

It is generally accepted that the Southern Caribbean deformed belt is an accretionary wedge related to southward subduction resulting from Eocene to Recent convergence of North and South America (e.g., Biju-Duval et al., 1982; Pindell et al., 1988; Pindell et al., this volume, Chapter 1). However, part of the NS shortening may be related to the northward tectonic escape

of the Maracaibo block (Burke, 1988). Application of the Global Positioning System (GPS) and the study of deep-seismic profiles may solve this question.

Leeward Antilles Arc

The arc is generally considered to be an extinguished portion of the Greater–Lesser Antilles volcanic island arc. However, it has been proposed (e.g., White et al., 1999) that some parts of the arc (e.g., Curaçao, Aruba) are not arc-related, but part of the Caribbean plateau basalt province. Some of the islands (e.g., Bonaire) are clearly arc related (Thompson et al., 2004). More geochemical work has to be carried out to constrain the tectonic setting of the islands.

The diachronous collision of the Leeward Antilles with South America must have happened in the Eocene in western Venezuela, whereas the collision in the east occurred in the Miocene. This hypothesis was based mostly on K-Ar age dates. As K-Ar ages are not always reliable, U-Pb (Wright and Wyld, 2004), $^{40}Ar/^{39}Ar$ (P. Copeland, 2004, personal commun.), and zircon and apatite fission-track (Beardsley and Avé Lallemant, 2004) dating will be carried out as part of the BOLIVAR project.

In many arc and forearc terranes, arc-parallel extension (arc-perpendicular normal faults) is the result of displacement partitioning due to oblique plate convergence and the curvature of the arc and forearc (Avé Lallemant and Guth, 1990). Are the Leeward Antilles segmented by this process? Seismic reflection studies (Levander et al., 2004) and kinematic analysis of exposed rock may answer these questions.

Belt of Tertiary Basins

The Tuy-Cariaco and Carúpano basins appear to be the result of east-west extension in pull-apart basins related to the

---

*E-mails: ave@rice.edu; j_sisson@netzero.com

Avé Lallemant, H.G., and Sisson, V.B., 2005, Epilogue, *in* Avé Lallemant, H.G., and Sisson, V.B., eds., Caribbean–South American plate interactions, Venezuela: Geological Society of America Special Paper 394, p. 329–331, doi: 10.1130/2005.2394(EPI). For permission to copy, contact editing@geosociety.org. ©2005 Geological Society of America.

east-west–trending strike-slip faults (Ysaccis, 1997). However, some of the extension may be the result of forearc-parallel stretching. Some of the extension might be related to divergence between the North and South American plates (Pindell et al., this volume; Pérez et al., 2001; Weber et al., 2001). Continental collapse is a possibility as well (F.A. Audemard, 2002, personal commun.), but east-west–striking normal faults are relatively rare (Avé Lallemant and Sisson, this volume, Chapter 7). The Bonaire Basin may have formed by any of these mechanisms or by the northward escape of the Maracaibo block (James, 2002). In order to understand the history of sedimentary basins, high-order sequence stratigraphy is highly desirable not only in the offshore basins, but also in the foreland basins (e.g., Di Croce, 1995; Di Croce et al., 1999).

Cordillera de la Costa Belt

How allochthonous is this belt? Are the calcareous and graphitic schists really Jurassic and Lower Cretaceous passive-margin deposits? How deep is the basal décollement? What is the real metamorphic age of the eclogites and blueschists? Are they mid-Cretaceous like the blueschists of the Villa de Cura rocks, and are the late Eocene $^{40}Ar/^{39}Ar$ ages an overprint? Are the blueschists diachronously emplaced like the Leeward Antilles island arc? More radiometric ages are needed.

Although the geology of the Cordillera de la Costa belt is similar to that of Margarita Island, there are important differences. The highest pressures at which the eclogites formed on Margarita are 12 kb (Pindell et al., this volume), but are 22 kb in the Cordillera de la Costa belt (Sisson et al., 1997). If this difference is real, the histories of subduction and exhumation in these two sites may be quite different.

Paracotos Belt

Are the rocks of the Paracotos belt, north of the Villa de Cura, equivalent to the Guárico Formation south of the Villa de Cura? What is the age of the belt? What is the age of the ultramafic–mafic complexes in the Paracotos?

Villa de Cura Belt

The Villa de Cura blueschist belt has generally been interpreted as a klippe (e.g., Smith et al., 1999). Recently however, it has been proposed that the belt is an imbricate slice that roots in the basal décollement of the entire Caribbean Mountain system (F.E. Audemard, 1997, personal commun.). Can seismic studies resolve this problem? Are the kinematics of the internal structure of the complex consistent with the kinematics in the other belts (John et al., 2004)?

A totally different tectonic model has been proposed in which the Villa de Cura belt is relatively autochthonous (Ostos and Navarro, 1985; see also Ostos et al., this volume, Chapter 2).

Serranía del Interior Fold and Thrust Belt

It is generally assumed that the south-vergent thrust faults in the Serranía foreland fold and thrust belt merge at depth with a basal décollement system. It is not known, however, at what depth this basal surface occurs. Neither is it known what kind of rocks occur between the presumed décollement and the exposed folded Cretaceous formations. Are they undeformed or folded Paleozoic sedimentary rocks or Precambrian basement rocks derived from the Guyana Shield? Or, are these rocks Tertiary or Cretaceous in age?

Displacement partitioning requires that coeval thrust and strike-slip faults merge into basal décollement. Can we image them seismically? Similarly, the Tertiary basin fill is deformed by normal faults that may merge into the same décollement.

How much is the continental margin stretched during the fragmentation of Pangea? Does the continental crust extend all the way to the Leeward Antilles (Zelt et al., 2004)? Another related question is the origin of the extremely negative gravity anomaly in the Maturín basin. Deep seismic reflection data may be necessary to solve these problems. In Chapter 10 (this volume), Hung presents six different NS balanced cross sections. While each of them is reasonable, only one can be correct. This problem may be solved by deep seismic studies.

Many NW-SE–trending faults cross-cut the Serranía del Interior. They don't fit common models of faulting. Are they inherited structures, perhaps old Jurassic transform segments, or are they lateral ramps?

How important is the Paleogene NS contraction that Pérez de Armas (Chapter 11, this volume) and Locke and Garver (Chapter 12, this volume) have found in the Serranía del Interior on the basis of fission-track dating? More age dating is needed to prove this.

REFERENCES CITED

Avé Lallemant, H.G., and Guth, L.R., 1990, Role of extensional tectonics in exhumation of eclogites and blueschists in an oblique subduction setting: Northwestern Venezuela: Geology, v. 18, p. 950–953, doi: 10.1130/0091-7613(1990)018<0950:ROETIE>2.3.CO;2.

Beardsley, A.G., and Avé Lallemant, H.G., 2004, BOLIVAR: Tectonic history based on brittle deformation features of the Netherlands Leeward Antilles island arc: Eos (Transactions, American Geophysical Union), v. 85, no. 47, p. F1714.

Biju-Duval, B., Mascle, A., Rosales, H., and Young, G., 1982, Episutural Oligo-Miocene basins along the north Venezuelan margin, *in* Watkins, J.S. and Drake, C.L., eds., Studies in continental margin geology: American Association of Petroleum Geologists Memoir 34, p. 347–358.

Burke, K., 1988, Tectonic evolution of the Caribbean: Annual Reviews of Earth and Planetary Sciences, v. 16, p. 201–230, doi: 10.1146/annurev.ea.16.050188.001221.

Di Croce, J., 1995, Eastern Venezuela Basin [Ph.D. Thesis]: Houston, Texas, Rice University, 225 p.

Di Croce, J., Bally, A.W., and Vail, P., 1999, Sequence stratigraphy of the eastern Venezuelan basin, *in* Mann, P., ed., Sedimentary basins of the world: Caribbean Basins: Amsterdam, Elsevier, p. 419–476.

James, K.H., 2002, A simple synthesis of Caribbean geology: http://www.ig.utexas.edu/CaribPlate/forum/james/james_carib_model.pdf (Accessed: April 2005).

John, A.M., Avé Lallemant, H.G., and Altamira-Areyan, A., 2004, BOLIVAR: Deformation history of the Villa de Cura blueschist belt, Venezuela: Eos (Transactions, American Geophysical Union), v. 85, no. 47, p. F1715.

Levander, A., Mann, P., Avé Lallemant, H.G., and Schmitz, M., 2004, BOLIVAR: The SE Caribbean continental dynamics project: Eos (Transactions, American Geophysical Union), v. 85, no. 47, p. F1712.

Ostos, M., and Navarro, E., 1985, Faja de Villa de Cura: Realmente un complejo de arco de isla alóctona?, *in* Espejo, A., Ríos, J.H., Pimentel de Bellizzia, N., and de Pardo, A., eds., Memoria, VI Congreso Geológico Venezolano: Caracas, Sociedad Venezolana de Geólogos, v. 10, p. 6615–6637.

Pérez, O.J., Bilham, R., Bendick, R., Velandia, J.R., Hernandez, N., Moncayo, C., Hoyer, M., and Kozuch, M., 2001, Velocity field across the southern Caribbean plate boundary and estimates of Caribbean–South American plate motion using GPS geodesy 1994–2000: Geophysical Research Letters, v. 28, no. 15, p. 2987–2990, doi: 10.1029/2001GL013183.

Pindell, J.L., Cande, S.C., Pitman, W.C., III, Rowley, D.B., Dewey, J.F., Labrecque, J., and Haxby, W., 1988, A plate-kinematic framework for models of Caribbean evolution: Tectonophysics, v. 155, p. 121–138, doi: 10.1016/0040-1951(88)90262-4.

Sisson, V.B., Ertan, I.E., and Avé Lallemant, H.G., 1997, High pressure (~2000 MPa) kyanite- and glaucophane-bearing pelitic schist and eclogite from Cordillera de la Costa belt, Venezuela: Journal of Petrology, v. 38, p. 65–83, doi: 10.1093/petrology/38.1.65.

Smith, C.A., Sisson, V.B., Avé Lallemant, H.G., and Copeland, P., 1999, Two contrasting pressure-temperature-time paths in the Villa de Cura blueschist belt, Venezuela: Possible evidence for Late Cretaceous initiation of subduction in the Caribbean: Geological Society of America Bulletin, v. 111, no. 6, p. 831–848, doi: 10.1130/0016-7606(1999)111<0831:TCPTTP>2.3.CO;2.

Thompson, P.M.E., Kempton, P.D., White, R.V., Saunders, A.D., Kerr, A.C., Tarney, J., and Pringle, M.S., 2004, Elemental, Hf-Nd isotopic and geochronological constraints on an island arc sequence associated with the Cretaceous Caribbean plateau, Bonaire, Dutch Antilles: Lithos, v. 74, p. 91–116, doi: 10.1016/j.lithos.2004.01.004.

Weber, J.C., Dixon, T.H., DeMets, C., Jansma, P., Mattioli, G., Saleh, J., Sella, G., Biham, R., and Pérez, O., 2001, GPS estimate of relative motion between the Caribbean and South American plates, and geologic implications for Trinidad and Venezuela: Geology, v. 29, no. 1, p. 75–78, doi: 10.1130/0091-7613(2001)029<0075:GEORMB>2.0.CO;2.

White, R.V., Tarney, J., Kerr, A.C., Saunders, A.D., Kempton, P.D., Pringle, M.S., and Klaver, G.T., 1999, Modification of an oceanic plateau, Aruba, Dutch Caribbean: Implications for the generation of continental crust: Lithos, v. 46, p. 43–68, doi: 10.1016/S0024-4937(98)00061-9.

Wright, J.E., and Wyld, S.J., 2004, Aruba and Curaçao: Remnants of a collided Pacific oceanic plateau? Initial geologic results from the BOLIVAR project: Eos (Transactions, American Geophysical Union), v. 85, no. 47, p. F1713.

Ysaccis, R., 1997, Tertiary evolution of the northeastern Venezuela offshore [Ph.D. Dissertation]: Houston, Texas, Rice University, 285 p.

Zelt, C.A., Magnani, M.B., Levander, A., Schmitz, M., Christeson, G.L., Mann, P., and Sawyer, D.S., 2004, BOLIVAR: Crustal structure across the Caribbean–South American plate boundary at 67.5°W: Results from wide-angle seismic data: Eos (Transactions, American Geophysical Union), v. 85, no. 47, p. F1714.

MANUSCRIPT ACCEPTED BY THE SOCIETY 5 APRIL 2005

Index

333

Beata Ridge: 8, 26, 243
Belize: 8–10, 225
Benioff zone: 23–24, 27, 246, 273, 310
Bergantín block: 252–53, 256–57, 267, 317–18
Bermeja complex: 10, 13, 22, 226, 242
Bermuda Rise: 181–83, 186, 189
Betijoque Formation: 75
Blue Mountains: 10, 16, 27
Boconó fault zone: 46, 56–57, 79–81, 253
Bogotá area: 56–57
Bogotá Formation: 38
Bolivar complex: 219
Bonaire
 geochemical analysis of: 144
 geochronology of: 79, 226
 Great Caribbean Arc and: 226
 lithology of: 3
 maps of
  geographic: 1
  geologic: 93, 120
  paleotectonic: 40
  tectonic: 2
  tectonostratigraphic: 272
  terranes/provinces: 225
  topographic: 54
 metamorphism in: 77
 protoliths: 226
 Villa de Cura belt and: 148
Bonaire basin: 174, 208–9, 224, 277, 291, 330
Boquerón oil field: 253, 262
Brasiliano orogen: 105
Brazil: 55, 141, 219
Broadband Ocean-Land Investigation of Venezuela
  and the Antilles arc Region: 329
Bucaramanga fault zone: 15, 46, 58
Buga Batholith: 19, 32
Burgüita Formation: 62, 64–65

C

Cabaiguan Formation: 22–23, 25
Cabo Blanco Group: 139
Cabo Codera area
 Cordillera de la Costa belt in: 4
 geochronology of: 114, 201–2
 maps of
  faults in: 194
  geographic: 1
  geologic: 93, 120, 194
  tectonic: 2, 158
  tectonostratigraphic: 272
Cacaguapa Schist: 11
Caledonian orogen: 55, 150
Calentura Formation: 36
California: 174, 186–87
Camatagua region: 72, 102–3, 274
Camatagüita Creek area: 283–87, 291–92, 296,
  299–300, 307
Campeche platform, map of: 8
Campur Formation: 28
Cangre Belt: 16
Caño Limón fault zone, map of: 73
Canoa Formation: 59–60, 64, 275
Cantagallo thrust: 70, 96, 111, 273–74, 282–83,
  286–88

Cantarranas Formation: 11
Capacho Formation: 59, 61–63
Capadare, maps of: 76
Caparo area, maps of: 57
Caparo fault zone, maps of: 79–80
Capiricual Formation: 74–76, 78
Caracas area
 maps of
  facies: 60, 63–64
  faults in: 71, 194
  geographic: 1
  geologic: 93, 120, 194, 224
  lithostratigraphic: 60
  lithotectonic: 174
  paleotectonic: 66, 74
  plate tectonics: 68
  sediment: 73
  seismic: 277
  tectonic: 2, 158, 209, 274
  tectonostratigraphic: 272
  terranes/provinces: 57
  topographic: 54
 petrogenesis of: 55
Caracas Group
 Antímano Formation: 59, 81, 122–23, 138–40
 Garrapata Formation and: 45
 geochronology of: 100
 geographic setting of: 59, 81
 Juan Griego Formation and: 82
 La Guajira Peninsula and: 83
 Las Brisas Formation. *see* Las Brisas Formation
 lithology of: 45–46
 maps of: 44, 138
 modeling of: 70
 Peña de Mora Formation. *see* Peña de Mora
   Formation
 petrogenesis of: 291
 Querecual Formation and: 45
 Sebastopol and: 81
 stratigraphy of: 82
 Villa de Cura belt and: 45
Carache fault zone, maps of: 79–80
Carapita Formation
 Capiricual Formation and: 75
 Chaguaramas Formation and: 75
 diapirism in: 323
 geochronology of: 255
 lithology of: 255, 319
 maps of: 40, 42, 74, 76, 317
 Merecure Formation and: 72–73, 75
 modeling of: 78
 Narical Formation and: 72, 324
 Oficina Formation and: 75
 oil and: 75
 petrogenesis of: 75, 255, 318–19
 in Serranía del Interior belt: 319
 structure of: 261, 268–69
 thickness of: 255
 wells in: 256
Caratas Formation: 39–40, 67–72, 255–56, 317,
  319, 323
Carbonera Formation: 40–41, 65–67, 69, 72–73
Cariaco area: 115, 252, 256–57, 267
Cariaco basin. *See also* Golfo de Cariaco
 Caucagua-El Tinaco belt and: 82

 faults and: 81, 208, 316, 329–30
 geochronology of: 81
 geographic setting of: 81
 lithology of: 81
 maps of
  faults in: 79
  geologic: 224
  lithotectonic: 174
  paleotectonic: 42
  tectonic: 209
  topographic: 54
 Paracotos belt and: 82
 petrogenesis of: 329–30
 Villa de Cura belt and: 82
Cariaco fault zone: 42
Caribbean Frontal Thrust. *See* Caribbean thrust belt
Caribbean Igneous Plateau
 Antilles and: 329
 Aruba and: 34, 243–44, 329
 Colombian basin and: 243
 Cordillera Occidental and: 243
 Curaçao and: 243, 329
 Duarte Formation and: 243
 Dumisseau Formation and: 243
 Galápagos Islands and: 224, 242–43
 geochemical analysis of: 244
 geochronology of: 18, 23–24, 224, 243
 Gorgona Island and: 243
 Hispaniola and: 120
 Inter-American Arc and: 23–24, 34, 46, 92, 225,
   244–45
 lithology of: 244
 Nicaragua and: 243
 Nicoya complex and: 243
 petrogenesis of: 24, 224
 San Jacinto belt and: 45
 Serranía de Baudo and: 243
 subduction of: 21
 trench choking and: 23–24, 34, 92, 225, 244–45
 Villa de Cura belt and: 245–46
Caribbean Mountain system
 Baragua Range: 1, 54
 Caucagua-El Tinaco belt. *see* Caucagua-El
   Tinaco belt
 Cordillera de la Costa belt. *see* Cordillera de la
   Costa belt
 geographic setting of: 3
 lithology of: 4
 Loma de Hierro ophiolite: 4, 70, 82, 227
 maps of: 8, 80
 Paracotos belt. *see* Paracotos belt
 San Luis Range: 1, 54
 Serranía del Interior. *see* Serranía del Interior belt
 Sierra de Perijá. *see* Sierra de Perijá
 Venezuelan platform and: 80
 Villa de Cura belt. *see* Villa de Cura belt
Caribbean plate
 Andes and: 32
 Bahamas and: 2–3, 121, 205
 basin evolution and: 3–4, 9, 25
 boundaries of: 2, 35, 253, 272–73
 Chortís block and: 9
 Cordillera Real and: 35–36
 crust/mantle structure: 23, 29, 224
 Farallon plate and: 35, 92, 121, 205